Ministries of Health and Healing

A Handbook for Health Ministries Leaders,
Educators and Professionals in
the North American Division

SECOND EDITION

Compiled by
DeWitt S. Williams, Ed.D., M.P.H., C.H.E.S.,
Kay Kuzma, Ed.D., and Leo R. Van Dolson, M.P.H., Ph.D.

With contributions from more than 45 health professionals

Advent*Source*: Lincoln, Nebraska

Published by the Seventh-day Adventist Church
North American Division
Health and Temperance Department
12501 Old Columbia Pike
Silver Spring, MD 20904
(301) 680-6733

For additional copies:
Advent*Source*
5040 Prescott Avenue
Lincoln, NE 68506
(800) 328-0525
www.adventsource.org

Revised 2002 by
Advent*Source*

ISBN 1-57756-009-4

Printed in the U.S.A.

Introduction

I think about Jesus walking around in Palestine 2,000 years ago, because I want to be like Him. He preached some. He visited with people and ate at their homes sometimes. But mostly He healed people. He'd walk into a town in the morning; when He left in the afternoon, there weren't any sick people left in town!

Aren't you glad to be part of a church that preaches the Gospel and the Three Angels Messages! I'm glad to be part of the Adventist Church. I'm also glad the Adventist Church is a friendly place that encourages people to get to know their neighbors, and I hope you've made friends with your neighbors.

But this Adventist Church won't reflect completely the image of Jesus until we tell people about healthy living. I believe God gave this church a special mission to help restore complete health in people. That's how we reflect Jesus to the communities around us. Just think of all the ways in which we share good health with our communities:

Adventist hospitals help millions of people each year live better, live longer, live stronger. They do this by performing surgeries as intricate as any hospitals in the world. They also do this by praying at the bedside of patients, by telling people about the Great Healer, by portraying Jesus in the pictures and literature throughout the hospital.

Adventist schools teach students principles of healthful living, right from first grade to graduate school. Every student in an Adventist school learns about exercise, about eating, about sleeping, about drinking plenty of liquids, about trusting in God.

Adventist Community Services helps build better health in our communities, whether it's through Disaster Response that provides clean water for people displaced by tornadoes and floods, or it's through community clinics in towns like Dayton, Ohio.

Adventist Health Ministers (that's you!) serve in an important way as well. The Health Ministries Department of the local Adventist church works in two ways to help God restore His image in men and women:

1) Health Education for our church members.
2) Health Evangelism for the communities in which we live.

The handbook *Ministries of Health and Healing* is a great resource for you as you lead out in doing what Jesus did, preaching a little, making friends in the community, and leading people to healthy lifestyles.

Don C. Schneider, President
North American Division
of Seventh-day Adventists

More than a hundred years have passed since God used Ellen White to educate Adventists about the advantages of healthful living. The principles she taught were based on exercise, adequate rest, a wholesome diet, abstinence from harmful substances, a positive mental outlook, and trust in divine blessings. Today, medical science has demonstrated the value of these same principles which are acknowledged and practiced in our mainstream culture. People who once resisted a change in lifestyle are now actively searching for the most current information and the best practices.

As we enter the 21st century, new technologies, better health care and instant information systems inform more people every minute than Ellen White could in her lifetime. Yet, there are more unhappy, addicted, overweight, sick people than ever. Information alone does little to alleviate their suffering. When people experience the support of informed and caring communities of faith, who understand that healing is the result of knowing Christ's love and grace, they will want to live healthy in response to Him.

Adventist Health Ministries in North America exists to help church leaders know how to give this kind of support. This book gives ideas for ministry that you may not have considered, and provides resources and information that is easy to use. My hope is that this *Ministries of Health and Healing* handbook will encourage every health ministries leader to fulfill God's divine purpose in giving His people this wonderful message of complete health.

Debra C. Brill
Vice President
North American Division

Table of Contents

Acknowledgements

For the second edition, we had several conference calls to discuss our procedure and what should be added and left out. My thanks go to Frank McMiller, Marilyn Renk, Audray Johnson, Desmond Frances, David Higgins and Fred Hardinge for their ideas and suggestions in this initial stage. Special thanks to Edith Woodruff for reading a large part of the manual looking for errors.

New chapters were written by Leilani Proctor and Vivian Raitz (Fairs and exhibits), Steve Veres (Van Ministry), Celeste Ryan and John Scharffenberg (Wellness Camps), Stephen Barrett (Quackery and Nutrition Fads). Special thanks to Dorothy G. Keith who typed and typed and typed and for her patience in overseeing the entire project. I thank Debra Brill, Vice President for Ministries, who suggested and provided a budget so that the task could be undertaken. Mack Rucker, for the second time, made financial arrangements for a writer and footed the bill for the chapter on the hospital systems of the church. We thank him for his willingness to help and cooperate in every endeavor that we have. It was a pleasure working with AdventSource again. Brad Forbes and Christal Gregerson did everything they could to help us make deadlines and produce a good product. Leo Van Dolson once again did a marvellous job of editing and integrating the myriad of comments that returned to my office.

Each chapter was sent out to about seven readers who sent their comments back to our office. I would like to thank each reader for their comments, their time and suggestions. If their names were listed in the list for the original volume(see next paragraph), I will not mention it again in this paragraph: Bernell and Marjorie Baldwin, Bill Bremner, Debra Carbi, Gary Case, Faith Crumbley, E. W. Dempsey, Bernice DeShay, Terry Dodge, Chris Donovan, Louis Edwards, Desmond Frances, Kiti Freiser, Dane and Vikki Griffin, Richard Hansen, Fred Hardinge, Jim Harmon, Richard Hart, Patti Herring, Don Hall, Dave Higgins, Gladys Hollingsead, Dwayne McBride, Frank McMiller, Ray Nelson, Kermit Netteberg, Bryce Pascoe, Sharon Pittman, Lou Preston, Richar O'Ffill, Mike Ortel, Mack Rucker, Beverly Rumble, Celeste Ryan, Marie Schaub, Raye Scott, E. Wayne Sheppard, Carlyle Simmons, Rose Stoia, Sidney Sweet, Agatha and Calvin Thrash, Tony Torres, Owen Troy, Nancy Wallack, Eunice Warfield, David White, and Al Williamson.

—DeWitt S. Williams

Contributors

Elvin Adams, M.D., a graduate of Loma Linda University, is a former associate director of the General Conference Health and Temperance Department. He retired after practicing in Texas, specializing in internal medicine.

Bernell Baldwin, Ph.D., is the science editor for the *Journal of Health and Healing*. He has taught for the schools of medicine and health at Loma Linda University and is currently a teacher at Wildwood Lifestyle Center and Hospital. His specialty is neurophysiology.

Stephen Barrett, MD, is a retired physician who has written over 34 books. He won an FDA award for fighting nutrition quackery.

Maxine Blome, M.S.N.E., C.N.A.A., Retired Parish Nurse Coordinator for Adventist Health in Roseville, California.

James Brackett, M.P.H., director for health ministries of the Nevada-Utah Conference, and former director of RESTORE (Reaching Seattle for Eternity), Seattle's medical evangelism project.

Jack Calkins, M.Div., M.S.P.H., (and Ann) currently serves as a pastor in New Conference & his wife is a freelance writer.

Donna Davis Cameron, Ph.D., is a health education consultant. She specializes in nutrition education and mental health issues and is a sought-after pianist.

Kimberly Carr was Communications Coordinator for Adventist Heath System, Sunbelt.

Roger W. Coon, Ph.D., formerly served as an associate secretary of the Ellen G. White Estate, Silver Spring, Maryland.

David DeRose, M.D., M.P.H., is assistant editor of the *Journal of Health and Healing* and is on the staff of the Lifestyle Center of America in Oklahoma. He is a specialist in internal medicine.

P. William Dysinger, M.D., M.P.H., was the former senior health advisor for the Adventist Development and Relief Agency (ADRA.) He spent many years in academic administration at Loma Linda University School of Public Health. He has lived and worked in both Africa and Asia.

Harvey Elder, M.D., is retired chief of the infectious disease section at the Jerry L. Pettis Memorial Veteran's Center in Loma Linda California. He is an expert in the clinical aspect of AIDS and spends much of his time doing AIDS education for pastors and laity.

Martin W. Feldbush, D.Min., B.C.C., Associate Director, Adventist Chaplaincy Ministries, General Conference of Seventh-day Adventists.

Vikki Montgomery is a health educator and writer living in Maryland. She is an editor for *Liberty* magazine.

Gwen Foster, M.P.H., is a graduate of Loma Linda University and a member of the Loma Linda Board of Directors. She is currently the Health Czar for Philadelphia and the originator of the Fitness for Life conditioning program. She was the host of a health program that was aired on one of the major networks in Philadelphia.

Gary E. Fraser, M.B., C.H.B., Ph.D., M.P.H., F.R.A.C.P., is a practicing cardiologist at Loma Linda University Medical Center and is professor of epidemiology and cardiology at Loma Linda University. He was appointed director of the Adventist Health Study in 1987.

Phil Garver, Ed.D., is chairman of health, physical education, and recreation, Southern Adventist University in Collegedale, Tennessee.

Gary L. Hopkins, M.D., Dr.P.H., C.H.E.S., is the director of the Institute for the Prevention of Addictions at Andrews University. Areas of special interest include: Teen pregnancy prevention; AIDS research and program development; substance abuse prevention in the community and with incarcerated individuals.

Don G. King, Dr.P.H., is president of Northeastern Conference. Formerly a pastor, and the secretary of the Alberta Conference in Canada.

Lee Anna Jackson served as the assistant editor of *Message* magazine. Jackson has been employed by several televisions stations in the New York City market. She has served as a media consultant, reporter, producer, and host for news, public affairs and other televisions programs.

Audray Johnson, R.N., directs health ministries and family life for the Southeastern California Conference.

Harry Krueger is a former pastor and hospital chaplain who directed the HeartBeat program and the Adventist Health Network for the North American Division.

Jan W. Kuzma, Ph.D., is a biostatistician and was a former director of research at Loma Linda University School of Public Health. He was president of Sentinel Research Services which produced the daily radio spot, "Got A Minute for Your Health?"

Kay Kuzma, Ed.D., Family specialist, speaker and founder of Family Matters. She has authored more than a dozen books on family life and hosted a daily radio spot, "Got A Minute for Your Family?"

Reuben Lorensen, M.Sc, M.P.H., Dr. P.H., C.H.E.S., Director of Preventive Care and Health Education at the Gimbel Eye Centre in Calgary, Alberta, Canada.

Aileen Ludington, M.D., is a graduate of Loma Linda University with over 25 years of practice focusing on preventive medicine. She has authored a number of books and co-authored several with Hans Diehl.

Emerson Miller is a Board Certified Social Worker, licensed Marriage and Family Therapist, and a licensed Chemical Dependency Counselor. For many years he was assistant professor of Social Work at Southwestern Adventist College.

Bruce Moyer, S.T.D. is at the Institute of World Missions at Andrews University, and is a specialist in pastoral education and AIDS resources.

Pat Mutch, Ph.D., is the academic dean of the College of Arts and Sciences at Andrews University. For many years she was the director of the Institute for the Prevention of Addictions at Andrews University and an assistant director for the General Conference Department of Health and Temperance.

Christine Neish, R.N., M.P.H., Ph.D., Associate Professor, Chairman of Health Promotion and Education at the School of Public Health, Loma Linda University.

Warren Peters, M.D., F.A.C.S., Director of the Center for Health Promotion, Loma Linda University. He practiced at Weimar and other self-supporting institutions before bringing his rich background in preventive medicine to Loma Linda University.

Jocelyn M. Peterson, R.D., M.P.H., L.D., Nutrition Consultant and Director of Dimensions in Food and Nutrition, Inc., Burtonville, Maryland.

Leilani Proctor, produces *The Health Connection* Catalog and is continually searching for the best in resources for the promotion of drug-free living.

Stoy Proctor, M.P.H., Associate Director of the General Conference Health Ministries Department and author of the Breathe Free™ stop smoking manual.

E. John Reinhold, D.D., D.N., Founder and director of Christian Care Ministry, a not-for-profit organization where Christians help Christians pay medical expenses.

Celeste Ryan, is editor of the Columbia Union Visitor and producer of Lifelines radio spots.

Monte Sahlin, M.A., former assistant to the North American Division President for Ministries and the North American Division ADRA Director. He has been a pastor and is involved in research and development in the North American Division.

Albert Sanchez, Dr.P.H., former Director Spanish Health Coordinator, Community Health Education at Pacific Health Education Center in Bakersfield, California.

Janey Scandiff is a member of the American Council on Exercise. She is currently president of Health Connection Network, a privately owned business outside of Chicago, Illinois.

Richard Schaefer, Director of Community Relations, Loma Linda Medical Center, and author of the history of Loma Linda called *Legacy*.

John A. Scharffenberg, M.D., M.P.H., Assistant Director of the General Conference Health Ministries Department. Formerly from Loma Linda University and Pacific Health Education Center. A dynamic speaker and author.

J. R. Spangler, now deceased, former director of the Ministerial Association for the General Conference of Seventh-day Adventists. He retired in 1990 after 28 years as editor of *Ministry Magazine*. His strong emphasis on evangelism has included pioneering efforts in health evangelism.

Gary D. Strunk, M.A., M.Div., M.P.H. is currently pastoring a church in California. Just prior to that he was Director of Religious Studies for the Pacific Health Education Center in Bakersfield California.

Walter C. Thompson, M.D., is a retired surgeon living in Illinois. He is the author of numerous books on health and an active pro-moter of the 3-ABN television ministry.

Agatha Thrash, M.D., Co-founder of Uchee Pines Institute, popular speaker, TV host, and author of dozens of books on health, natural remedies and the complete vegetarian diet.

Leo Van Dolson, Ph.D., former editor of *Life and Health* and professor at the School of Public Health, Loma Linda University. He is the author of a number of books on health and is active in local health evangelism.

Steve Veres, is a pastor and director of the Michigan Van Ministries.

Caroline Watkins,, is a mental health consultant as well as a human resources developer and consultant.

DeWitt S. Williams, Ed.D., M.P.H., C.H.E.S., is director of Health Ministries for the North American Division.

About this Handbook

The first edition of this manual was prepared during 1996 so that it could be ready in 1997, the Year of Health and Healing. New information, new leaders and new concepts are constantly being brought to our attention. This second edition attempts to bring you the latest. We have added five new chapters and an index.

A handbook which attempts to list materials, speakers, programs, organizations, and resources is almost out of date by the time it is published. We have made an attempt to find all the current information we could, but we realize that we may have made omissions and mistakes. If you notice something that needs to be corrected, added, or deleted, please send this information to NAD Health Ministries Department, 12501 Old Columbia Pike Silver Spring, MD 20904. Indicate the chapter and page where this information belongs. If you have a book or video that has been omitted, please send a copy for review. When the next revision is made, this information will be available.

Truth is progressive. This is especially true about health issues. More and more research is confirming what Ellen White wrote a century ago, yet not all health professionals agree on various issues in the health arena, especially on such hot topics as diet and natural remedies. We have chosen to list all the resources from Adventist organizations that we learned about without judgment. It is our prayer that we can help one another to build a temple of truth by taking the best from various sources and comparing them with *The Ministry of Healing and Counsels on Diet and Foods*.

From time to time the North American Division has made small variations in department names in various promotional materials in order to reflect their work more meaningful.

In an attempt to make this handbook user-friendly, we have duplicated telephone numbers and some resource information in various chapters so you don't have to read the entire manuscript to find the information you need.

Although there is a chapter on resources, some resources have been listed in chapters under various topics and are not duplicated in the resource chapter. Prices listed are U.S. prices unless noted.

Bible texts are from the King James Version, unless otherwise noted.

Not all 800 numbers will work from Canada, therefore, we have attempted to list the regular number wherever possible, except in Appendix F where toll-free hotline numbers are given. Hundreds of individuals helped us in bringing together the information that is in this manual. We want to thank those who were not recognized as contributors, but provided a valuable service to us.

A Challenge to Follow the Blueprint

Ellen White said that we will never finish the work until we work the cities as God would have us. She said that in this work, gospel ministers and medical missionary workers or health professionals are to be united. (See *A Call to Medical Evangelism and Health Education*, pp. 14, 15.)

Hospitals will never be able to fully care for North America's healthcare needs. In the United States, fifty years ago, healthcare expenditures were $2 billion a year; today they are $2 billion every day. Despite decreases in inpatient volumes over the past five years, healthcare spending continues to rise and is projected to comprise 18 percent of the nation's gross domestic product by the year 2000. In addition, an estimated 37 million U.S. citizens, or one out of every seven, have no health insurance. Although the statistics for Canada and Bermuda differ from that of the United States, there is still an urgent need for adequate healthcare throughout North America.

Churches can be church-based preventive healthcare centers. With more than 350,000 congregations in the United States, churches outnumber hospitals by a huge margin. Congregations deal with 150 million people regularly, not just when they get sick, or become incapacitated. In North America, Adventists have nearly 5,000 churches and fewer than 75 hospitals. The mere *physical presence* of our churches is a tremendous asset because they are everywhere.

Then there is the personnel of the churches. In North America there are more than 850,000 Adventists—volunteers, as it were—who could be trained for medical missionary work. Many physicians, nurses, and other health professionals are already trained.

Finally, there is the *power* that churches offer. Many organizations offer stop-smoking clinics, cooking schools, and other life-changing programs. But none of them offer the life-changing power found in Jesus Christ.

North America is our mission field. Men and women are sick, overweight, over-drugged, and confused. We've had our health message since 1863. Now is the time to accept the challenge to get "health reform" to the masses.

Wouldn't it be wonderful if Adventists could say to North America, "we have 50,000 trained health professionals who can go into the cities and towns and restore people to health; we have nearly 5,000 churches that are prepared as community-based health prevention centers ready to help"?

Our churches have a moral responsibility to answer the call. What if each church served its immediate neighborhood by conducting classes in healthful living or offered basic medical screening? We should be involved, not from a secular agenda imposed on us, but from the spiritual injunction to care for the sick, the poor, and the oppressed.

Imagine churches, Adventist Community Services centers, hospitals, and schools in a given area networking together. Some of our large cities have more than 20 churches. Most of the time, each one works independently. What if they worked together, planning their marketing strategies and training others?

Now is the time to reach out to people in North America. We have the right arm of the message. Let's use it.

My prayer is that this book will empower those who want to reach out and minister to the hurting, the helpless, the hugless, the homeless, the least and the last. Together we can make a difference in the lives of hundreds of thousands of people. Together we can work God's blueprint for health evangelism, doing a noble work for God and blessing humanity. Together we can win souls for Christ.

I like the thought of Bertha Von Suttner, "After the verb 'to Love', the verb 'to Help' is the most beautiful verb in the world." *Ministries of Health and Healing* will help you help somebody who needs your help. And at the same time it will help you help yourself. For as James Barrie once said "Those who bring sunshine to the lives of others cannot keep it from themselves."

—DeWitt S. Williams
Director Health and Temperance Department
Seventh-day Adventist Church
in North America

1

The Adventist Philosophy of Health Ministry

The Seventh-day Adventist health message is more than veggie burgers and tofu; sitz baths and stop smoking plans. *There is a religious connection.* The practical reason for a health ministry is that those with clear minds are able to better understand the will of God, and those with healthy bodies are better able to serve others.

Health is God's Will

A health ministry, which includes healing, disease prevention and health enhancement, needs to be built on a foundational belief that good health is God's will. Such a foundational belief *mandates* a health ministry.

While it may be argued that death, disease and suffering are in the broad sense God's will (for they are the natural consequences of human's God-given freedom to choose to transgress the laws of life) it may also be argued that sin and its consequences are contrary to God's beneficent will for His creatures.

In seeking to relieve suffering and putting a halt to sin, we are cooperating with God's efforts to restore the universe to harmonious compliance with His laws of life. With rare exceptions, loss of life through capricious storm, earthquake, injury, illness and premature death are not the will of God. (See *The Great Controversy*, pp. 589, 590.)

God created the human race to live eternally, but the entrance of sin brought disease and death. Until the flood it was common for people to live 700 years or more. Methuselah, Noah's grandfather, lived 969 years. Noah survived 950 years. But after the flood, Abraham lived a mere 175. By the time the Jews left Egypt and entered the promised land their life span had shrunk to approximately what it is today.

What was responsible for the dramatic reduction in life span? Many suggest it was the flesh foods that God allowed man to eat after the flood to shorten a life of sin. But eating God's original plant-based diet and obeying God's health principles can help reverse this trend. Studies on Adventist populations suggest vegetarians who exercise these principles live six to twelve years longer than the general population. (See research findings in Chapter 23.)

If you lived longer and healthier, imagine the wisdom you would acquire! Think of what a powerful witness you could be for Christ if you remained disease free. Consider the number of people you could win if you brought just one person a year to God for each extra year you lived. What a difference you would make for the gospel.

God's promise is, "My son, do not forget my teaching, but keep my commands in your heart, for they will prolong your life many years and bring you prosperity (Prov. 3:1-2, NIV). If we live healthier and longer, we will be better equipped to serve God and meet the needs of others.

God created our bodies as temples of the Holy Spirit. God wants to dwell in us. Paul twice declared to the hedonistic Corinthians that God intends our bodies to be spiritual temples for His Holy Spirit (1 Cor. 3:15; 6:19). God claims to "own" these "temples," both by His original act of creation (Eph. 2:10) and subsequently by the redemption price paid at Calvary (1 Cor. 6:20). Because God has a lot invested in our bodies He wants them to be treat-

> "Disease never comes without a cause. The way is first prepared, and disease invited by disregarding the laws of health ."
>
> —Ellen White, *Selected Messages*, book 2, p. 469.

ed according to His "Owner's Manual"—the Bible.

God redeemed us (our bodies) through Jesus Christ and wants to restore us to His image. In his article, "What Is the Adventist 'Health Message'?," Roger Coon says, "The goal of the Christian religion, in theological terminology, is 'redemption'—the restoration of what once was, in both humans and their world, thus bringing both back to their original ideal state." Then he quotes Jim Gilbertson as saying, "God formed us; sin deformed us: salvation through Christ transforms us'" (*Adventist Review*, Dec. 9, 1993, p. 17).

Biblical Basis for the Adventist Philosophy of Health

- *We are God's creation to do good works.*

  "For we are his workmanship, created in Christ Jesus unto good works, which God hath before ordained that we should walk in them" (Eph. 2:10).
- *We have a sacred, moral obligation to maintain these "dwellings" in optimum physical condition.*

  "I beseech you therefore, brethren, by the mercies of God, that ye present your bodies a living sacrifice, holy, acceptable unto God, which is your reasonable service" (Rom 12:1).
- *We were redeemed by Christ, and are to honor and glorify God in our bodies; we must not "defile" them in any way.*

  "What? know ye not that your body is the temple of the Holy Ghost which is in you, which ye have of God, and ye are not your own? For ye are bought with a price: therefore glorify God in your body, and in your spirit, which are God's" (1 Cor. 6:19, 20).
- *The belief in the soon coming of Christ calls for a dedication of the complete being to God.*

  "The very God of peace sanctify you wholly; and I pray God your whole spirit and soul and body be preserved blameless unto the coming of our Lord Jesus Christ" (1 Thess. 5:23).

God Holds Us Accountable for Our Health

On this Biblical basis rests the belief that there is an accountability to God for the preservation of health, and that the person who knowingly violates simple health principles, thereby bringing on ill-health, disease, or disability, is living in violation of the laws of God. The smoker who brings cancer of the lungs upon himself or herself; the drinker who develops cirrhosis of the liver; the irregular eater, or the overeater, or the one who indulges in excessive quantities of heavy or rich food and develops serious digestive disease; the corpulent, intense, non-exercising business person or professional who is overtaken with a heart attack—all these are in greater or less measure responsible for the ills they suffer and bear some guilt for neglect of the bodies entrusted to them.

This fact makes our relationship to the entire question of health a highly practical one, not an emotional, ritualistic, or legalistic one. If, as Adventists believe, Christians have the same responsibility to preserve their health as they have to preserve their character, promotion of a wider understanding of basic health principles assumes an important role in religion and theology.

In the light of these facts, Adventists concern themselves with the care of the sick, helping to bring relief to those who suffer. They further endeavor through education to promote desirable habits and practices of health whereby disease is lessened or prevented and the body preserved in health.

Susannah Wesley, mother of the founder of Methodism, aptly said, "Whatever weakens your reason, impairs the tenderness of your conscience, obscures your sense of God, decreases the strength and authority of your mind over your body–that thing is wrong, however innocent it may be in itself."

—Quoted by C. B. Haynes, "Church Standards No.5," *Review and Herald*, October 30, 1941, p. 7.

The Challenge

The Bible warns that in the last days even the elect will be deceived. If ever we needed a time for clear thinking and spiritual discernment, it's now. God speaks to our minds through the Holy Spirit and commands our bodies to serve. If our overburdened bodies dull our thinking, the Lord has a difficult time getting through to motivate us.

Isn't it time for us to think about Jesus Christ as being more than a "fire escape" from destruction? Isn't it time for us to present our bodies to the God who teaches us to care for his holy temples? Our health and vigor can point the way to true inner joy and peace for a lost and materialistic "boomer" generation. This is the reason for the health message.

The first humans lived at a time before degenerative diseases. Because God wanted Adam and Eve and the entire human race to be healthy, He:

1. told them to eat nuts, grains, and fruit
2. gave them work to keep their bodies exercised
3. commanded them to rest one day out of seven
4. established marriage and families to give them a social support system.

God certainly didn't suggest the lifestyle that causes the American population of 285 million to suffer more than 700,000 annual deaths from heart attacks, more than half a million from cancer, and more than 160,000 from strokes. Most of these deaths occur at an early age in the sixties

Adventist Lifestyle Profile: *Mavis Lindgren*

*P*lagued with severe lung ailments since childhood, it wasn't until she reached her early 60s that Mavis took responsibility for her own health.

While she was attending a series of lectures by Dr. Charles Thomas from Loma Linda University, she began to walk every day. She prayed as she walked that the exercise program might help her worsening lung ailment, weakened heart, and skeletal muscles. Decades of inactivity had added twenty extra pounds to her five-foot-two frame. Over the months, she increased her walking distance. Before long, she took up jogging. She lost the extra weight and her lung ailment disappeared. (She often says, "I haven't been sick a day since.")

The running increased. Soon she went on the trail six days a week, five miles at a time—and loved it. At age 70, she entered the Sacramento Pepsi 20-Mile Run. She not only finished the twenty miles, but set a record for her age group. She has since gone on to finish other marathons (26.2 miles) where she also set records for her age group, only to come back and reset the record on several occasions. But she says of her races that she doesn't compete with others, she races only against herself.

A vegetarian, Mavis eats a high-carbohydrate diet and *averages* fifty miles of running a week. She believes that although the process of aging is inevitable, it is possible to maintain a higher level of fitness throughout the decline by adhering to simple, healthful habits. She also says that in addition to proper nutrition, sufficient rest, and exercise, the fourth component of a balanced lifestyle is gratitude of heart.

The headline on the sports page of the November 9, 1993, *New York Times* read, "Don't Look Back, Father Time, Mavis Lindgren, 86, Is Gaining on You."

—*Jan W. and Kay Kuzma*

(From: *Energized!: One-a-day devotionals for body, mind and soul.* Hagerstown, MD: Review and Herald Publishing Association, 1997. Used by permission.)

Adventist Lifestyle Profile: *Charlotte Hamlin*

"*There's* no great accomplishment just in living many years," said an active 91-year-old. "Nursing homes are filled with medicated survivors–as if that has to be the fate of those who reach old age. But to live to those ages and still be independent, physically active, and mentally alert, *that* is an accomplishment."

And that's exactly what Charlotte Hamlin has been doing as she sets walking and cycling records across the country. "The closer we live by the laws of nature," she says, "the better we will feel and the longer we will live." What are the laws of nature? According to Charlotte, the secret's in the acronym "FRESH START": **F**resh Air, **R**est, **E**xercise, **S**unshine, **H**appiness, **S**imple diet, **T**he use of water, **A**bstemiousness, **R**estoration and **T**rust in divine power.

Charlotte, nearing her eightieth birthday cycles from 50 to 80 miles a day and has proven to millions that we can stay productive and healthy at any age. From 1973 until she retired in 1986, she organized and directed a summer health screening program, and founded the Three C's, a risk evaluation program that tested for potential risk for coronaries, cancer, and CVA (stroke).

In 1986, Charlotte retired from her post as assistant professor of nursing at Andrews University to establish *Fresh Start*, a health conditioning live-in program.

Ready to quit? Not Charlotte. When she was 68, she and her son Gene formed a non-profit organization Global Trek International.

The same year she walked and cycled from coast to coast, leaving Southern California in March 1987 and arriving 67 days later at Charleston, South Carolina. She made a 32 day trek across Europe that fall. The following year her 9,000 miles of pedaling took her through portions of Israel, Pakistan, India, Thailand, China, Japan, Guam, Hawaii, and she finished at her birthplace in Canada on her seventieth birthday.

An article about Charlotte carried the title, "Too Fit to Quit." Not a bad epithet as she pedals around the world, reminding us that God has a work for us to do, regardless of our age.

—*Jan W. and Kay Kuzma*

(From: *Energized!: One-a-day devotionals for body, mind and soul.* Hagerstown, MD: Review and Herald Publishing Association, 1997. Used by permission.)

and seventies—far from Methuselah's 969 years. Put another way, our present style of living generates heart attacks, cancer, and strokes—three-fourths of the causes of all deaths. Researchers insist that these premature deaths are due primarily to our diet and lifestyle.

In 1863 Ellen White was given a 45 minute vision that emphasized the importance of re-establishing the original health principles in the lives of God's people. God made it clear that health considerations were more than secular concerns. "Healthful living", said Ellen White, "is a sacred duty which God has enjoined upon reasonable beings, formed in His image, to keep that image in as perfect a state as possible" (*Spiritual Gifts*, vol. 4a, p. 148).

That is why the health message is such an important part of the outreach of the Seventh-day Adventist church. That's why the church in 1863 began publishing a health journal called *The Health Reformer* and has continued to publish health and temperance magazines. That's why the church began medical institutions and training programs for medical missionaries. And that's why, today, Seventh-day Adventists have a department of Health Ministries at every level of the church structure and a Health Ministries Leader in every Adventist church.

The health message is the "right arm" of the message. And you have the honor and responsibility to lead out in this important work in your church.

An Imaginary Interview Between J. R. Spangler and Ellen White

In *Ministry* (September, 1970, pp. 3-5), J. R. Spangler published an imaginary interview with Ellen White using various quotations from her voluminous writing about the importance of health. Her counsel from the 1860's until her death in 1915 is relevant to health ministries personnel today. Hopefully, this interview will inspire you to promote the health message among your church members and your local community.

JRS: *Mrs. White, the attention of the world today seems to be focused more and more on healthful living. Do you believe we should capitalize on this fact?*

EGW: "No subject which is presented to the inhabitants of our cities should command so large an interest as that which concerns physical health" (*Temperance*, p. 196).

JRS: *Do you think our health message can be used as a tool for evangelism?*

EGW: "I can see in the Lord's providence that the medical missionary work is to be a great entering wedge, whereby the diseased soul may be reached" (*Counsels on Health*, p. 535).

JRS: *Why do you call it an "entering wedge" and just how is [an individual] elevated spiritually by placing emphasis upon healthful living?*

EGW: "If we would elevate the moral standard in any country where we may be called to go, we must begin by correcting their physical habits. Virtue of character depends upon the right action of the powers of the mind and body" (*Ibid.*, p. 505).

JRS: *Of course, you understand that prejudice is strong against our faith and sometimes we are known as health faddists. How strongly do you favor a health approach for breaking down prejudice?*

EGW: "When I heard that Dr. Kellogg had taken up the medical missionary work, I encouraged him with heart and soul, because I knew that only by this work can the prejudice which exists in the world against our faith be broken down" (*Ibid.*, p. 532).

JRS: *Could you clarify this point, further?*

EGW: "Doors that have been closed to him who merely preaches the gospel, will be opened to the intelligent medical missionary. God reaches hearts through the relief of physical suffering" (*Medical Ministry*, p. 246).

JRS: *So you think it is easier to reach a person spiritually through his/her physical needs?*

EGW: "In affliction, many are humbled in spirit, and words in favor of the truth spoken to them in tenderness by one who is seeking to alleviate physical sufferings, may touch the heart" (*Counsels on Health*, p. 503).

JRS: *What about using a health approach in those areas where Adventism is unknown, such as a dark county?*

> "It is the Lord's design that the restoring influence of health reform shall be a part of the last great effort to proclaim the gospel message."
>
> —Ellen White, *Medical Ministry*, p. 259.

EGW: "In new fields no work is so successful as medical missionary work. If our ministers would work earnestly to obtain an education in medical missionary lines, they would be far better fitted to do the work Christ did as a medical missionary. By diligent study and practice, they can become so well acquainted with the principles of health reform, that wherever they go they will be a great blessing to the people they meet.

"For thirty years the necessity of health reform has been held before our people. By the practice of its simple principles, the sick and suffering are relieved, and fields otherwise unapproachable, become most interesting fields of action. The seeds of truth, cast into good ground, produce an abundant harvest" (*Medical Ministry*, p. 239).

JRS: *Are you saying a health approach not only prepares the soil for gospel seed planting but is effective in reaping a harvest?*

EGW: "When connected with other lines of gospel effort, medical missionary work is a most effective instrument by which the ground is prepared for the sowing of the seeds of truth, and the instrument also by which the harvest is reaped" (*Ibid*, p. 240).

JRS: *What relationship should medical missionary work have to the Three Angels' Messages?*

EGW: "Again and again I have been instructed that the medical missionary work is to bear the same relation to the work of the third angel's message that the arm and hand bear to the body" (*Counsels on Health*, p. 513).

JRS: *But don't you think that our modern system of medical treatment is sufficient for the human race today and that in these last days our entire time should be occupied in preaching spiritual themes only?*

EGW: "The gospel of health is to be firmly linked with the ministry of the word. It is the Lord's design that the restoring influence of health reform shall be a part of the last great effort to proclaim the gospel message" (*Medical Ministry*, p. 259).

JRS: *But, Mrs. White, we ministers are so busy in our program. How can we be expected to learn all*

about the body and its functions? We need help. What do you suggest?

EGW: "So far as possible, it would be well for evangelical workers to learn how to minister to the necessities of the body as well as the soul; for in doing this, they are following the example of Christ. Intemperance has well-nigh filled the world with disease, and the ministers of the gospel cannot spend their time and strength in relieving all in need of help. The Lord has ordained that Christian physicians and nurses shall labor in connection with those who preach the word. The medical missionary work is to be bound up with the gospel ministry" (*Ibid*, p. 240).

JRS: *Your answer amazes me! Do you mean medical personnel should be out working side by side with the ministers in teaching truth?*

EGW: "If our physicians and our ministers can work together in the presentation of truth to the people, more can be reached than could be influenced by the minister laboring alone" (*Medical Ministry*, p. 263).

"The physician and the minister should realize that they are engaged in the same work. They should labor in perfect harmony" (*Ibid.*, vol. 7, p. 111). . .

JRS: *Just how serious are you about preachers and other soul winners having a knowledge of health principles to the extent of teaching it to others?*

EGW: "Every gospel worker should feel that the giving of instruction in the principles of healthful living is a part of his appointed work. Of this work there is great need, and the world is open for it" (*The Ministry of Healing*, p. 147. . .

JRS: *Can you give us any other reasons why ministers should be deeply interested in promoting a health program?*

EGW: "I wish to tell you that soon there will be no work done in ministerial lines but medical missionary work. The work of a minister is to minister. Our ministers are to work on the gospel plan of ministering. . . .

"You will never be ministers after the gospel order till you show a decided interest in medical missionary work, the gospel

---

All who habitually, persistently flout the observance of health principles will in the end be destroyed in God's final judgment, (see *Testimonies*, vol 4, p. 652; *The Acts of the Apostles*, p. 239; *Conflict and Courage*, p. 165) not so much because they broke one of His health laws as because they destroyed the only channel of communication with Him, thereby losing the capacity (and eventually even the desire) for truly knowing and loving Him (the "first... great commandment"). Thus, in the end, "God destroys no man. Everyone who is destroyed will have destroyed himself"
(*Christ's Object Lessons*, p. 84).

—*Roger W. Coon.*, "What Is the Adventist 'Health Message'?" *Adventist Review*, Dec. 9, 1993, p. 17.

Adventist Lifestyle Profile: *Hulda Crooks*

*H*ulda Crooks first climbed 14,495 foot Mount Whitney, North America's highest mountain, in 1962 at age 66 and continued to climb it nearly every year after that until she was 88.

When she was 91 years old she climbed Japan's 12,388 foot Mt. Fuji, reaching the summit on July 24, 1987, the oldest woman ever to do so. Six weeks later she again climbed Mt. Whitney. But these aren't the only climbs she has made. Incredible as it may seem, between her 81st and 90th birthdays she climbed 97 peaks. When someone challenged her to climb the avalanche of steps leading to the top of the Capitol Dome in Washington, D.C. (steps are sometimes more difficult than a mountain trail) Hulda Crooks accepted the challenge—and won. When she was 94 her doctor told her she had the heart and lungs of an 18 year old.

Among the many honors bestowed on Hulda, perhaps the most surprising to her came in 1991 when the California State Legislature named a mountain peak near Mt. Whitney, after her—Crooks Peak.

She celebrated her 100th birthday with the publication of two books: *Conquering Life's Mountains* by Hulda Crooks, and a book about her, *Grandma Whitney*, by William Andress & Winnie Gohde.

She lives by the philosophy that "muscles, not used, atrophy. Bones, not put under stress, lose minerals and become weak. Joints, not moved sufficiently as in walking, working, or other forms of exercise, become stiff from disuse. The blunt facts are that your body needs intelligent care."

Hulda has proven that a lifestyle change can take place at any age. She describes her teen years as being nervous, anemic, and perpetually tired. At age 31, when she was overweight and not physically well, her physician-husband encouraged her to become more physically active. Following his advice changed her life. Since then she has said that we can't separate diet and exercise. "The diet provides the materials for the body's functions. The exercise is absolutely essential in keeping up a good circulation. If we don't exercise, the circulation is sluggish and that affects the entire body, the mental as well as the rest of the body."

Hulda's life is an inspiration to all, regardless of age, to get up and get going!

—*Jan W. and Kay Kuzma*

(From: *Energized! One-a-day devotionals for body, mind and soul.* Hagerstown, MD: Review and Herald Publishing Association, 1997. Used by permission.)

Hulda Crooks passed away on November 23, 1997.
She celebrated her 100th birthday May 19, 1996.

of healing and blessing and strengthening" (*Counsels on Health*, p. 533). . .

JRS: *I've heard some ridicule the concepts God has given us through you regarding health principles. How do you feel about this?*

EGW: "Guilt rests upon us as a people who have had much light, because we have not appreciated or improved the light given upon health reform. Through misunderstanding and perverted ideas many souls are deceived. Those who teach the truth to others and who should be shepherds of the flock, will be held accountable for their willing ignorance and disregard of nature's laws. This is not a matter to be trifled with, to be passed off with a jest" (*Counsels on Health*, pp. 505, 506).

JRS: *What do you think the future holds for our medical missionary work?*

EGW: "We shall see the medical missionary work broadening and deepening at every point of its progress, because of the inflowing of hundreds and thousands of streams, until the whole earth is covered as the waters cover the sea" (*Medical Ministry*, p. 317).

JRS: *Let me express appreciation to you for giving us such valuable insights of a work we should have taken up long ago. We hope to see a change of emphasis in our movement regarding the use of our health message as an evangelistic entering wedge.*

What is the Adventist Health Message?

Some might define the Adventist health message by listing the eight natural remedies mentioned by Ellen White, "Pure air, sunlight, abstemiousness, rest, exercise, proper diet, the use of water, trust in divine power—these are the true remedies" (*The Ministry of Healing*, p. 127). Weimar Institute's acronym for the true remedies is NEWSTART: **N**utrition (proper), **E**xercise, **W**ater, **S**unlight, **T**emperance (self-control), **A**ir, **R**est, and **T**rust in divine power.

Others would simple say that the Adventist health message is:

#1: To promote good health habits; and speak against those things which ultimately destroy the body temple, such as,

- Eating or drinking harmful substances
- Insufficient physical exercise
- Overwork—often coupled with insufficient rest or relaxation
- Impure thoughts (The opposite of those things which are true, honest, just, pure, lovely and of good report as mentioned that we should think upon in Phil. 4:8)
- Improper posture
- Abuse of bodily organs by overeating, overexertion, straining, constriction, etc.
- Lack of sufficient pure water, fresh air, and sunshine.
- Using addictive substances.(True temperance means moderation in the use of all that is health-producing, and total abstinence from all that harms and hurts.)

#2: To promote the original diet given by God to Adam and Eve (fruits, nuts, grains, and vegetables) as the diet that develops optimum physical health and spiritual growth and well-being.

- Meat, poultry, and fish, together with dairy and poultry products, are increasingly undesirable and unsafe because of:
- Disease in the animals themselves
- Contamination from chemical agents (and even at times radioactive agents)
- Potentially harmful effects, physiologically and spiritually, upon body, mind, and character.

#3: To promote natural remedies. Whenever possible in attempts at physical healing, natural remedies (including trust in divine power) are the preferred therapeutic agencies. Poisonous drugs and substances should be avoided whenever and wherever possible. But there is a legitimate place for some drugs, anesthetics, immunizations, x-rays, and prophylaxis (e.g. the use of quinine-like medications for the prevention of malaria). (See *Selected Messages*, book 2, pp. 279-284.) The list of safe, valuable, life-saving medications has expanded considerably since Ellen White's lifetime, but the preferred remedies are natural ones.

#4: To share the principles of health with others. Ellen White suggested: "We must go no faster than we can take those with us whose consciences and intellects are convinced of the truths we advocate. We must meet people where they are. . . . In reforms we would better come one step short of the mark than to go one step beyond it. And if there is error at all, let it be on the side next to the people" (*Testimonies*, vol. 3, pp. 20, 21).

#5: To provide healing services and training, such as:

- The establishment of health-care centers for the healing of those afflicted with illness and disease.
- The teaching of preventive methods and practices by means of which illnesses and disease may be avoided.
- The establishment of training schools for health professionals and workers.

A Testimony for the Health Message

*M*ore than ten thousand Christians were in membership of an organization I founded as an alternative to conventional health insurance. Our members share one another's medical bills on a not-for-profit basis. As CEO I weighed 278 pounds, was on heart medications, a pain medication for arthritis, and had reoccurring diverticulosis. Because of my weight I was told I did not qualify for the program I founded. At this time the only health message I knew was to stay away from poison mushrooms!

Then an Adventist member sent me *Counsels on Diet and Foods*. I devoured the book in a day, being amazed to discover that the author, who is on the cutting edge of current health issues, wrote most of the content before the turn of the century.

While straightening out my lifestyle using the principles I read in Ellen White's book, and dropping over 70 pounds along the way, I answered a telephone call from Dr. Jan Kuzma, inquiring about our ministry. As the Lord worked things out, I had travel plans to be in Tennessee the following week and was drawn to visit with this brilliant biostatistician regarding health issues.

After visiting the Kuzma household a second time and becoming impressed with the Christian witness I found, I inquired about the doctrines of the Seventh-day Adventist Church. Jan gave me a booklet called, *Your Friends the Adventists*. That weekend I sought out the local fellowship of Seventh-day Adventists and kept my first Sabbath. Within a week an Adventist Pastor from Virginia, inquiring about our program, upon my request to learn more, sent me the book, *Seventh-day Adventists Believe....*

As a result of attending the ASI Convention at Spokane and being influenced by Dr. John and Jane Sines and others, we initiated a very aggressive wellness program in our ministry. By that time I had been a complete vegetarian for a year. My energy levels were akin to those I remembered in my college years. I had no arthritis and no heart skips or extra beats. After 35 years of being enslaved to coffee and my taste buds, I was free. My cholesterol levels went from the mid 250's to the low 130's. My triglycerides dropped to below 100 from the mid 700's. My blood pressure dropped into acceptable ranges from borderline high. In short I was "born again." In the meanwhile my wife, married sons and wives, son at home, and our ministry staff, all joined my lifestyle as the result of studying the model.

The Christian Care Ministry and the Medi-Share Program is now a beacon to the whole Christian community on health issues. Nine of our board members are Adventists, most of our staff and health counselors are Adventists, and I have been a Sabbath keeper for almost two years. Our ministry sponsors vegetarian cooking classes, regional health seminars for our members, and a newsletter dealing with health issues. We refer dozens of our members to lifestyle centers under the care of Adventists. Hundreds of books have been distributed to our members authored by Adventist authors like Doctors Hans Diehl and Aileen Ludington, Richard Hansen, and Agatha Thrash.

After taking 2,200 hours of formal training in Bible studies, I discovered that I had missed many truths. What a joy it is to share those truths as well as the Health Message to thousands all over the world.

— E. John Reinhold

(For more information about the Medi-Share program, to receive the Helping One Another *newsletter, or to contact John about speaking appointments, contact: Christian Care Ministry, P.O. Box 1779, Melbourne, FL 32902; (800) 374-2562.)*

What Does the Health Message Have to Do With Salvation?

It helps prepare people for Christ's second coming. God has designed a special program to help prepare people for Christ's second coming. The health message requires an emphasis on medical missionary work which helps to bring new life into our churches as the members turn outward in helping to show God's love to their neighbors in need.

Health workers and gospel workers need to develop a cooperative working relationship if this last movement is to succeed. Because human beings cannot be separated into body, mind, and soul—they are an integrated whole—health workers need to know how to relate to spiritual matters and ministers need to know how to relate to physical health.

"Those who are willing to inform themselves concerning the effect which sinful indulgence has upon the health and who begin the reform, even from selfish motives, may in so doing place themselves where the truth of God can reach their hearts. And, on the other hand, those who have been reached by the presentation of Scripture truth, are in a position where the conscience may be aroused upon the subject of health. . . . He who cherishes the light which God has given him upon health reform has an important aid in the work of becoming sanctified through the truth, and fitted for immortality" (*Counsels on Health*, p. 22).

> "Of all people, those seeking to bring about changes in lifestyle should be the most courteous and tactful. This type of teaching is best done by example and is successful only by the grace of God who gives both the desire for change and the power to bring it about.

"Sanctification is not merely a theory, an emotion, or a form of words, but a living, active principle, entering into the everyday life. It requires that our habits of eating, drinking, and dressing be such as to secure the preservation of physical, mental, and moral health, that we may present to the Lord our bodies—not an offering corrupted by wrong habits but—a living sacrifice, holy, acceptable unto God. Rom 12:2" (*Counsels on Health*. p. 67).

By obeying health principles, Christians "earn" nothing toward salvation and eternal life (*Spiritual Gifts*, vol. 4a, pp. 148, 149), they only "earn" better health. God gave us health laws in order that, through obedience, we can experience the cause and effect phenomenon and be healthier and happier as we avoid harmful practices. As Roger Coon puts it, "We thus observe His health principles, not in order to be saved, but rather because He already has redeemed us. We are motivated by love for God. A clear mind enables us to understand God's will; a strong body enables us to do it. But salvation itself is not a matter of eating and drinking (Rom 14:17), and salvation does not come to us at the end of a knife, fork, or spoon!" ("What is the Adventist Health Message?" *Adventist Review*, Dec. 9, 1993, p. 18).

The Health Message is Based on Christ's Method of Ministry

Adventists believe that, at the Fall, all aspects of human nature—the physical, the intellectual, and the spiritual—were affected, and that Jesus, who said He had come to restore that which was lost (Luke 19:10), seeks to save the whole man. In His ministry Christ touched these three dimensions: He preached the gospel of the kingdom (spiritual), He healed those who were mentally deranged (intellectual), and He restored those afflicted with disease (physical).

Through His continuously operating power by which He also upholds the universe (Heb. 1:3), God is the One who heals our diseases (Ps. 103:3). But at times He involves His servants in that ministry of healing as with Moses and the brass serpent or Elisha and his many acts of healing. Moses also *taught* health. He established an enviable health education program whose laws were to be in the hands of the priest-physicians and to be read in the hearing of the congregation every seven years (Deut. 31:9-12).

The ministry of Jesus was characterized by teaching, preaching and tireless restoration of the sick and suffering (Matt. 4:23-25; 8:1-3;14-16, Acts 10:38). The charge He gave to the apostles, "Preach, saying, 'The kingdom of heaven is at hand, Heal the sick, cleanse the lepers,'" (Matt. 10:7, 8), linked healing and preaching. So did His commission to the 70 in Luke 10:9 and His commission to the church in Mark 16:15, 18. By the example of Jesus and His commission to preach, to teach, and to seek healing, the church is authorized to do all in its power to relieve pain and suffering, and to help prevent illness and accident.

"Christ, the Great Medical Missionary, is our example. Of Him it is written that He went about all Galilee, teaching in their synagogues, and preaching the gospel of the kingdom, and healing all manner of sickness and all manner of disease among the people. He healed the sick and preached the gospel. In His service, healing and teaching were linked closely together. Today they are not to be separated" (Ellen White, as quoted by O. A. Olson, *Review & Herald*, Oct. 29, 1914). "The life of Christ and His ministry to the afflicted are inseparably connected.... An intimate relationship should ever exist between the medical missionary work and the gospel ministry. They are bound together in sacred union as one work, and are never to be divorced. The principles of heaven are to be adopted and practiced by those who claim to walk in the Saviour's footsteps. By His example He has shown us that medical missionary work is not to take the place of the preaching of the gospel, but is to be bound up with it. Christ gave a perfect representation of true godliness by com-

bining the work of a physician and a minister, ministering to the needs of both body and soul, healing physical disease, and then speaking words that brought peace to the troubled heart" (*Counsels on Health*, p. 528).

Jesus was a health educator. He taught the Law, and He taught a relationship between sin and disease (John 5:14). He gave instruction on how people's needs were to be met. When we follow Jesus' example, it helps greatly in preventing physical, emotional and spiritual sickness. (See Matt. 6:33.)

Ignorance is No Excuse

"To make natural law plain, and to urge obedience to it, is a work that accompanies the third angel's message. Ignorance is no excuse now for the transgression of law. The light shines clearly, and none need be ignorant; for the great God Himself is man's instructor. All are bound by the most sacred obligations to heed the sound philosophy and genuine experience which God is now giving them in reference to health reform. He designs that the subject shall be agitated and the public mind deeply stirred to investigate it; for it is impossible for men and women, while under the power of sinful, health-destroying, brain-enervating habits, to appreciate sacred truth."

—Ellen G. White, *Counsels on Health*, p. 21

Health Education

In Adventist philosophy, the concept of "having a body" to care for is replaced by the goal of being a healthy person. We don't just "have bodies," we are bodies.

Ellen White on the Miracle of Healing

"We cannot heal. We cannot change the diseased conditions of the body. But it is our part, as medical missionaries, as workers together with God, to use the means that He has provided. Then we should pray that God will bless these agencies. We do believe in a God; we believe in a God who hears and answers prayer. He has said, 'Ask and ye shall receive; seek, and ye shall find; knock, and it shall be opened unto you.' Matt. 7:7."

—Ellen White, *Review & Herald*, Dec. 5, 1907.

The whole person (physical, mental, social, and spiritual) is viewed as a part of a community whose health is influenced by that of other individuals. For that reason health education involves the cooperation of concerned people, a variety of official and voluntary agencies, professional societies, and churches in promoting necessary changes in order to achieve optimum health and safety.

Because proper provision of food, clothing, and housing within a safe and healthy environment is closely related to community health concerns, careful attention also needs to be given to family living and planning.

The Adventist philosophy of health ministry involves taking advantage of scientific therapies, but views the task of personal and community health as being largely contingent upon personal choice. Because so many of our current diseases are lifestyle related, it becomes incumbent on us to teach people how to free the system from the results of the violation of God-given health principles.

The major goal of Adventist health education is to teach the whole person the responsibilities, opportunities, and decisions essential for the creation of that condition of happiness and whole-ness we call health while living on this earth, and to prepare the individual for the greater happiness and health that will be experienced in the world to come.

Meeting Felt Needs

In Toronto, Ontario, Canada, in 1985, during a time when Sunday closing laws were a front-page controversy, a seminar on the issue of Sunday closing was conducted by the Seventh-day Adventist Life Team. Advertising in the Toronto Star cost $2,300. Three calls were received and 2 people attended. At about the same time, a vegetarian cooking school, called "Western Vegetarian Eating" was conducted in the same place by the same team. Advertising in the Toronto Star cost $400. It produced 65 calls and 100 people attended. Actually we can present as much Bible truth in Western Vegetarian Eating as we can in a Sabbath-Sunday Seminar. People were baptized as a result of that cooking school. No wonder we are told "Take hold of the medical missionary work, and it will give you access to the people" (*Counsels on Health*, p. 533).

People are interested in health. And we are in position to reveal the love of God through our health ministry. The cry of human felt need is a Macedonian mandate to the Seventh-day Adventist Church.

God has placed Seventh-day Adventists at the crossroads of interest in many nations through their record of good health. The Adventist church was born in the dawn of the scientific revolution. We now live in an age of science. Science is the language of advertising, persuasion, expert opinion, epistemology, origins of life and exploration of the universe. With the advent of statistics we now are able to document scientifically that Seventh-day Adventists are healthier and live longer than the average population in every country where they have been studied. This scientific evidence provides tangible, measurable, hard evidence to the world that following the Bible is beneficial. It speaks loudly in a language that people of this generation understand. Adventists have received more press in scientific journals, popular magazines and

Adventist Lifestyle Profile: *Carrol S. Small, MD*

Carrol, born September 16, 1910, has been an active, lifelong church member. Since 1937, he has taught pathology at Loma Linda University as a full professor and has a wall filled with plaques for excellence in teaching. He has also served as president of the San Bernardino County Medical Society, Chairman of the Pathology section of the California Medical Association, President of the Medical Alumni Association and has held memberships on numerous boards.

The real changes began in his life in 1937 when he agreed to teach a course in healthful living. Carrol decided to obey his own recommendations. He and his wife changed their diets and stopped using meat, caffeine, excess sugar, and high-fat foods. Although they had occasionally used medications such as aspirin, they stopped and became, in their own words, "drug-free vegetarians." When he reached the age of 82, not only was he in good health, but he had a cholesterol level of 140.

Today, Dr. Small says, "I adhere to and recommend a non-alcoholic, non-tobacco, vegetarian diet, plus exercise, rest, study, and much trust in God's power and guidance. This program has given me a long life and happiness."

When he was 75, he became the editor of their *Loma Linda University Medical Alumni Journal* and held that position for the next seven years.

At 88, he still is teaching pathology to medical students. In addition to keeping current with the field of pathology, in the last few years he also has helped with a church-sponsored program that tutors high school students in subjects such as physiology and biology. He laughingly admits that before beginning this tutoring, the last biology book he read was in 1928.

What's the secret to Dr. Small's long and active life? He says, "I learned that our bodies are temples for God's Spirit, and that we should keep them free of contamination."

—Jan W. Kuzma, *The Live-Longer Lifestyle*

newspapers for their health than for any other thing they have done in the last 100 years.

"Seventh-day Adventists are handling momentous truths. It is our duty to understand and respect the principles of health reform. On the subject of temperance we should be in advance of all other people" (*Testimonies*, vol. 9, p. 158).

Last-day Ministry

The gifts of the spirit are to be active in the church until the work of the church is complete (Eph. 4:13). One of those gifts is healing (1 Cor. 12:9), another is teaching (Eph. 4:11). Each gift is to be active in building up the church in quantity and quality. Working on the assumption that healing must be attended by corollary instruction of what caused the illness and how to prevent

further illness, health education must be an active ministry of the church.

Another spiritual gift is prophecy (Eph. 4:11). Our philosophy of health and healing can be derived entirely from the Bible, but the Bible prophetically forecasts special messages from Jesus in the last days known as the "Testimony of Jesus" or the "Spirit of Prophecy" (Rev. 12:17; 19:10). These messages forcefully direct our attention to the role, the importance, and the "how" of health. A complete understanding of health must embrace all that is contained in these prophetic messages lest in essence we be found ignoring that portion of the Bible which predicts this gift.

Adventist Lifestyle Profile: *E. Harold Shryock*

*F*ew names are more closely connected with Loma Linda University than that of Shryock. In fact, if you were to walk through the lovely, tree-studded campus, you would likely come upon Shryock Hall, the anatomy building built in 1936 and named for Harold Shryock's father. Harold, who was born in 1906, has lived almost his entire life at Loma Linda, moving there with his family when he was four years old.

Perhaps best known for his journalistic accomplishments, Harold was a columnist for a number of journals and has written 621 articles and 13 books, the last ones completed when he was 79 years of age. Most of his writings emphasized how to live so as to avoid illness. However, in response to the personal problems and concerns of students, he wrote about personal relationships, marriage, and parenthood. He still continues to pursue his writing career. His latest challenge is writing a historical sketch of Loma Linda University's School of Medicine.

In addition to eating a good diet, Harold has been an enthusiastic cyclist. During most of his adult life, he has ridden five to ten miles daily before breakfast. He gave that up in the early 1980s, when his attention turned to caring for his ailing wife for almost ten years until her death in 1992. He now walks a mile before breakfast. He eats two low-fat, low-cholesterol meals a day, "because," he says, "it's more convenient and makes it easier for me to maintain a proper weight."

In 1970, an article about him began, "Men tend to take on statistical configurations if they do much living, and if they live long enough. E. Harold Shryock, M.D., is a man who qualifies" (Keld J. Reynolds, "Vessel of Honor," *The Youth's Instructor*, February 17, 1970, p. 9).

—Jan W. Kuzma, *The Live-Longer Lifestyle*

What about Miracles?

Because the spiritual gift of healing in the ministry of Christ and the early church consisted largely of miracles the question needs to be asked, Why should not the Seventh-day Adventist Church seek to perform miracles rather than establish hospitals and do health education?"

For one thing, the circumstances and beliefs of Jesus' day were different from ours. It was commonly believed that people who had serious diseases and infirmities were under the curse of God and could not be saved. To counter this prevailing belief, Jesus healed prodigiously both Jew and Gentile. By healing them He removed the "curse" and conveyed the truth that the sick could be forgiven and saved.

Some miracles can be expected and are seen in the church, but in the last days the second beast of Revelation 13 is to perform deceiving miracles to help erect an image to the beast. The miracles, which characterize the work of this beast, include miracles of healing which appear to ratify its doctrines as authentic. In contrast, the followers of God are characterized as those who keep the commandments of God and have the testimony of Jesus. To avoid the possibility of appearing like those who follow the beast we would do well to stress the greater miracle of a regenerate heart which restores believers to harmony with the laws of God, including His laws of nature that lead to health and healing. (See Chapter 8.)

During the reorganization and education of Israel, God set forth a comprehensive proclamation of the laws of life (Rom. 7:10; Lev. 18:5) and promised freedom from disease on condition of obedience (Deut. 7:11-15; Ex. 15:26). This was and is God's preferred method of restoring people to health—through the natural results of intelligent obedience to the laws of life. While a measure of Divine interposition still is needed to enable people to obey and to protect them from illness, if people obeyed faithfully, miraculous healing would seldom be needed.

A major part of the work of the gospel is to empower people to develop the fruits of the Spirit which includes self control (Gal. 5:23; 2 Peter 1:6). This leads to control over their lives and restores them to obedience to the commandments of God and the laws of life. A teaching ministry does this more effectively than miracles.

Those seeking to bring about changes in lifestyle should be the most courteous and tactful. This type of teaching is best done by example and is successful only by the grace of God who gives both the desire for change and the power to bring it about.

Summary

God is intensely interested in our total well being. His detailed health instructions in the Bible; the healing ministry of the prophets and of Jesus; and His commissions to heal, teach and preach; in addition to His love within our hearts for our neighbor and the plaintive cry of human need provide powerful justification for the Seventh-day Adventist Church to be highly active in a health ministry. Jesus has blessed us with messages from His own lips in the Spirit of Prophecy, enabling His remnant church to enjoy a measurable advantage in health and longevity which send a signal to the world in scientific language that God's Word is relevant and beneficial in these last days. Seventh-day Adventists, taking the entire Bible as their guide, are to flow out in streams of living water to the world, healing, teaching and preaching in the name of Jesus Christ.

Joseph Bates, The First Adventist Health Reformer

*M*ariner, reformer, Advent preacher, one of the founders of the Seventh-day Adventist Church. He was born July 8, 1792, at Rochester, Massachusetts, near New Bedford. At the age of 15, he set out from his home to follow the sea. He experienced shipwreck, capture, forced service in the British Navy, and was for two and a half years a prisoner of war in England, being released in 1815. After being restored to his home and family, he continued his career as a merchant seaman, becoming a captain in 1820. In 1818, he married Prudence Nye, a childhood friend.

In 1821, Bates gave up the drinking of ardent spirits. The following year, he resolved to drink no wine, and soon after gave up smoking and chewing tobacco, as well as the use of profane language. Before 1838, he had abandoned the use of tea and coffee, and, in 1843, he discontinued the use of flesh foods. Thus, before Seventh-day Adventists were organized into a religious group, Joseph Bates was an enthusiastic supporter of the health principles that this body came in time to embrace.

After Bates' conversion to Christianity in the middle 1820's, he commanded a temperance ship on which he allowed no intoxicants, no swearing, and no washing and mending of clothes on Sunday. He conducted morning and evening worship, but in spite of these rigid rules the rough crew adapted themselves very well to this strict regimen. Earlier in 1824, a New Testament that his wife had placed in his trunk stimulated the beginning of a spiritual awakening. Sobered by the death of a crew member, he surrendered his life to Christ and began daily Bible study and prayer. Upon reaching home he was baptized and attended religious meetings, and, in 1827, joined the Fairhaven Christian church, to which his wife belonged.

In later years, nearly all the early church pioneers were incapacitated with illness from time to time—but not Joseph Bates. Not only did the captain give up flesh food in 1843, but he resolved also to eat no more butter, grease, cheese, pies, or rich cakes. It was not until 20 years later that Ellen White received her comprehensive health vision at Otsego, Michigan. But even after that, it took many Adventists longer to adopt the health principles that would make them healthier, happier, and holier.

2

Community Health Promotion

Early in their history Seventh-day Adventists became involved in teaching people to live healthy lives. At no time has this service become more crucial to the population of North America than during the 21ST Century. "Health reform" is now a major political issue in the United States, and a primary concern of the governments of Canada and Bermuda.

Today more than ever activists from the Adventist Church are needed to take a stand for health issues related to substance abuse and tobacco smoke in public facilities. In the same way that the Five-Day Plan to stop smoking caught wide public attention in the 1960s, Adventist health ministries need to gain significant visibility and prominence for their fitness and health promotion efforts today.

The Need for Health Promotion

The need for health promotion through screening and education is starkly evident in the light of the large number of deaths that result from preventable conditions. Table 1 summarizes the latest statistics showing the diseases that are killing Americans. Most experts agree that many of them are preventable through health education. More than half of all preventable deaths are related to tobacco. With nearly half a million deaths per year attributable to tobacco use and secondhand smoke, the "jury" is in—tobacco kills. In addition to liver disease, mental health problems and other diseases, alcohol use is related to half of all fatal motor vehicle crashes. (See David Nieman, *The Adventist HealthStyle; Why it Works*, Hagerstown, MD: Review and Herald Publishing Association, p. 43.)

Table 1

Deaths and percent of total deaths for the 10 leading causes of death: United States, 1999

Rank	Causes of death and year	Deaths	Percent of total deaths
	All causes	2,391,399	100.0
1	Diseases of heart	725,192	30.3
2	Malignant neoplasms	549,838	23.0
3	Cerebrovascular diseases	167,366	7.0
4	Chronic lower respiratory diseases	124,181	5.2
5	Accidents (unintentional injuries)	97,860	4.1
6	Diabetes mellitus	68,399	2.9
7	Influenza and pneumonia	63,730	2.7
8	Alzheimer's disease	44,536	1.9
9	Nephritis, nephrotic syndrome and nephrosis	35,525	1.5
10	Septicemia	30,680	1.3
	All other causes	484,092	20.2

National Vital Statistics Report, Vol. 49, No. 11, October 12, 2001

One of the most significant public health phenomena of the previous decade has been the increasing pervasiveness of cocaine as a drug of choice. From 1976 to 1985, emergency room episodes involving cocaine in consistently reporting programs increased from 1,015 to 9,043, a nine-fold increase. (See *Cocaine Client Admissions*,1979-1984, U.S. Alcohol, Drug Abuse, Mental Health Administration, DHHS Publication Number ADM 87-1528.)

In Canada the incidence of smoking and the use of alcohol is somewhat higher than in the United States. Canada's Health Promotion Survey in 1990 found that 32 percent of men and 29 percent of women were smokers, down from 36 percent of men and 33 percent of women in the 1985, survey, but higher than the 28 percent of men and 23 percent of women smokers in the U.S. in 1993. Alcohol consumption remained relatively constant in Canada while it declined in the U.S. Eight in ten Canadians had a drink in 1990, the same as in 1985, while in the U.S. this figure dropped from 65 percent to 61 percent of the population. Stress on the other hand is more of an American problem. About one in eight Canadians report that their lives are very stressful, while 27 percent of women and 20 percent of men in the U.S. say they are under a lot of stress. (See Charlotte A. Schoeborn, "Trends in Health Status and Practices: Canada and the United States," *Canadian Social Trends*, Winter, pp. 16-21; "Provincial Differences in Health Practices,"*Canadian Social Trends*, Summer, pp. 30-34.)

"Community" Health Risks are "Personal" Health Risks

The statistics listed in the previous section indicate that "community" health risks are personal health risks that require personalized health education. It is the goal of health educators to identify specific community risks, to offer preventive community health education, and to help translate that education into action strategies not only for their communities but also for the "at risk" individuals in their communities. The following three individuals entered the "statistics pool". Their stories, unfortunately, are not unique even though the persons are.

After escaping the terrors of a Nazi detention camp George C. and his wife joined the throng of immigrants headed for safety in North America. Sponsored by caring relatives, they began a new life. Starting with a simple, one-bedroom home for their expanding family, they eventually built a lovely home literally "brick by brick." George was a skilled machinist whose skills were much in demand in the burgeoning manufacturing after the war. They had adopted much of their new homeland's habits, including chain smoking. Several packs of cigarettes per day were the norm. Nearing retirement, and anticipating the fruits of many years of long labor, George was scheduled for a routine physical examination. A lump in the right lung proved to be lung cancer.

Bill R.'s idol was Lenny Bruce, the coarse, caustic commentator of the Viet Nam era. No one was particularly surprised. Before the word "dysfunctional" became a part of our national vocabulary, Bill's volatile family fit the description. But he was a "gentle spirit," evoking the image of the "flower children" of the times. With his rounded, wire-frame glasses and perpetually tousled look, Bill often was classified as a "druggie." No one knows which came first, the accusation or the habit. But Bill eventually graduated from marijuana to a hallucinogenic to heroin. Many close to him sent warnings, but the needle was his friend. Just like Lenny Bruce…. Then marriage to a nurse and a young child seemed to break the spell. But only for awhile. The needle always was there when things got rough. And it didn't criticize or talk back. Bill's naked, AIDS-ridden body was discovered in a seedy, downtown walk-up. The needle was right beside him along with a note. "Just like Lenny Bruce…" everyone said.

Beulah R. was a model employee. As a single woman, she literally devoted forty-three years of her working life to the same employer. Being the front desk clerk of a downtown hotel, she had "seen it all" and loved to laugh her deep, throaty laugh at all the "goings on." Not much escaped the attention of "Miss Beulah." Her desk was the command center around which swirled endless activity. The front lobby was filled from early morning to late night with the "regulars"–men who were the town's retired or temporarily laid off. Their talk, along with their cigarette and pungent cigar smoke, permeated the air. No one even had a name for "secondhand smoke." Not yet. When Miss Beulah finally quit and moved to the Lutheran Retirement Home, her first order of business was a complete physical. Diagnosis: lung cancer. Cause: secondhand smoke. "Miss Beulah" was a non-smoker.

How Adventists are Meeting the Need

Since its inception, the Seventh-day Adventist Church has promoted a philosophy of health and healing. While developing health-care institutions which belt the globe, a health-promoting way of life has been taught to the church membership. Teachings based on broad principles, found in the Sacred Scriptures and more explicitly expressed in the counsels given by Ellen White, have in recent years been increasingly substantiated by the findings of scientific research. These findings have clearly demonstrated the health superiority of Seventh-day Adventists, especially of those who more closely adhere to the health philosophy of the church. Local Seventh-day Adventist churches and health-care units offer hundreds of community health education classes each year. These classes include smoking cessation programs, drug education and prevention, stress control clinics, vegetarian cooking schools, nutrition workshops, and other health-related seminars designed to meet community felt needs. More recently, as a result of community health needs assessments, classes centered on domestic violence, parenting skills, family finances, and grief or loss recovery have been added.

The Better Living Center of Chicago

The Better Living Center of Chicago is a case in point. According to Roberto Cepida, director of the center since 1990, "We are serving a population of both Hispanic and Polish extraction in the East Village area. We have definitely seen an increase in serving the elderly population with

their emergency food needs. And we are now offering classes in both drug prevention and parenting skills as well as tutoring for eighth graders. This is a special concern since there is a fifty percent dropout rate for Hispanic high school students in the Chicago area." Pastor Cepida also stresses the importance of cooperating with other agencies (American Cancer Society, American Heart Association, etc.) to best serve the needs of a community. Duplication of effort, in both the planning and operational stages, can be avoided through interagency communication, coordination, and cooperation.

Greater Kansas City Real Truth Crusade and the Adventist Youth Health Team

Health programs provide particular opportunities to work closely with public evangelism. For example an Adventist Youth Health Team worked as part of the Greater Kansas City Real Truth Crusade in the summer of 1993. For nine weeks, about 30 young adults from Oakwood College and the Central States Conference conducted a community health project. It included intensive health lectures and training each morning, operating a summer urban day camp in the afternoon and health practicums in the evening. The team members were tutored by Adventist health professionals in four areas of skill, including the 12-step approach to overcoming addictions and 48 hours of comprehensive training in nutrition. Kansas City residents were invited to attend a week-long "Finger-licking Good Cooking School" taught by the team.

CHIP: Coronary Health Improvement Project

CHIP is a 30-day, community lifestyle education program that is one of a kind! Church members and community graduates alike are overjoyed with their improved health. Many are eager to sign up friends and relatives so that the call for more CHIP programs keeps expanding!

This dynamic video-based, life-changing experience targets the lifestyle diseases of the 21st Century—Obesity, Diabetes, Hypertension, Heart Disease and Osteoporosis. It is enormously popular wherever it is conducted and has won many friends for the Seventh-day Adventist Church while influencing many hundreds to improve their health. It is especially attractive to the more educated and affluent population.

Hans Diehl, DrHSc, MPH, FACN, is the founder of CHIP and principal speaker in the Video-CHIP series. Originally he presented this program in person to large audiences in the U.S., Canada, Australia and elsewhere. Today, however, Dr. Diehl comes to local communities through Seventh-day Adventist Churches across North America by way of Video-CHIP.

While we are very supportive of residential lifestyle programs, CHIP participants may achieve similar results right in their local community for much less money while at the same time developing a network of helpful friends and resources. Participants continue to work closely with their personal physician while attending CHIP and are encouraged to share their clinical outcomes. Best of all, the program remains in the community, offering regular follow-up support and programming through the local Seventh-day Adventist church.

The Community Response:

The results are thrilling. About 100 CHIP Chapters currently cover North America from Alaska to Florida, from Connecticut to California, and from the Yukon to Newfoundland. Hundreds of participants are reveling in their new lifestyle and improved health while at the same time making fast friends with their local Seventh-day Adventist CHIP leadership.

From CHIP to CHURCH: An Ongoing Journey

*F*ive years ago our family started on a journey much like Abraham and Sarah. God had the journey well planned, but it was different than the plans Lavetta (my wife) and I had.

In 1995, my wife went to a home school workshop sponsored by the Three Angels SDA Church in Wichita, Kansas. Dr. Raymond and Dorothy Moore were the presenters for the workshop. While there, Lavetta picked up a brochure on a new "pilot project." That project was the initial CHIP program at Three Angels. Lavetta participated in the first CHIP class. During the first week our family went from what Dr. Diehl calls a S.A.D. diet (Standard American Diet) to eating whole grains, fruits, vegetables, and legumes.

During the month of CHIP the retired assistant pastor of Three Angels, and his wife, befriended Lavetta and later began a Bible study with our family. Between them and their son*s family, we went through the book of Daniel (with Revelation thrown in on the side!).

The next few months we read and studied, on our own, about the SDA Church. Lavetta even found a book in the public library entitled Seventh-day Adventists Believe... containing the 27 fundamental doctrines. Within a short period of time, we were convinced that the SDA church was, and is, the true remnant church carrying out the message of the Three Angels message of Revelation. We soon joined the church and became active members in the CHIP program in Wichita. Over the next three to four years we were strengthened, built up, and challenged with the health message of our church.

Having been a cardiovascular Physician Assistant, for about twenty years, I knew the relationship between diet and disease. CHIP brought this into a clearer and more relevant focus for me.

Over the last year God opened various doors. In August of 2000 we left our home in Wichita and headed to a land we "knew not." We ended up in Lincoln, Nebraska, where I became the Clinical Director of the Physician Assistant program at Union College. What a journey it has been. Because of the CHIP health message as one of the "arms of the Church," our family has been brought into a closer, more loving relationship within the Lord*s arms

(CHIP testimony from Clifford Korf)

Here is just a sampling of the feedback from the communities and churches where CHIP is conducted:

- From a lay pastor of another denomination in Lumby, BC: "The Seventh-day Adventist Church has given us a beautiful model of servanthood here in our community."
- Overheard in an Adventist physician's office in Brewster, WA: "Isn't it wonderful what the Seventh-day Adventist Church is doing for our community?"
- One small Adventist Church in Central California had a very poor reputation in town due to some unfortunate events in their early history. Today that same church parking lot is never so full as when there is a CHIP program going on. The entire community is talking about CHIP!
- At the Wichita, KS CHIP program over a dozen new members can trace their first contact with the Adventist church to a CHIP program.
- In Groveland, CA, four or five CHIPPERS have attended the Bible studies held at the Adventist physician's office.
- The Lodi, CA CHIP program has seen baptisms and incorporates regular spiritual presentations from their enthusiastic pastor, a CHIP graduate himself.

CHIP in Your Local Church Looks Like This:

- **Free Information Sessions repeated on several occasions offer an opportunity to explain the program, answer questions, register people and sign them up for HeartScreen # 1.**
- **HeartScreen # 1 (Pre-Test) includes a review of medications, fasting lipid profile and blood sugar, lifestyle assessment, height, weight, blood pressure, and a heart healthy breakfast.**
- **16 Video-CHIP Lectures are presented in classes that meet four days a week for four weeks. Dr. Hans Diehl is the dynamic lecturer in this compelling video series complete with superb graphics, illustrations, and humorous stories. Local presentations**

provide for live interaction, heart-healthy recipe samples, and lots of fun. Participants receive a textbook, workbook, notebook, and other materials.
- **Applied Nutrition Workshop and Shopping Tour (optional) teach valuable grocery shopping and cooking skills.**
- **HeartScreen # 2 (Post-Test) measures the changes in lifestyle, clinical outcomes, and medications over the 30-day period.**
- **Graduation provides a time to celebrate the progress of each participant with a special meal, diploma, CHIP pin and CHIP kitchen knife.**
- **Alumni Organization: This meets on a regular basis for learning, inspiration, and encouragement. This is where the lifestyle and friendships are cemented.**

CHIP Connects With Your Church Like This:

CHIP connects with your local church through the Adventist CHIP Association. This Association is a grass root, volunteer-driven organization that grew out of a need for inspiration and fellowship among local CHIP Chapters. It also provides support and training for the development of new CHIP Chapters.

You may contact the Association for a CHIP Information Kit and Director Application. The Kit contains a CHIP promotional video, a testimonial video, information on how to start CHIP in your church, a MicroCHIP plan, order forms, a list of resources people and more.

The Association distributes manuals that provide detailed information on how to implement the local program. The Association also conducts training seminars and provides for ongoing support to church CHIP Chapters through email, phone calls and newsletters.

Our Mission Statement:

It is the mission of the Adventist CHIP Association to help the local church to provide its community with a church-sponsored, scientifically sound, community health education program that will:

- Bring healing to the whole person—body, mind, and soul;

- Create lasting friendships for the church;
- Stimulate interest in the larger picture of Bible truth.

We believe that the local Seventh-day Adventist Church has the potential of becoming a recognized place for health and healing in its community. Our mandate is clear: "Health reform is one branch of the great work which is to fit a people for the coming of the Lord. It is as closely connected with the third angel's messages as the hand is with the body." *Counsels on Health* p. 20. We believe CHIP in the local church is helping to fulfill this high calling.

CHIP in your local Church

For churches wanting to start a CHIP program, contact the Adventist CHIP Association, (866) 732-2447 toll free for a CHIP information kit and Director application. (Web site: www.sdaCHIP.org; e-mail: info@sdaCHIP.org).

Key Elements of the Problem

To concerned Christians, the "need" of health education per se is intrinsically related to the sin problem. As sinners, existing in an environment that bears the marks of several thousand years of abuse, we are both victimized by and victims of our own unhealthy environment. Like the old

Bicycle Bob and His Wife Theresa

*W*hen Bob Anderson was 66 he retired as a building contractor because of debilitating arthritis in his lower back. "I could hardly make it out to the mailbox," Bob said, "so I started driving my old car the 200 feet to get the mail. I had no energy. I was 60 pounds overweight, smoked three packs of cigarettes a day, and was always short of breath."

Theresa's health wasn't much better. She suffered from high blood pressure and diabetes, was overweight and extremely depressed.

Then Dr. Hans Diehl came to their town of Creston, British Columbia, with a *Live with All Your Heart* seminar (now referred to as CHIP). The message was simple: "Our diets are killing us. Our excesses in meat, rich dairy products, sugar, alcohol, salt, and tobacco—all the good things in life—must go or we'll eat and drink ourselves into early graves."

Getting the results of the *HeartScreen* health evaluation jolted the Andersons into action. Their blood pressure, cholesterol and blood sugar were all too high. When they realized their rich diet and sedentary lifestyle was contributing to their heart disease, diabetes, hypertension and osteoarthritis, they dumped their vodka down the sink, and filled three garbage bags with the "junk" food they cleaned out of their fridge. They burned Bob's cigarettes in their fireplace (a 35 year long habit) and started walking. First just one block, then two, three, five—and more.

They say God can make crooked things straight, and that happened to Bob. By the sixth month his back pain disappeared, he stood straight, and walked without a limp. Their blood pressure, cholesterol and blood sugar levels returned to normal. Both took up bicycling, shed 50 pounds each, and three years later, at age 69, Bob cycled 3,210 miles from Creston to Ottawa, Ontario in 60 days.

Theresa says, "No more are we simply 'enduring' retirement. We are living our lives to the hilt! We both have bicycles and love life on the road. And as our physical health improves, we are growing spiritually. We've been 'born again,' and are active in our church. Now we have a purpose, and a sense of direction in our lives."

—Aileen Ludington

(From: *Energized! One-a-day devotionals for body, mind and soul.* Hagerstown, MD: Review and Herald Publishing Association, 1997. Used by permission.)

maxim, we have literally "made our own bed and now must lie in it."

In a 1992 statement entitled "Caring for God's Creation," the General Conference Committee states, "The human decision to disobey God broke the original order of creation, resulting in a disharmony alien to His purposes. Thus our air and waters are polluted, forests and wildlife plundered, and natural resources exploited. Because we recognize humans as part of God's creation, our concern for the environment extends to personal health and lifestyle. We advocate a wholesome manner of living and reject the use of substances such as tobacco, alcohol, and other drugs that harm the body and consume earth's resources; and we promote a simple vegetarian diet." (See Appendix C for entire text.)

Health education in any locale, especially in large urban areas with diverse ethnic mixes, is a daunting task. It assumes that the health activists have an accurate knowledge of the real needs of their target population. It also is based on the assumption that the target population has a desire to be educated regarding their personal health habits. Behavior change is inevitably "easier said than done."

"Sustaining behavior change is crucial to the effectiveness of health education programs," according to Steven Shea of the Department of Medicine and School of Public health, Columbia University (*American Journal of Public Health*, Vol. 82, No. 6; June 1992, p. 786). Shea points out that an important task for many community-based programs is the transfer of intervention elements to existing organizations. Some of the obstacles to this process include a lack of resources in local health departments, school systems and voluntary organizations. The requirement for technical expertise or specialized training can also be an obstacle to this transfer, as can the need for appropriate insurance.

In poor communities of large cities, where such programs could have their greatest impact, additional challenges include the lack of a local government, a health department, or a media market specific to the target community, as well as the lack of community-based health organiza-

tions such as the American Heart Association, American Cancer Society, or Weight Watchers.

A key issue in assessing community prevention programs is whether they reach the poor, minorities, groups of low educational attainment, and Hispanics, Asians, and other groups that may present language or cultural barriers to main-stream messages and communication channels.

What is the public health challenge now? It is to identify effective programs and program elements, to disseminate them, to scale them up to the state and national level, to sustain funding, to monitor effectiveness, and to ensure that the programs reach the populations most at risk. (*Ibid.*, p. 786)

A Biblical View of Health Education

Perhaps the greatest health principle given to the Israelites was the invitation to love God supremely, depending totally on Him. Disease prevention and long life were promised to all who entered into a relationship with Him. (See Exodus 23:25, 26.)

Throughout scripture, health is intimately tied to both mental and spiritual well-being. For example, Psalm 6:2b, 3a: "O Lord, heal me, for my bones are in agony. My soul is in anguish" (NIV). Or Psalm 31:9, 10, "Be merciful to me, O Lord, for I am in distress; my eyes grow weak with sorrow, my soul and my body with grief. My life is consumed by anguish and my years by groaning; my strength fails because of my affliction, and my bones grow weak" (NIV).

Proverbs 3:7, 8 advises, "Do not be wise in your own eyes; fear the Lord and shun evil. This will bring health to your body and nourishment to your bones" (NIV). "My son, pay attention to what I say; …keep them [my words] within your heart; for they are life to those who find them and health to a man's whole body," Proverbs 4:20-22 adds (NIV). "The fear of the lord is a fountain of life…. A heart at peace gives life to the body, but envy rots the bones" (Proverbs 14:27a, 30, NIV).

Probably the most popular "health verse" in the Bible is found in 3 John 2. "Beloved, I wish above all things that thou mayest prosper and be in health, even as thy soul prospereth."

In *The Adventist Healthstyle: Why It Works*, David Nieman provides this overview of health principles from the Old Testament pertaining to sanitation, diet and sexual behavior as they apply to both infectious and lifestyle disease prevention:

Mankind's original diet was to come totally from the plant kingdom (Gen. 1:29, 30; Gen. 3:18). Men and women strayed from this ideal, and God then laid down several safeguards for the Hebrew people when they desired to include meat in their diets. No blood or fat was to be consumed (Lev. 3:17; 7:22-27; 1 Sam. 2:16). This decreased the level of saturated fat and cholesterol, greatly reducing the risk of heart disease and cancer. [Certain flesh foods also were proscribed as being unclean (see Lev. 13:1-23; Deut. 14:3-20).]

People who abstained from alcohol were to be held in high esteem (Num. 6:3, 4; Judg. 13:4) Many rules for sanitation were given, including the burial of human excrement (Deut. 23:13-15), procedures to prevent foodstuffs from contamination or spoilage (Ex. 16:19; Lev. 11:31-40; 19:5-8), personal bathing and washing of garments (Gen. 35:2; Ex. 19:10; Jer. 2:22; Eccl. 9:8), quarantine for those with major infectious skin diseases (Lev. 13, 14; Num. 5:2-4). Each of these rules safeguarded the spread of infectious diseases among the Israelites.

God made it plain that husband and wife were not to commit adultery and were to have sexual relations only with their spouse (Gen. 2:24; Ex. 20:14, Lev. 18:1-22). Sexual relations with animals were also prohibited (Ex. 22:19; Lev. 18:23; 20:15, 16). These rules would effectively prevent the spread of sexually transmitted diseases (pp. 23, 24).

For Seventh-day Adventists, the writings of Ellen White give added impetus to the deep-seated relationship between physical, mental, social, and spiritual health. In her classic *The Ministry of Healing* she states, "From Him [Christ] flowed a stream of healing power, and in body and mind and soul men were made whole" (p. 17). "Whatever injures the health not only lessens physical vigor, but tends to weaken the mental and moral powers" (p. 128). "The relation that exists between the mind and the body is very

intimate. When one is affected, the other sympathizes.... Courage, hope, faith, sympathy, love, promote health and prolong life" (p. 241).

Adventists have long espoused the delicate interworkings of mind and body. What affects the one certainly affects the other. This mind/body relationship has enjoyed a resurgence of interest due to recent public television documentaries, magazine and professional journal articles and best-selling books. An openness on the part of many unchurched people to discuss "spiritual" matters has been one of the side-effects of this mind/body inquiry. "Total health" now implies more than just your physician's stamp of approval.

Contemporary Community Health Promotion Approaches

Health education methods have changed significantly in recent years. The traditional offering of classes and seminars has been joined by a number of other methods that are more suited to the current attitudes, dynamics and trends among the population in North America. In order for your church to successfully conduct health education, it is necessary for you to utilize methods that will work in your community—that will attract people and engage them in learning and change their health practices. Described below are several community health education programs, elements of which can serve as models for Adventist programming:

Model 1. The Planned Approach To Community Health (PATCH) project and the Community Chronic Disease Prevention Program (CCDPP). Both programs were developed within the last decade by the U.S. Centers for Disease Control (CDC) and operate in conjunction with state health departments.

PATCH involves local communities, state and local health departments, and the Centers for Disease Control in a partnership to plan, develop, implement, and sustain local health promotion programs. The Community Chronic Disease Prevention Program is a similar partnership that is specific to heart disease and cancer health promotion intervention programming.

In both programs, communities that wish to participate form an advisory committee composed of representatives from local health and social agencies and from the general public. With training and technical assistance from the Centers for Disease Control, a locally-developed "community action plan" is put into effect.

It is important to note that both PATCH and CCDPP are needs-based in their assessment of health risks. They encourage community input and involve the community in the assessment process. The support that the Centers for Disease Control offers in disseminating these approaches leads to greater vertical linkages among the national, state, and local organizations, and increases networking within each of these levels.

The PATCH and CCDPP models use data gathered within the community to set priorities and seek to reinforce and strengthen existing social networks by developing core advisory groups of individuals and organizations. The models also work to generate a stronger capacity for health promotion in the local community groups and networks. This is accomplished by training for community leaders and by facilitating greater community awareness of health risks, as well as greater organizational capacities to address these risks.

Communities across the U.S. which are involved in PATCH are generally satisfied with the process. The Planned Approach To Community Health has experienced success in mobilizing and empowering African-American residents of urban public housing projects, and generally can be adapted to meet the unique needs of culturally diverse communities, including those outside the United States.

Seventh-day Adventist health professionals and lay persons desiring to plan and present health promotion programs can learn much about the kind of planning needed and perseverance in working toward widely-accepted community health programs from carefully studying the recommendations for the PATCH and CCDPP approaches.

Model 2. Healthy Cities Healthy Cities is a health promotion initiative being conducted in more than 300 cities around the world. This particular model began in Canada and Europe. Healthy Cities Indiana is typical of projects in the U.S. which are adapting the Canadian models to their local context. Healthy Cities Indiana is a collaborative effort between the Indiana University School of Nursing Department of Community Health Nursing, the Indiana Public Health Association, and six Indiana cities—Fort Wayne, Gary, Indianapolis, Jeffersonville, New Castle and Seymour. This program began in 1988.

Healthy Cities uses a process of enabling people to have a unified voice for health in order to bring about planned change to improve community life, services and resources. A healthy city is a combined effort of government, business, the arts, science, religion—the community as a whole.

A unique part of the Indiana program is community leadership development that supports local problem solving and action in health. Community leaders exist in any city but they may not know their potential in health promotion. Healthy Cities Indiana prepares community leaders to take an active role in promoting healthy public policy. There are several phases in this process:

1. *Commitment.* The mayor and local health officer sign a commitment for broad-based participation in the placement of health as a priority on the city's agenda and in the adoption of policies that promote health.
2. *A Healthy City Committee is Formed.* The committee is composed of a community-wide public-private partnership of people willing to be actively involved in the healthy city process.
3. *Community Leadership Development.* Project staff assist community leaders in developing their skills in the healthy cities process. Compilation of data, consultation with health specialists, statewide workshops, are key parts of this leadership development process.
4. *Action-research.* Each of the healthy cities committees is involved in identifying their city's strengths and health problems. Specific recommendations are then developed for local action.

5. *Provision of Database Information to Policy Makers.* The local committees promote the development of healthy public policy through long range city planning. Specific programs are targeted.

6. *Evaluation.* A local self-study questionnaire has been put together as one measure of community leadership development.

The Healthy Cities Indiana Resource Center has on file introductory information on healthy cities including videotapes, audiotapes, bibliography, resources for on-site consultation, and is a distributor for Healthy Cities working papers. For more information, contact Healthy Cities Indiana, Indiana University School of Nursing, 1111 Middle Drive, Indianapolis, IN 46202. (Adapted from: *American Journal of Public Health*, Vol. 81, No. 4; April 1991, pages 510-511.)

You will be more effective in your health promotion program if you become aware of how entire communities can work together in meeting the population's needs and the possibilities of networking with activities and health leaders in your area.

Gwen Foster, the dynamic former Director of Health Ministries for the Allegheny East Conference, now is Health Czar for the city of Philadelphia. One challenge she met when she started her work there was the fact that Philadelphia was the fattest and most unhealthy city in the United States. The Mayor and Gwen have teamed with the Philadelphia 76ers to create a citywide health revolution. Together they challenged Philadelphia to lose 76 tons in the year 2001. Gwen worked out a schedule of ten weekly health and fitness challenges:

1. Select a health buddy.
2. Drink more water.
3. Increase physical activity.
4. Enjoy more fruits and vegetables.
5. Eat foods high in fiber and vegetable protein.
6. Take time to breathe deeply.
7. Schedule time for rest and play.
8. Adjust your eating schedule.
9. Get adequate amounts of sunlight.
10. Give someone a reason to smile.

(For more information on her 76 Tons of Fun approach, go to www.phila.gov or call (215) 686-2000).

Model 3. Public Health Week. Los Angeles has developed a yearly Public Health Week in which local Adventists have participated. The Public Health Programs and Services (PHP&S) Branch of the Los Angeles County Department of Health Services began a strategic planning effort in January, 1986 to meet new disease trends, curb rising healthcare costs, consolidate limited resources, and handle shifting demographics. A strategic plan was designed to assess the opportunities and challenges facing the agency over a 5-year horizon. Priority areas were recognized, and seven strategic directives were formulated to guide PHP&S in expanding public health services to a changing community.

Health promotion was acknowledged as a critical target of the strategic planning process. Among the most significant results of the health promotion directive was the establishment of an annual Public Health Week in Los Angeles County. Beginning in 1988, one week each year has been selected to enhance the community's awareness of public health programs and the leadership role PHP&S plays in providing these programs to nearly nine million residents of Los Angeles County.

Events in Public Health Week include a professional lecture series and the honoring of an outstanding public health activist and a media personality who has fostered health promotion. It is an extensive community outreach effort, featuring an array of open houses, tours, displays, video presentations, disease screening, mobile immunization clinics, trivia games, health fairs, smoking cessation programs, and contests involving children. Community groups and churches can participate in the week of activities in a variety of ways.

The intensive media coverage of Public Health Week provides an opportunity for aggressive education of the community on vital wellness issues. The strategic methodology employed by PHP&S, with its emphasis on long range, proactive planning, is receiving national recognition and could be adopted by similar agencies wishing to enhance their image and develop unique health promotion projects in their communities. (See *Public Health Reports*, Vol. 107, No. 1; January-February 1992, pp. 110-112.)

Watch for opportunities in your area to tie your programs into a citywide health emphasis.

Model 4. The People of Color Against AIDS Network (POCAAN) Some population groups are hard to reach with health education programs. In the wake of the 1992 civil disturbances in Los Angeles, a study of urban teenagers added to the unhappy news about race relations in America. By junior-high age many Black youth would rather die than take conventional drug and safe-sex messages to heart.

The "hip-hop" generation, researchers said, shuns advice from health education stemming from either white culture or mainstream Black culture. African-Americans are dying in disproportionate numbers, along with other young people, adults and newborns marginalized by race, lifestyle, and/or poverty. AIDS, substance abuse, related diseases, and infant mortality hit these communities hardest.

Health educators who develop services and programs for "at-risk" populations such as these face a formidable challenge in marketing them. Unfortunately, many health educators still consider information prepared for white, middle-class families to be "one size fits all." Yet, although 19 percent of the U.S. population is Black and Latino, 45 percent of AIDS cases were from these segments. If conventional methods won't work, what will?

Summary of Recommendations for Improving Community Health Promotions Programs

Stage	Recommendations
1. Community Needs Assessment	1. Consider doing a community capacity assessment (demographic study) prior to initiating a community needs assessment.
2. Analyzing Needs Assessment Data	2. Do not overly rely on risk factor surveys for various health problems.
3. Setting Priorities Based on Data	3. Analyze needs assessment data rapidly for community planning.
4. Reaching Consensus on Priorities	4. Allow flexibility in determining priority health problems.
5. Developing Activities	5. Do not "front-load" consultation; technical assistance should be available throughout the program process.
6. Implementing Activities	6. Emphasize multiple interventions around one chronic condition at a time. (Don't try to cover the waterfront!)
7. Process Outcomes	7. Fund at least one full-time local coordinator and adequate building space. Develop and encourage local leadership.
8. Institutionalization	8. Before institutionalizing your program see the institutionalization criteria for PATCH and CCDPP.

The People of Color Against AIDS Network is a pilot project that has pioneered an approach for reaching the hard-to-reach with healthcare information. It demonstrates the practical success of the following principles:

1. *The need to influence community norms in order to influence individual behavior.* "One way we find out what community norms are is by hiring people who have a strong sense of their racial home communities, plus represent a number of subcultures within those communities," explained POCAAN Director Fullwood. Another way is to use focus group research to surface issues, or conduct a survey of knowledge, attitudes and beliefs about health in the community.

2. *The use of peer educators to empower the community in propagating health values and practices.* Young people of color get AIDS information via other young people of color. Latinos and African-American women visit community gathering places to educate women and girls about AIDS and infant mortality. They make neighborhood young people the "backbone" of the organization.

3. *Network with other community groups to take advantage of already-established points of contact.* POCAAN works with a number of organizations to reach its audiences. Initially, POCAAN outreach workers set up information tables at Black and Asian community festivals, Latino fiestas, and Native American pow wows. From this experience grew opportunities to do AIDS education within community-based organizations and at conferences and forums.

4. *Solve the payment problem for the client in advance.* If a service can't be free, it has to be within the range of what local community residents can afford.

5. *Make information accessible.* POCAAN develops printed materials in the desired language instead of translating from English and takes literacy levels and street vernacular into account. Health information is delivered to the target audience so people do not have to take initiative to get it.

6. *Spend time and money in unconventional ways.* In place of hosting a traditional health fair, POCAAN recently staged "Health'n the Hood" at a Seattle housing project. Health information booths were secondary elements. A puppet show advised children how to pick up syringes and why people with AIDS need care and understanding. A rap contest with prizes elicited creative disease-prevention messages from teens. Coloring books, clowns, free food and music added to the mix. For a packet of sample health-information brochures, comic books, and foto-novels available from POCAAN, write People of Color Against AIDS Network, 5100 Rainier Avenue South, Seattle, WA 98118. (Adapted from: Healthcare Marketing Report, Vol. 11 No. 1; January 1993, pp. 1-6.) Learning about programs like POCAAN can inspire you to think of creative ways you can reach the "unreachable" in your area.

What Can be Learned from these New Models?

Notice the summary chart of recommendations for improving community health promotion programs. Here's an important observation: "It may be unrealistic to assume that lay people are willing and/or able to take the initiative and lead a community health promotion effort. Such an effort requires passion for the issues, expertise in planning and program development, an appreciation for existing community networks, leadership skills, and, most of all, time. Without accounting for such factors, even the best models are not likely to produce the desired outcomes" (Goodman, Steckler, Hoover and Schwartz, *American Journal of Health Promotion*, January-February 1993, pp. 208-217). (See Summary of Recommendations for Improving Community Health Promotion Programs.)

Seventh-day Adventist Action Plan for Outreach

Ellen White had a vision for health ministry as the key strategy for Adventist outreach. "How shall we reveal Christ? I know of no better way

...than to take hold of the medical missionary work in connection with the ministry" (*Medical Ministry*, p. 319). "Much of the prejudice that prevents the truth of the third angel's message from reaching the hearts of the people, might be removed if more attention were given to health reform. When people become interested in this subject, the way is often prepared for the entrance of other truths. If they see that we are intelligent with regard to health, they will be more ready to believe that we are sound in Bible doctrines" (*Counsels on Diet and Foods*, p. 76).

This vision has continued to be important to Seventh-day Adventists. The North American Division has established a strategic plan for health outreach which seeks to mobilize the vast numbers of Adventist health professionals and other church members who want to volunteer for health outreach, by organizing Adventist Health Network (AHN) in both urban and rural areas. AHN builds on the best contemporary ideas for health promotion as well as the rich Adventist heritage of health values and knowledge. (See Chapter 16 for further information on AHN.)

The Breadth of Adventist Health Work.

Health work is a phrase common to Adventist usage, meaning not only the profession of medicine but other phases of the healing arts such as nursing, dentistry, dietetics, the various paramedical techniques, and health education. The following categories may be enumerated:

a. Education of health professions and allied health professionals.
b. Preventive medicine and health education centers, better living centers, health enhancement centers, lifestyle centers, or conditioning centers.
c. Clinical medicine and dentistry.
d. Health evangelism.
e. Healthcare institutions and other facilities.
f. Health food production and restaurants, nutrition programs.
g. Temperance institutes and drug abuse prevention programs.
h. Mental health ministries.

Seventh-day Adventists hold that it is in the very nature of Christian life and faith to exercise compassion toward those who need help, to aid both soul and body. This concept is tersely stated in the motto of the Loma Linda University School of Medicine: "To make man whole." It is this high motivation that leads Christian people to give emphasis to various forms of medical ministry.

Outside North America, many kinds of Adventist medical work and health ministry are employed under varying circumstances to conform to the requirements of each country, as resources are available. In larger metropolitan centers of more advanced countries, modern, well-equipped hospitals are developed in keeping with local standards and needs. Except where larger facilities are built to be used as teaching centers, small towns or rural areas of newly developed countries are well served by smaller hospitals or by well-equipped clinics or dispensaries. In certain areas, medical units take the form of medical launches.

In the non-Christian countries of the world, medical work of some form may be the only Christian activity permitted. Hospitals, clinics, maternity centers, well-baby clinics, or simple dispensaries are cordially accepted where ministers are not allowed. Sometimes the health work is connected with the Adventist Development and Relief Agency (ADRA).

Any ministry to the sick in the spirit of Christ is a communication understood by all. It is for this reason that in many instances medical ministry of some form is the medium of choice for entry into new or difficult lands. More and more, effort in health education and public health, which emphasizes healthful living, is receiving governmental favor where curative medicine alone may be regarded as competitive with local practitioners. On the lay level, church members in every country are encouraged to learn simple health principles and to engage in local health and welfare work. Ellen White makes it plain that "We have come to a time when every member of the church should take hold of the medical missionary work" (*Testimonies*, vol. 6, p. 289). And

Closing the Health Gap: *An Appeal from DeWitt Williams*

*N*ot long ago I was invited to the Interfaith Health Resources Center which belongs to the Carter Center at Emory University. The invitation letter said, "The mission of Interfaith Health is to encourage faith groups to improve the individual and collective health of their members and the local and global communities they serve."

I didn't know quite what to expect as I checked in and looked through the materials reserved for me. Former President Jimmy Carter had invited 150 key leaders involved with health programs within faith groups. More than 70 percent of churches surveyed claimed involvement with at least one health-related activity. We discussed five interrelated gaps that need to be closed in order to improve health.

Gap 1: Apply what we know: Carter asked, "What would happen if the 145 million members of faith groups in the United States served just the immediate neighborhoods by putting on classes promoting healthy living or offering basic medical screening tests?" Every year an average of $2,700 per person is spent in the United States in the name of health. Less than five percent goes toward prevention. Adventists know how to do the Five-day and Breathe Free stop smoking plans, and cooking schools, etc. But do we apply all we know?

Gap 2: Do what we say we believe: It is important for faith groups to identify and act on their tradition of social justice and health responsibilities. The tradition shouldn't stem from a secular agenda imposed on faith groups, but from a Bible injunction to care for the sick, poor, and oppressed. Adventists have long affirmed the value of health as an ideal for every member and have promoted health as a part of community outreach. Yet, which conference or church is implementing these beliefs fully?

Gap 3: Replicate successful models: The Carter foundation pointed out that nearly everything that ought to be done is being done somewhere by a church, a synagogue, a mosque, or temple. Almost any problem has been successfully confronted somewhere. But successful working models are rarely known outside their particular circle of interest. Adventists need to know what is being done among Seventh-day Adventists and other faith groups. And we need to take the best ideas and implement them in our communities.

Gap 4: Breaking out of isolation: We believe we have "the health message." We say it is *our* right arm. It opens doors to bring people into our church. Learning from others is hard enough. Cooperating is harder. Can we partner with a Catholic church to make our communities healthier? Can we team up with a Methodist hospital and a Moslem health clinic?

Gap 5: Move beyond parochial limits of time and distance: This final gap reflects the understanding that we are part of a created order and responsible for it. Our actions create ripples beyond the span of our living years and beyond the circle of those we personally know. Yet we are so easily isolated by barriers of denomination, race, culture, economics, language, age, and distance.

I left the conference feeling that it was wonderful to know that there is a national movement of faith and health, a movement based on a prevention ethic. If the movement catches on, Adventists may no longer be in the forefront of health outreach. Maybe we've hoarded our health principles too long, and God sees that it's time, like with the Jews and their treasure of salvation, to take the health message to the Gentiles. We've had it since 1863. The door of opportunity still is before us. Let's close the gaps and help make healthy communities.

that "The medical missionary work should be a part of the work of every church in our land (*Counsels on Health*, p. 514).

Prevention: The New Philosophy of Health Education

The ad was catching, "If you're in perfect health, call a doctor." Many of us grew up with the philosophy "wait until you get sick then call the doctor." But health professionals have finally caught on to the fact that regular visits to the doctor while you are well can protect your good health and improve your chances of preventing or surviving serious medical problems.

Prevention is in! Dr. Dean Ornish, who had such phenomenal success with reversing heart disease and appeared on the cover of *US News* and *World Report*, says "It's easier to prevent illness than to reverse it.... Simple changes increase the joy of living. You don't have to be sick to notice the improvement when you change your diet and lifestyle. People lose weight, they feel lighter, happier, freer, more full of joy. The simple changes can be very powerful. The implications of all this go way beyond treating and preventing heart disease."

In 1960, Johnny Q. Smoker was not 100 percent sure he wanted to stop smoking. He knew that he enjoyed his smoking habit but he also had a nagging doubt that he was not as fit or as active as he had been. When he saw a sign at a local Seventh-day Adventist church that advertised the 5-Day Plan to stop smoking, he came and was shown *One in 20,000*, a rather gruesome film of the actual operation of a patient who had lung cancer. He was told all the facts about cigarette smoking and had to be convinced that smoking was really bad for him.

Since January 1964 when the Surgeon General made the official proclamation that smoking causes lung cancer, there has been a proliferation of information to the public. The American Cancer and American Lung Society, wellness programs on the job, and private organizations have jumped into the stop-smoking arena. Since 1966, smoking among American adults has dropped from 42 to 25 percent and it keeps falling. Only the serious addicts continue smoking. But from 1991 to 1997, the prevalence of current cigarette smoking among high school students increased 32 percent."

Our approach to conducting a stop-smoking program today is not to use gruesome fear tactics and it's not necessary to give half the information that was necessary in 1960. Our Breathe Free™program must still offer support and encouragement. Health education and health behavior does not need to be based on the negatives. We can use the carrot and stick approach of offering people a more abundant way of life. Dry facts, piles of statistics, and scare tactics are not necessary today.

A recent issue of *Vegetarian Times* affirms that 12.4 million people in the United States are vegetarians. This is a great and wonderful time to do health education! Ellen White says every church should have cooking schools. In today's prevention conscious society, hundreds of people will come to our cooking schools. Twenty years ago, vegetarians were looked upon as strange. Their diet was looked upon as rabbit food. But this is not the case today.

Don't be overwhelmed with the comprehensive community health education programs presented in this chapter. Not every church has the resources to plan a community-wide project, but every church can do something. And every member can do something to promote the health message. Hopefully Earl and Dottie Allen's story will inspire you. Before Dottie's death, the Allens owned a motor home and went from church to church conducting cooking schools. Their program was called "Meals that Heal." This is the story in their words:

We have seen God open doors for us to talk about the health message and to present cooking workshops and health seminars.

Our phone rang rather insistently last September, and as I ran to answer it an enthusiastic voice on the other end said, "Dottie! This is Gay," Now I had no idea who I was talking to. But she certainly was a very enthusiastic person.

She explained to me that she had been watching Earl and myself as we spoke on 3ABN (Three

Angels' Broadcasting Network) doing cooking demonstrations. She said, "I've been following the lifestyle you suggest and I can see that it certainly is God's natural way."

"The reason I'm calling," she said, "is because I understand that you and Earl will be going to Arkansas to present some talks. I just wish I could join you, but I can't. I was wondering if on your way to Fayetteville, you could stop in North Little Rock where we live, and present a health seminar for us and our friends.

"I explained to her that we were totally booked up, both coming and going. She was so disappointed. "Our Catholic church has never had a health seminar."

As I hung up the phone and began to explain to Earl how badly I felt to say no, the telephone rang again. This time, it was a class in South Carolina that was canceling because they were having a Revelation Seminar, and thought they would be too tied up to have the health seminar immediately following it.

Providentially, this was the very weekend that Gay wanted—that one that would follow our being in Fayetteville. So, of course I delightedly called her back and made the arrangements.

So we found ourselves guests of this Catholic couple who were paying for the seminar, and holding it in the Seventh-day Adventist church. We thought that was rather remarkable. Sixty people attended.. It was so exciting! Gay had three girls. And the entire family now follows God's natural simple way of eating, without refined products.

Her oldest daughter was going to be confirmed in the Catholic church. They had a pizza party and cokes. As the priest offered them to her daughter, she said,"No. I don't care for any, thank you." The priest said,"Oh! Won't your mother let you eat that?" She replied, "Oh, my mother will let me, but I don't choose to because my body is the temple of God, and I don't think He'd want those things in it.

"When we came back to hold another health seminar in Charlotte, North Carolina, a woman came in and said, "Do you remember me?" And I'll have to say we didn't. But nevertheless, she remembered us. She told us, "My first contact with Seventh-day Adventists was through your health seminar in this church." She said, "A short time later they had evangelistic meetings. Because I had learned so much, I came back to see what else Seventh-day Adventists believe. Now I'm a happy member of this church.

"In the fall, we had the opportunity of going to a church near Hendersonville, North Carolina.

A young man named David also attended the seminars. He was overweight, diabetic, had high cholesterol, and many other lifestyle problems. He was a very silent member of the class.

We invited the people on the Sabbath after we spoke to come and be part of the fellowship dinner. David also came. After the seminar was over, the church had us come back each month for three months for one class as a follow-up to keep the people excited about what they were doing. We would have a dinner and do about a 40-minute health talk, and give them recipes for the healthful food that they were eating.

After we left, David felt impressed to write a letter to the local newspaper. The response was just overwhelming. The letter that he had written to the editor explained that he couldn't understand why so many people went to weight-watchers programs, and paid big money to do this, when at the Seventh-day Adventist church—free—he had learned more than any doctor or chiropractor had ever been able to tell him. He now had his weight and diabetes under control. His cholesterol was down by 48 points, where his doctor had not been able to obtain these results. He was so thrilled!

He mentioned in the letter that we followed the principles taught by the Seventh-day Adventist church through the Bible and the writings of Ellen G. White. He explained that there was no pressure applied for the people to do this. We told them the best, and it was up to them to choose which part of it they wanted to do. David is now preparing for baptism (Dottie Allen, personal correspondence).

A Wonderful Opportunity

There are approximately 6,649 hospitals in the United States. They will never be able to cure all of the diseases in America. But there are also more than 5,000 Seventh-day Adventist churches in North America. Wouldn't it be great if each church was a community based prevention center? What if we had a network of retired persons living in motor homes like the Allens scattered across North America giving cooking schools on a regular basis? What a wonderful time to do health education and health evangelism!

3

The Mission and Organization of Adventist Health Ministries

History of Adventist Health Ministries

Joseph Bates, as early as 1827 began working for the cause of temperance. But the first united move to start a temperance program came in 1863 with the organization of the Seventh-day Adventist church.

In the April, 1877 issue of the *Health Reformer*, Ellen White penned the words, "True temperance teaches us to abstain entirely from that which is injurious, and to use judiciously only healthful and nutritious articles of food."

Shortly after that the church organized the American Health and Temperance Association, which later became the International Health and Temperance Association. In 1893 the SDA Medical Missionary and Benevolent Association was organized for over-all guidance of the denomination's medical work, including temperance, with J. H. Kellogg, M.D., as president.

Later, an attempt of the General Conference to bring this more or less independent body into closer denominational control resulted in the withdrawal of the association from its denominational connection. In 1905 the Medical Missionary Department (or council) of the General Conference was organized. The temperance work, however, continued to be conducted primarily by the American Temperance Society, and later by a separate Temperance Department.

The Medical Missionary Department name was changed to the Medical Department at the General Conference and, in the late sixties, the name was changed to Health Department. In 1980, when departments were being down-sized, it was voted to combine the departments of Health and Temperance. Then in 1996 the North American Division recommended that the name Health and Temperance Department be changed to Adventist Health Ministries Department.

The Organizational Structure of the SDA Church

NAD stands for the North American Division of the General Conference of Seventh-day Adventists. The United States, Canada, and Bermuda comprise the NAD territory. The following is the basic structure of the Seventh-day Adventist Church: A group of churches comprises a conference. The North American Division has 4,911 churches, 461 companies and 58 conferences. A group of conferences form a union. There are nine unions in the North American Division.

The local church health ministries leader is elected by the church nominating committee as is any other church officer. The health ministries leader is responsible to the church board (and is probably a member of that board). The health ministries leader works with the church pastor, the health ministries committee—if there is one, and the director of Health Ministries at the conference.

The conference Health Ministry director is responsible to the conference president, and works with the directors of Health Ministries at the union and division levels.

Areas of Concern and Responsibility

The Department of Health Ministries currently provides the following functions for the church:

1. Serves as a resource for information and counsel on health and temperance affairs.
2. Advises the church and its departments and agencies, in the development and administration of health and/or temperance policies and programs.
3. Promotes a healthful lifestyle among church members through literature, programs, and Sabbath services.

4. Provides through publications, services, and programs, an ongoing witness to the world concerning the physical, mental, and soul-destroying effects of tobacco, alcohol, and other harmful substances.

5. Sponsors and/or organizes societies to effectively involve church and non-church organizations in united endeavors to promote the non-use of tobacco, alcohol, and other harmful substances.

6. Encourages involvement in the evangelistic thrust of the church by developing and using health and temperance programs and media that will gain the trust and confidence of people.

Why Change to Adventist Health Ministries Department?

*C*hange is difficult, but sometimes it's necessary. Changing times and conditions dictate new approaches to the same problem. For several years now strong voices have been advocating that the name of the Health and Temperance Department was no longer relevant. The basic problem was with the word "temperance." The North American Division Health and Temperance advisory studied this question in January 1996 and unanimously recommended renaming the department to Adventist Health Ministries Department. Here are the reasons:

1. *Clarity*: The word "temperance" is not understood in our culture today. Most people think it means "moderation." I had one non-Adventist man tell me, "Yes I drink wine, but I drink it *temperately*." Older members know that temperance means total abstinence from anything that is harmful, and judicious use of things that are good. But the younger generation has not been exposed to that concept.

2. *Consistency*: Today, the term "health" is a broader, more inclusive word. People understand that cigarette smoking and addictions of all types are detrimental to ones health. They understand that the avoidance of harmful drugs comes under the term "health." Years ago when the department was founded the term "health" was primarily linked to healthcare institutions or public health work. Today health and wellness are synonymous.

3. *Opportunity*: The word "ministries" imparts the idea of service and outreach, "Temperance" does not convey this concept. Adventist Health Ministries is a name that implies taking advantage of the opportunities around us to care for the hurting, helpless, and hopeless and to bring them to a state of wellness. Ministries implies using the right arm lovingly to open doors for the gospel message that we are preaching.

4. *World-wide Unity*: At the World Health and Temperance Director's Summit in March 1996, with all of the World Health and Temperance Directors present, this problem was discussed and a recommendation was made to the world divisions that, "whereas the general public has difficulty in understanding the meaning of the word 'temperance' as it has a connotation for moderation rather than abstinence, and whereas the word 'temperance' is difficult to be translated in other languages, and whereas several divisions have already adopted the name of 'Health' (without using Temperance, i.e., the Adventist Health Department is the official name of the South Pacific Division), it was voted to give study to changing the Department's name but maintaining the word 'health.'"

To those who feel we are straying from the temperance work that Ellen White so strongly advocated in her book, *Temperance*, I want to assure you, that *temperance will remain the core of our work*. It is, after all, one of the fruits of the Spirit (Gal. 5:22, 23). Changing a name to be culturally acceptable does not change our mission!

—DeWitt S. Williams

7. Provides support of Seventh-day Adventist healthcare institutions, clinics, and health/temperance programs. This is done through memberships on boards, inspections, assistance in recruiting personnel, cooperation with community programs, and support for spiritual ministries including the work of chaplains.
8. Maintains liaison with Seventh-day Adventist health professional organizations such as dentists, dietitians, nurses, optometrists, and physicians.
9. Promotes and/or sponsors health and temperance seminars and workshops.
10. Develops and/or catalogs resource material for health and temperance education and programs through the Church Resources Consortium.

Mission for Adventist Health Ministries

Adventist health ministries is dedicated to promoting an integrated wellness lifestyle through modeling and through needs-based, scientifically supported, gospel-oriented materials. The aim is to raise health awareness and standards in all the communities of North America. The Division Health Ministries Director promotes the following goals:

Goal 1: To create geographic networks of Adventist churches for the purpose of:
- Certifying Lifestyle Consultants, Specialists, and Trainers (See Chapter 22.)
- Sharing concepts for successful local ministries
- Scheduling major wellness events

Goal 2: To publish the health ministries newsletter HealthWorks once every two months..

Goal 3: To schedule national Breathe Free™, Regeneration, and other specialty training programs.

Goal 4: To inform Adventist churches of the growing incidence of AIDS within the church, and to educate members in prevention and loving responses to people affected by the virus.

Goal 5: To encourage the Adventist community, especially elementary, academy and college students, to adopt and maintain a healthy, drug-free lifestyle.

Goal 6: To conduct vegetarian congresses and to train a core of vegetarian instructors.

Goal 7: To use satellite links—Adventist Communication Network (ACN)—to train workers and to reach out to the public through such programs as HeartBeat.

Job Description for Conference Directors of Health Ministries

Most conferences have health ministries directors who carry various responsibilities depending on their organizational structure. Each conference has its own job description for the health ministries director. The following is a generic job description:

Purpose: To uphold the healthful lifestyle given by God and to develop and promote its wise presentation as a means of introducing others to the fullness of the gospel message which encompasses the physical, mental, social, and spiritual nature of humankind.

Accountability: The conference health ministries director is accountable to the conference president.

Qualifications:
1. Possess and demonstrate a deep interest in personal and public health, health education and health evangelism.
2. Be competent in planning, equipping, implementing and evaluating health programs, utilizing youth, laity, and health professionals.
3. Be educated in the area of health and preferably to hold a health professional degree (e.g. M.P.H., M.D., R.N., D.D.S., Dr.P.H., etc.)
4. Engage in continuing education in health annually and be active in one or more appropriate professional organizations.

Functions:

1. Maintain communication with local church health ministries leaders to motivate and encourage, as well as make sure they are aware of the resources available.
2. Promote a healthful lifestyle among church members through literature, programs, seminars, workshops, and Sabbath services.
3. Train youth, laity, pastors, and health professionals to conduct health education/evangelism programs.
4. Promote publications, services, and programs that provide an ongoing witness to the world concerning the physical, mental and soul-destroying effects of tobacco, alcohol, and other harmful substances.
5. Sponsor or support organizations such as Youth Alive (formerly AY2Y), Collegiate Adventists for Better Living (CABL), and others to effectively involve church and non-church parties in united endeavors to promote the non-use of tobacco, alcohol and other harmful substances.
6. Publicize news-worthy health education and health evangelism activities in the conference through the pages of the union paper.
7. Encourage participation in special projects and emphasis during the year such as:
   - Temperance Emphasis Day (usually in January/February): The sermon and other presentations emphasize drug-free living. The Listen, and The Winner subscription campaigns are also promoted at this time.
   - Health Education Emphasis Week (usually starts the first week and ends the second week in October). The sermon, special seminars, fairs, health screening and other health promotion events are held at this time. The Vibrant Life (the church's health outreach journal) subscription campaign is promoted at this time.
8. Plan with the administration for health programs at camp meetings, special speakers for workers' meetings, and the marketing of health programs to the local church via the pastors.
9. Educate food service directors to improve the healthful quality of food served at our churches, schools, youth camps, camp meeting, and other conference and church-sponsored meetings.
10. Chair and give leadership to the conference health ministries committee.
11. Appoint, where possible, area coordinators for health education/evangelism. The area coordinators are members of the health ministries committee and work as assistants to the director in planning and coordinating all health-related activities within the conference.
12. Work through the area coordinators to assist the church and the pastor in planning a year-round health ministries program for the church.
13. Give support to Youth Alive drug-free programs in conference schools in the following ways:
    - Encourage Adventist schools to send representation to Adventist youth conventions.
    - Encourage each school to organize action groups that will present drug, alcohol and tobacco education programs to students in public schools.
    - Encourage SDA schools to be active in alcohol, tobacco and other drug education so the peer pressure among youth will not push them to drink, smoke, and use drugs.
14. Attend and participate in health ministries advisory meetings.
15. Encourage and promote wide circulation of Ellen White's health publications.
16. Make budgetary provision for the acquisition of health screening vans and health expo displays for county fairs and other community events.
17. As the budget allows, maintain a current library of health resources, (e.g. training manuals, participants' materials on various programs, audio-visual resources [slides and videos], approved speaker lists of health topics and health programs), and make sure all requests for resources are promptly supplied.

An Example of What Happens when Leadership Believes in Health!

Alvin M. Kibble, President of the Allegheny East Conference in Pine Forge, Pennsylvania is putting his money where his mouth is by committing his conference to excellence in ministry for every dimension of the whole person—mental, physical, social, and spiritual.

During an October 26, 1993, press conference, Kibble presented the plan entitled, "Toward the Year 2000—Fit and Free!" to his conference team of pastors, educators, Bible instructors, office staff, parishioners and members of the press, a senator, a National Institutes of Health official, and other dignitaries.

Kibble then began working with Gwen Foster, the conference health ministries director, in planning probably the most unique camp meeting in church history to certify Allegheny East pastors and church members in Pennsylvania, New Jersey, Delaware, Maryland, Virginia, and Washington D. C., as Lifestyle Consultants, Specialists and Trainers—the three levels of Lifestyle certification offered through the conference.

Kibble and his conference team have taken seriously the counsel of Ellen White over 100 years ago, that pastors and churches should be involved in health outreach to the community. Kibble feels that it's time the conference leadership empowers every pastor and member to use this "right arm" of the message as a vital entering wedge. Through the health message many will be led to Christ. That's why their goal is that every church and company in the conference will become a church-based center for health ministry by the year 2000.

The week-long camp meeting was held in the summer of 1995 on the campus of Hampton University. Excitement ran high as 1200 began and completed their certification programs inspired by messages from such national figures as Dr. Lyn Behrens from Loma Linda University, Dr. Samuel DeShay, former General Conference Health Director, and Dr. DeWitt Williams, who is directing health ministries for the North American Division.

Lifestyle Specialist Certification (Level 2) was offered in three different areas:

The Vegetarian Cuisine Instructors class was offered by Dr. Bethany Jackson, former Chairman of the Department of Nutrition at Andrews University; Natural Remedies and Hydrotherapy was taught by staff from Hartland Institute; and Dr. Richard Neil, former Chairman of the Department of Health Promotions at Loma Linda University, taught Stress Management. In addition, Gwen Foster offered the class, Training the Trainer, to certify individuals as Lifestyle Trainers (Level 3), empowering them to present health seminars in their local churches.

As these Lifestyle certified individuals begin working in their churches the focus will be on the African American community. Their goal is to promote health and disease prevention to reduce health risk behaviors associated with hypertension, diabetes, cancer, stroke, infant mortality, homicide, and AIDS.

Allegheny East is moving to be a health leader in the black community because they believe the religious community is the best group to deal with health issues and make a lasting difference in the lives of others.

Apparently word has already gotten out. Dr. Kay James, who was the State Health Commissioner of Virginia at the time, requested Allegheny East Conference provide this same training to empower and certify others in black communities.

Conference Health Ministries Director Profile — *E.W. Dempsey*

$\mathcal{E}$. W. Dempsey, a graduate of Andrews University, taught and coached in a public school system in North Georgia for 22 years and is a former nursing home owner and administrator. He is currently the innovative Adult Health Director of the Georgia-Cumberland Conference Health Department.

Under the leadership of President Larry Evans, four initiatives were developed, one of which is total health. The initiative includes helping conference personnel and church members, as well as the community, understand and practice a healthy lifestyle. Other Departmental officers serve as Youth, and Children's Health Ministries directors. All of them also have responsibilities in other areas of work for the conference such as: prison ministries, lay evangelism, and Pathfinders. These directors are members of the conference Church Ministries Committee, which is chaired by the Church Ministries director.

Dempsey helped developed a wellness program for the conference staff. A professional health organization was used for individualized testing. The results were used for the setting of personal goals. During the ensuing months many shed pounds and lowered their blood pressures. A walking program was implemented. Using an aerobic equivalency walking system, the staff "walked" from Calhoun, Georgia, to the General Conference Session in Toronto, Canada and back home. There have been other successful "walking" destinations.

Dempsey divided the conference geographically into 13 regions, each region having a director. The Regional Director endeavors to get acquainted with the health ministries leaders in his region, encouraging them to set up health committees in their churches, and assisting them with their needs for resource and speaker ideas, and planning for specific health events in each of their churches.

These directors are members of the Health Evangelism Council, which is a subcommittee to the conference Church Ministries Committee. There are also several members at large, who are interested in health evangelism. The Council meets three times a year, usually in January, May (at camp meeting), and September. The chairperson of the Health Evangelism Council is a volunteer lay person who also serves as an "assistant" to the health department director.

The Mission of the Health Evangelism Council is to uplift Jesus in the church and community through following His steps in health ministry. The committee also plans the camp meeting health program and explores ideas for regional rallies and local health emphasis days. The method of holding the regional rallies is optional. It may be a one-day event or a weekend event. The committee also helps set annual goals for the Health Ministries director as well as discusses new resources and materials.

Some of the activities that Dempsey has developed include a five-minute "Health Watch" video issued quarterly by the Adult Health Ministries and Communication departments. It usually consists of two reports about group and/or individual activities. A copy is sent to each church.

Three times a year he and his associate send an "Exciting Health Happenings" newsletter to all pastors and church health leaders. It tells what is being done in the health arena throughout the conference and lists resources and gives suggestions intended to help the church health leaders. A monthly newsletter, written by a medical doctor, is sent to the pastor and church health leaders. This is designed for photocopying and sharing with the church members.

Job Description for a Church Health Ministries Leader

Qualifications

A deep interest in personal health, health education, and health evangelism; good organizing abilities; membership in the church in good and regular standing.

Responsibilities

The following is a comprehensive job description indicating the scope of possibilities a church health ministries leader can become involved in. The health ministers leader, in cooperation with the health ministries committee, can determine the specific responsibilities that are necessary to meet the needs of each church and community.

1. *Health Awareness*

These events help people become aware of their personal health needs and the available resources to meet those needs. A need may be something indispensable to good health such as nutritious food, or it may be something desirable to enhance enjoyment of life such as a new jogging suit.

Community awareness: To plan events such as health screening and testing, information articles in newspapers, radio and television spots, public advertising, health fairs, or cooperation with national health events such as The Great American Smokeout, World Health Day, and the National Cholesterol-Screening Program.

The purposes of community awareness events are:

- To increase the health awareness of the participant.
- To attract the community to the Seventh-day Adventist church.
- To establish friendships between church members and the community residents.

Church awareness: To plan and supervise effective church health ministries awareness programs on the dates set aside in the church calendar for this purpose:

- Temperance Emphasis Day (usually in January/February): The sermon and other presentations emphasize drug-free living.

Conference Health Ministries Director Profile Con't

The Conference health department office has an extensive lending library of videos and other seminar materials for use by the Georgia-Cumberland Conference churches. A "Health Ministries" section also is included in the conference website www.gccsda.com which includes a copy of the monthly newsletters, a lending library list, schedule of upcoming health events, a list of recommended speakers, resource materials, and other helpful information.

The department also gives assistance to local churches in the conducting of health fairs. In 2001 health testing was offered to Georgia-Cumberland teachers at their teachers' convention. In 2002 there will be an on-going pastoral wellness program that will include testing, education, and personal consultation.

The conference strongly urges all health workers to become certified in health evangelism. In conjunction with the North American Division Health Ministries Department, E. W. and his associates have developed a Level 1 certification program as well as inviting specialists from the Division to provide Level 2 instruction and certification. This gives the workers the opportunity to become more knowledgeable about valid health information and health ministry outreach methods. Further information about the Three-level Lifestyle Certification program is outlined in chapter 22.

—*Vivean Raitz, Lay Assistant to E. W. Dempsey and Chairperson of the Health Evangelism Council*

Local Church Health Ministries Leader Profile *Leona Alderson*

Leona Alderson taught home economics for 41 years—17 in elementary schools and 24 at Kingsway College. In 1991 she retired from teaching and has been conducting vegetarian nutrition classes in Oshawa, Ontario.

"We teach pure vegetarian cooking. That's what the public wants. No eggs, milk, or cheese. When people call to ask about our class, their first question is, 'Do you use dairy products?' Some say: 'I have a lactose intolerance,' or 'I want to be a vegan and I want to make sure I get the necessary nutrients without eggs,' or 'My doctor told me I must not eat eggs, especially the yolks, because of the cholesterol.' They seem very, very happy when I tell them we don't use any of these products."

When someone registers for the class, Leona asks them where they heard about it. She likes to know whether it was the newspaper, TV, a poster, or a friend. Many say something like this, "Well, we had a visiting pastor at our church last Sunday and she talked about protecting the environment. It was World Ecology Day and one thing she recommended was to quit eating animals." Then she gives Leona's name and telephone number and when the next class starts.

"She" is Susan Gange, pastor of the United Church. She has attended a total of six series. "I call Pastor Gange my PR person. She not only promotes our classes in her sermons but I send her posters which she puts up in her church."

There are more "PR" people. Bill belongs to the Christian Brethren Church. When he first saw the cooking class ad in the paper 11 years ago, he casually looked at it. He was interested but he didn't really want to come because he thought Adventists were a cult and he didn't want to get mixed up in a cult. His father had just recently died of a massive heart attack in the Ukraine. His family ate a lot of sausage loaded with fat. He cut the ad out of the paper and saved it. He said to himself, "The next time they advertise I'll take a chance." So, that fall, he came and he still comes—10 years later.

"He's another one of my PR people," says Leona. Last summer he was at a Bible camp and talked about the virtues of vegetarianism. He told a lady about this wonderful cooking class he had taken. She lives 100 miles from here. He expounded so eloquently that she decided to drive the long distance every night to participate."

"Last spring our classes were so big we couldn't really get acquainted with everybody so now we divide them into groups of six or eight with an Adventist facilitator in each group. We spend a portion of each program getting acquainted with them in small groups."

People all over the area are searching for the principles of vegetarianism that God has given to our church. Leona Alderson is doing her part and God is blessing this health outreach.

—DeWitt S. Williams

The Listen, and The Winner subscription campaigns are also promoted at this time.

- Health Education Emphasis Week (usually starts the first week and ends the second week in October). The sermon, special seminars, fairs, health screening and other health promotion events are held at this time. The Vibrant Life (the churches health outreach journal) subscription campaign is promoted at this time.

2. *Health Promotion/Disease Prevention*

The purpose of health promotion/disease prevention programs are:

- To provide information and strategies for lifestyle change.
- To help motivate participants to actually make lifestyle changes.
- To support and encourage participants as they make changes.

- To improve the participants' quality and length of life.
- To develop lasting friendships between caring church members and participants.
- To help participants understand the interrelationship of body, mind, and spirit.

The health ministries leader's objectives for the health promotion/disease prevention area are:

- To plan, supervise, and market a cyclic 1-5 year education program for church members and for the community at large, such as smoking cessation, addiction prevention and support groups, AIDS awareness, nutrition education and cooking schools, weight control, stress management, physical fitness education, employee wellness, coronary risk reduction, and parenting/family life.
- To participate and encourage the participation in conference or union-wide seminars in health leadership to prepare more effective health promoters.

3. *Health Information/Bridge Building Events*

These events and activities are designed to introduce participants to an understanding that health includes not only the biological or physical dimensions but also the mental, social and spiritual. Objectives might include:

1) To assist in the planning of events that have a social/spiritual component, such as the following:
   - Giving personal Bible studies on health topics.
   - Helping with fellowship dinners and parties.
   - Planning a health series for camp meeting.
   - Developing out-patient or residential health-conditioning programs.
2) To foster the study and reading of periodicals and Ellen White books through small group discussions or church health education programs. Reading materials should include:
   - Magazines: (such as: *Vibrant Life, Listen, The Winner, The Journal of Health and Healing* (Wildwood)

- Ellen White books (such as: *The Ministry of Healing, Temperance, Welfare Ministry, Counsels on Health, Counsels on Diet and Foods*)
- Other books about the health message, such as *Legacy* (about Loma Linda University), and Take 10 (see chapter 5)

4. *Special Nurturing Activities*

The purpose of nurturing activities is to maintain and continue lifestyle improvement by updating information on a regular basis and to share strength through the community of believers learning and growing together. Specific objectives might include:

1) To plan and supervise one or more special activities such as:
   - Health promotion between Sabbath School and church by using short presentations with slides, videos, or posters.
   - Giving sermons on health
   - Community support activities with county and volunteer health agencies
   - Film and slide programs
   - Neighborhood health visitations and surveys
   - Health/Bible study series
   - Bloodmobile sponsorship
   - Literature racks
   - Retreats
   - Walking, jogging, or health clubs
   - Dental health promotion
   - Mental health promotion
   - Radio spots
   - Health fairs
   - Health conditioning centers

2) To acquaint new members and converts with the health message. This might be accomplished by:
   - Providing each new member with the pamphlet, "Good Health in One Package" available from *The Health Connection*. This little pamphlet explains the eight basic principles of health and temperance. (See Chapter 4 for a more complete list of resources for new members.)

- Invite the new church members to members' homes and fellowship dinners to acquaint them with vegetarian food.
- Loan or give new members the Ellen White health classics, especially The Ministry of Healing.
- Invite new members to camp meeting and other special health ministries meetings.
- Ask new members to assist in your local church health ministries outreach programs.
- Send new members to conference-sponsored training seminars on health topics.

3) To encourage young people to participate in the appropriate health ministries and health/temperance peer education programs.
  - For teens, this is Adventist Youth Alive
  - For college-age young people it is Collegiate Adventists for Better Living (CABL) For information on these programs contact the Institute for the Prevention of Addictions at Andrews University (616) 471-3558. (Also see Chapter 10 on Youth Ministries.)

5. *Records and Reports*
     To keep records of programs and activities and to report them quarterly to the church board and conference Health Ministries director. Include the following:
  - Participants in health programs (Count Person Visits (PV), i.e. the number of individuals at each session held.)
  - Follow-up activities of community members
  - Income and expenses
  - Names of church members who are health professionals (physicians, dentists, nurses, physical therapists, and others)

4

Getting Started: Help For the New Health Ministries Leader

Congratulations!

Being elected health ministries leader for your church is an honor. You've accepted the position, but chances are you have mixed feelings. You are happy because you know how relevant health is. You hear government leaders talking about healthcare. You see special features on television and in magazines about health, and you are hoping that under your leadership your church can make a difference. At the same time you are apprehensive. You may not be exactly sure what to do. Here are some steps to follow that will help you be more effective in promoting health ministries work.

Step 1: Pray that God will direct your planning and give your church a special health ministry.

The health message is the right arm of the gospel message. God will direct the health work to reach individuals who could not be reached in any other way, if we rely on His guidance.

Step 2: Read through the remaining chapters in this handbook in order to be aware of the information that is available.

Step 3: Look for supplies.

Probably you will find a lot of health ministries supplies stashed away at your church. Find your predecessor and ask if there are any supplies, good books, films, videos, or magazines available. What programs did he/she organize? Did he/she have an activities calendar for the year? It would be beneficial to see what was done and to know which programs were successful before planning your program for the year.

It is important to have a file cabinet to keep your supplies and information organized. Periodically the conference, union, and other organizations send excellent resource materials to your church. You may not need them right now, but if you file them away, you will have them when you need them. Many churches have a file cabinet for the health ministries leader. If your church doesn't, ask the pastor and the board to purchase a good filing cabinet. It will help to keep you organized and it will be a wonderful treasure chest of knowledge for the person who succeeds you. A file with a good lock will help you keep your videos and slides in a safe place. It is best to keep these church materials in a safe and accessible place at the church, rather than in your home.

Step 4: Find out what resources are available to you.

Start by reading the resource chapter of this handbook. The North American Division (NAD) and many of the conferences have supplies that they can lend (e.g., films and videos from their libraries). They might also be willing to conduct training programs.

Ask the pastor for the names, addresses, and telephone numbers of your conference health ministries directors. If you have a specific question about your role as a health ministries leader, call your conference.

For all other information, the North American Division maintains a "help desk" for local leaders at **Adventist PlusLine, 800-732-7587.** PlusLine is committed to providing live ministry phone support to active church leaders, and pastors throughout North America. If you have a question that needs answering, call them. NAD also has a 24-hour **FaxPlus** service that you can call toll free: (800) 474-4732. Follow the verbal instructions to find what health information is available to be faxed to you. This information is changed periodically, so this is a good service to check on a regular basis. Fill in the blanks below:

> My conference is:
>
> My conference health ministries director:
>
> Office phone:

Those on the internet should check the health ministries web page frequently: NAD Adventist.org/HM.

Step 5: Order current health catalogs.

Although you may already have health resource catalogs in your file, new material is constantly becoming available. Be sure you have current copies of the following catalogs: The free *Health Connection Catalog*, published at the Review and Herald Publishing Association, contains drug prevention and health promotional teaching materials. Call (800) 548-8700 and ask for the Adventist edition. Also a number of catalogs containing a wide variety of resources for the local leaders are available from Advent*Source* by calling (800) 328-0525.

Step 6: Write a mission statement, goals, and a job description.

A clear mission statement, goals, and a job description will increase your effectiveness. To guide you in developing these, see the mission statement and goals for North America, and the job descriptions for the conference and local church health ministries leaders in Chapter 3. You may want to adopt or modify these for your use.

Step 7: Form a health ministries committee.

If your church does not already have a health ministries committee you will want to establish one. Your committee should include the pastor, the local elder, the church ministries leader, the communication leader, and one or more health professionals. A small working committee of individuals interested in health promotion is more productive than a large uninvolved group; yet the more people you involve in planning, the more

ownership they will take in supporting your health ministries activities. If there is any question about your mission statement, goals, and job description, make that the first item on your agenda. It is good to plan at one sitting the health ministries activities you want to have for the entire year. You will need to have additional meetings to complete specific planning.

Step 8: Determine the health needs of your church and community.

You may want to do a survey to find out what you can about the population of the area you serve. When the information is gathered and analyzed it may give you some idea as to how to best plan your activities. For instance, you may want to find out the health status and health knowledge of your own local congregation. If you do any community outreach, you may want to survey the community to assess its needs. Is it a healthy community? Do they prefer a program on AIDS rather than a stop smoking program? Would more people come to an activity in the morning or at night? On which days of the week are they most likely to attend? Surveys can yield very useful data if properly planned.

You can design your own or modify those included in Chapter 5. Make sure you scratch where people itch!

Step 9: Use special health days to build awareness.

The Church Calendar

The North American Division has set aside **two important** annual Health ministries promotion days.

1. *Temperance Emphasis Day* (sometime in January/February). This day is set aside to create an awareness of our Temperance journals: *The Winner*, a drug prevention magazine for children and *Listen* for teens. Church members should be encouraged to subscribe to these publications for their own children and grandchildren and to fund gift subscriptions for SDA children in both church schools and public schools.

2. *Health Education Emphasis Week* (second week of October). Keeping church members

aware of the importance of health and educating new members on the current Health ministries topics are two of the major responsibilities of a local leader. This responsibility should be carried out at every opportunity, but the second week of October is a special time for emphasis. This is a unique opportunity to increase the level of awareness and the practice of health principles in your local church. Health emphasis week usually begins the first Sabbath of October and ends with the following Sabbath. This is the time to promote the importance of getting a Vibrant Life subscription for every family in the church, and for members to give gift subscriptions as a witness to friends, neighbors, and leaders in the community. Vibrant Life is the official outreach health journal published by the church for nonprofessionals. It provides informative material on health and the Adventist lifestyle in a way that makes it attractive to non-Adventists.

Ask your pastor if a sermon on health can be preached and plan something special in conjunction with these events. Hundreds of churches throughout the North American Division will be participating with you. This is an excellent opportunity to network with another church in your area, especially in large cities. Many churches working together can put on an attractive program.

National or World Health Days

In addition to the health emphasis events on the NAD church calendar, you may want to observe national or world health emphasis days. You can get the U.S. National Health Observances Calendar by calling the National Health Information Center at (800) 336-4797 or (301) 565-4167. Either wait on the line for an information specialist or indicate that you are interested in publications.(www.health.gov/nhic)

Decide which dates you will observe. Rarely will you be able to observe all of the dates. It is better to have a smaller number and place strong emphasis on them. Choose your dates and then send for materials from the organizations that sponsor them. Here are some important days or events you may want to observe: The American

Association for World Health (202) 466-5883 has information and ideas for celebrating three events. (www.aawhworldhealth.org)

- World Health Day: April 7
- World No Tobacco Day: May 31
- World AIDS Day: December 1

Red Ribbon Week (alcohol awareness encouraging young people to take a stand against alcohol) is observed in October. Contact the sponsoring organization, National Family Partnership, 11159 B. So. Town Square, St. Louis, MO 63123, (314) 845-1933 for materials and the Red Ribbon booklet. Clear the dates you plan to observe with your pastor to make sure the emphasis will meet church board approval. To be successful you need the support of your church.

Step 10: Start Networking.

A network is a person-to-person or group-to-group connection. It helps you find and share information. Networking is reaching out and joining hands with people with similar goals and interests. Networking means adding your strength to someone else's, rather than working alone.

Identify all of the health professionals who belong to your church. Do you have nurses, physicians, dentists, dietitians, physical therapists, or people with public health degrees? These will be people that you can call on to help promote and participate in your programs. They can be speakers, and additional hands, arms, and resources for you. Start networking with them now.

Identify others in your community that can help you. The yellow pages of your phone book may help. Almost every community has a Heart Association, a Cancer Society, a Lung Association, etc. They can help you on your big activity days. Usually they have qualified speakers who can give presentations for your health promotion programs, for special AY (Adventist Youth), Friday night vespers, Wednesday night prayer meetings, or even Sabbath morning. Many groups have slides or video programs, and various screenings that they do free of charge. Is there a hospital close by? Is there a university with a nutrition department or a medical school? All of these have potential speakers. Join hands and network with them.

Step 11: Read the NAD Health Ministries newsletter.

Several years ago, the North American Division Health Ministries Department began publishing a newsletter, *H&T Update*. This eight-page newsletter had a calendar of events, helpful articles, news and information, profiles of health professionals, and resources you can use. The newsletter name has now been changed to *HealthWorks* and it is a four-page.

HealthWorks is usually published every two months. If you are not receiving the newsletter call Advent*Source* (800) 328-0525 and ask to be put on the mailing list.

Step 12: Consider sponsoring new member programs.

Review suggestions made at the end of chapter 3. Your objective is to introduce every new member to the Adventist lifestyle and to get them active in some form of health ministry.

Introduction to a Healthy Diet: To encourage new members to have a healthful diet, you might provide the following:

- Acquaint them with vegetarian cookbooks. (See the Health Connection Catalog.)
- Ask a dietitian or trained nutrition instructor to hold cooking classes for the new members once a year. The conference health ministries director may be able to refer you to a qualified instructor.
- A special effort should be made to invite new members to established Adventist homes for representative vegetarian meals and fellowship.

Step 13: Consider certification.

The North American Division has prepared a Lifestyle Certification program to empower church members to be more effective health promoters. There are three levels: Consultant, Specialist, and Trainer. The requirements for certification cover the basic aspects of health educa-

tion. When you are finished with Level 1 you will know how to take personal responsibility for your health and share simple health principles with your church and family. In Level 2 you take training in specialty areas, such as stress management, smoking cessation, or vegetarian cooking instruction. Level 3 is a training course and apprenticeship for those wishing to teach certification courses. The full description of the Lifestyle Certification program can be found in Chapter 22. With the completion of certification you and other committed lay persons and professionals will be equipped to meet people's needs and share your faith as you share the health message.

Step 14: Marketing the Adventist health message

Dr. Ben Carson summed up what Ellen White once said about seizing the moment with two succinct words: "THINK BIG!" The point was that when opportunities for ministry present themselves, you should not be satisfied with ordinary attainments.

As Seventh-day Adventists, we believe we have "the health message." Unfortunately, we have not succeeded in getting this message out as effectively as possible. In most of our churches, the typical pattern followed for health outreach is to find someone who can do a cooking school, advertise it in the bulletin, and then pray some non-Adventists will show up. While this may have worked in the past, most will acknowledge that it no longer does. Instead of relying on outdated methods, we need to follow the example of successful corporations and businesses and market what we have to offer.

Typically, corporations spend more money marketing their products than they do on the products themselves. Nothing is left to chance. Millions of dollars are spent on research and analysis targeting potential consumers. When it comes to finding our potential audiences we most often fail to do our homework. If your church would like to think big in its health ministry, consider the following suggestions:

Community Research

- Check with the YMCA/YWCA and area health clubs. What are they doing? Coordinate with their services and assist them in programming.
- Contact local hospitals. What are local hospitals doing for community health education? Plan so your programs can complement their programs.
- Network with church members. Make a list of the large companies and corporations where your members work. See if doors can be opened for your church to assist with corporate health programs.
- Visit elementary and high schools. Ask school authorities if you can provide assistance in the areas of substance abuse, healthful home economics, or even provide an occasional noon meal.
- Go to the Chamber of Commerce. Get to know the receptionist. You'll be surprised how much local information they can provide. Offer to speak or do health screenings at the chamber breakfast or luncheon meetings. Network with chamber members.
- Survey local sporting goods stores. See if they will co-sponsor some of your programs (perhaps a race or walk or sports team with donated prizes).
- Contact local clubs and organizations. Make your services available to area Lions and Rotary Clubs, etc.
- Participate in annual holiday parades and health fairs. Consider building a float or booth that depicts health concepts. Health Expo booth materials can be ordered from The Health Connection.
- Contact area physicians. Place complimentary literature in doctors' offices and key community areas.
- Visit wellness groups in your community. Go to their programs and exchange ideas. Many benefits can come from this kind of networking.

Advertising Strategies

- Newspaper: Contact your local newspaper and find out what the rates and schedules are. Get to know the general editor as well as the religious and community events editor. Often they will accept well-written articles for publication without cost that will advertise your programs more effectively than a purchased ad.
- Flyers and posters: Have a group of church members help distribute your fliers and posters.
- Personal invitations: Invite the mayor and fire and police chiefs to your programs. With their permission, get photos of them at the programs for future public relations campaigns.
- Radio and TV: Provide area stations with Public Service Announcement spots. Offer to do interviews and/or demonstrations.
- Radio call-in programs: If there are physicians in your church, work to get them on radio or TV for an information/call-in program prior to your event.
- Editorials: Write a column on health for the local paper.
- Signs and billboards: Make sure your signs are readable and attractive. You may consider tying helium balloons to them for added attraction and pizazz. Billboard rental companies, as well as those who handle bus cards and signs in subways, usually donate a certain amount of space each year to non-profit, charitable organizations. Your only cost is the production of the signs. You are not likely to be considered if you contact them in the name of the church. Use the name of the denomination's separately-incorporated charitable agency, Adventist Community Services (ACS).

Now you have enough information to get started, it's time to get busy. Remember that God said, "Beloved, I wish above all things that thou mayest prosper and be in health" (3 John 2). He wants your church to be healthy and to reach out to the community through health. Health programs break down prejudice and begin the process through which the Holy Spirit can work to bring the community into a relationship with your church.

Have a healthy year!

5

Step-by-step in Health Evangelism

Health Evangelism is an aspect of gospel work that presents basic health principles and offers practical instruction in health and sensible health habits as an avenue to a more abundant life and a sound Christian faith. Almost from its inception, the Seventh-day Adventist Church has promoted health evangelism through its ministry, its medical institutions, and its professional personnel.

The Adventist denomination is quite unique in this aspect as no other church organization has health and health ministry so closely tied to their belief system as does this one. Such a development did not come by accident. It came by design–God's design–through the inspired words of Ellen White.

Concerning the evangelistic role of physicians, Ellen White wrote:

"Let the medical workers present the important (Adventist) truths . . . from the physician's viewpoint. Physicians of consecration and talent can secure a hearing in large cities at times when other men would fail. As physicians unite with ministers in proclaiming the gospel in the great cities of the land, their combined labors will result in influencing many minds in favor of the truth for this time" (*Medical Ministry*, p. 248).

Beyond the organized medical work, Ellen White was given the message that every minister should become involved in medical missionary work:

"Medical missionary work . . . is to be connected with the gospel ministry. It is the gospel in practice. . . . I wish to tell you that soon there will be no work done in ministerial lines but medical mission-

ary work. The work of a minister is to minister. Our ministers are to work on the gospel plan of ministering. . . . You will never be ministers after the gospel order till you show a decided interest in medical missionary work, the gospel of healing and blessing and strengthening. . . . The Lord wants every one of His ministers to come into line. Take hold of the medical missionary work, and it will give you access to the people. Their hearts will be touched as you minister to their necessities" (*Counsels on Health*, p. 533).

Evangelism was not to be carried on separately from the health message. Many Seventh-day Adventist evangelists make health and nutrition a part of their public program. Health correspondence lessons and special health features are a part of most Adventist radio and television programs.

Because abstinence from the use of tobacco and alcohol, and other drugs is a requirement for church membership among Seventh-day Adventists, there is a continuing program of education against their use along with stop smoking programs conducted by minister-doctor-laymen teams.

Many different forms of vegetarian cooking classes are being conducted for the public. Other health evangelism programs include home nursing classes that stress simple home treatments, first-aid classes, weight control, physical fitness, dietary control of heart disease, stress management, cancer risk prevention, and other classes and seminars designed to meet people's felt needs.

Many Adventist medical institutions carry on strong health evangelistic programs, employing health educators to coordinate evangelistic programs with chaplains, doctors, and nurses both in North America and overseas.

The Purpose of Medical Missionary Work

There are some who ridicule the concept that the purpose of our health ministry is evangelistic. They suggest that we should do health education without putting any "hooks" in it. But God has not called us to medical missionary work just to make healthy sinners out of people who come to our programs. Ellen White in no uncertain terms spells out God's purpose for health ministry:

"The minds of men must be called to the Scriptures as the most effective agency in the salvation of souls, and the ministry of the word is the great educational force to produce this result. Those who disparage the ministry and try to conduct the medical missionary work independently are trying to separate the arm from the body. What would be the result should they succeed? We should see hands and arms flying about, dispensing means without the direction of the head. The work would become disproportionate and unbalanced. That which God designed should be the hand and arm would take the place of the whole body, and the ministry would be belittled or altogether ignored. This would unsettle minds and bring in confusion, and many portions of the Lord's vineyard would be left unworked" (*Testimonies*, vol. 6, pp. 288, 289).

In combining the arm and the body in health evangelism, we are reaching out to those who ordinarily would never consider attending an Adventist series of doctrinal meetings. Naturally, it takes more time to bring these people step-by-step to an understanding of our message, but when you do you end up with Adventists committed to the kind of lifestyle most conducive to a living experience with Christ.

Step-by-step in Health Evangelism

Many engaged in health evangelism have learned that, before conducting a series of health evangelistic meetings for the public, it is essential to train church members in the healthy lifestyle that is to be presented to the public. That becomes an essential first step in health evangelism.

Step 1: Preparing the Church:

Because Adventist church members often are somewhat gospel hardened to the health message and often less receptive than the general public, they must be taught health principles, the advantages of the Adventist lifestyle, and the methods of health evangelism.

One way of doing this is to hold a medical missionary training program such as the Take 10 Seminar on the Golden rules of Dynamic Living (Materials available from The Health Connection. Toll-free phone: 1-800-548-8700). Your objectives in such a church training program are to lead to a realization of:

1. The urgency and advantage of using medical missionary work to finish the gospel task.
2. The necessity for personal practice of health principles.
3. How each member can be trained to use medical missionary outreach programs.

Organize the members into small companies for conducting specific health programs.

Continuing research is being funded on the advantages of the Adventist lifestyle. See Chapter 23 for up-to-date information. (Programs on the Adventist Advantage can be ordered from The Health Connection).

Once church members become convinced that healthy habits strengthen the immune system, which gives them added protection against lifestyle diseases such as cancer, heart disease, and stroke, they should be ready to make some

---

See Chapter 24

For the latest information on Health Exhibits. Use the 12 easy steps of CELEBRATIONS to illustrate your health booth. Order from The Health Connection, 800-548-8700.

---

personal lifestyle improvements, experience the benefits, and then share what they have learned with those about them.

Step 2: Begin with a Health Expo or Health Fair or other community screening programs:

Include community health agencies and put these on at a public auditorium or shopping mall. Include various screening programs. Most important—have registration sheets for specific community health education classes. It is essential to use some type of community health interest survey in order to learn what type of health programming is most needed in your community. (See sample surveys at the end of this chapter.)

Health screening can be conducted in several different formats, such as:

- Screening vans–mobile units that take screening tests to the curbside in central cities or suburban shopping center parking lots.
- Screening booths or tables-set up in shopping malls, at county fairs, and any other setting where people congregate.
- Health fairs–large events involving a number of different health organizations. (See chapter 24 for additional information.)
- Health risk management programs-a combination of screening tests with stress management or specific disease risk prevention seminars.

Specific Information about how to conduct health screening programs is not included in this book because many such programs, including complete planning guidelines, step-by-step procedures, medical protocols for different screening tests and camera-ready masters, videos, or Power Point presentations are available from several denominational supply entities. *The Health Screening Handbook* is available from Advent Source (800) 328-0525. (See chapter 21 for other programs and where they are available).

Step 3: Offer Classes that Meet the Felt Needs Indicated on Health Interest Surveys:

Attempt to offer those programs that are unique to your community rather than competing with what other health agencies are doing. Some possibilities:

1. Welcome Baby program.
2. Vegetarian cooking classes, such as Healthy Holiday Recipes.
3. Physical Fitness programs. (Marathon or health run).
4. School temperance and drug abuse prevention programs.
5. Programs in doctor's, dentist's offices.
6. Radio and TV health hint presentations.
7. Prison ministry.
8. Home finance and budgeting seminars.
9. How to Get the Most Out of Bible Study seminars.
10. Gardening, craft, and hobby classes, and, of course,
11. Classes on how to overcome harmful health habits (smoking, drinking, narcotics, gambling, obesity, etc.)

NEWSTART® Health Expo

Eight beautifully illustrated exhibit centers present an easy-to-follow plan of protection from disease and even disease reversal. It includes computerized health evaluations, consultations, home health care demonstrations, screening programs, food demonstrations and samples, video films, free gift drawings, and explanations of the eight natural remedies. (Available from Dorothy Nelson: Health Expo Lifestyle Programs, Weimar Institute, P.O. Box 486, Weimar, CA 95736 (800) 525-9192 ext. 7013.)

Simple blood pressure screening at fairs or in community department stores or malls also has proved to be effective in generating community interest in planned health seminars. Interest surveys should be filled out no matter what type of community contact you use.

The best place to hold these seminars is in a Better Living or Health Enhancement Center. If you cannot do so, try to find some neutral location. Most people will shy away from coming to a church. But if you have nowhere else to hold these classes, doing so in a church does help tie those who come to participate in church activities. If you hold the seminars in a church, use a fellowship hall or classroom rather than the main chapel.

Dr. Elvin Adams, who has successfully held health evangelism programs in churches, promotes this use of churches, saying "The best way to change the reputation of the local Seventh-day Adventist church is to do something useful for neighbors and friends. The purpose of evangelism is to help our secular friends develop a personal relationship with Christ and to develop a fellowship in the church. In our materialistic society the church is not as relevant as it once was.

HeartBeat '96 by Satellite in Centerville, Tennessee

*T*he air was electric with tension as the expectant audience at the Martin Memorial Seventh-day Adventist Church waited for Dan Matthews to open the HeartBeat '96 Adventist Communications Network (ACN) down-link seminar on Tuesday evening, May 21. The 66 participants had received the results of their individual computer generated heart disease risk analyses and were anxious to hear their interpretation and to learn what they could do to reduce their risk of heart attacks. They were not disappointed. All who attended stated the seminar met their expectations and 96 percent committed to repeat their participation next year.

When asked what they appreciated most about HeartBeat '96, the Centerville participants' response ranged from expressions of appreciation for its low cost and affordability to appreciation for the evident interest and concern the panel of specialists had in helping people to understand and correct their individual problems. All realized they were receiving the latest heart disease information available. One participant particularly expressed appreciation over being able to obtain information from more than one doctor. Others were excited to hear questions asked from the audience in Centerville and have them answered live by the panel of experts in California. One stated that the seminar "made me realize that I need to do something about my weight and diet." Another expressed appreciation for "the information and challenge to do better." One stated "I learned about things I have not thought about before." Others simply said "everything was great" or that they "liked it all." A local practicing doctor who attended the seminar stated "it couldn't have been better!"

The Martin Memorial S.D.A. Church in Centerville, TN has a small active membership of 23 and is the only Adventist church in Hickman County, a rural county in middle Tennessee with a population of approximately 15,000. God has blessed the witness and prayers of this small band of believers, however, and the church regularly has in attendance on Sabbath more than 50 worshippers, including 10 to 15 non-Adventists. Centerville is blessed with a dedicated Adventist pastor, but he has two other larger churches in his District and is able to be in Centerville only one Sabbath out of every four.

HeartBeat '96 began with the enthusiastic endorsement of the concept by the church membership and they have followed through with magnificent support. (More than half the church members directly assisted by giving time and effort to various aspects of the program.)

Support was obtained from the four local practicing physicians and the Community Hospital. In fact, the local hospital cosponsored the program by providing the facility for screening and blood drawing and using its telephone operators to make all appointments. Contacts with local businesses and industries generated a lot of interest. The largest local bank and nursing home

An emphasis on the advantages of a Seventh-day Adventist lifestyle can reverse this trend." He believes that the true home of health evangelism should be the local church. If a church consistently offers a wide variety of programs to the public it will come to enjoy a unique reputation in the community. People will come to realize that the solution to all of life's problems is found at the Seventh-day Adventist Church. He is convinced that health evangelism will not enjoy its greatest

measure of success until its home base is firmly established in the local Seventh-day Adventist church.

Another reason why there may be some advantage in using local churches for health evangelism programs is that the church facility can comfortably handle any size group—and it's free. Renting an auditorium can be expensive.

agreed to pay the entire fee for their employees to participate in HeartBeat '96 and several other businesses encouraged their employees by giving them time off to obtain the screening.

A paid advertisement was placed in the local weekly Hickman County *Times* and the paper reciprocated by two good news stories and three different public service announcements. The local radio station also gave a number of public service spot announcements about the event. A survey of the HeartBeat participants indicated that 35 percent learned of the program through the newspaper; 27 percent participated at the encouragement of their employers; others were motivated to participate by a friend (19 percent) or because of known disease in their family (15 percent). Less commonly mentioned, but helpful were announcements that were made in several local churches and the radio announcements.

It is obvious that HeartBeat '96 met a felt need in Hickman County; 84 percent of participants indicated that they had long felt a need for something like this before they heard of HeartBeat '96. Their serious interest is also indicated by the fact that more than half committed to future participation in follow-up programs of low-fat cooking/nutrition classes or exercise/physical fitness programs. Strong interest was also expressed in weight control/obesity treatment and stress management seminars. Significant, but lesser interest, was shown in stop smoking programs. Of those participating, 96 percent gave information so they can be notified of future health programs.

A brief analysis of the 66 Centerville HeartBeat participants shows that 32 percent were male; 68 percent were female; 26 percent of all participants were under age 40, 62 percent between age 41 and 65, and 12 percent were over age 65. Ethnic background was not recorded, but we were happy to have a good representation from our minority population. 41 percent of all participants had their registration paid by their employers; the rest were paid personally. All but five participants were from the local Centerville telephone exchange; only one came from outside Hickman County.

The benefits of HeartBeat '96 to the Martin Memorial Seventh-day Adventist Church are numerous. 1) The Adventist Health Network and Martin Memorial Church gained a great deal of scientific credibility and name recognition—56 out of the 66 participants were non-Adventists. 2) A large number of non-Adventists attended an Adventist church for the first time and in a friendly and non-threatening environment. 3) Strong interest for future programs was generated. 4) It was an excellent demonstration of the power and capability of satellite television. The Martin Memorial church believes that many more people will be willing to attend Net '96 because of this positive experience with HeartBeat '96.

The Adventist Communication Network and the Adventist Health Network are providing much needed and appreciated assistance to such small rural churches as the Martin Memorial. Centerville, Tennessee has been deeply affected by this most recent community service program. May God be glorified by its impact!

—P. William Dysinger, local HeartBeat Coordinator

Breathe Free™: The Plan to Stop Smoking

The church's first smoking cessation program was designed by Dr. J. Wayne McFarland and Chaplain Elman J. Folkenberg between 1959 and 1961. Called the five-Day Plan to Stop Smoking, it was one of the first smoking-cessation programs available in the United States. At that time the General Conference Temperance Department also produced one of the first films on smoking and health—*One in 20,000*. During the next 20 to 25 years this plan was successful in helping millions of smokers stop smoking.

In 1985 the plan was revised and was named the Breathe-Free Plan. In 1993 it was again revised to allow time for small group work and discussion with less attention given to a lecture format. The time was extended to nine sessions and the official title became: Breathe Free: The Plan to Stop Smoking.

The materials provided for the Breathe Free plan consist of nine annotated scripts designed for the expert or the novice in conducting a smoking cessation program, plus a director's manual giving detailed information on how to plan, promote, and implement the program.

There are a number of items available to enhance the effectiveness of the program: novelty buttons; a personal plan booklet that guides each participant through each session, diplomas at the end of the nine sessions, at six months, and at one year; posters, nine videos and many demonstration devices.

Breathe Free seeks to empower the individual to reach four major objectives: physical preparation, mental conditioning, social support, and spiritual regeneration. It assists participant in becoming knowledgeable and active in the process of behavior change, opening up to them a vision of personal choice, individual responsibility, freedom to act, and power to direct their own lifestyle.

Some Adventist Health Seminar Packages

A number of kits have been developed that enable health professionals or other volunteers to conduct successful, effective health education events. Almost all of these include an instructor's guide and materials to be handed to the group participants. Some include audio-visuals and advertising materials.

Breathe-Free Plan to Stop Smoking is the replacement for the Five-Day Plan. Nine sessions designed for a four-week period are available through The Health Connection, the health ministry resource center for the Seventh-day Adventist Church in North America. The program includes scripts for the minister and doctor. Also posters, personal plan booklets, etc. It recommends an introductory meeting several days before beginning the program, and also recommends a follow-up schedule. Videos and Power Point are available which can be purchased from The Health Connection. A Stop Smoking video series by Detroit cancer surgeon, Dr. Art Weaver also is available.

Stress Beyond Coping. A most practical Stress Seminar based on a lifestyle approach. The seven keys to coping include nutrition, exercise, sleep and other health principles that can also be used as stand-alone short talks. Includes an instructor's manual with word-for-word scripts for six two-hour sessions. The seminar materials also include a CD-ROM with Power Point illustrations, participant work book sets, and overheads. Everything you need for your first seminar can be purchased at a special savings price from The Health Connection (Catalog number 35290–Introductory Package). Useful for both a Lifestyle Seminar and for use as a bridge-building step in health evangelism.

Cooking Schools and Nutrition Workshops are an Adventist tradition. Several program designs have been published over the years. (See chapter 9 for suggestions on kinds of cooking schools and how to conduct them.)

Eight Weeks to Wellness. Motivates participants to make two lifestyle changes they select

from the following topics:
   Week 1–Developing a Healthy Lifestyle
   Week 2–Becoming More Physically Active
   Week 3–Low Saturated Fat/Cholesterol
   Week 4–Eating Enough Fiber
   Week 5–Achieving/Maintaining a Healthy
     Weight
   Week 6–Dealing With Dependencies
   Week 7–Coping With Stress
   Week 8–Preventive Exams and Safety

Eight Power Point presentations are included in the package available through The Health Connection.

Step 4. Bridge Building:

Because our ultimate goal is to lead people to Christ and into His kingdom we have not finished our task when we have led them to stop smoking or lose weight. Some type of bridge program that emphasizes the spiritual but does not get into heavy Adventist doctrine helps those not yet ready to become Adventists understand the importance of the spiritual in total health. However, the attempts to bridge between health and evangelistic programs will result in only very limited success *if the program is not meeting felt needs.*

Once the confidence of the public has been obtained in a health program, spiritual principles should be introduced to give the Holy Spirit the opportunity to prepare their hearts and minds to be more receptive to the fuller, doctrinal message that is presented in an evangelistic program. A health program may be made evangelistic by introducing an individual to God as the agent of change in behavior. This type of evangelism is relatively narrow and focused on the problem which brought the individual to the class. Everyone who comes to a Seventh-day Adventist stop smoking program should learn that God helps smokers quit, obese people to lose weight, and the rest of us to cope with stress. In fact, God provides the answer to all of life's perplexing problems. This type of focused health evangelism will not review the wide spectrum of distinctive doctrines held by the Seventh-day Adventist Church and it should be presented as free as pos-

---

Every Church a Training School

"The medical missionary work should be a part of the work of every church in our land. Disconnected from the local church it would soon become a strange medley of disorganized atoms." —*Testimonies*, Vol. 6, p. 289.

"Every church should be a training school for Christian workers…. There should be schools of health, cooking schools, and classes in various lines of Christian help work. There should not only be teaching but actual work under experienced instructions." —*The Ministry of Healing*, p. 148-9.

---

sible from the jargon which is used in traditional church circles.

Those conducting health evangelism programs should realize that it is God who produces the feeling of discontent with one's lifestyle and prompts an individual to come to a Seventh-day Adventist health program. An individual is sitting in your audience because God brought him/her to your church so behavior could be changed.

In your health evangelism program you should develop rather completely the theology of behavior change. (See Chapter 6.) Once a person experiences deliverance from one problem the individual will be anxious to tackle other programs and eventually ask about the spectrum of beliefs of the Seventh-day Adventist Church.

Some question whether placing the spiritual material early in a health program will cause people to be offended and seek assistance elsewhere. This should not be the case if it is directed toward the problem with which they are struggling. They have come for help and are desperate to learn any secrets you might have which would deliver them from the problem they are trying to overcome.

Perhaps the only way in which Seventh-day Adventist health programs can be unique is in the inclusion of a spiritual dimension in a program of behavior change. It is likely that most of the people in the audience will already have tried to change their behavior in other programs and have repeatedly failed because they never were pointed to God as the One who brings about change in the life. True health evangelism presents God as the source of help, and the more abundant life.

In Pursuit of Excellence is a 12-session health evangelism series designed to provide the missing link between the health programs you have been offering and the spiritual results you want. This program allows you to present health in a non-judgmental, caring way, position your church as a wellness center for your community, and make the Bible appealing to the secular mind as you blend health information with the gospel to save the soul as well as the body.

Take Ten. Ellen White challenges: "To make plain natural law, and to urge obedience to it, is a work that accompanies the third angel's message."—CH 21. She adds: "Since the laws of nature are the laws of God, it is plainly our duty to give these laws careful study. . . . Ignorance in these things is sin."—CD 18. Concerning the need to educate people in the laws of health, we read:

Christ's Methods

"Christ's method alone will give true success in reaching the people. The Savior:
1. Mingled with men   (CONTACT)
2. as one who desired   (CONCERN)
   their good.
3. He showed His   (COMPASSION)
   sympathy for them,
4. ministered to their   (COMMITMENT)
   needs
5. and won their   CONFIDENCE
6. Then He bade them,   (CONVERSION)
   "Follow me."
                    —*The Ministry of Healing*, p. 143

"It is the duty of every person, for his own sake, and for the sake of humanity, to inform himself in regard to the laws of life, and conscientiously to obey them. . . . We can not be too often reminded that health does not depend on chance. It is a result of obedience to law."—MH 128.

Take Ten is intended to be a "bridge" program that leads those attending from interest in physical health to an understanding of wholistic health. It is God's intention to restore the image of God in man physically, as well as mentally, socially, and spiritually. With this basic philosophy in mind, those attending are led to recognize that the Creator's laws are essential for health and happiness. When this is understood, people begin to grasp the fact that there is a strong connection between health and religion and that religion plays an important role in the health of body and mind. When they complete this seminar they should be ready for more specific examination of the Adventist faith. The seminar involves many practical applications to lifestyle and behavior change. It leads those attending to make many of these applications themselves, thus making it easier for them not only to understand but to apply in their own lives. (This seminar is available from The Health Connection. It includes Instructor's manual, video presentations, and/or Power Point presentations. Plans are underway to combine this with a twelve step to wellness seminar now being prepared by The Health Connections.)

Step 5. Health Evangelism Series:
This should be a full-message series that ties in brief health presentations with the doctrines of the Adventist. An excellent resource is the "Life Net" series prepared by Dan Matthews of the Lifestyle Magazine television series for use with Net '96.

In connection with these meetings, a strong personal work and Bible study program should be conducted in the homes of those attending in order to make sure they understand and accept the truths being presented and to make these truths applicable to the individual's needs and Christian growth. In all evangelistic endeavors, nothing can be accomplished without the guidance of the Holy Spirit and much prayer.

Personal Health Evangelism

Most think of health evangelism as a large church sponsored program where a number of church members participate in a planned outreach to the community. That's the type of health evangelism we have focused on in this chapter. But health evangelism doesn't have to be big, church sponsored, or even church based. You don't even need a committee to do it. Health evangelism is something anyone can do. There is no excuse for not having a part in the health evangelism work. You are never too young or too old to live your lifestyle, share your personal testimony, or use your particular gifts in some aspect of the health work. If one of the outreach programs in this chapter inspires you, go for it. But if not, begin praying, asking God how He can use you in a way that fits you, your personality and your talents. That's what the Benton sisters did, and here's their story: In 1992 three teenager "singing" sisters from Lakeport, California prayed, "Lord, show us how we can evangelize in our own town. We go singing and sharing everywhere but what can we do at home?" Audrey, Trishonna, and Emberly Benton grew up on a little farm in Northern California. They enjoyed milking goats and gathering eggs. Eventually the Benton family developed allergies to dairy products, and began noticing many friends and relatives were suffering because of their rich American diet. As their health awareness grew the Benton sisters began exploring new ways to cook without using animal products, refined fat or sugar. Their goal was to revise everyone's favorite recipes without sacrificing looks or taste, using foods in their natural, unrefined state. The result is that they didn't give up anything—but gained everything, including a nation-wide ministry. The Bentons now have a television series on 3ABN where they demonstrate their vegan recipes, sing together, and minister. They conduct cooking schools not only in their own hometown, but around the United States, and their book, *What's Cooking in the Benton Sisters' Kitchen*, has been reprinted many times. God has a ministry for everyone who is willing to pray, "Lord show me how I can evangelize in my own town." For more information contact the Benton Sisters Ministry, PO Box 552, Lakeport CA 95453; (707) 263-5871; answering machine (707) 262-0901.

A Challenge from Ellen White

"To make plain natural law, and to urge obedience to it, is a work that accompanies the third angel's message."
—*Counsels on Health*, page 21.

"Since the laws of nature are the laws of God, it is plainly our duty to give these laws careful study…. Ignorance in these things is sin."
—*Counsels on Diet and Foods*, page 18.

"Concerning the need to educate people in the laws of health: "It is the duty of every person, for his own sake, and for the sake of humanity, to inform himself in regard to the laws of life, and conscientiously to obey them…. We can not be too often reminded that health does not depend on chance. It is a result of obedience to law."
—*The Ministry of Healing*, page 128.

Sample Health Interest Surveys (See the following page.) Proper planning with a statistician or someone who knows about randomization and sample size will help you obtain reliable information from your interest survey. If you use the interest surveys with a health screening program, you will want to obtain the *Health Screening Handbook* which can be ordered from Advent Source (800)328-0525.

Total Health Community Interest Survey

Which of the following Seminars Would You Find Helpful?

Physical Well-being:

❑ Physical Fitness Class
❑ Vegetarian Cooking Class
❑ Healthy Holiday Recipes
❑ Stress Control
❑ Breathe-Free Stop Smoking Plan
❑ Weight Control
❑ Cancer Prevention

Social Well-being

❑ Marriage Encounter
❑ Raising Teenagers
❑ Wills and Estates
❑ Personal Family Finances
❑ How to be a Hero to Your Kids

Improving Skills:

❑ What Every Driver Needs to know About Basic Car Maintenance
❑ Computer Skills
❑ Internet Use
❑ Bread Baking
❑ Welcome to Wellness Seminar

Understanding the Bible:

❑ How to Get the Most Out of Bible Study
❑ Sat. Morning Neighborhood Children's Bible Class
❑ Vacation Bible School
❑ Understanding Daniel and Revelation

Indicate which days are best for you to attend:
❑ Sun ❑ Mon ❑ Tue ❑ Wed ❑ Thurs ❑ Fri ❑ Sat

❑ Morning
❑ Afternoon
❑ Evening

Please notify me as to where and when the seminars checked will be offered:

NAME _____ PHONE_____

ADDRESS_____

6

Health Behavior Change: Taking Personal Responsibility

Most people have largely surrendered control of their health to professionals rather than taking personal responsibility by following a healthy lifestyle.

An important prerequisite to being an effective health evangelist to others is the ability to take personal responsibility for your own health. It's one thing to know all the right answers but another to do it. Being a living example of the principles you teach, and having experienced first-hand the struggles of taking control of your life and making the lifestyle changes that you knew you should will give you credibility and a compassionate heart for those who are still fighting the battle.

It takes time to change a habit because what you are doing is changing an established pathway in the brain to another one. For example, take the sensation of hunger between meals. Most people will get up, go to the kitchen, find something that tastes good, and eat it. Once you learn that it's better for your weight and your digestive system to not eat between meals you must replace that old automatic response with a new chosen response. You must override your automatic pilot! Your decision now is based on information, not feelings. You know if you have had an adequate meal that the sensation is probably the body needing more water rather than more food. So you drink a full glass of water and stay out of the kitchen, and the hunger sensation ceases.

The first few days are the hardest because the rut to the old behavior is far deeper than the new pathway you are trying to establish. But the longer you use the new pathway the deeper it will become, until that action becomes your automatic pilot. You may always be tempted with your old habit, but the frequency and strength will decrease over time.

To reinforce the fact that a change will be worth the effort, there is a study conducted by Dr. Lester Breslow and his team that shows that living health practices can result in longer life. They asked 7,000 residents of Alameda County in Northern California a variety of questions, such as whether they smoked, drank alcohol, exercised, were overweight, ate breakfast, slept seven or eight hours a night, and snacked between meals.

After following the group for nine years, the team learned that 38 percent of the men aged 60–69 who adopted no more than two of the health practices, had died. By comparison, of those who had adopted four or five practices, only 24 percent had died. For women, 38 percent who adopted no more than two had died, while only 9 percent of those who adopted four or five had died. This study shows that anyone—even after age 60—who adopts good health practices can decrease the risk of dying prematurely from such major diseases as heart disease, cancer, and stroke. (See Lisa F. Berkman and Lester Breslow, *Health and Ways of Living: The Alameda County Study*, New York: Oxford University Press, 1983.)

Based on this study, consider your own health habits. Chances are you don't smoke or drink alcohol, but what about other habits?

Do you get enough exercise?

Are you overweight?

Do you eat a wholesome breakfast?

Do you get at least 7 or 8 hours of sleep?

Do you snack between meals?

Do you drink enough water?

Do you eat too much fat or sugar?

Do you control negative thinking?

Is your life as balanced as it should be?

Most of us are something like the patient who, being lectured by his physician about his

It is Impossible to "Break" Bad Habits

Most people talk about "breaking" bad habits. But to be exact, habits are really never broken, only changed. The habit pathways in your brain are like ruts in a road that will always be there. That's why unless you have a plan and work it, it's easy to fall back into unhealthy ways. Since you can't "break" old habits, your focus must be on retraining your brain to use new pathways. These new habits must be repeated again and again to establish the rut! That's why it's so important to stick with your resolve for 21 days. After that time, as you are beginning to make new pathways in your brain, it should be easier.

Here are positive statements you may want to copy and say to yourself as you retrain your thinking.

- I am breaking bad habits.
- I am no longer doing things that go along with the unhealthful habit.
- I am turning my mind to positive thoughts.
- I am developing a supportive environment.
- I have set a date for making the break—and I am going to do it.
- I am successfully working my lifestyle change plan.
- I may not make big changes at once, but I will change.
- I have set a tiny goal in the direction I want to go.
- Each time I reach success, I reward myself.
- Each week, I will take one more tiny step toward my goal.
- I won't punish myself for failure.

—Jan W. Kuzma, *The Live-Longer Lifestyle*

need for better health habits, complained: "I didn't come here to be told that I'm burning the candle at both ends. I knew that already. What I came for was more wax !"

Health information in and of itself does not help us much unless we choose to make use of it. Our problem is that, until we become sick, we find our present habits and life style so comfortable that we resist change. It isn't that we lack interest in the subject of health. This topic fascinates most Americans nowadays. Bookstores and magazine racks are flooded with up-to-the-minute health information. But, until we perceive a practical application to our immediate needs, most of us are happy to be up to date without bothering to apply what we know. Our real need is for a powerful motivation that will make us want to adopt a healthier lifestyle.

At rare moments we seem to be able to look beyond the horizons of our present way of life. When we do, we catch a breath-taking view of the wide band of potentialities available to us. Often this happens when we see someone we know making a drastic improvement in lifestyle. If flabby old George can look and feel ten years younger, then we can too. We can wake up in the morning feeling full of vigor and vim, knowing that this day is going to be the best of our lives. How? That is what the rest of this chapter is about. When you understand the psychology of health behavior change, you will be better able to make the continuing lifestyle changes to improve your own health, while at the same time being a more effective health evangelist to others.

How to Turn Information into Reformation

Sometimes the most intelligent people act foolishly. Knowledge at times even gets in the way of wisdom, as when the scientifically oriented reject faith in God because they cannot empirically establish His existence in the laboratory. The wisest man who ever lived testified that true wisdom begins with "the fear of the Lord (Prov. 9:10)."

In this setting *fear* means respect for. Those who respect both themselves as children of God and the Creator's laws that are designed to provide maximum life and health, not only experience better health, but also soon learn that doing so promotes real happiness. People cannot be separated into little compartments called "physical," "mental," "social," "emotional," and "spiritual." One of the greatest health discoveries of recent years is that the mind can contribute more to the state of illness than microbes can. The five components of our being that are listed above are so interrelated that what affects one affects all.

Writing in the February, 1977, issue of *Psychology Today*, Kenneth Pelletier gives this key to the mounting health problem he terms "afflictions of civilization." From the standpoint of the whole person, it becomes clear, he tells us, "that a person's mind and body work as a single unit and that health exists when they are in harmony." He concludes that "staying healthy involves much more than simply seeing a doctor when we become ill. How we live—including what we eat, our family life, our working day, and many other large and small details of our routine—is critically important in keeping us healthy."

Because most of the major diseases we now face are rooted in causes involving everyday living, they cannot be contained or controlled neatly in hospitals or laboratories. Evidence of this is seen in the fact that death rates from chronic diseases have risen dramatically over the last 50 years in spite of the tremendous advances being made in the field of acute care. Our high-technology, acute-care system is not designed to deal efficiently with lifestyles, nutrition, health behavior, lack of exercise, and the stress and tension that are recognized as being among the major causes of chronic disease.

The 1979 Surgeon General's report entitled *Healthy People* states: "The health of the Nation's citizens can be significantly improved through actions individuals can take themselves. . . . For the individual often only modest lifestyle changes are needed to substantially reduce risk for several diseases. And many of the personal decisions required to reduce risk for one disease can reduce it for others. Within the practical grasp of most Americans are simple measures to enhance the prospects of good health, including:

- elimination of cigarette smoking;
- reduction of alcohol misuse;
- moderate dietary changes to reduce intake of excess calories, fat, salt and sugar;
- moderate exercise;
- periodic screening (at intervals determined by age and sex) for major disorders such as high blood pressure and certain cancers; and
- adherence to speed laws and use of seat belts.

Widespread adoption of these practices could go far to improve the health of our citizens."—Page 10.

Later in the report the Surgeon General states: "Beginning in early childhood and throughout life, each of us makes decisions affecting our health. They are made, for the most part, without regard to, or contact with, the health system. Yet their cumulative impact has a greater effect on the length and quality of life than all the efforts of medical care combined."—Page 119.

The report adds: "Consider, too, the strikingly lower cancer rates among certain groups of Americans compared to those for the general population. Seventh-day Adventists neither smoke nor drink, and about half follow a milk, egg, and vegetable diet. For this group, not only is their cancer incidence, for those cancers strongly related to smoking and drinking, less than one seventh that of the general population; even their cancer incidence at other sites is only half to three-fourths as high."—Page 119.

The Motivating Power of Religion

Why do people with strong religious convictions often have better health? The one ingredient essential to success in any resolve we make to improve our health habits is motivation. The woman whose husband promised her a fur coat if she would stop smoking naturally lost most of her motivation not to smoke after she got the coat.

A fascinating study conducted with those who were attempting to stop smoking demonstrated that religion was one of the most powerful motivating factors in permanently quitting smoking. It was found that those who have strong religious motivation for stopping are more likely to do so and to never smoke again than are those who do not have this kind of motivation (Waingrow, S. M. Report from National Clearinghouse on Smoking and Health, USPHS. O. W. Elsinger, "Psychological Predictors of Smoking Recidivism," Journal of Social Behavior, Dec., 1971).

Sam gave up both smoking and drinking at the same time. It was the most difficult struggle he had ever been through. He discovered that it took all the help he could find. Fortunately his

---

Principles for Overcoming

We cannot overcome on our own. Our adversary is too strong for us. But he is a defeated foe. We must realistically face up to our weaknesses, but at the same time remember that Jesus has gained the victory for us if we will let Him win the battle for us. Some ways we cooperate are:

1. Avoid places and situations that you know are likely to tempt you. Run, don't walk, away from temptation.
2. Overcome evil habits by replacing them with good habits. Particularly concentrate on developing the best health habits you can.
3. Hide God's word in your memory to help recognize His will in every situation. Carry Bible promise cards with you to refer to when tempted to fall back.
4. Develop such a great love for Christ that you would rather die than disappoint Him. When tempted, concentrate on what Jesus would do rather than on the temptation.
5. Be constantly in an attitude of prayer and communion with God.
6. Attend group therapy sessions, helping others gain the victories you are gaining. Pray for the members of your group at a specific time each day. If a church member, attend Sabbath School, church services, and prayer meetings faithfully.
7. If you do not yet belong to one, organize a prayer and study group with five or six friends who live in your area.
8. Do not neglect Bible study. Spend some time each day contemplating the life of Jesus.

When Satan comes to dispute your position, call on the Lord to rebuke him, When he is tempting and bargaining with you, appeal to God's Holy Word. "It is written." And when he uses another individual to tempt or attack you, trust in Christ to rebuke that person and to defend you.

—*Leo Van Dolson*

---

family and friends supported him. But that was not enough. When everything else failed him he turned to God in a desperate bid for divine help and found the help he needed. Sam gave his life to God and developed a new and powerful motivation for not smoking or drinking, as well as receiving help in keeping his cravings from overpowering him. The unaided human will often is powerless to overcome the temptations that destroy health of body and mind. That is where trust in divine power can be most effective.

Notice this wonderful promise that the Bible holds out to those who find temptation assailing them: "There hath no temptation taken you but such as is common to man: but God is faithful who will not suffer you to be tempted above that ye are able; but will with the temptation also make a way to escape, that ye may be able to bear it" (1 Corinthians 10:31).

People who have acquired spiritual values do have an advantage. They accept as the motivating power for all that they do a sense of strong commitment to God and His way and will in their lives. This includes a sense of responsibility to keep their bodies in as healthy a condition as possible in order to be able to serve God better and be a blessing to those about them.

Use Positive Motivators

Too often in our approach to sharing we leave the impression that what we're suggesting is BITTER rather than BETTER. And then we wonder why people shy away from it. Too often we stress the negative rather than the positive. We act as though we know what is best and others better listen to what we have to say if they want to know what's for their own best good. Sometimes, in fact, we're so intent on getting our particular message across that we aren't even aware of what the problem is that's causing others to continue doing that which isn't good for them.

Take for example a teacher who catches a 7th-grader smoking. The ensuing dialogue might run something like this:

"Oh, you shouldn't do that!"
"Why not?"

"Why, because it's bad for you. You'll get heart disease, lung cancer and emphysema."

Then what if the teacher went to the principal to get help in arranging for a series of films to be shown to the 7th grade. Films, naturally, on heart disease, lung cancer and emphysema!

Would that take care of the problem? Probably not. It would be much better if the teacher would try to find out why the child had taken up smoking and deal with the basic cause. Usually one of two reasons will come out. Either he'll say, "I want to be like Dad and Mom" or "the fellows will call me `chicken' if I don't."

What is needed? Obviously not a lecture on heart disease, lung cancer and emphysema. The children who are having this very real problem need to know how to be like Mom and Dad without ruining their lungs; or what to do when someone calls them "chicken."

Actually, the key to the right approach in bringing about health behavior change was written many years ago. It is found in the health classic, *The Ministry of Healing*. "It is of little use to try to reform others by attacking what we may regard as wrong habits. Such effort often results in more harm than good. In His talk with the Samaritan woman, instead of disparaging Jacob's well, Christ presented something better. `If thou knewest the gift of God,' He said, `and who it is that saith to thee, Give Me to drink; thou wouldest have asked of Him, and He would have given thee living water.' He turned the conversation to the treasure He had to bestow, offering the woman something better than she possessed, even living water, the joy and hope of the gospel. This is the illustration of the way in which we are to work. We must offer men something better than that which they possess, even the peace of Christ which passeth all under-standing. We must tell them of God's holy law, the transcript of His character, and an expression of that which He wishes them to become" (pp. 156, 157).

Note the statement that "it is of little use" to attack the wrong habits of others. Why is this so? Because those involved become defensive about their pet habits and tune out those trying to help them. What then is the most effective way of bringing about a change in a person's lifestyle? In a pleasant, optimistic, affirmative, and positive way we must demonstrate that there is something better. That makes good sense, doesn't it? Many will move in the right direction once they truly understand the benefits to be realized.

We need to approach suggested behavior change, whether it be stopping smoking or just learning to drink five to six glasses of water each day, as a joyful, happy thing to do—something that will help us experience the "more abundant life" Christ offers in John 10:10.

The Desire of Ages enlarges on Jesus teaching "something better" this way: "In the sermon on the mount, [Jesus] sought to undo the work that had been wrought by false education, and to give His hearers a right conception of His kingdom and of His own character. Yet He did not make a direct attack on the errors of the people. He saw the misery of the world on account of sin, yet He did not present before them a vivid delineation of their wretchedness. He taught them of something infinitely better than they had known. Without combating their ideas of the kingdom of God, He told them the conditions of entrance therein, leaving them to draw their own conclusions as to its nature. The truths He taught are no less important to us than to the multitude that followed Him" (p. 299).

Did you catch what was said above? Not just "something better" but "SOMETHING INFINITELY BETTER." That's what God wants to offer people through us once we have found it for ourselves.

Everybody Fails at Something

The desire for change is followed by developing a plan of action. There are hundreds of programs offered by a variety of institutions and organizations which promise quick, sure fire results to help people change their health behavior. But old habits and old ways of doing things die hard. Often short term behavior change success is followed by long term failure. Something comes up or some unexpected stress at home or work causes people who have changed destructive habits for a while to slip back into the old ways. This is followed by a sense of frustration, guilt, and a loss of self-esteem.

Some who succeed in breaking a harmful habit end up substituting a new destructive habit for the old one. Some who are successful in quitting smoking begin to gratify their oral desires with food instead of cigarettes. The resulting obesity does not carry the risk of lung cancer but may increase the risk of heart disease. Not all change means success.

Although everyone can change some bad habits, everyone has harmful habits they cannot change. Some resign themselves to being stuck with this habit for the rest of their lives. Others keep trying to change, but never achieve more than limited or short-term success. But their is another way out of the human dilemma. Change is possible.

God Gives Success

Every desire to do right or to do better has been planted in the human mind by God. God wants to give you success in overcoming harmful habits, and He can and will if we will cooperate with Him in the way He has outlined in the following AAA plan:

1. ADMIT. *First, we must admit that we cannot change by ourselves.* We may have tried many times only to learn that it is impossible to make the needed change through the exercise of our own will.

2. ASK. *Second, we must ask God specifically to help us.* This request does not always have to be made on bended knee or in church. But some way you must acknowledge your inability to change yourself and turn to the God who alone can give you the victory. You can even ask Him to make you willing to be willing. After having done so you still may be uncertain and not feel any different, but you have started the process God outlines and can claim His promised intervention in your life.

> "After we have done all we can for ourselves, making the best use of the advantages within our reach, then we may look to God with earnest prayer to do by His Spirit that which we cannot do for ourselves."
>
> —Ellen G. White, *Gospel Workers*, p. 91

3. ACT. *Third, we must do something about it.* Faith is demonstrated in action. If the problem is smoking, throw away the cigarettes and ashtrays. Have the house fumigated. If overweight is the problem, start exercising and substitute a low-calorie, low cholesterol diet. Plan specific strategies for meeting overwhelming urges. Avoid circumstances that trigger strong desires to return to harmful habits. Keep praying as you recognize that it is God who is giving you success. The old behavioral modification techniques you tried before that didn't seem to work can work now with God's special help. Your efforts will be rewarded with success where before there was only failure. Be sure you give the credit to God.

God will not allow you to fail. Once you have done all **you can** God will do all **you can't**. All you do is never enough but what you do is necessary. God will supply what you lack and will bring success. Of course, you are free to resume your old habits at any time. But when you do it is not a failure on God's part. It takes a conscious choice to give up God's help. Nevertheless, God's help is still there. You may lose a battle, but you don't have to lose the war.

"After we have done all we can for ourselves, making the best use of the advantages within our reach, then we may look to God with earnest prayer to do by His Spirit that which we cannot do for ourselves."—*Gospel Workers*, p. 91.

Some think that once a habit has been turned over to God the old habit never threatens to return. Unfortunately this is not true. One obese lady who had lost 40 pounds observed that the struggle was a continuous one. She acknowledged that unless she talked with God about breakfast she would overeat at breakfast. Unless she talked with God throughout the morning she was likely to graze all morning long. Without a commitment of her obesity problem to God at each meal and throughout the day she would meet with failure. God promises long term success only to those who maintain a long term relationship with Him.

God does not want us to be satisfied with overcoming just one problem in life. Once a habit has been broken and a new behavior acquired, it's time to move on to a new victory—to a new lifestyle increasingly productive of good health. What surprises many is that when they gain victory by God's help over a harmful health habit they find their mental and spiritual health improves too. Our lives become a string of successes instead of a string of failures.

What About Disease and Disability?

Many who live with a bad lifestyle already have developed disease or disability. What happens when they begin a new lifestyle? If a person has developed emphysema as a result of long-term smoking that degree of emphysema will not change when they discard cigarettes, but neither will the disease progress. But the risk of heart disease and cancer will be drastically reduced almost immediately. God does not necessarily deliver us from the results of an unhealthy lifestyle, but He does offer us forgiveness, freedom from guilt, and the satisfaction and well-being that come from finding a new relationship with Him and living the more abundant life.

The Christian's Advantage

Because they largely are caused by harmful lifestyle today's health problems are more difficult to cope with than the epidemics of the past. Health educators need to be more aware than most have been that one of the most useful and effective instruments of health behavior change is found in religion—not only as a strong motivation factor, but also in the commitment to keep well through the recognition that our bodies need to be recognized as the temple of God.

The Christian also has the advantage of resources not available to those who attempt behavioral change without God's help. Christians can depend on the power of God, the work of the Holy Spirit, the support of the organized church, the power of intercessory prayer, and the wealth of promises and information found in the Bible. Not only does the Bible present special keys to health behavior change, but it also presents case history after case history of those who found victory over a variety of temptations and harmful habits. Here is the best source to find our God-given potential and power to live healthier, happier, holier lives.

Ten Steps to Changing Your Lifestyle

1. Prepare. Educate yourself. Read all you can on why you should change, how to avoid relapse, and the benefits you'll experience.

2. Decide what you want to change. Work on one lifestyle change at a time.

3. Make a plan, and determine a start date.

If you want to lose weight, your plan might include:
- Take half size portions
- Chew each bite 20 times
- Only eat when you are sitting at the table
- Stay out of the kitchen unless preparing meals
- Buy only healthy food
- Omit desserts, or omit weekday desserts
- Drink water every time you feel hungry, unless it's mealtime.

4. Tell someone about your plan, so you become accountable to them. Get support from your family and friends. Join a support group.

5. Anticipate potential stumbling blocks. Visualize resourceful ways to overcome. For example, if you're tempted at coffee breaks to eat donuts, keep an apple with you and eat that instead.

6. Give yourself permission to fail and forgive yourself when you do. Don't give up because you occasionally fail. Don't let derailments be permanent. Get back on your program as soon as possible (certainly within 24 hours). The only area where it's important not to regress is when you're dealing with addictions. Whether it's food, cigarettes, alcohol or caffeine drinks, relapse to former addictions can cause binge behavior that makes it more difficult to get back on the wagon again.

7. Set small weekly goals you can likely achieve. Make a chart, so you can monitor your progress. Remind yourself every day (and say aloud) "Inch by inch everything's a cinch."

8. Reward yourself for your achievements. Enjoy your success, no matter how small it may seem. Say to yourself, "This is progress." Now do something really kind for yourself. Do something you enjoy, such as going to see a concert or taking a bubble bath.

9. Continue motivating yourself. Post notes around the house, the office, and inside your car to remind you of your goals and progress. Listen to motivational tapes.

10. Claim your ultimate Resource. As a Christian, you have an additional resource—an important one—God's willingness to help you achieve success. "I can do all things through him [Jesus Christ] who gives me strength," wrote the apostle Paul (Phil. 41:13 NIV). You may want to choose a number of "power" verses from the Bible and keep them accessible to read or repeat when you're facing a temptation. Such verses can be an important tool on your road to a successful lifestyle change.

When you're tempted to quit your exercise program, for example, remember the promise, "No testing has overtaken you that is not common to everyone. God is faithful, and he will not let you be tested beyond your strength…" (1 Cor. 10:13 NRSV)

When you push your cart past the candy bars at the supermarket, repeat, "So whether you eat or drink or whatever you do, do it all for the glory of God." (1 Cor. 10:31 NIV)

When your car keeps trying to pull into Dunkin' Donuts, keep your foot on the accelerator and say, "Yea, though I walk (drive) through the valley of the shadow of death, I will fear no evil: for thou art with me…" (Psalms 23:4)

(Adapted from The *Live-Longer Lifestyle*, by Jan W. Kuzma.)

7

Natural Remedies

Adventists have become known over the years for their judicious use of natural or simple remedies that can be administered in the home. A proper diet, which is a "natural remedy" was a major part of health reform. The other area was the therapeutic use of water and the utilization of charcoal and simple herbs in the healing process. Although medical science has moved toward an emphasis on synthetic medication therapy—since "pills" and "potions" are easy to administer and have passed the rigors of clinical trials and proven statistically "effective"—simple home remedies continue to be a popular seminar topic when presented in health evangelism programs.

The presentation of this topic, however, should not encourage people to use simple remedies in the place of well-established medical care prescribed by a reputable physician. There are circumstance where modern medicine does offer more appropriate, safer, and proven remedies, and if one has access to these, it would be a mistake to use a natural remedy when something more effective is available.

What did Ellen White Mean by "Natural Remedies"?

Ellen White taught that mental, physical and spiritual remedies have an effect on the whole body. Her lists of "natural remedies" for the physical well-being included such things as:

- Proper diet (*The Ministry of Healing*, p. 235).
- Purity of life (*Selected Messages*, vol. 2, p. 287).
- Simple herbs (*Ibid.*, p. 295).
- A spirit of gratitude and praise (*The Ministry of Healing*, p. 251).
- Well-regulated work (*Testimonies for the Church*, vol. 2, pp. 555-557).
- Exercise, preferably walking (*The Ministry of Healing*, p. 240).
- Trust in the divine power of God (*Ibid.*, p. 127).

- Rest (*Ibid.*).
- Sunlight (*Ibid.*).
- Temperance/self-control (*Ibid.*).
- Water (*Testimonies*, vol. 5, p. 443).
- Pure air (*Ibid.*).
- Body cleanliness (*Ibid.*).
- Clean, sweet premises (*Ibid.*).

The Adventist church has actively promoted each of the above "natural remedies" that has been given scientific credence in the modern medical community. Even the sound physiologic base of vegetarianism, certain herbal remedies, and the value of a firm spiritual commitment are now respected among health professionals. These natural remedies are preventive in nature. But what about the more therapeutic remedies, such as the use of charcoal, herbs and hydrotherapy? Should the promotion of these be a part of our health education programs? What Ellen White has to say about these remedies, in contrast to different drug therapies that were practiced in her day, gives us insight into the practical common sense approach that has become the Adventist heritage.

Charcoal:

It is unclear whether Ellen White's recommendation for the use of charcoal was a direct revelation from God to her, or a commonly used home remedy that fit with the overall counsel of God to use simple remedies. Often God inspired Ellen White with a concept that she then developed from her own life experiences.

For example, she wrote, "I have ordered the same treatment for others [charcoal poultices] who are suffering great pain, and it has brought relief and been the means of saving life. My mother had told me that snake bites and poisonous insects could often be rendered harmless by the use of charcoal poultices" (*Selected Messages*, bk. 2, p. 295).

Here are seven cases where she prescribed charcoal.

1. **1899:** Bloody dysentery and malaria, and possible "mortification," which is humiliation to the point of death.
   Rx: Charcoal water to drink and poultices to bowels and stomach. (*Ibid.*, p. 299)
2. **1889:** 18-month-old child with an infected insect bite on his knee.
   Rx: Charcoal poultices, then incision and drainage. (The case was told to emphasize the need for a hospital in the area.) (*Ibid.*, pp. 299, 300).
3. **1897:** Cases where the sick were suffering great pain, and physician had given up.
   Rx: Charcoal poultices wet in boiled smartweed. (In this letter to Dr. J. H. Kellogg she added, "I expect you will laugh at this; but if I could give this remedy some outlandish name that no one knew but myself, it would have greater influence..." (*Ibid.*, 294).
4. A young woman with fever and not expected to live but a few more hours. Dr. Merritt Kellogg asked Ellen White if she had any light on this case for him.
   Rx: Charcoal from the blacksmith's shop, poultices to stomach and sides. Relief came in 30 minutes. (*Ibid.*, p. 295)
5. **1903:** Some forms of indigestion.
   Rx: Drinking charcoal mixed with a little olive oil. (*Ibid.*, p. 298)
6. **1908:** Bruised and inflamed hands from work injuries.
   Rx: Charcoal poultices (*Ibid.*, p. 295).
7. **1897:** Severe inflammation of the eyes.
   Rx: Charcoal poultices, put in a bag, and dipped into hot or cold water and applied to the eyes. (*Ibid.*, p. 294).

It's interesting to note that today these cases would probably be taken to the emergency room for treatment; perhaps intravenous rehydration and massive infusions of antibiotics prescribed. But every emergency room in America stocks powdered charcoal. It is the treatment of choice for acute poison or drug overdose problems. It is the most highly adsorptive compound known. It is cheap, safe, and effective. It even lowers cholesterol and relieves intestinal gas when used internally. And it is a simple remedy that we should learn how to use in our work as health evangelists.

For instance, if a person has a digestive upset a dozen or more charcoal tablets taken with water usually settles things down nicely without acid rebound, heavy metal hazards, or drug side effects.

It's a wonderful healing agent for inflamation. The signs of inflammation are: redness, heat, swelling, and pain or tenderness and change of function. Charcoal is the strongest adsorptive agent known to pull the "poisons of inflammation" out of the body. Read about it in *Selected Messages*, book two, in the chapter on Remedial Agencies, beginning on page 292.

Every private home should have charcoal on hand as a ready antidote for poisoning, and as a cleansing agent in infections and various metabolic disturbances. Orally administered charcoal is effective in preventing many intestinal infections. All studies show that charcoal is harmless when ingested, and when it comes in contact with the skin. Charcoal is without a rival as an agent for cleansing and assisting the healing of the body (Agatha and Calvin Thrash, *Home Remedies*, Seale, Alabama: New Lifestyle Books, 1981, p.143).

Herbs

Ellen White used herbs as beverages, and for medicinal preparations. For example she was fond of clover flowers brewed into a tea. She said she once took a little tea or coffee for the treatment of nausea and sea sickness. (*Selected Messages*, Bk. 2, p. 302-303). She also mentions hop tea for insomnia and that "a cup of tea made from catnip herb will quiet the nerves." (*Ibid.*, p. 297)

As late as 1908, Ellen White admonished J. A. Burden and others bearing responsibility at Loma Linda that "there are many simple herbs which, if our nurses would learn the value of, they could use in the place of drugs, and find very effective" (*Ibid.*, p. 295).

Dr. Warren Peters, former Director of the Center for Health Promotion at Loma Linda University, in a position paper presented to the General Conference of Seventh-day Adventists on "The Use of Natural Therapeutics In a Contemporary Medical Setting," states, "In her [Ellen White's] letter to the leaders of the fledgling medical school, she went on to discuss the value of charcoal treatments and other simple remedies. She warned them to avoid drugs that weaken the system. Yet catnip leaves [which she herself used] contain a volatile oil which forms 70-99 percent of a drug called nepetalactone. It carries cats through six distinct phases each lasting about ten minutes. The reaction during the phases range from stretching and euphoria to sexual stimulation. Four cases of catnip abuse in humans have been reported. These simple remedies are pharmacologically active substances and can be harmful if not used with care" (p. 7).

Herbalist, Dr. Varro E. Tyler, Ph.D., writes, "True herbalism encompasses scientific testing, honest reporting of the results, and safe use of effective herbs by informed practitioner and the public. It also includes the production and ethical marketing of herbal products. True herbalism, which brings honor to the wonder-filled world of plants, does exist as part of the science of pharmacognosy. However, there is a dark side to herbalism which I call Paraherbalism." He then describes some myths of paraherbalism. For example:

Myth 1: A conspiracy by the medical establishment discourages the use of herbs.

Myth 2: Herbs cannot harm, only cure (Some plant constituents are among the most toxic substances known.)

Myth 3: Whole herbs are more safe than their isolated active constituents.

Myth 4: Natural and organic herbs are superior to synthetic drugs.

Myth 5: Reducing the dose of a medicine increases its therapeutic potency. (This is contrary to all natural law and physical principles.)

Myth 6: Astrological influences are significant.

Myth 7: Physiological tests in animals are not applicable to human beings.

Myth 8: Anecdotal evidence is highly significant.

Myth 9: Herbs were created by God specifically to cure disease (Varro E. Tyler, "False Tenets of Paraherbalism," *Nutrition Forum*, 1989; vol. 6: p. 41).

These myths were promoted as truth in Mrs. White's day. Isn't it interesting that she emphasized first and foremost lifestyle measures, which have proved to be essential to wellness, and safe simple remedies as secondary therapies? Herbs have a place in the "simple remedy" category, but one must be careful.

First, herbs can be effective in cases of sickness, but should not be used as an everyday potion. God abundantly supplied in the fruits, grains, nuts and vegetables everything that was needed to maintain our health.

Second, single agents should be prescribed, not multiple mixtures of dubious origins!

Herbs are drugs. They are crude forms of pharmaceutical agents that have both beneficial and deleterious effects. But because in the United States herbs are categorized as "food" instead of "drugs," strict parameters are not placed on their manufacture and distribution—as long as the label does not make certain claims. Without restrictions, there is no motivation to submit herbs to the rigors of research, therefore more is known about the effect of synthetic drugs in this country than about herbs. This has opened the door to a certain amount of quackery, and the continued promotion of the myths that Dr. Tyler has mentioned.

In Europe, herbs and drugs are classified in the same category and must be submitted to vigorous research to determine their effectiveness. This has resulted in the discovery of a number of extremely beneficial herbs in the treatment of disease.

For example, Ginkgo has proven to be effective in conditions of decreased cerebral blood flow. Echinacea or coneflower stimulates the activity of various types of phagocytes and may increase the production of interferon. That's why it's so effective in helping you resist the common cold. St. John's Wort is now being used successfully in Europe for treatment of sleep disorders. But more importantly, scientists have now shown that this ancient herb contains hypericin and psuedohypericin that have shown "dramatic anti-retroviral activity and low toxicity at effective doses. Clinical trials are now being conducted to determine if this herb will be effective in treating AIDS.

What should our role be in the use of herbs? Dr. Peters suggests in his briefing paper, "We can be leaders in the investigation and use of legitimate herbal therapies. The effectiveness, safety, and potential side affects of therapeutic botanicals should be taught along with the usefulness of other medicinal preparations." (p. 10)

Hydrotherapy vs. Drug Therapy

Even though hydrotherapy has become the hallmark of simple remedies, and offers the care and the personal touch of "real" medical missionary work, it is interesting that Ellen White did not write extensively about it.

She and her husband, James, did spend time at Dr. James Caleb Jackson's treatment center called "Our Home" in Dansville, New York, which offered hydrotherapy treatments. Mrs. White also chose hydrotherapy as the preferred method of treatment when her son Willie became sick. The White's were planning to go to Dr. Jackson's facility to learn about such things as the baths, the dripping sheet, the pail douche, the sitz bath and the foot bath, as well as Sylvester Graham's diet of simple vegetarian foods free of spices, rich gravies, or fat. But before the Whites could go to Dansville, personal tragedy struck.

Here is the story:

"Their oldest son, Henry, developed complications of pneumonia following a simple upper respiratory infection. They sought the help of their family physician, when Henry's condition worsened. The physician used the wisdom of his day and administered harsh medications. Henry died and was buried in the Oak Hill Cemetery in Battle Creek, Michigan. Can you imagine the thoughts that were going through the minds of these bereaved, overworked parents as they made the long journey back to Michigan with the body of their oldest son? You can begin to understand the fervor and vehemence of Ellen White's warnings against conventional therapies! The American health reform movement which was gaining popularity, and the inspiration of God on these topics must have taken on new meaning.

Not long after this, their youngest son Willie became similarly ill. Without hesitation the White's called in some of their friends and for five days administered hydrotherapy to him. This is what Mrs. White wrote about the experience:

"The next day Willie was very sick. He was wandering. He did not seem to see or hear me when I spoke to him. His heart had no regular beat, but was in a constant agitated flutter. We continued to look to God in his behalf, and to use water freely upon his head, and a compress constantly upon his lungs, and soon he seemed rational as ever. He suffered severe pain in his right side, and could not lie upon it for a moment. This pain we subdued with cold water compresses, varying the temperature of the water according to the degree of the fever. We were very careful to keep his hands and feet warm.... I had retired, sick, and could not sleep for anxiety for several hours.... I dreamed that an experienced physician was standing by my child, watching every breath, with one hand over his heart, and with the other feeling his pulse. He turned to us and said, 'The crisis has passed'" (*Spiritual Gifts*, vol. 4, pp. 151-152).

This experience and others led Ellen White to call for families to take responsibility for their own health. They must have clean, disease-free environments with plenty of fresh air and sunlight. She urged mothers to become skilled in the simple remedies that could be used at home.

Since the Adventist system of medical care emerged from the hydropathic reform movement— which held the same abhorrence of drug treatments and the same emphasis on vegetarianism, fresh air, sunlight, moral uprightness, and the search for individual perfection—why is hydropathy dead and the Adventist health system alive? There is no national organization of hydropathic healing, but there is a Seventh-day Adventist network of healthcare facilities and practitioners that not only span the Americas but also the world. What made the difference?

Dr. Peter's answer to this is that the Adventist health reform remained a "movement" and did not become an institution. Ellen White was receptive to the prompting of the Holy Spirit. In vision she saw the need for training doctors and nurses in emerging health fields. She saw angels standing in the operating rooms guiding the hands of God-fearing surgeons. Ellen White wrote in 1899 to the medical superintendent of the Battle Creek Sanitarium, these words, "Who has been by your side as you have performed these critical operations? Who has kept you calm and self-possessed in the crisis, giving you quick, sharp discernment, clear eyesight, steady nerves, and skillful precision? The Lord Jesus has sent His angel to your side to tell you what to do. A hand has been laid upon your hand. Jesus, and not you, has guided the movements of your instrument" (*Testimonies*, vol 8, pp. 187-188).

The very same year she stated, emphatically, "It is our privilege to use every God-appointed means in correspondence with our faith, and then trust in God, when we have urged the promise. If there is need of a surgical operation, and the physician is willing to undertake the case, it is not a denial of faith to have the operation performed" (*Selected Messages*, bk. 2, pp. 284-285).

The drugging practices of the 19th century were appalling and deserved condemnation. Medical practitioners had very little if any formal education. With few exceptions it consisted of an apprenticeship with another practitioner for six months to a year. There was no formal education in anatomy, physiology, or least of all, pharmacology. Even after medical schools were established, President Eliot of Harvard University, lamented in 1871, "It is fearful to think of the ignorance and incompetence of most American doctors who have graduated at American schools. They poison, maim and do men to death in various ways, and are unable to save life or preserve health" (Theodore Puschmann, *History of Medical Education*. New York, NY: Hartner Publishing Co., Inc., 1966, p. 534).

Even the botanical or "natural doctors" were not immune to the harsh treatment of the human body. Some suggested that one half teaspoonful of cayenne pepper in sweetened hot water should be given to restore internal heat to the body. Others said that teas prepared from local roots, barks, leaves and berries, and mixed with brandy were good for digestive problems.

Without any understanding of physiology or the etiology of diseases, physicians were trained to give large doses of poisonous preparations for the symptoms that the patient complained of. If the desired results of dehydration were not immediately obtained other compounds were given.

Is it any wonder that Ellen White would write, "Mercury, calomel, and quinine have brought their amount of wretchedness, which the day of God alone will fully reveal. Preparations of mercury and calomel taken into the system ever retain their poisonous strength as long as there is a particle of it left in the system. These poisonous preparations have destroyed their millions, and left sufferers upon the earth to linger out a miserable existence. They are victims of poisonous preparations, which have been, in many cases, administered to cure some slight indisposition, which after a day or two of fasting would have disappeared without medicine" (*Selected Messages*, vol. 4, p. 139). Dr. Warren Peters writes:

Ellen White's recommendations regarding the use of quinine give us a valuable perspective on her counsels regarding the use of drugs. Quinine was frequently used by allopathic practitioners for any and every symptom. Large doses were used for simple fevers caused by upper respiratory infections as well as for malaria and other infectious diseases. Ellen White called for a reform in this matter. She equated quinine with opium, strychnine, mercury, and other poisons.

The agent that caused malaria was not yet known. But one of the symptoms of malaria was fever, and it became common practice for people living in malaria infested areas along the Mississippi River to take quinine each day with breakfast. They found that by taking small doses each day the chills could be avoided, yet they were never cured, and they needed continuous treatment. Dr. S. P. S. Edwards was a Seventh-day Adventist physician at the Tri-City Sanitarium in Moline, Illinois from 1904 to 1909. Because of the writings of Ellen White, he refused to use quinine for malaria. Instead he tried to use hydrotherapy. According to him, neither the hydrotherapy nor the low doses of quinine that the people took on their own ever cured the malaria. As more became known about malaria, several doctors began to use larger doses of quinine over a very short period of time and found that they could destroy the infective agent. Dr. Edwards tried coupling the larger but short doses of quinine with hydrotherapy to overcome the side effects of the drug. This regimen was effective, and the lives of many people were saved. Ellen White visited the sanitarium some time later. When she heard of the method that he was using successfully, she said, "This is different from what I refer to in my testimonies. Like using ether or chloroform for surgery, you use one or two doses to kill the cause and do not continue to dose the patient day after day as is done in so many places. It is the repeated drugging that I have condemned" (This experience was written in a letter by S. P. S. Edwards to Elder F. D. Nichol in 1957).

The doctor then goes on to tell how Ellen White sent W. C. White to Dr. Edward's room one day in 1910, when Dr. Edwards was visiting the St. Helena Sanitarium. Elder White brought him a letter addressed to Mrs. White from an Elder Fulton in the South Sea Islands. In the letter Elder Fulton stated that the workers and members were

dying of malaria, but because of Ellen White's statements they would not use the curative quinine. Ellen White asked Dr. Edwards to write out his experiences on the Mississippi River malaria outbreak. When the letter was completed, Ellen wrote across the bottom, "P.S. If quinine will save a life, use quinine. Ellen White." (S. P S. Edwards Letter to Elder F. D. Nichol, 1957).

Although there is no direct quotation from Ellen White that she modified her stance on quinine, there are other indications that she continued to adapt her medical counsel as new evidence was presented. As blood transfusions became medically possible, she reflected on this treatment for Dr. Kress who was ill. "There is one thing that has saved life—an infusion of blood from one person to another; but this would be difficult and perhaps impossible for you to do. I merely suggest it" (*Selected Messages*, vol. 2, p. 303). Dr. Kress was dying from pernicious anemia, a deadly nutritional disease at that time. He had over-reacted to the health reform instructions and consumed such a sparse diet that he was deficient in several vital nutrients. Here Ellen White, a layperson, was suggesting to the doctor one of the most advanced medical practices of their time.

A similar example is found in her use of vaccinations for smallpox. While her hydropathic contemporaries were condemning the use of vaccination, she herself was vaccinated and urged her domestic staff to do the same. (*Ibid.*) Ellen White was a progressive health reformer who praised God for scientific advances.

She even used a primitive form of radiation therapy for a skin lesion on her face. She may have thought it was cancer. In a letter to her son Willie in 1911, she states, "For several weeks I took treatment with the X-ray for the black spot that was on my forehead. In all I took twenty-three treatments, and these succeeded in entirely removing the mark. For this I am very grateful" (*Ibid.*). Apparently using radiation therapy for a suspected cancer was not inconsistent with her call for the use of simple remedies. Medical knowledge today has progressed to such a point that this treatment would be considered quite radical. Now there is a better understanding of the biology of skin lesions and skin cancer. But at the time Mrs. White used the most advanced medical treatment that was available.

On January 10, 1910, I. H. Evans, E. E. Andross, and H. W. Cottrell wrote to Ellen White requesting clarification as to her view of establishing a full program of medical education to become licensed physicians and nurses. Many were shocked when she suggested this, in light of her many statements about the importance of simple remedies.

They wrote, "But there is a difference of opinion between us in regard to what you mean when you use the term, 'a medical school.' Some hold that when you speak of a 'medical school,' you mean a school where the Bible is made prominent, where all features of our faith are taught, and where the message is given in its fullness; in addition to which we give an outline of the treatment of simple diseases, the care of the sick, and such things as will qualify the student to go into a foreign field, or even into a city, and do intelligent medical missionary work.... Others hold that when you use the phrase 'a medical school,' you mean, in addition to the foregoing, a fully equipped medical school that teaches the Bible and the truth, as before said, but that gives such a thorough training along medical lines as will qualify the students who take the course, to pass State Board examinations and become registered, qualified physicians for public work.... We are very anxious to preserve unity and harmony of action. In order to do this, we must have a clear understanding of what is to be done" (I. H. Evans, *Medical Practice and the Educational Program at Loma Linda*, Ellen White Publications, General Conference, Washington D.C., Letter to Ellen White, Jan. 25, 1910, p. 83).

Many are still asking the same question today. After reading most of what Ellen White wrote about medical work, they come to a conclusion about what that work should be. Some still see it as hydrotherapy and a rejection of any modern advances in science. Others see it as the latest advance in technical medical care and a total rejection of the earlier emphasis on natural remedies. Others see it as a combination of using natural remedies wherever possible, incorporating modern advancements in science that can be used in properly diagnosing disease and advancing the welfare of the patient, while excluding as much as possible those drugs and procedures that have powerful toxic side effects or that might unnecessarily harm the patient.

Ellen White answered the concerned leaders of 1910 who waited only two days before this reply came to them: "The light given me is, we must provide that which is essential to qualify our youth who desire to be physicians, so that they may intelligently fit themselves to be able to stand the examinations required to prove their efficiency as physicians. They should be taught to treat understandingly the cases of those who are diseased, so that the door will be closed for any sensible physician to imagine that we are not giving in our school the instruction necessary for properly qualifying young men and young women to do the work of a physician.... The medical school at Loma Linda is to be of the highest order, because those who are in that school have the privilege of maintaining a living connection with the wisest of all physicians" (*Ibid.*, pp. 83-84). (See Chapter 18 on Loma Linda University.)

With uncanny accuracy, Ellen White's counsel has guided the Seventh-day Adventist church to avoid the pitfalls of spurious remedies that contaminated the reform movement of the nineteenth century. Although mesmerism and phrenology were part of the water-cure methods, she refuted these. Ellen White warned, "This entering in of Satan through the sciences is well devised. Through the channel of phrenology, psychology [mysticism—not psychology as we know it today], and mesmerism, he comes more directly to the people of this generation, and works with that power which is to characterize his efforts near the close of probation" (*Selected Messages*, vol. 2, p. 351).

The irregularities of the skull have no relationship to personality, character, or state of health as the proponents of phrenology claim. Instead the skull becomes a tool for divination much as the palm is used by the fortune teller. Today iridology, or the iris of the eye has been substituted for the skull in medical quackery. Again, one must be careful, and continue to be leery of mystical procedures that are not based on scientific evidence. Ellen White never lost sight of the primary core of the health message that God had given to her. It was and always will be the reformed style of living. Modern advances would help with the treatment of disease, *but preservation of health would still be through the natural remedies of exercise, fresh air, sunlight, a nutritious diet and an abiding confidence in God.* The Seventh-day Adventist reform movement survived and out-lived all the other "health reform" sects of the 19th century—the homeopath, the allopath, the phrenologist, the herbalist, and the like. It remained a movement that could encompass and incorporate the scientific advances in the under-standing of God's intricate creation. It moved. It adapted. While at the same time it remained true to the principles of health first revealed in 1863.

Recommendations for Continued "Health Reform"

Here are some conclusions and recommenda-tions that Dr. Warren Peters made on June 14, 1993 to the General Conference of Seventh-day Adventists in his briefing paper called, "The Use of Natural Therapeutics In a Contemporary Medical Setting."

1. The first remedy in disease is a good lifestyle. This is to be the centerpiece of the Seventh-day Adventist health reform mes-sage. Natural therapies, or any therapies for that matter, must be secondary to helping people think, feel, and act in accordance with God's plan for wholeness.
   RECOMMENDATION: Intensify and diver-sify health education within and without the church. Where feasible, join with medical agencies such as the American Heart Association, American Health Federation, and American Cancer Societies to promote healthful living.

2. Self-doctoring is still a necessary art. Heath care will become more and more scarce as economics limit services to those individuals with the most acute and severe diseases. We must reform our wasteful, overutilization of healthcare for the financially privileged and the despicable neglect of the poor.
   RECOMMENDATION: Teach home reme-dies for the simple diseases. Every cold does not need a $100.00 visit to the doctor. Sprains, bruises, bites, headaches, and flu can be cared for at home, if the church has trained its members and their neighbors.

3. The wise use of pharmacological prepara-tions whether of a crude or a refined nature is still important. However, many people use these preparations to excess. Whether Tylenol or golden seal, both may be unneces-sary if more simple therapies such as water cures were still taught.
   RECOMMENDATION: Train healthcare workers in pharmacology, including the pharmacology of botanicals. They in turn can educate patients and others in the most sim-ple remedy possible. Loma Linda medical students are not exempt.

4. Unfortunately, many conservative Seventh-day Adventists are attracted to spurious remedies. Education in physiology is the greatest protection we can give against health fraud and quackery. It will also form a bul-wark against spiritualistic healing methods.
   RECOMMENDATION: Intensify efforts in health training within the Adventist educa-tional system and our church. Teach general nurses-aid level anatomy and physiology. Actively identify spurious practices that enter the church. If a person is healed or suc-cessfully practices these mystical remedies and diagnostic techniques, it is very hard to give them up. Prevention is the first line of defense. Pastors must be better trained to identify health scams.

5. Spiritual healing is the primary focus of all medical health work. It must be given the

broad exposure and emphasis that is essential.

RECOMMENDATION: In-depth investigation and implementation of methods for addressing spiritual needs of patients at all levels of Seventh-day Adventist medical facilities. Roll back the trend of secularization of healthcare. Teach private practitioners of the healing arts how spiritual issues can be addressed. All Adventist training programs must model this behavior. This is of utmost importance.

6. There need not be a gulf of separation between the use of the most advanced medical methods and the promotion of the simplest self-care modality that has been proven to be effective. Ellen White did not have a conflict between recommending that nurses be taught to use herbs and at the same time recommend a medical educational institution that had the highest reputation within the emerging American Medical Association. She could recommend to the churches' leading physician the use of charcoal poultices for abdominal pain and receive the most advanced radiation therapy for her skin lesion. The separation of preventive medicine, acute care medicine, and self-care into often antagonistic elitist camps is wrong, wasteful, and confusing.

RECOMMENDATION: Form a study group that can bring together the various factions within the church. Self-care must be taught as part of all levels of healthcare professionals. This will break down prejudice.

7. Many faithful Adventist chiropractors are still using unnatural or supernatural methods.

RECOMMENDATION: Facilitate an Adventist association of chiropractors for those who may want to reform their methods.

8. Many well meaning Adventist physicians have laid aside their heritage of "lifestyle-based medical care." They have replaced it with "a pill for every ill."

RECOMMENDATION: Restudy, at the highest level of our medical school, the curriculum for our medical students. Do they receive the "Adventist Heritage" of training in hygiene and physiology? More importantly, do they see this type of medical care modeled by their professors, or do they see and hear their roots treated as an embarrassment?

9. The observations and recommendations of this report are biased toward North America and its culture. The applications of the health reform principles can only be considered as illustrative and not definitive for other cultures. Sanitation and hygiene reform may contribute the highest return in terms of health for some cultures. Simple therapies or folk remedies of other cultures may have proven value. Others may be deleterious.

RECOMMENDATION: Develop culture-specific interpretations of health reform. Prioritize areas of greatest need. The emphasis of vegetarianism may not be appropriate where getting enough calories from any source is the primary issue for survival.

The Use of Natural Remedies in Personal Evangelism

Over the years, many have said it was the personal involvement of some neighbor or friend who treated them with natural remedies that sparked their interest in the Adventist church. For example, "My mother was sick and a neighbor came over and gave her hydrotherapy treatments." Or "When I was a kid I had a terrible infection on my leg that wouldn't heal. The doctors were threatening amputation. An Adventist woman came over, prayed with us, applied poultices, prescribed 15 minutes of sunlight on the wound each day, and made sure I was fed a natural foods diet with lots of water. Each day as she gave me the treatments she talked about the Bible. To the amazement of all, the wound healed, and my folks started attending the Adventist church."

Today, people seem to be rediscovering the fact that these simple remedies work. This chapter gives some reasons why they work along with a few practical remedies that you can share with others. Armed with a love for your friends and neighbors, these remedies, and God's bible truth, you can be a personal health evangelist. But first start in your own home.

With just a little attention, time, and care you can save money and the erosion of your immune system by the use of natural remedies. Here is how to get started.

Why Go Nature's Way?

Antibiotics are losing their grip. The panacea days of penicillin are gone. Resistant germs are multiplying rapidly in animal factories where cows, chickens, and pigs are fed antibiotics by the ton even in their routine food. Antibiotics are often used in clinics for trivial and even not indicated purposes. AIDS patients are multiplying by the thousands. When the human host is immuno-compromised even weaker germs are given a chance to multiply and get stronger and tougher. Result? Ever more resistant strains and old easy-to-kill germs have become more aggressive and deadly. The new bugs are getting tougher!

For decades we have been treating the body like it was made in Detroit. The quick-fix approach using drugs is not wise enough. It is backfiring! What is involved? A drug is a foreign substance of a poisonous nature. Many times these side effects don't show up Monday morning. The modern sciences of immunology and physiology are explaining how today's drug use can compromise tomorrow's resistance, not only to similar troubles but to new diseases of a far more complicated nature. Autoimmune diseases, complicated damage to the DNA system, to the joints, to the liver, kidneys and other organs of the body are increasing ominously. The God of Nature makes the rules and has given us the principles. That classic of health wisdom, *The Ministry of Healing* continues to be a standard-bearer.

When To Use Natural Remedies

There is a time to get medical help. If your leg is broken, plus who knows what else, don't self-medicate by drinking seven cups of "boneset." Go immediately to the emergency room. With any disease or significant health problem step one, is to get an accurate diagnosis. What is wrong, why is it wrong, and what can be done about it? Modern medicine shines in this step. Wouldn't it be great if the establishment knew as much about nutrition and natural remedies as they do about high technology. Fortunately, many common ordinary health problems can be assessed and dealt with at home.

The best time to use natural remedies is before you are sick! Prevention works. For instance a good brisk walk early each morning is the best therapy for dozens of diseases and conditions. It tones up the entire body from the brain through the nerves and the endocrine glands to every cell of the body. As little as 15 minutes a day of exercise will reduce heart attacks.

Another winning natural remedy is rest, spelled S-L-E-E-P. Two hours of deep sleep, blessing the brain with delta waves, is worth more than four hours of shallow sleep after midnight. The brain has billions of tiny batteries. When they are charged up you are charged up. After several nights of good sleep and several days of real exercise you not only will feel better, but you also will be better. Creativity and productivity go up. The blues tend to go away. Tonight's sleep builds for tomorrow's excellence.

Let physicians teach the people that restorative power is not in drugs, but in nature. Disease is an effort of nature to free the system from conditions that result from a violation of the laws of health.
[1] In case of sickness, the cause should be ascertained.
[2] Unhealthful conditions should be changed,
[3] wrong habits corrected.
[4] Then nature is to be assisted in her effort to expel impurities and to reestablish right conditions in the system.

—Ellen G. White, *The Ministry of Healing*, p. 127.

Another helpful natural remedy is the hydrotherapy treatment known as an early morning shower. Use warm water for cleanliness then finish off with a brief brisk cool shower. Day by day keep lowering the temperature until you end your warm shower with a really brisk cold climax. Then rub down vigorously with a towel. This is physiological coffee! But it's different. Instead of giving you weaker and weaker nerves you develop stronger and stronger nerves. You will find that after good sleep and with regular exercise and this natural tonic you are ready to see more in the Bible that you have in months. Bible texts, principles, and people will come alive.

Stress Headaches

But suppose things have piled up on you just when your vitality is down. You get a stress headache. What can be done? Knowing something about physiology can help you understand what to do about a headache.

There is a rule in physiology that the blood goes to where the action is. This is called the Loven Reflex. Local dilation of the blood vessels occurs where this action happens and the brain also orders general constriction or narrowing of the blood vessels over the rest of the body. So hours of eye work or head work with details chasing details around in circles causes your head to feel the stress and tension. This results in too much blood in the head. Too much blood in the thin-walled veins of the head brings on this headache.

What should you do? First get into a quiet room, dim the lights, put both of your feet into deep warm-to-hot foot bath. (If you have compromised blood vessels or nerves in your feet or legs be careful about elevating the temperature of the water.) Then put a pinch of yellow ground-mustard powder into the water. Then place a quite cool, or cold, wash cloth wrung out of water on your forehead.

Here is how Dr. Bernell Baldwin, a physiologist describes what happens next. The nerves in your underused feet will send a nerve FAX. "Send us more blood quickly." Your overused head will reply in tired cooperation, "Ooh...kaaay." Then

chemoreceptors in the skin of the feet and legs will get on the body's internet. "Quick, send us blood for a change, now!" This pull-therapy from the feet will be reinforced by push-therapy from the skin of the forehead. "Brain, get this excess blood out of here!" This focused combination therapy helps the brain balance the circulation and the vascular headache tends to subside.

Remember that most pain killers "cut the wire instead of putting out the fire." Natural therapy is rational, scientific, and builds today for better physiology tomorrow.

Warning! If the headache does not yield promptly to simple natural measures, go to a physician immediately. Many a brain tumor has grown beyond curability by using stronger and stronger pain killers.

Migraines

A real migraine headache is a different ball game. People who suffer from migraines will tell you that the more healthy the lifestyle they live, the fewer and milder their migraine episodes. There is an important genetic component to this condition. Sometimes a liberal use of chipped ice, in ice bags or doubled bags from the supermarket, when used to cover the head may relieve the pain.

Conscientiously living the healthy abundant lifestyle and faithfully paying attention to offending food sensitivities (such as eating large amounts of cheese, or large milk shakes, especially late at night which cause toxic effects of tyramine in the blood) combined with the use of steady Christian stress control techniques can often mitigate migraine attacks to such an extent that they cease to be monthly traumas.

Sore Throats

These usually come from strong germs and weak immune systems adding up to scratchy, raw, even painful throats. One way to tip the balance against the germs is to bring moist heat to the area of the throat by putting a hot towel around the throat. Keep it there until it loses its noticeable heat. Then contrast this with a towel dipped in cold tap water, wrung out and

Natural Remedies at Battle Creek Sanitarium

"One hundred years ago, in the day of Dr. John Harvey Kellogg, people from all over the world came to the Seventh-day Adventist Sanitarium in Battle Creek. Many of these cases had been given up as hopeless—yet a surprisingly large proportion recovered at the sanitarium. The reason the people kept the 1,200 bed institution filled was that the treatments encompassed the best of the several different schools of the healing arts and avoided the harmful aspects. Principally the Battle Creek Sanitarium used enlightened diet therapy far in advance of that day, hydrotherapy, some manipulative therapy, along with the scientific use of all good medical procedures of the time. This therapeutic combination accomplished outstanding results with practically no harmful side effects. While some surgery was performed and some drugs administered, these treatments were rare compared to the carefully done physiotherapeutic procedures. The physicians were master physiologists, far in advance of physicians of later years. The Battle Creek Sanitarium developed hydrotherapy to its greatest degree in modern times."

—Agatha and Calvin Thrash, *Home Remedies*, Seale, Alabama: New Lifestyle Books, 1981, p. 5.

wrapped around the throat just for a moment. Then off and back with the fine comfortable heat all around the throat. This hydrotherapy helps shift the pH or acidity of the local secretions so that a natural antibiotic called lysozyme can attack the bugs.

More oxygen, more fresh white blood cells, and more blood flow helps shift the tide of battle between the body and the germs. It is important for the feet to be toasty warm. You can't tell by just subjective feeling whether your feet are really warm. A feeling of "OK" may be 20 degrees too low. Cold feet mean unbalanced circulation. And cold feet lead to the weakening of resistance in the nose, throat, and respiratory tract.

Another fast way to give a boost to the throat is to take two glasses of water. One warm and one tap water. Put half of a teaspoon of salt in each glass and stir well. Next, gargle with this warm saline solution. When it cools spit it out and gargle briefly with the cold. Then the heat, then the cold. It's easy, it's fast and it helps. Often you can nip a sore throat in the bud with these simple methods.

As a further safeguard, after gargling put a heating compress on the throat. Here is how to make a heating compress. Find an old worn out handkerchief or any cotton cloth two or three fingers wide and long enough to go completely around the neck. Dip it in cold water and wrap it all the way around the throat. Next, wrap a warm wool sock, like a boot sock, around the neck, completely covering the cotton. Carefully safety-pin the wool in place and pin the lower edge so there is no air gap between the compress and the shirt, blouse or nightwear. Then do something daring! Go to bed early. Ask the Great Physician to tell you why you got this. Then ask Him to bless the simple remedy. He will. Remember this tremendous promise: "Natural means, used in accordance with God's will, bring about supernatural results" (*Selected Messages*, vol. 2, p. 346).

If the throat feels raw and hurts, fix up a vaporizer, even a teakettle or suitable container on a hotplate located near enough to the bed but securely positioned so that it will not tumble and either burn somebody or damage something with water or fire. With the vaporizer safe and solid, put some eucalyptus oil in it. The eucalyptol in the oil has been found to be a phytochemical that can help the body fight viruses. This provides aroma therapy as it smells good too.

Don't forget sensible moderate nutrition. Use plenty of fruit and cut out excess sugar and junk food. If these simple measures don't work get professional help as soon as you can. Presumptive neglect in this matter can ruin heart valves or kidneys.

Influenza

Some forms of the flu are dangerous. After World War One the flu virus became so deadly that approximately 20 million people were killed in the epidemic. This was as many or more than all the military deaths caused by the war. During the epidemic, Adventists demonstrated that good old fomentation treatments would save lives and help fight the flu. Drugs do poorly against such viruses because the germs penetrate inside the cells of the body where drugs and antibiotics can't do much.

Now the good news. If at the first early sign of influenza an effective heating procedure is administered by a knowledgeable practitioner the body's immune system can overcome the virus before it seriously attacks the lungs. Dr. Charles Thomas of Desert Hot Springs, California has demonstrated for years that a Russian Bath (steam bath with the head out) or other serious heating procedure of the chest and lungs, followed by putting the patient to bed, can have wonderful results. With the Lord's blessing it is common in the morning to find that the patient is well and happy! On the other hand, if those coming down with flu use only symptomatic drug therapy for a day or so they usually come down with the flu and are sick with a fever for a week or so. When the virus is stronger or the patient is older or weaker pneumonia may set in. This is when things get dangerous. Even then, hydrotherapy helps the immune system heal the patient.

Fomentations: Upper Division Hydrotherapy

At least one adult in every home should be familiar with fomentations. A fomentation consists of a hot moist cloth wrapped in a comfortable soft liner placed, in this case, over the chest. Clean, old blankets can be made into fomentation cloths and kept for ready use. Dry them completely before putting them away. They should be about as thick as your finger to hold the heat. Moist heat speeds up enzymes. It brings more blood, oxygen, and thousands of fresh new immune cells ready to fight the invaders. A warm room without drafts provides the right setting for good hydrotherapy.

Before treatment cover the bed with plastic so that a little spill of water won't spoil the bed for resting or sleep. Prepare a cold compress for

The National Council Against Health Fraud can help you stay on top of health quackery and fraud. Their newsletter features briefings on products, resources and news. Dr. William Jarvis is director of the center and is a professor of preventive medicine at Loma Linda University. For more information write or call, National Council Against Health Fraud, P. O. Box 1276, Loma Linda, CA 92354. Phone (909) 824-4690.

the head. Place one thicker fomentation lengthwise on the bed and have the patient lie on it. When the patient is lying down provide a foot tub about half full of water for the feet. This pulls blood to the feet. Then place a fomentation across the chest for about three minutes or until it has lost its heat. Be careful not to injure either the skin or the person while attempting to help. Start the treatment on the comfortable side when it comes to temperatures. Then increase the heat modestly—no need to overdo heat at all. If you do it right, it will feel so good that they will look forward to another treatment. Excessive heat backfires because it injures instead of helps. After two or three minutes of the delightful heat soaking into the tissues of the chest, it is time to flush out the old blood in the veins and bring a fresh batch of fighters. Here is how. Lift off fomentation number one. Then rub the chest with a cold cloth for a few seconds. Dry the chest nicely. Then apply fomentation number two.

Observe the patient sympathetically. Ask if there are any hot spots. Bony prominences may become too hot. If so, lift the fomentation up slightly and rub under the fomentation. It feels good. Don't just leave, linger. Ask, now how does it feel. If OK, then check the hot foot bath to make sure it is hot enough and renew the cold compress to the forehead. Next, repeat the sequence two more times on the chest. Finish the treatment with a shower, or a cold mitten friction, or a graduated shower in which the temperatures at the end are stepped down gradually to coolness.

Then put the patient to bed for a least half an hour during the day. If you are giving this treatment in the evening, put the patient to bed

Eight Doctors for the Price of None

*H*arold Hardtummy has become disgustingly healthy. When his friends, who tend to be flabby and smoke like old-fashioned steam engines, see Harold purposely striding in their direction, they scatter like saloon keepers used to at the approach of Carrie Nation. You see, Harold has taken seriously the plethora of health warnings that are hurled at Americans today from every side, whereas his friends have not.

Sometimes warnings can be more frustrating than helpful. A classic example comes from England. Zoo officials there discovered recently that they had paid more than 100 pounds to visitors for articles stolen by monkeys. But what puzzled them most was that the favorite item being snatched was eyeglasses. An investigation revealed that the monkeys grabbed the glasses when the visitors leaned over to read a sign on the cage that was difficult to see. The sign said: "Warning! These monkeys snatch glasses."

When it comes to health warnings, our frustrations do not center around our ability to read, hear, or understand. The messages come through loud and clear from all sides. That's the problem. We are so inundated with these health warnings that we have come to the place where our heads are swimming and we cannot remember them all. It seems that everything we do, eat, smell, feel, or even listen to has the potential of damaging our health.

How can we keep up with the plethora of environmental and health concerns and warnings that bombard us daily? Many seem to be almost contradictory. Isn't there an easy-to-remember, simple program that can be followed by those interested in prevention and natural remedies?

Yes, there is! Some time ago I visited the Weimar Institute in California. Their basic program is health conditioning, designed to improve the health of those who are suffering from cardiovascular problems. I found those about to graduate from the program more than enthusiastic about what had been accomplished for them in a few short weeks. One healthy-looking woman beamed as she told me that during the three weeks she had been there her blood pressure, which had been 210/116, had returned to 110/78 without her having to take medication of any kind. Her cholesterol level, which had been quite a bit above normal, had come down dramatically.

Prominently displayed on one wall in the health education classroom at Weimar is the motto, I Choose the Better Life. On the opposite wall hangs a large poster that lists the guiding principles of the basic NEWSTART® program based on the natural remedies outlined in the health classic, *The Ministry of Healing* by Ellen White:

Pure air, sunlight, abstemiousness, rest, exercise, proper diet, the use of water, trust in divine power—these are the true remedies. Every person should have a knowledge of nature's remedial agencies and how to apply them. It is essential both to understand the principles involved in the treatment of the sick and to have a practical training that will enable one rightly to use this knowledge.

The use of natural remedies requires an amount of care and effort that many are not willing to give. Nature's process of healing and up building is gradual, and to the impatient it seems slow. The surrender of hurtful indulgences requires sacrifice. But in the end it will be found that nature, untrammeled, does her work wisely and well. Those who persevere in obedience to her laws will reap the reward in health of body and health of mind (p. 127).

—Leo Van Dolson

for the night. Watch the diet carefully. Because excess sugar inhibits white cell activity seriously, serve moderate meals, heavy on fruit. Patients who are careful and thorough in using natural remedies tend to recover speedily after sickness and often are stronger and have more energy than before they were sick.

Conclusion

Psalm 103:3 refers to the Lord, "Who forgives all your iniquities, Who heals all your diseases." How reasonable and wise it is to follow the Creator's counsel in the methods of healing.

Sources For More Information
(Contact your Adventist Book Center)

Dail, Clarence MD, and Charles Thomas Ph.D. *Hydrotherapy: Simple Treatments for Common Ailments* (Brushton, N.Y.: Teach Services, Inc., 1995), pp. 146. This revised work contains gems of illustrated treatments for the home. It is simple to follow, authoritative, and moderate in tone.

Hansen, Richard A., M.D., *Get Well at Home: Complete Home Health Care for the Family*,(Poland Spring, Maine: Shiloh Medical Publications, PO Box 1057, Cresswell, OR 97426). A documented journal is published four times a year and has an article in each issue on natural remedies as well as other useful serious articles on health.

Thrash, Agatha, M.D. and Calvin, M.D., *Home Remedies*, Seale, Alabama, New Lifestyle Books, 1981.

Hardinge, Mervyn G., *Drugs, Herbs, & Natural Remedies*, R & H Publishing, 2001.

Divine Healing and Prayer for the Sick

When Hiram Edson first heard the preaching of the Second Advent message, he held the office of steward in the Methodist church in Ontario County, New York. This was about 1839. Edson became one of the shining stars among the Adventist pioneers. An insight into the place divine healing held among these early Adventist is brought to light in a story that involves him.

"One evening at the close of his work Brother Edson entered his house and sat by the fire, since it was chilly. It seemed as though by an audible voice the conviction came, "Go, heal thy sick brother." There was a neighbor, very ill, whose case had been given up by the doctor. Startled. Edson thought, "The day of miracles is past." At once he was plunged into a terrible experience of darkness. In distress he appealed to the Lord to save him from ruin. "Go, heal thy sick brother," came again. In response, he said, "Anything, Lord, to save me from this predicament."

"Then all was normal. He pulled on his boots and made his way to the man's house. There the family, fatigued, had lain down to rest and had fallen asleep. The candle had burned down so that only a flickering light was left. By it Brother Edson made his way to the bed, and laying his hand upon the man, said, "Brother, the Lord Jesus make you whole." Immediately the man rose to his feet and walked the floor, praising the Lord.

"This aroused the family, who came into the room to see what caused the commotion. Brother Edson said to the man, "You are enjoying something that I am not, and I want to share it with you." So they bowed in prayer, and the Holy Spirit's presence was so manifested that some of the family were converted. Then Brother Edson went home, and the family retired.

"In the morning the healed man went out to the roadside to cut wood. The doctor drove up, and recognizing him, called him by name, saying, "Is that you? How is this? I expected to find you dead!" I am a well man," his former patient replied; "the Lord has healed me." The doctor drove on. The day passed.

"When the time came to go to the evening meeting, Brother Edson hitched up his team, took his family and the healed man, and drove to the meeting. The church was filled to about its capacity. The pastor gave a short discourse without any apparently emotional appeal. Following this, opportunity was given for testimonies. Several responded, including the healed man. Then, speaking in an ordinary tone of voice, the pastor said, "If there are present those who desire special prayer in their behalf, please stand." Immediately the whole congregation was on its feet. There followed a revival that continued for three weeks, and many were converted" (*Pioneer Stories Retold*, pp. 25-27).

Such miraculous intervention of God in behalf of the sick was not limited to the early pioneer days of the Adventist Church.

When Leo Van Dolson and his twin brother were five years old, the brother, Fred, was run over by a car with faulty brakes. It was coming down a steep street in San Francisco much faster than it should have been. Suffering from a severely fractured skull, Fred was unconscious for several days. Because the doctor held out little hope for him, his parents, who had grown up in the

Adventist Church but were not practicing their religion, called Adventist ministers to pray for his healing. When Fred was healed even the doctor attributed his recovery to divine power. This miracle led directly to the Van Dolsons becoming Seventh-day Adventist church members.

Leo's first pastorate was in the Brookings-Gold Beach district in Oregon, where Roy and Rose Slaybaugh were living. Leo moved there soon after Roy's miraculous healing (recorded in Rose Slaybaugh's book, *Escape From Death*). Most of the members of the Gold Beach church at that time had joined the church because of the impression this miracle made.

Although in modern times the Lord has preformed many miracles of healing in answer to prayers for and by Seventh-day Adventists, many Adventists feel that something is missing. They do not see widespread miracles such as those performed by Peter and Paul in the early Christian period. Is there a missing ingredient in our health ministry?

In response to that question we might ask, Is there any healing other than divine healing? When the surgeon removes an offending organ has he "healed" the patient or has he only made it more likely that healing will occur? What goes on in the patient's body after the surgeon has sewn the cut edges of the wound together? Does he control the healing process, or is he merely cooperating with natural forces planned long ago in the mind of the Creator? The physician may set a broken bone, but can he make it grow together again?

Obviously, the hand of the Creator still works in the healing and restoration of our bodies. He has made provision for the body to fight off infection and disease to begin with, and to heal itself when afflicted with disease. Is it unrealistic then, for human beings to turn to their Creator when overwhelmed by sickness and disease? If God is interested in us, as the Bible indicates, can't we expect Him to respond sympathetically to our prayers for healing? Not only can we expect it, but God Himself has established a plan for us to follow when we turn to Him for the healing of our physical infirmities, just as He has estab-

lished a plan for recovery from spiritual infirmity. His plan is not limited to just those fully committed to Him, but is one way He has provided for those who have not yet learned to know and trust Him to be impressed by His love for and interest in them.

When Christ ordained His twelve disciples and sent them out to minister to the needs of the people in the surrounding countryside, "He gave them power against unclean spirits, to cast them out, and to heal all manner of sickness and all manner of disease" (Matt. 10:1). Luke adds that "They departed, and went through the towns, preaching the gospel, and healing everywhere" (Luke 9:6). When Jesus later sent out the seventy, He demonstrated that the work of teaching and healing was not to be limited to ordained ministers; He commissioned these lay workers: "Into whatsoever city ye enter. . . heal the sick that are therein, and say unto them, The kingdom of God is come nigh unto you" (Luke 10:8, 9). That this plan included the church throughout the ages is made plain in the Great Commission, "Go ye into all the world, and preach the gospel to every creature. . . . And these signs shall follow them that believe; . . . they shall lay hands on the sick, and they shall recover" (Mark 16:15-18).

God's modern prophet emphasizes Christ's intention that we continue this type of ministry today.

"Christ is the same compassionate physician now that He was during His earthly ministry. In Him there is healing balm for every disease, restoring power for every infirmity. His disciples in this time are to pray for the sick as verily as the disciples of old prayed. And recoveries *will follow*; for "the prayer of faith shall save the sick." We have the Holy Spirit's power, the calm assurance of faith, that can claim God's promises. The Lord's promise, "They shall lay hands on the sick, and they shall recover" (Mark 16:18), is just as trustworthy now as in the days of the apostles. It represents the privilege of God's children, and our faith should lay hold of all that it embraces. Christ's servants are the channel of His working, and through them He desires to exercise His healing power. It is our work to present the sick and suffering to God in the arms of our faith. We should teach them to believe in the Great Healer. The Saviour would have us encourage the sick, the hopeless, the afflicted, to take hold upon His strength" (*The Ministry of Healing*, p. 226. Italics supplied).

Ellen White specifically warns against going to extremes and fanaticism in this type of ministry. She also suggests that it be done quietly and on a house-to-house basis.

"Those who engage in house-to-house labor will find opportunity for ministry in many lines. They should pray for the sick and should do all in their power to relieve them from suffering.... Many can be reached only through acts of disinterested kindness. Their physical wants must first be relieved. As they see evidence of our unselfish love, it will be easier for them to believe in the love of Christ" (*Welfare Ministry*, p. 81).

Who is Qualified for This Type of Ministry?

It is not education or even ordination that prepares us for the Christ-ordained mission of healing the sick, but instead a close, confident, trusting experience with Him. Most of all, we must be filled with the love of Christ. "The power of love was in all Christ's healing, and only by partaking of that love, through faith, can we be instruments for His work. If we neglect to link ourselves in divine connection with Christ, the current of life-giving energy cannot flow in rich streams from us to the people" (*The Desire of Ages*, p. 825).

When thinking of the qualifications essential for those whom Christ can use in healing the sick through prayer, the issue at times is confused by the fact that prayers for the sick by ministers who later were proved to have been leading unworthy lives have been answered. The following experience reported by Ellen White may help

us understand how God can answer prayer for divine healing under such circumstances:

"A case was held up before me of _____, a minister; eighty miles he was sent for, to pray for a sick sister who sent for him in compliance with the teaching of James. He went and prayed in earnest, and she prayed; she believed the minister to be a man of God, a man of faith. Physicians had given her up to die of consumption. She was healed immediately. She arose and prepared supper, a thing she had not done for ten years. Now the minister was vile, his life was corrupt, and yet here was a great work. He took the glory all to himself.

"Then again the scene mentioned above passed before me. I saw that the women was a true disciple of Christ; her faith was that she should be healed. I saw their prayers: One was misty, dark, fell downward; the other prayer was mixed with light or specks which looked to me like diamonds, and arose upward to Jesus and He sent it up to His Father like sweet incense, and a beam of light was immediately sent to the afflicted one and she revived and strengthened under its influence. Said the angel, God will gather every particle of true, sincere faith; like diamonds shall they be gathered up and will surely bring a return or answer; and God will separate the precious from the vile" (*Selected Messages*, book 2, p. 347).

The church as a whole has a responsibility: "In order to be purified and to remain pure, Seventh-day Adventists must have the Holy Spirit in their hearts and in their homes. The Lord has given me light that when the Israel of today humble themselves before Him, and cleanse the soul-temple from all defilement, He will hear their prayers in behalf of the sick and will bless in the use of His remedies for disease. When in faith the human agent does all he can to combat disease, using the simple methods of treatment that God has provided, his efforts will be blessed of God" (*Testimonies*, vol. 9, p. 164).

Conditions for Answers to Prayer for Healing

There are conditions that God knows it is best for us to meet before we can expect His full blessing in this matter.

"In the word of God we have instruction relative to special prayer for the recovery of the sick. But the offering of such prayer is a most solemn act, and should not be entered upon without careful consideration. In many cases of prayer for the healing of the sick, that which is called faith is nothing less than presumption.

"Many persons bring disease upon themselves by their self-indulgence. They have not lived in accordance with natural law or the principles of strict purity. Others have disregarded the laws of health in their habits of eating and drinking, dressing, or working. Often some form of vice is the cause of feebleness of mind or body. Should these persons gain the blessing of health, many of them would continue to pursue the same course of heedless transgression of God's natural and spiritual laws, reasoning that if God heals them in answer to prayer, they are at liberty to continue their unhealthful practices and to indulge perverted appetite without restraint. If God were to work a miracle in restoring these persons to health, He would be encouraging sin. It is labor lost to teach people to look to God as a healer of their infirmities, unless they are taught also to lay aside unhealthful practices" (*The Ministry of Healing*, p. 227).

The major condition to being healed in answer to prayer is the individual must be willing to live in harmony with both the natural and spiritual laws of God. Additional conditions found in the Spirit of Prophecy include: (1) close self-examination; confession and forsaking of sins (see *Testimonies*, vol 2, p. 146); (2) calm faith and courageous trust in God's unfailing love (see *The Ministry of Healing*, p. 229); (3) self must be entire-

ly surrendered (see *Testimonies*, vol 9, p. 166); (4) education in healthful practices that lead to reform (see *The Desire of Ages*, p. 824).

How should these conditions be presented to the person asking for prayer for healing? We have been given specific directions:

"Sin has brought many of them where they are—to a state of feebleness of mind and debility of body. Shall prayer be offered to the God of heaven for His healing to come upon them then and there, without specifying any condition? I say, No, decidedly no. What, then, shall be done? Present their cases before Him who knows every individual by name.

"Present these thoughts to the persons who come asking for your prayers: We are human; we cannot read the heart, or know the secrets of your life. These are known only to yourself and God. If you now repent of your sin, if any of you can see that in any instance you have walked contrary to the light given you of God, and have neglected to give honor to the body, the temple of God, but by wrong habits have degraded the body which is Christ's property, make confession of these things to God. Unless you are wrought upon by the Holy Spirit in special manner to confess your sins of private nature to man, do not breathe them to any soul.

Christ is your Redeemer; He will take no advantage of your humiliating confessions. If you have sin of a private character, confess it to Christ, who is the only Mediator between God and Man. "If any man sin, we have an advocate with the Father. Jesus Christ the righteous." 1 John 2:1 (*Counsels on Health*, pp. 373, 374).

How to Pray for the Sick

The scriptural plan for healing the sick is found in James 5:14, 15; "Is any sick among you? Let him call for the elders of the church; and let them pray over him, anointing him with oil in the name of the Lord: And the prayer of faith shall save the sick, and the Lord shall raise him up;

and if he have committed sins, they shall be forgiven him." In addition to this specific instruction, much detailed information on how to pray and actually what to say in such prayers is given in the Spirit of Prophecy: "The case should be committed to the Lord in calm faith, not with a storm of excitement" (*Testimonies*, vol. 2, p. 147). This apparently rules out any method of showmanship that encourages a spirit of excitement. We also are told plainly that "our petitions must not take the form of a command, but of intercession for Him to do the things we desire of Him" (*Ibid.*, p. 149). In the early days Ellen White and her associates did not fully understand this. But they soon learned that it was not God's will for them to demand that the sick must be healed:

"When we come to Him we should pray that we might enter into and accomplish His purpose, and that our desires and interests might be lost in His. We should acknowledge our acceptance of His will, not praying Him to concede to ours. It is better for us that God does not always answer our prayers just when we desire, and in just the manner we wish. He will do more and better for us than to accomplish all our wishes, for our wisdom is folly.

"We have united in earnest prayer around the sickbed of men, women, and children, and have felt that they were given back to us from the dead in answer to our earnest prayers. In these prayers we thought we must be positive and, if we exercised faith, that we must ask for nothing less than life. We dared not say, "If it will glorify God," fearing it would admit a semblance of doubt. We have anxiously watched those who have been given back, as it were, from the dead. We have seen some of these, especially youth, raised to health, and they have forgotten God, become dissolute in life, causing sorrow and anguish to parents and friends, and have become a shame to those who feared to pray. They lived not to honor and glorify God, but to curse Him with their lives of vice.

"We no longer mark out a way nor seek to bring the Lord to our wishes. If the life of the sick can glorify Him, we pray that they may live; nevertheless, not as we will but as He will. Our faith can be just as firm, and more reliable, by committing the desire to the all-wise God, and, without feverish anxiety, in perfect confidence, trusting all to Him. We have the promise. We know that He hears us if we ask according to His will" (*Ibid.*, pp. 148, 149).

How to actually present our prayers in such a way as to express quiet confidence in and submissiveness to the will of God is explained in *The Ministry of Healing*, pp. 229, 230.

"In prayer for the sick it should be remembered that "we know not what we should pray for as we ought." Romans 8:26. We do not know whether the blessing we desire will be best or not. Therefore our prayers should include this thought: "Lord, Thou knowest every secret of the soul. Thou art acquainted with these persons. Jesus, their Advocate, gave His life for them. His love for them is greater than ours can possibly be. If, therefore, it is for Thy glory and the good of the afflicted ones, we ask, in the name of Jesus, that they may be restored to health. If it be not Thy will that they may be restored, we ask that Thy grace may comfort and Thy presence sustain them in their sufferings."
God knows the end from the beginning. He is acquainted with the hearts of all men. He reads every secret of the soul. He knows whether those for whom prayer is offered should or would not be able to endure the trials that would come upon them should they live. He knows whether their lives would be a blessing or a curse to themselves and to the world. This is one reason why, while presenting our petitions with earnestness, we should say, "Nevertheless not my will, but thine, be done." Luke 22:42. . . . The consistent course is to commit our desires to our all-wise heavenly Father, and then, in perfect confidence, trust all to Him".

What to Expect and Do After Praying

Probably the most awkward moment in a prayer service for the sick comes in knowing what to say and advise after prayer has been offered. The Lord has given instruction in this matter too. Careful study of the following points should enable us to share much beneficial counsel with those for whom we have prayed and with their relatives.

Realize that not all the sick are healed

"There are cases where God works decidedly by His divine power in the restoration of health. But not all the sick are healed. Many are laid away to sleep in Jesus. . . . From this we see that if persons are not raised to health, they should not on this account be judged as wanting in faith" (*Ibid.*. p. 230).

Take advantage of rational remedies

"God's miracles do not always bear the outward semblance of miracles. Often they are brought about in a way which looks like the natural course of events. When we pray for the sick, we also work for them. We answer our own prayers by using the remedies within our reach. Water, wisely applied, is a most powerful remedy. As it is used intelligently, favorable results are seen. God has given us intelligence, and He desires us to make the most of His health- giving blessings. We ask that God will give bread to the hungry; we are then to act as His helping hand in relieving hunger. We are to use every blessing God has placed within our reach for the deliverance of those in danger".

"Natural means, used in accordance with God's will, bring about supernatural results. We ask for a miracle and the Lord directs the mind to some simple remedy. We ask to be kept from the pestilence that walketh in darkness, that is stalking with such power through the world; we are then to cooperate with God, observing the laws of health and life. Having done all that we possibly can, we are to keep asking in faith for health and strength. We are to eat that food which will preserve the health of the body. God gives us no encouragement that He will do for us that we can

do for ourselves. Natural laws are to be obeyed. We are not to fail of doing our part" (*Selected Messages*, book 2, p. 346).

Persevere in prayer

"There are precious promises in the Scripture to those who wait upon the Lord. We all desire an immediate answer to our prayers and are tempted to become discouraged if our prayer is not immediately answered. Now, my experience has taught me that this is a great mistake. The delay is for our special benefit. We have a chance to see whether our faith is true and sincere or changeable like the waves of the sea. We must bind ourselves upon the altar with the strong cords of faith and love, and let patience have her perfect work. Faith strengthens through continual exercise. This waiting does not mean that because we ask the Lord to heal there is nothing for us to do. On the contrary, we are to make the very best use of the means which the Lord in His goodness has provided for us in our necessities" (*Counsels on Health*, pp. 380, 381).

Preparation for death not a denial of faith

"Many who seek the Lord's healing mercy think that they must have a direct and immediate answer to their prayers or their faith is defective. For this reason, those who are weakened by disease need to be counseled wisely, that they may act with discretion. They should not disregard their duty to the friends who may survive them, or neglect to employ nature's agencies for the restoration of health. Often there is danger of error here. Believing that they will be healed in answer to prayer, some fear to do anything that might seem to indicate a lack of faith. But they should not neglect to set their affairs in order as they would desire to do if they expected to be removed by death" (*The Ministry of Healing*, p. 231).

To be educated in healthful living

"In the early history of our work, many were healed by prayer. And some, after they were healed, pursued the same course in the indulgence of appetite that they had followed in the past. They did not live and work in such a way as to avoid sickness. They did not show that they appreciated the Lord's goodness to them. Again and again they were brought to suffering through their own careless, thoughtless course of action. How could the Lord be glorified in bestowing on them the gift of health?

"When the light came that we should begin sanitarium work, the reasons were plainly given. There were many who needed to be educated in regard to healthful living. As the work developed, we were instructed that suitable places were to be provided, to which we could bring the sick and suffering who knew nothing of our people and scarcely anything of the Bible, and there teach them how to regain health by rational methods of treatment without having recourse to poisonous drugs, and at the same time surround them with uplifting spiritual influences. As a part of the treatment, lectures were to be given on right habits of eating and drinking and dressing. Instruction was to be given regarding the choice and the preparation of food, showing that food may be prepared so as to be wholesome and nourishing and at the same time appetizing and palatable. . . . God designs that by means of these agencies of His own planting, the rich and the poor, the high and the low, shall find the bread of heaven and the water of life. He designs that they shall be educated in right habits of living, spiritual and physical. The salvation of many souls is at stake" (*Counsels on Health*, pp. 469, 470).

Health gained through service for others

"One of the surest hindrances to the recovery of the sick is the centering of attention upon themselves. Many invalids feel that everyone should give them sympathy and help, when what they need is to have their attention turned away from themselves, to think of and care for others. . . . While we offer prayer for these sorrowful ones, we should encourage them to try to help those more needy than themselves. The darkness will be dispelled from their own hearts as they try to help others. As we seek to comfort others with the comfort therewith we are comforted, the blessing comes back to us. The fifty-eighth chapter of Isaiah is a prescription for maladies of the body and of the soul. If we desire health and the

true joy of life, we must put into practice the rules given in this scripture. Of the service acceptable to Him and its blessings, the Lord says:

"Is it not to deal thy bread to the hungry,
    When thou seest the naked, that thou cover
        him;
    And that thou hide not thyself from thine
        own flesh?
Then shall thy light break forth as the
    morning.
And thine health shall spring forth speedily."
(*The Ministry of Healing*, pp. 256, 257).

Expanding Our Ministry for the Sick

In the light of this instruction, it is evident that Adventists should be doing more than we have been in heeding Christ's commission to pray for and heal the sick. This is not to be done in mass-healing sessions that feature showmanship and sensationalism, but in quiet, calm visits from house to house as part of an over-all medical missionary program that ministers to the physical, social, mental, and spiritual needs of those with whom we come in contact. Our effectiveness will depend on our humbling ourselves before Christ and cleansing the soul temple from every defilement. Combine this prayer ministry with the use of the simple remedies God has given and educate our neighbors to reform their habits of living and come into conformity with both natural and moral law. Those for whom we pray are to be led to confidently trust in God and pray with us that His will be done. After prayer they are to cooperate with Him in His plan for their lives and especially to share the blessings they have gained with those more needy than themselves.

Although this kind of service represents only one branch of last-day medical missionary work, it needs to be implemented much more than it has been. Ministers need to study the Lord's instruction and share it with church members. The church, then, must assume a great responsibility for self-examination and the laying aside of sin that might hinder this work, going forth in the confidence that Christ has given us today the same power and ability to fulfill the commission that He gave to His disciples long ago. As channels of Christ's working we "shall lay hands on the sick, and they shall recover" (Mark 16:18).

9

Nutrition Education

The Garden of Eden could be called the garden of Eatin' because Adam and Eve were given access to a world of good food. Yet even in Eden they were to exercise self-discipline and self-control. Of thousands of fruit-bearing trees one—just one—was placed off limits. Undoubtedly, the fruit on the forbidden tree was not much different than that on the other trees. It was chosen by God arbitrarily to be the test of their love and self-discipline.

The fruit of that tree fascinated Eve because it was forbidden. It also was deadly because eating it would be a symbol of rebellion and a denial of God's love and goodness. In a sense we, too, live in a Garden of Eatin' surrounded by a wealth of delicious, nutritious dietary choices. But there is a strong temptation to make wrong food choices. For some reason the junk food "apples" appeal to our perverted tastes more than the "apple a day that keeps the doctor away." And it still is true that anything harmful to physical well-being adversely affects our spiritual well-being.

"Because the avenues to the soul have been closed by the tyrant Prejudice, many are ignorant of the principles of healthful living. Good service can be done by teaching the people how to prepare healthful food. This line of work is as essential as any that can be taken up. More cooking schools should be established, and some should labor from house to house, giving instruction in the art of cooking wholesome foods. Many, many will be rescued from physical, mental, and moral degeneracy through the influence of health reform. These principles will commend themselves to those who are seeking for light; and such will advance from this to receive the full truth for this time" (*Counsels on Diets and Foods*, p. 472).

Nutrition is a widely recognized and vital part of health promotion. Seventh-day Adventists have been blessed with special counsels on nutrition, personal health and lifestyle. This knowledge represents a treasure which can be shared with those who wish to improve their health. Nutrition should be integrated into all evangelistic outreach efforts.

The ability to prepare healthful and palatable food has been likened in value to "ten talents." Many individuals within the church have such talents. Because of the importance of nutritional cooking, the Adventist church provides the "Vegetarian Cuisine Instructor's Course" for those wishing to conduct vegetarian cooking classes in their communities. This 30-hour training course, taught by instructors with masters degrees in nutrition, goes beyond the basics in cooking into theoretical nutritional principles. The Vegetarian Cuisine Instructor's Manual may be purchased through The Health Connection by calling (800) 548-8700.

Participants completing the requirements for this course receive a certificate which is good for a period of 5 years. Those who continue their education in this field by reading designated nutrition material may have this certificate renewed at the end of the 5 years. You may arrange for such a course to be taught in your area by requesting it of your conference leadership. Often a church will send one or two individuals to such a course and pay for the manual and the expenses to attend the course.

Once you have a qualified instructor you can plan cooking seminars. You may hold these in the church or in another facility, four nights for one week, or one night for four weeks, or any other combination. Many find two nights a week for two weeks is best.

Many types of cooking seminars can be held. Most churches start with a basic vegetarian cooking seminar, then offer follow-up classes in such things as bread baking, food for healthy hearts, or healthy fast foods. Because of the on-going need and interest in cooking, many churches offer cooking seminars twice a year or more. The following are a sample of some of the innovative nutritional programs you might want to model.

Vegetarian Cooking Seminars

General seminars on vegetarian cooking are conducted at local churches to educate the church members, new converts, and those in the community who are interested in the vegetarian concept as it relates to healthful eating. Here are some suggestions to help in your planning.

Sample Program Evaluation

How many sessions of the program did you attend?

Has the program fulfilled your expectation?
[ ] Yes   [ ] No   [ ] Partly

Rate the following aspects of the program on a scale of 1-5 (circle one number on each line.)

	Poor				**Excellent**
Demonstrations	1	2	3	4	5
Recipes	1	2	3	4	5
Nutritional information	1	2	3	4	5
Handout materials	1	2	3	4	5
Helpfulness of personnel	1	2	3	4	5
Practical sessions	1	2	3	4	5

What aspect of the program did you enjoy most?

What other topics would you have liked to have seen covered in the program?

Do you have suggestions for improvements?

A general survey should be filled out by church members to obtain their specific needs. The topics listed on the survey may vary from vegetarian dishes to making whole grain bread in an hour. After completion of the survey, the most favored topic should be the first class scheduled. One month's notice is enough time to inform the members of the proposed class. Notices should be placed on bulletin boards at the church and in the church bulletins. Two weeks before the class the health ministries leader or a designated person should make an announcement from the pulpit to members and others interested in the class. A coordinator should be assigned to be responsible for the overall program. Invite those interested to preregister for the class. This enables the coordinator to contact the speaker or instructor ahead of time so adequate preparations can be made for necessary materials and grocery shopping. A small fee should be requested to cover the cost of the materials and the recipes that are demonstrated.

It is a good idea to have door prizes at the end of the cooking class and recipe books that can be purchased. Program evaluations should be filled out by each participant in the class at the end of the session.

The title you give the cooking school makes a great deal of difference. Some will be influenced to come with one title while another group would rather come if the same class were titled something else. To help you choose a concept or title, here are descriptions of some successful food ministries.

• *Cooking to Prevent Heart Disease program.* Topics include: the major risk factors such as the P/S ratio, the amount of saturated fat recommended, when treatment is recommended, and the amount of cholesterol in the diet. This program is a good follow-up to the HeartBeat Coronary Risk Evaluation program and an excellent way to "sell" the vegetarian diet.

• *Fast Food Cookery* or a *Microwave Cooking* class teaching how to cook by just using a microwave, are popular seminars for busy people.

• *Cooking for Bachelors* or single people has proven to be successful.

• *Vegetarian Cooking:* At one time a cooking school called "Vegetarian Cooking" would not attract many. Now many will respond because it is a vegetarian cooking school. People will expect to get considerable information concerning the advantages of the vegetarian diet. One could discuss the cost of vegetarian foods for the nutrients purchased compared to meat. Or one could discuss how the vegetarian diet reduces the risk of heart disease or cancer. One could spend one evening just discussing the adequacy of the vegetarian diet—how easy it is to get enough protein for example. Be prepared for questions on vitamin B 12 as that always comes up. You could discuss the advantages of the vegetarian diet from the standpoint of the environment or ecology; or from the physical fitness standpoint—the muscle glycogen is higher on such a diet and results in almost three times the usual endurance in marathon races.

• *Weight Control:* Weight control is a big thing in the United States. Nearly everyone wants to know how to cook with fewer calories. Include food demonstrations each night. You might also follow up a weight control program with a *Low Calorie Cooking School.* In this way you would create a built-in-audience.

• *Natural Food Cooking:* People like the idea of a "Natural Food Cooking" school.

• *Low Sodium Cooking* schools can be held for those on an extremely low salt diet. Even for hypertensives, 0.6 teaspoon of salt a day is permitted. Coronary bypass surgeons often remove all salt from the patients so they have less danger of congestive heart failure. These patients don't need to stay on such a diet long after the surgery but the surgeon forgets to tell them they can go off of it. Most people who have been on no salt diets prefer to not use substitutes. It is now known that sodium chloride or salt is a lot worse than sodium combined with something other than chloride. Even most of the low sodium

---

It's All in the Name

One time a new employee and his wife wanted to do a vegetarian cooking school. I was already doing one to prevent heart disease. I said that would be fine. So they did theirs just about two weeks before I was to do mine. I thought that no one would now come to mine. However, they had 80 at theirs and I had 80 at mine just several weeks later. They both would prevent heart disease and they were both vegetarian schools, but an entirely different group of people came to each because of the different titles.

—John Scharffenberg

---

recipe books call for baking powder containing sodium. However, with "Low Sodium Cooking" you usually will get a smaller audience.

• *Sugarless Desserts:* Scharffenberg states: "In Honolulu one time I only had time for a one night cooking school. I named it 'Sugarless Desserts.' We showed the sugarless banana cream pie made from cashews and dates on the TV program. More than 80 people came out to a little church for this one night on sugarless desserts. People know a lot of sugar is not good for them yet they like the sweet taste, so a night in any cooking school with sugarless recipes goes over really well. We have a night in our heart disease preventive cooking school just on this because most desserts are not healthy from the heart standpoint. By the way, that banana cream pie never got out of that TV studio alive."

• *Low Budget Cooking.* A cooking school just on "Low Budget Cooking" goes well because everyone wants to know how to do this. You can discuss bulk purchasing, storage, buying less packaged items and gardening. Vegetarian products are much less expensive for the nutrients purchased compared to meat and fish.

• *Let's Do Lunch.* Many people want to know what to do about "lunch." Talk about school lunches, taking a lunch to work, lunching at home or lunching out at a restaurant. Hand out menus from various restaurants and ask the people to select the best or most healthful lunch. They often forget to ask for things not on the menu. Or tell them to imagine going to work with two one-quart thermos jars containing their lunch. They could have hot rice in one and tofu and vegetables in the other.

• *Gourmet Cooking.* Women, especially, like to attend a cooking school that is named Gourmet Cooking or Decorative Cooking. If the food is attractively served most anything can be called "gourmet." It is amazing that almost every church has someone who is gifted at fixing up foods in an exquisite manner.

• *Diet for Athletes*. Many people, particularly the younger set, are interested in physical fitness. Show how endurance is increased almost threefold with a high carbohydrate diet (a vegetarian diet), and how the saturated fat decreases the oxygen supply the red blood cells deliver to body tissues. The best diet for athletes is a low fat vegetarian diet since as much as 68 percent of the saturated fat in the diet comes from animal products.

• *Low Fat Cookery* attracts many. Everyone has heard that Americans are eating too much fat.

Once when I was at a medical meeting in Los Angeles, I took a box of zwieback, a jar of peanut butter, and a thermos full of hot thickened grape juice. It made a very satisfying meal. I invited a Ph.D. biochemist to come to the car with me to share this lunch. He thought it was delicious and wondered who had ever thought up that meal. At least it was much more healthful than the steaks most of the physicians rushed out to get.

—John Scharffenberg

Not only are overweight people aware of it, but also people with heart problems and those concerned about cancer.

• *Single Food Cooking Schools*. Just taking a single food item and showing all you can do with it creates much interest, like in *The Bean Cooking School.* Discuss how to counteract the flatulence problem. Expound on the advantages of beans for diabetics because of the low glycemic index, or for those with high cholesterol because beans contain much soluble fiber and help lower serum cholesterol. Show how this kind of food greatly reduces colon cancer risk. You could do a similar thing with potatoes or fruit.

• The *One Dish Meal* is another interesting cooking school. It's amazing how many one plate dinners you can prepare, such as a noodle ring with peas in the center of the ring, or a taco salad.

• *Cooking To Prevent Cancer.* When Dr. Scharffenberg was asked to help in programs for patients with cancer, he says, "I tried to discuss what to do if you're nauseated, you lack appetite, or you have difficulty in swallowing. None of that went over too well. But as soon as I discussed what to do to prevent cancer, people were very interested even though they already had cancer. Usually such patients will get their friends out to a program on what to do to prevent cancer. I talk about a vegetarian diet and the advantages of the 20 or more substances in plant foods that help prevent cancer. Then I show the many mechanisms by which meat may help to bring on cancer. I present how eating less fat and especially fewer calories is needed to keep the weight down since weight increases cancer risk. The advantages of beans, cruciferous vegetables, and antioxidant vitamins also should be discussed."

• Try "_____*In The Kitchen*" (INK). It is quite interesting to do a program for a particular group of people. For example, have a program to train pastors to cook. In the Caribbean Islands they called it "Pastors in the Kitchen" or "PINK." If it was just for men it was called "Men in the

Kitchen" or "MINK", or for women it was Women in the Kitchen" or "WINK," and for kids it was "Kids in the Kitchen" or "KINK."

With some of these cooking schools it is well to get the entire family to come. Some have a lower charge if the family attends. Of course, singles might be upset, but you can tell them they can have the same break if they bring someone with them.

What makes a cooking school interesting is to have children doing some demonstrations, or involving the audience in doing some of them, or having men who are not used to the kitchen up front demonstrating.

• *Making Your Favorite Recipes Healthy.* One interesting type of cooking school or a one-night emphasis in a cooking school is teaching people how to modify recipes from something tasty but unhealthful to something tasty and healthful. People see in magazines many recipes they would like to try, but don't because they call for unhealthful ingredients. They need to learn how to modify these recipes, substituting healthful ingredients for unhealthful ones. One may even have healthful recipes but they may not be tasty. An example of a healthful and tasty recipe is changing the usual waffle recipe made from 99 percent refined ingredients to an oatmeal waffle topped with fruit instead of syrup.

• *Healthful Holiday Cooking Schools.* These can be provided seasonally on such occasions as Easter, Thanksgiving, and Christmas. Demonstrate low-fat recipes to replace traditional high-fat ones. Emphasize good taste and attractive decorations.

More Ideas for Successful Cooking Schools

There are an almost endless variety of possibilities when it comes to conducting cooking schools, but if you only know how to do one type and it's successful, go ahead and keep repeating it. Some have done the same type of cooking school twice a year for many years, attracting a new group of people each time. Dr. Scharffenberg reports doing this: "The cooking school was on how to prevent heart disease. Naturally with new

information coming out, I updated the educational material I used for each occasion. However, the town was big enough to draw about 80 people each time. Yet the town was small enough (200,000) that when friends who had attended the cooking school at different times, would meet, they could talk about the same recipes. It was almost as if they had been at the cooking school at the same time."

Most people know how to mix, dump, pour and stir, but they do not know why they should cook the way you are telling them to do. Therefore, do not do in front of them what they already know to do. Have the simple steps already done and demonstrate the more unusual ones. Use the time for giving good sound information on why they should do what you are teaching them to do. You wonder what you are going to say at all these programs, but you will be surprised at the great ideas that come up when you get a team together.

The most important part of the program is spending time with people personally. The break in the middle of the 2-hour evening cooking school is extremely important. This is the time when many people ask questions of a religious nature. You should also be at the program early to talk with people and stay afterwards to do the same.

With a little brainstorming, many kinds of cooking schools could be planned. When you get a group of people together at any church, all kinds of ideas will pop up, and many of them will be excellent ideas. If your first committee meeting is not too fruitful, you may have to meet several times until you're well acquainted with each other. However, if for some strange reason you don't have ideas of what to do, contact a dietitian in some nearby town and he or she will have many suggestions for you—or take the Vegetarian Cuisine Instructor's course.

Plan your health programs for the year in advance. You need to know whether or not you are going to do a weight control program for the community. If you are, do not discuss in detail weight management in a different kind of cooking school. However, if you are not planning to do a weight program, talk in detail about cooking to control your weight. Plan your visual aids and other illustrations. Instead of using all your good visual aids at a cooking school, save some for your weight control program. Vary the visual aids you use from program to program.

The Sunday Afternoon Cooking School

The time of the week to hold a cooking school has always been a problem because of such conflicting factors as Wednesday night prayer meetings and Monday night football. Tuesday and Thursday programs seem to draw more people. Again Scharffenberg shares this experience: "Often l have been asked to conduct cooking schools in distant locations and I didn't have time to spend two weeks or even one week. So I developed the Sunday afternoon cooking school. We started about 1:30 PM and would go for about 4 1/2 hours with food demonstrations, and close at 6 PM with a meal. Into that time period I could present most of my scientific information on how to prevent heart disease. This is a complete cooking school in one session and the people really enjoyed having it completed in that time span."

Holding Informal Cooking Schools at Home

A cooking school does not have to be held in a church or an official facility. It can be done in a home, in your own kitchen or that of one of the class member's with just 10-15 people. It is a good way to get acquainted with different people in the community.

In this program each class member helps in providing the food demonstrations, and in experimenting with recipes. Some dishes are prepared at home and brought for tasting while others are prepared right there in the kitchen.

Cooking Schools on Video

Cooking By the Book is an excellent, widely accepted cooking school produced by Marcella Lynch, a home economics teacher in Mountain View, California. She demonstrates how to prepare wholesome, nutritious food with simple recipes based on the nutrition principles of

Scripture. There are 13 videos of approximately 26 minutes each, and an accompanying cookbook. Available through The Health Connection.

Check with your local Union or Conference Health Departments or Adventist resource agencies listed in chapter 21 for current cooking school videos that are up-to-date and scientifically accurate. Several well-done nutrition videos also are available through The Health Connection, such as:

- *The Search for the Fountain of Youth*—on the Adventist lifestyle.
- *The Vegetarian Advantage.*
- *Eating for Life*—hosted by Mike Farell and other celebrities showing the adequacy and advantages of a vegetarian diet.
- *The Great Grain Robberies*—How refining grain destroys nutrients.
- *Sugar's Sour Side*—How to avoid the harmful aspects of sugar.
- *Trapped in the Spider's Web*—Caffeine's harmful effect.

Visual Aids and Resources

When hunting for visual aids for your nutrition programs see The Health Connection Catalog or talk to one of their representatives: call (800) 548-8700 or Fax 1-888-294-8405.

Poster: Vegetarian Food Pyramid Poster. The following information is available from The Health Connection in a beautifully designed poster.

Nutrition Council Position Statements

These statements in pamphlet form are from 30 of the denomination's top nutritionists and include the most up-to-date information on controversial nutrition issues. These are ideal for nutrition lectures, cooking schools, new member classes, and professional patient information racks. Bulk rates are available. Here is a list of topics: (New topics are added regularly)

- Dietary Fat
- Herbs and Herbal Teas
- How Diet Can Lower Cancer Risks
- Meat Analogs as Part of the Vegetarian Lifestyle

- Planning Fellowship Dinners
- The Vegetarian Dietary Lifestyle
- Vitamin B 12 for the Vegetarian
- Use of Caffeine
- Use of Vitamin and Mineral Supplements

One of the easiest ways to present nutritional principles is to use visual illustrations or demonstrations. Here are some examples:

1. Weight Control

Hand out tape measures and have the audience do their waist to hip ratios. Involve the audience in the learning process as much as possible. Discuss what these ratios should be (0.85 or less for women and 1.0 or less for men) and about the dangers of elevated ratios.

Have those present calculate their own Body Mass Index. The formula is:

$$\frac{\text{weight (kilograms)}}{\text{height}^2 \text{ (meters)}}$$

or

$$\frac{\text{weight (lbs) x 704}}{\text{height}^2 \text{ (inches)}}$$

If using a calculator it is easier to tell people to divide by the height once and then to divide by it again the second time. The ratios for normal weight are 20-24. If their results are 25-29 they are overweight and if they are over 30 the person is obese. (An Omron Body Fat Analyzer is much simpler to use–Order from The Health Connection (800) 548-8700.

Another interesting demonstration is to put on paper plates the amount of food that equals 100 calories. Do this with a lot of foods. Show how four heads of lettuce are not going to make them fat, but that sliver of pie might.

Discuss the Calorie Nose-Dive. We teach people not to eat this or that and soon they are not getting enough calories to survive. Show them how they can eat all they want and not get fat. Put on plates two cups of grated carrots, six cups of string beans and nine cups of summer squash and you have about 500 calories. This will take perhaps four plates. Tell them they must eat this twice a day (on the two meal a day program) to get 1000 calories. They should eat at least that much or they might get too skinny, which would give the weight control program a bad reputation.

2. Decreasing the Use of Sugar

Call a gentleman from the audience. Give him a box of sugar cubes. Use the 1/2 teaspoon size sugar cubes. Ask him to count very loudly the number of cubes he places into a pyrex pie plate and you will stop him when he gets as many as Betty Crocker's standard Banana Cream Pie recipe calls for. It will take 64. Then continue for the berry pie recipe; it will take 96. The apple pie also will take 96 and the lemon pie, 144. Do this after you have demonstrated your sugarless banana cream pie.

Have 5 apples on the table and a model of a banana split. They both have the same amount of sugar. Ask, Can we then allow our children to have a banana split in place of five apples if it's just the same? Then explain the differences. In the

---

The Vegetarian Food Pyramid: A Daily Guide to Food Choices

Eat Sparingly: Vegetable fats and oils; sweets, and salt.

Eat Moderately:
- Low-fat or non-fat milk, yogurt, fresh cheese, and fortified alternative group: 2-3 servings.
- Legume, nut, seed, and meat alternative group: 2-3 servings.

Eat Generously:
- Vegetable group: 3-5 servings.
- Fruit group: 3-5 servings.

Eat Liberally: Whole grains, bread, cereal, pasta, and rice group: 6-11 servings.

A "Total Plant Food" Pyramid also is available from The Health Connection.

natural state one will not usually eat that concentrated quantity of sugar. The sugar in the apples is absorbed slower, so that the high blood sugar level is not followed by a low level. The banana split also comes packaged with cholesterol and saturated fat, compared to the pectin in the apple.

3. Soda Drinks and Your Teeth

Get a dentist to give you some teeth he has extracted and place them for 4 hours in some coke with some water. Then take them out in front of the audience and put them in ink.

4. Decreasing Fat Consumption, Especially Animal Fat

Have two plates one with a baked potato with Loma Linda Gravy Quick, frozen peas, and 3 gluten steaks while the other has a baked potato with 2 pats of butter, frozen peas and a fake model of a 6 oz. Porterhouse Steak. Compare 475 vs. 878 calories; 47 percent less calories vs. 85 percent more calories; 12.4 g fat vs. 58 g fat; 25 percent of the calories from fat vs. 60 percent of the calories from fat; linoleic acid 6.3 g vs. 1.5 g; saturated fats 1.4 g vs. 28.5; and cholesterol 0 vs. 268 mg.

Teach the audience how to calculate the ratio of polyunsaturated to saturated fatty acid. Have two participants come forward and separate the foods from a shopping bag into polyunsaturated foods (P/S greater than 1) vs. saturated fat foods (P/S less than 1).

Have tray 1 with 1/2 cup whole milk, 1 cup low fat milk, and 20 cups nonfat milk. All have the same amount of fat—5 g. Have tray 2 with 0.4 oz. broiled T-bone steak, 1/2 chicken breast, 1/3 frankfurter, 1/3 cup chili con carne with beans; each has 5 g fat. Have tray 3 with 6 jumbo potato chips, 10 French fries (each 3/5 in. long), 2/3 cup potato salad, and then 25 baked potatoes (this will take up the whole of another tray) and each of these has 5 g fat. Have tray 4 with 1/9 avocado, 10 olives, 4 apples, 25 medium bananas and each food contains 5 g fat. Have tray 5 with 1 egg, 1 pat butter, 1 teaspoon salad dressing, 1 oz. peanut butter and each food has 5 g fat. Have tray 6 with 1/2 cup cooked soybeans and 5 cups cooked kidney beans and each food contains 5 g fat. Have tray 7 with 4 cups cooked brown rice, 2 cups cooked oatmeal, 1 1/2 in. arc of apple pie and each food contains 5 g fat. With this illustration people learn where the fat is. Hand out a sheet with these facts on it. This is quite an impressive demonstration.

5. Fiber

Show how these foods have equivalent fiber contents:

5   slices whole wheat bread = 40 slices of white bread
2   large shredded wheat biscuits = five 1 oz. cups of corn flakes
1   orange = five 6.5 oz. cups orange juice
1   apple = ten 6.5 oz. cups apple juice.

6. The Best Foods

Draw concentric circles on the blackboard. The bull's eye represents the best of foods. Have about five different areas where the participants could place foods, from the best at the bull's eye to the worst in the outer circle. Ask them what foods they would put in each of the categories from 1 to 5. It is surprising how close they come to the way it ought to be.

7. Quizzes

There are a variety of quizzes that can be given. For example, list two foods and ask which has the most iron.

At this point you might be thinking, I'm not a nutritionist and I wouldn't know how to do this. You can always find someone not far from you (a dietitian or a cook) who could come and spend an hour or two with you and give you ideas and information. But you don't even need that kind of help. It is surprising that when a group gets together many unique and interesting ideas can be dreamed up as to how to illustrate a topic. Spend a little time in brainstorming and you will come up with many good ideas.

Puppets

Puppets can be used to teach health principles. Often these programs are done with inappropriate or silly representations. They can, how-

On the Meatless Wagon

*R*obert ignited a roar of joyous approval at the Vegetarian Supper Club cooking school when he began explaining his reasons for taking the course: "These are going to be my Meat-alcoholics Anonymous meetings. I really have been overdoing my meat consumption, and I want to learn how to prepare another kind of protein." He detailed the extent of his perceived addiction, including the exact ounces of meat he had been devouring daily. Then he set off another rumble of laughter by concluding, "So I came here to get on the wagon."

Americans have been formally getting on the wagon ever since the phrase became popular in the late 1800's. And as anyone who has been on any kind of "wagon" can tell you, eliminating the loved and the familiar requires commitment and fortitude. The friendship and support of other people trying to make the same or similar change helps a lot. Robert can tell you all about that. He stuck with his class for all five training sessions.

At the International Tasting Event finale to the cooking school, Robert's face reflected the peace and joy of an overcomer. Several weeks later he announced he had prepared every recipe in the course manual, and apparently his friends had tasted it all. "When's the next class?" he asked. "I have a lot of friends who want to come!"

The bottom line of support for everyone making lifestyle changes, whether it's getting enough sleep, getting enough exercise, or getting on a meatless diet, is the Great Enabler. He provides the power to hold on and hold out—to stay on the wagon of wholesome change. However, when your face is set like flint to do God's will, it certainly helps to have friends who'll encourage you.

That's why I'd suggest joining a support group of people who are eating vegetarian style or doing (or stopping) whatever you have set your face toward. If you don't know anyone nearby to turn to, ask your omniscient Father to direct you to someone He has ordained to supply the encouragement you need.

—Faith Crumbly From: Energized! A one-a-day devotional for body, mind and soul. Hagerstown, MD: Review and Herald Publishing Association, 1997.

---

ever, be effective when used appropriately. Puppet programs not only attract young people and children but also adults. The Health Connection catalog has a large number of puppet presentations available.

Other Aids

Handouts help people remember what was presented. A sample copy of *Vibrant Life,* the church's outreach health journal offers recipes in each issue, and is a good give-away. A door prize could be a free subscription to this magazine. The *Vibrant Life* special vegetarian issue titled, "Going Meatless," is an excellent resource. (See Chapter 21 on resources for bulk price lists and other materials.)

To Keep Updated

To get the latest information from the scientific literature, order the NAD Health Ministries Department *HealthWorks* newsletter by calling Advent*Source* (800) 328-0525 to have your name put on the mailing list. It is written to provide practical information that you can use in your programs. You can also use current books on nutrition. (See Appendix E in this manual for some recommended books.)

How to Get People to Come to Your Programs

Some are afraid to start a program for fear no one will attend. Often only a few come out when we should be getting through to many people.

The Vegetarian Food Pyramid

A Daily Guide to Food Choices. This
little pamphlet is provided by the General
Conference Nutrition Council and is a
great handout for cooking school.
To order call (800) 548-8700.

What do you do to get a crowd out? Advertising is the key to successful attendance. Many local newspapers and media outlets are quite willing to give free promotion to health prevention programs. Also prepare attractive flyers that can be circulated in health professional offices, pharmacies, health fairs, community health agencies, and by church members to their friends and neighbors.

One of the most important thing is to have a quality program. But how is that done? You must present information that is on the cutting edge of science. Don't just tell people in a cooking school to cut down on fatty meats. They have heard that message for years. Point out why their intake of cholesterol should be as close to zero as possible and support your argument by scientific studies. Show them that saturated fat does not damage the arteries if there is no cholesterol in the diet. That will be new to most of them, and you must be prepared to base what you present on good studies.

Have the staff dressed well, as if they were going to a banquet. Right away that indicates quality. Have music playing as the attendees enter the room and have people greet them at the door. Give them something to read as they wait for the program to begin. Have staff participating who are up-to-date scientifically. Do everything possible to have the individuals present participate in the learning process by doing something.

It is important to have the program on a routinely scheduled basis. This way, people can plan on it. The program should be held at least once a year and at the same time of the year on a regular basis. More community referrals will be made if your nutrition program is a continuing program, or held quarterly.

The more programs a church conducts, the better the response will be to all the programs. The HeartBeat Coronary Risk Evaluation program helps to feed all the others. A weight control program helps get people into the cooking school, the physical fitness program and the stress control program. A cooking school can motivate people to attend the HeartBeat program to find out what their risk of heart attack is. A diabetes control program can funnel people into the weight control program, the HeartBeat program, as well as the physical fitness program. Smokers certainly should come to the cooking school because many of the hazards that have been attributed to smoking actually come from poor eating habits.

A newspaper feature article is the best mass media avenue. Personal word from one person to another also is an excellent way of getting the message out. Satisfied customers from previous programs are sure to tell their friends. Developing a mailing list of all who attend any of the programs is important. Radio and TV are not as effective unless your ad is on 6-7 times a day for a week or so.

It is better to have different speakers instead of two hours of just one person. No matter how good a speaker is some prefer another type of speaker. One person could serve as master of ceremonies for the two-hour program but several people should participate in the program.

More Creative Ideas Promoting Good Nutrition
Breadbakes

Breadbakes are where everyone brings a package of one or more of the ingredients. The group then puts them together, dividing what is needed by each member of the group. They take these home and bake the bread.

The Vegetarian Supper Club

Faith Crumbly, the editor of Sabbath School Leadership magazine, has used the idea of getting acquainted with people in the community by inviting them to supper. The result is what is called, The Vegetarian Supper Club which offers vegetarian cooking schools and weekly support groups that meet at different members' houses for lunch, brunch, dinner, or a party. The Vegetarian Supper Club is a place for vegetarians to meet, greet, eat, and share information, recipes, ideas, fellowship and encourage each other in following the vegetarian lifestyle. Once every three months, the entire group meets for a grand affair with entertainment, speakers, and good food. If you would like to contact the Hagerstown Vegetarian Supper Club for tips on how to get started, call the Hagerstown SDA Church (301) 733-4411.

Sunday Lunches

John Scharffenberg describes his experience with this program: "At Pacific Health Education Center we had Sunday luncheons once a month where there was a charge of just enough to cover costs for the meal. We had it from 11:00 AM to 1:00 PM with as many as 600 in attendance. When we first started people were lined up around the block waiting to get in. By opening the doors 30 minutes early we managed to get people in without a long wait. People were attracted by the totally healthful menu. The food was cholesterol-free and sugar was kept extremely low. Sunday school teachers would bring their Sunday school class with them to try the foods. We had the room nicely decorated and usually featured something special. We had violinists play, going from table to table. I tried to present a five-minute health talk but found it didn't work. People wanted to have a social time and were not interested in health information on such an occasion. However, the meal itself presented the health information. Everyone had a copy of the recipes in that meal and a listing of future programs as a way to advertise all the programs for the year. We always had at least 300 in attendance with 80 percent or more being non-Adventists." The Sunday Lunch still is a part of the Pacific Health Education Center outreach to the community.

Breakfasts

Many people don't know what a good breakfast is. They think a really good breakfast consists of bacon and eggs, pancakes with syrup and other high-fat foods. Yet it is easier to serve breakfast foods than other foods to people not used to a good diet in a way they will find tasty. Pacific Health Education Center (PHEC) began running HeartBeat programs and serving a complimentary breakfast to the participants who had

---

HeartBeat at the Pacific Health Education Center

People come to the program in the morning before they have eaten anything and pay a small fee for the program. They fill out a health questionnaire, have their blood pressure checked and their blood drawn by a nurse or lab technician. The blood is sent to the lab and analyzed with a report returned for total, LDL, HDL cholesterol, triglycerides, uric acid and glucose. Because they have not had breakfast they are given orange juice after the blood is drawn. The results of the test and the information on their lifestyle is put into the computer by your church secretary. The HeartBeat computerized program will generate recommendations for each person's needs.

The participants in the program return perhaps two weeks later for a group discussion of what the lab results mean and what they should do to lower their risk of heart attack. They are free to ask questions during this discussion and following the meeting many stay for another hour or two asking about their particular results. In the audience may be people who have had their blood drawn at different times or in different places in the town. You might be surprised to see so many people attending because at the testing there may have been only 5-10 in the room at a time. At this follow-up meeting people are given their reports. If they cannot return for some reason the report is mailed to them. The participants at this time also are given a coronary risk evaluation booklet listing the major factors leading to heart disease.

—John Scharffenberg

---

come after a fast for their blood test. Others also were welcome to eat breakfast for a small fee. This program is a regular Monday morning feature at PHEC. It's a good way to get acquainted with people, to learn about their problems, and to help them. If breakfasts are commonly provided in local areas for Ministerial Association monthly meetings, why can it not be done for other groups with whom you would like to make contact?

Fairs

At fairs, food such as vegetarian burgers can be sold, or a booth can be set up providing samples of vegetarian food. Be sure to have lots of literature promoting a healthful diet.

The Health Connection has a ten foot by five foot Celebrations exhibit banner and a pamphlet that goes along with it, as well as a step-by-step instruction book called, How to Plan a Health Exhibit. A coordinated give-away pamphlet titled,

---

I think someone should develop a seminar on scientific thinking regarding food. Perhaps it could be titled "Seminar on the Meaning of Food Facts and Figures," or "How to Lie with Food Facts and Figures!" This seminar would be one that would make people think seriously when they are told something about food, because much of the nutrition information being promulgated today is inaccurate. For example, a bread maker promoted their loaf of bread as being lower in calories. They stated it had 50 percent less calories per slice of bread. It was true because their slices of bread were half as thick as other breads being sold. Just ask the audience which sheep eat more grass—black or white sheep? Naturally white sheep eat more grass because there are more white sheep. People need to learn how to think critically in order to make better judgment calls when they hear various advertisements.

—John Scharffenberg

For information on "How to Read the New Food Labels," by the American Heart Association, call (800) 242-8721.

Good Health in One Package, offers a positive introduction to the Seventh-day Adventist lifestyle.

Fellowship Dinners

The General Conference Nutrition Council has a position statement on fellowship dinners that can be useful to your local church as a guideline in conducting fellowship dinners. These statements are available in pamphlet form at The Health Connection. At the beginning of your church's officers terms, the pamphlet, Planning Fellowship Dinners should be presented to the social committee and other committees involved with food service in your church .

Fellowship dinners present an opportunity for church members to share ideas of good nutrition, strengthen friendships, and celebrate God's goodness. In the days of Israel there was a coming together for feasting and socializing. "As a means of education an important place was filled by the feasts of Israel…. Three times a year seasons were appointed for social intercourse and worship…. So far as possible, all the household were in attendance; and with them, as sharers of their hospitality, were the stranger, the Levite, and the poor" (*Education*, pp. 41, 42).

Here are a few of the guidelines from the General Conference position statement:

The usual time for a fellowship dinner is after the church service…. Fellowship dinners are to be scheduled in advance so there is time for members to plan and prepare. A set plan for every Sabbath or a regular Sabbath scheduled each month makes this possible. Fellowship meals should be open to all. This includes members, visitors from out-of-town, Adventists from other churches, and non-Adventist neighbors and friends from the community. All should be made to feel welcome remembering the biblical injunction to entertain strangers, for thereby some have entertained angels unawares (Heb. 13:2).

Occasionally some church facilities will not accommodate all the members so other arrangements will need to be made.

When possible hold fellowship dinners where kitchen facilities have adequate refrigeration, freezing, heating, serving, and seating capacity. Church leaders are encouraged to provide such facilities necessary for the social and health evangelism programs of the church.

It is suggested that a fellowship dinner coordinator be chosen with several assistants, so that one person is not burdened with the full responsibility.

Fellowship meals may consist of a full dinner menu to include: entrees, cooked vegetables, starchy foods, salads and/or relishes, breads, beverages, and simple healthful desserts. Other ideas for meal planning include soup and salad menus, theme meals, holiday type meals, ethnic cuisine and 'build your own meal' from simple ingredients…. [such as a] salad or sandwich bar.

The meal needs to be planned carefully. When not planned, a potluck encourages members to bring whatever they choose resulting in too much of one type of food and not enough of another. It also is a poor witness when unhealthful food is served. Perhaps specific Sabbath School classes could be assigned to organize the meal. Or those whose names begin with A-F would bring an entree; G-K a vegetable and bread; L-O a tossed salad and nuts; P-S a fruit dessert; T-Z a fruit juice.

Guidelines should include: Choosing delicious meatless recipes which are nutritious, and attractive. Choose recipes which people will want to try at home. Consider the individual needs of the congregation—total vegetarians, ethnic groups, etc. Promote fresh fruit and whole grain desserts rather than those high in refined sugar, refined flour, fat, and salt. Select pure fruit juices and caffeine-free cereal beverages rather than high-sugar drinks. Of course alcoholic beverages are out of place. Provide printed recipes. Limit the variety.

Do not over-react if someone brings something that should not be served. Instead, in a tactful way and at the right time give the General Conference Nutrition Council's guidelines. Remember what Jesus did when he went out to eat as described by Ellen White:

Vegetarian Diet: Hot Subject for TV

One time the Los Angeles County Medical Society invited us to do a TV program on the vegetarian diet. We had Hulda Crooks in her hiking gear and discussed how much greater endurance a person has when on a high carbohydrate diet. We had bicycles in the studio and discussed the study of the nine Swedish athletes' endurance records on bicycles when their diet was changed for just three days. On the high carbohydrate diet the endurance was almost three times greater than when on the high fat and protein diet. We ended with a nicely set table and eating a vegetarian meal together. The program was a 30-minute program. The first month or so we got about 40,000 responses asking for more information—and another 30 to 40 thousand came later. Our problem then became how to pay for the postage to answer their questions.

—John Scharffenberg

"While Christ accepted invitations to feasts and gatherings, He did not partake of all the food offered Him, but quietly ate of that which was appropriate for His physical necessities, avoiding the many things that He did not need. His disciples were frequently invited with Him, and His conduct was a lesson to them, teaching them not to indulge appetite by overeating or by eating improper food. He showed them that portions of the food provided could be passed by, and portions chosen…. Christ went to these feasts because He wished to show those who were excluding themselves from the society of their fellow men how wrong their course of action was. He wished to teach them that truth was given to be imparted to those who had it not. If they had truth, why keep it selfishly to themselves. The world is perishing for want of the living Truth (*Manuscript Release* 7, p. 412).

Such fellowship dinners can provide an educational opportunity as an alternative or in addition to cooking schools. In this way, the vegetarian cuisine can be shared with non-Adventist friends in the community.

Nutrition Seminars

Many kinds of seminars can be conducted concerning nutrition or where nutrition forms a large component. (For more resources see Chapter 21.)

• *Cancer Risk Reduction Seminar*: John Scharffenberg was the first to develop cancer prevention seminars. He says, "Some criticized it because they said cancer could not be prevented. Now everyone knows that half of the cancers may be prevented, as documented in the *Abundant Living* Series. But because of the criticism at the time (1986) the name of the cancer prevention seminar was changed to "Cancer Risk Reduction Seminar." (Available from The Health Connection.) This seminar can be given in four sessions of two hours each. Session one covers the size of the problem, the official dietary recommendations and the subject of tobacco and lung cancer. The second addresses cancers of women with a focus on nutrition. The third, colon cancer, again with an emphasis on nutrition, and the possible mechanisms whereby food might be involved in producing cancer. The fourth is entirely on foods of various types and their link to cancer.

• *Weight Control* programs often draw the largest attendance. There are many overweight people in the country who are willing to pay to

Has the Time Come?

*I*f you want to start a lively discussion that often leads to controversy, bring up a subject where daily practice varies so widely you almost never find two people alike. Discuss something that even the experts disagree on widely—debate all the time.

Yet, since this is something vital to our spiritual development, God has interjected the matter of what we eat right into the middle of His discussions of spiritual growth. Why?

From the very beginning, God knows what we sometimes forget—that what we put into our bodies forms the building blocks of life both physically and spiritually. Not only is our strength of body impacted, but our clarity of mind as well. "The spiritual as well as the mental and physical powers suffer under the influence of unhealthful food. The conscience becomes stupefied, and the susceptibility to good impressions is impaired" (*Child Guidance*, p. 379).

What about today?

Since we are so bombarded with reports of contaminated and diseased foods in today's world, it is important to ask if anything in our diet is unhealthful. A recent article in *Newsweek* magazine illustrates the urgency of that question. The cover story on how resistant we are becoming to antibiotics described the impact animal products have on human beings.

"Farm animals receive 30 times more antibiotics than people do…Resistant strains emerge just as they do in humans taking antibiotics—and remain in the animal's flesh even after it winds up in the meat case…. The superbugs spread from farm animals to people through raw or under-cooked meat…. The threat could be even greater to those who down a milkshake with their burger. Milk is allowed to contain a certain concentration of 80 different antibiotics …. With every glassful, people swallow a minute amount of several antibiotics…. Tests discovered traces of 64 antibiotics at levels find an easy method of losing weight. In 1997 the *Abundant Living* Series plans to publish a program developed by Dr. Glen Blix of Loma Linda's School of Public Health with an emphasis on nutrition and exercise. Practical demonstrations should be presented each evening. Five basic principles need to be presented: no snacks; cut down on empty and refined calories (oils & shortening, sugar, refined cereals, alcohol); cut down on cholesterol and saturated fat (meat, dairy products, and eggs); eat a good breakfast and little or no supper; and eat more low caloric density foods; and the possibility of fasting one day a week. It is important to present these principles in a positive, encouraging way.

• A *Dietary Control of Heart Disease* seminar (*Abundant Living* series) is being revised and updated. Along with this seminar the participants and their families should be invited to a meal containing no cholesterol.

• *Blood Pressure Control.* Another nutrition seminar that is much needed is one on blood pressure control. In this seminar, you can teach people how to take blood pressure. You may invite a company that sells sphygmanometers to come and explain the various types of equipment. They usually give sizeable discounts that night for those wishing to purchase any of the equipment. During this seminar discussions focus on such topics as rational therapy-weight control, low sodium diet, stress control, exercise, abstinence from alcohol.

• *Smoking and Nutrition.* In a stop smoking program much of what is presented deals with what the smoker needs to know about nutrition. Smokers consume more cholesterol and saturated fat than non-smokers. Even though they are thinner their waist to hip measurement is worse than those who are non-smokers. Smokers consume less fruits and vegetables and therefore get less vitamin A and C. When they stop smoking a little

---

'that raise health concerns.' They could produce resistant germs in milk drinkers" (*Newsweek*, March 28, 1994).

True to His promise, God has not left us in the dark on what is best. Here is counsel it seems to me needs to be carefully considered as we move closer to the end.

"But I wish to say that when the time comes that it is no longer safe to use milk, cream, butter, and eggs, God will reveal this. No extremes in health reform are to be advocated" (*Counsels on Diet and Foods*, p. 359).

"The disease upon animals is becoming more and more common, and our only safety now is in leaving meat entirely alone.... Because of meat eating, many die, and they do not understand the cause" *Counsels on Diet and Foods*, p. 412).

"Eating the flesh of dead animals is deleterious to the health of the body, and all who use a meat diet are increasing their animal passions and are lessening their susceptibility of the soul to realize the force of truth and the necessity of its being brought into their practical life" (*E. G. White Letter* 54, 1896).

Has the time come to cease using all animal products? I can't make that decision for you. All I can do is share a sample of the counsel we have been given. Whatever you decide, please remember this is a personal matter between you and God, not something to push on others. Nor should we judge another less faithful if they make a decision different from ours. And if you do decide to change, expect difficulty, "For the sinful nature desires what is contrary to the Spirit, and the Spirit what is contrary to the sinful nature" (Gal. 5:17 NIV).

Sincerely your friend,
Tom Mostert, Jr.,
President, Pacific Union

(From: *Pacific Union Recorder*, May 2, 1994, p. 2)

Nutrition Newsletters

*T*he following newsletters have good nutrition information. Not all, however, advocate the Adventist lifestyle. Order a sample issue before subscribing to make sure the material presented will be helpful to you.

Environmental Nutrition: A monthly newsletter on the latest findings in the area of diet, nutrition and health. Regular subscription rates are $30 U.S. or $38 in Canada. Write to: Environmental Nutrition, PO Box 420451 Palm Coast, FL 32142-0451, or call (800) 829-5384.

Health Quarterly: A quarterly Christian newsletter on general health issues including good nutrition, specifically for those who are interested in preventing cancer and other nutritional diseases. ($10 yearly) HealthQuarters Lodge (associated with Health Quarterly) is an 11 day residential program to get cancer patients on a good anti-cancer diet and lifestyle program. For more information contact Health Quarterly at 4141 Sinton Rd. Colorado Springs, CO, 80907. Call (719) 593-8694 or for orders (719) 522-9759.

Nutrition Action Healthletter: This newsletter published 10 times a year that will keep you up-to-date with the latest nutrition information in a user-friendly way. Easy to read and use. Annual membership is $24 a year ($36 Canadian). Nutrition Action Health Letter, 1875 Connecticut Ave., N.W., Washington, D.C. 20009. E-mail subscription inquiries: circ@essential.org

Today's Family Matters contains information about the importance of a good healthy lifestyle and diet for the family. This bimonthly publication is edited by Greg and Donna Spann of Cornerstone Services, Inc. 9005 Macsvega Court, Lorton, VA 22079 or call (703) 339-6467.

Tufts University Diet & Nutrition Letter: This newsletter contains up-to-date research information in the areas of diet and nutrition. For more details write Tufts University Diet & Nutrition Letter, 6 Beacon Street, Suite 1110, Boston, MA 02108. New subscription information: P. O. Box 57857, Boulder, CO 80322-7857. Phone (800) 274-7581. In Colorado (303) 447-9330.

University of California at Berkeley Wellness Letter: A Newsletter for Nutrition, Fitness and Stress. For more information write or call, Wellness Letter Subscription Department, P. O. Box 420148, Palm Coast, FL 32142. Phone (904) 445-6414.

Vegetarian Nutrition & Health Letter: An 8 page newsletter published by Loma Linda University. Published 10 times per year and can be ordered by calling 888-558-8703.

For other newsletters on health see Chapter 21.

gain in weight usually follows. Caffeinated beverages seem to make the smokers want to smoke. It is more difficult to get off cigarettes if one is still consuming coffee. Smokers' heart attack rates have dropped percentage-wise more that non-smokers' rates. This is an indication that their diet has changed. Wherever possible a nutritionist or dietitian could be an active member of the Breathe Free™ team.

Food Service Directors' Workshop

When a much-needed and much-appreciated food service directors' workshop was presented at a camp meeting at Camp Hope, British Columbia, Canada, approximately 20 people participated in the workshop. They were people at all levels. Some had been in food service work and others were new to the field but wanted to get into this type of work. The Adventist church is in desperate need of qualified food service workers.

This group ran the camp meeting food service, saving the conference expense because it was done without charge to the conference. The students didn't pay tuition—their working in the kitchen was the laboratory part of the course. Lectures were given by a qualified teacher in this field. The areas covered were organization and management, personnel management, food production and service (including recipe standardization and computerization), food preservation methods, financial management, managing a nutrition system, menu planning, food procurement, and food selection. In addition a cooking school for the people attending the camp meeting was held. The participants in the Food Service Workshop also attended.

At this camp meeting all the meals served were total vegetarian. Soy milk was served. Low-fat or non-fat milk was available but, at another location so those wishing it would have to make an effort to get it. A physician at the outset was sure those responsible for this program would get a lot of flack. This probably was because he did not realize how good this food could be when properly prepared. When those attending filled

---

Nasco Nutrition Teaching Aids

This catalog contains hundreds of food replicas for use in seminar presentations and displays. You'll also find a listing of videos, slides, books and more. Write or call, Nasco Nutrition Teaching Aids, 901 Janesville Ave., Fort Atkinson, WI 53538; (414) 563-2446; Fax (414) 563-8296.

---

out an evaluation form, a 98 percent rating was received for attractiveness, taste, and variety. If more conferences could arrange these workshops, they would not only save money but also would provide workers in the areas where the church now has great need for personnel and in addition, educate members on health and nutrition principles.

Camp Meeting Food Service

Camp meeting is a good time to educate Adventist people on proper eating habits. At one camp meeting printed cards with a Spirit of Prophecy quotation on one side and a scientific statement on the other were placed on each table. People were invited to pick them up and take them home. A different card can be provided for each meal. Here are two examples:

Card #1. "Let the diet reform be progressive....Tell them that the time will soon come when there will be no safety in using eggs" (*Counsels on Diet and Foods*, p. 356).

"I wish to say that when the time comes that it is no longer safe to use milk, cream, butter, and eggs, God will reveal this.... The question of using milk and butter and eggs will work out its own problem" (*Ibid.*, p. 359).

"In all parts of the world provision will be made to supply the place of milk and eggs" (*Ibid.*, p. 359).

"People everywhere should be taught how to cook without milk and eggs so far as possible, and yet have their food wholesome and palatable" (*Ibid.*, p. 470).

The other side of the card had this: "How did you like the potato salad? Did you miss having the eggs in it? The latest survey of the membership of the Adventist Church in Canada and the United States noted that 23 percent no longer use eggs. At the General Conference session in San Francisco in 1960 among those surveyed only 6-7 percent did not use eggs. The Nutrition Council of the General Conference recommends that we learn to cook without eggs, especially the egg yolks. Eggs are the single greatest source of cholesterol in the American diet. The Inter-Society Commission for Heart Disease Resources recommended in 1970 for all to avoid egg yolks. You may wish to try scrambled tofu for breakfast in place of scrambled eggs."

Card #2. "If meat is discarded, if the taste is not educated in that direction, if a liking for fruits and grains is encouraged, it will soon be as God in the beginning designed it should be. No meat will be used by His people" (*Counsels on Diet and Foods*, p. 82).

"Again and again I have been shown that God is bringing His people back to His original design, that is, not to subsist on the flesh of dead animals" (*Ibid.*, 82).

And on the other side of the card was this: "Do you like these vegetarian meals? The latest survey of Adventists in Canada and the United States found that 41 percent are vegetarians. There are another 22 percent who eat meat less than once a month. This helps to explain why Adventist men have only 45 percent of the expected heart attack death rate. Adventists have only 50 percent of the expected cancer death rate. Adventist men (at age 40) who are vegetarians live 3.7 years longer than those who are not vegetarians". Or you could print a health message from your conference president.

Nutrition and Health Correspondence Courses

Home Study International offers three college level, accredited courses in health and nutrition. For more information contact: Home Study International, P.O. Box 4437, Silver Spring, MD 20914-4437, or (800) 782-4769. These are:

• HLSC 140 **The Human Body in Health & Disease** (4 credit units) A survey of the structure, function, health, and disease of the human body. Emphasis is placed on the understanding of the physiologic mechanisms that maintain each body system. A general foundation in the vocabulary of anatomy and physiology is a primary part of the course. Normal body structure and function are used as the basis to present information on human health and disease principles. Student must submit certificates of completion for the *International or American Red Cross Standard First Aid and Safety and Cardiopulmonary Resuscitation* courses.

• HLTH 200 **Health Principles** (3 credit units) A study of physiology, including the principles governing community and personal health and the methods of applying these principles to successful daily living.

• NUTR 300 **Nutrition** (3 credit units) A course designed not only to provide an introduction to the relationship between nutrition and good health, but to explore the basic medical and chemical aspects of nutrition.

Non-academic Courses

The closest product available to a non-academic correspondence course is the Lifestyle Home Seminar materials sent out to the general public as a service of Lifestyle Magazine. *Nutrition* by David Nieman and *Keys to Wellness* by Jim Wood, (on the eight natural remedies) are excellent sources of good nutritional information people can study on their own. They don't return the lessons for grading. These Home Seminars are available from Lifestyle Magazine Home Seminars, Box 1000, Thousand Oaks, CA 91359-9965. Allow 4 weeks delivery.

Offer Your Services to Schools

Have you thought of conducting a health week for one of our schools? Dr. Scharffenberg had this experience: " We did it in quite a few of our boarding academies. We had a team approach. We taught the chemistry classes about cholesterol and linoleic acid. We took over the Bible classes and discussed such things as meat from the Spirit of Prophecy standpoints. We had the worship periods in the various dormitories. Then we also had a daily chapel period. We made good use of the home economics classes, too. Work with the food service director in having the foods served correlate with what you are teaching. Some of these programs were just like a week of prayer. At one school the students called for a special meeting on the Thursday of that week and voted to ask the administration to take candy bars out of the school store.

"You might provide school assembly programs for Adventist and public schools. We have often given nutrition lectures to all the school teachers in a public school district. We have also presented a series of lectures once a week in a foods or health and wellness class of a high school."

Children's Programs

The Health Connection has cassette tapes with children's songs teaching nutrition. There is even a Vacation Bible School program on food and nutrition written by Judi Rodgers called, *Jesus' Kids in the Kitchen.*

Prayer Meetings

Here is a challenge from Dr. Scharffenberg: Would you like to double your attendance at prayer meeting? It can be done. I know because I did it. If you are old enough to remember the program our Church promoted called Testimony Countdown, you'll recall how those attending would read a section in the *Testimonies* and then discuss at prayer meeting what they had read. I remember at the La Sierra church seeing 400 out for prayer meeting. Most of our churches have very few attending prayer meeting.

With the church members' interest in the Spirit of Prophecy and health, something like Testimony Countdown could be promoted. I assigned material to be read from the Spirit of Prophecy before the next prayer meeting and handed out scientific material on the same subject. Then we came together to discuss it. The interest was great. Try it. It works!

Adventist health promotion programs have been called an "entering wedge" which prepares the way for acceptance of spiritual truths. At the cutting edge of the entering wedge is nutrition ministry as attested by the widespread interest in the subject on the part of North Americans.

10

Health Promotion with Youth

Because of their energy, enthusiasm, opinions, and ideas, children and youth can minister effectively in the health and temperance arena. Older adults today are impressed by young people who are committed to moral values and youth respond to their peers much more readily than to adult health educators. This chapter outlines programs that involve young people in health promotion. The youth of the church can be challenged to work as Jesus did using the methods He so often used.

Health Ministries Programs for Youth
Youth Alive (formerly AY2Y)

Youth Alive is a positive, peer program which uses local clubs led by youth (with the support of adult advisors) to reach other youth and children with a message of drug-free living. The former AY2Y was adapted for church sponsorship and launched in 1988 in the NAD to halt the trend of Adventist teens becoming involved with alcohol and other drugs. The new Youth Alive program operates primarily at the high school level. Following are its key features:

1. Promotes positive alternatives. The program focuses on positive alternatives to handling problems so that the use of alcohol, tobacco, and other drugs is seen as unnecessary and undesirable. The program features personal support and encouragement of all participants. Positive interpersonal communication is taught.

2. Peer oriented. Youth are trained to take the initiative to teach and encourage other youth and children in choosing to live drug free.

3. Focuses on prevention. The objective is to help children and youth make a personal commitment to abstain from alcohol, tobacco, and other drugs, or to stop using them if they have begun experimental or casual use. There are five elements of the Youth Alive program: (1) a totally drug-free message; (2) a youth-helping-youth ori-

entation; (3) activities demonstrating that drug-free living is fun; (4) personal support through small "family" groups of 10-12 youth; 5) a philosophy of honor, dignity, and respect for self and others. A strong spiritual component is threaded throughout all five elements.

The greatest strength of Youth Alive is seen when the members get active in their local communities by forming local clubs. Clubs are led by youth who are experienced in peer prevention and who have made a commitment to living free of drugs. Regular group meetings are held for planning, socializing, personal growth and support. Many clubs organize special outreach projects such as a drama team or puppet ministry. Clubs also sponsor drug-free social activities.

Youth Alive conferences are three- to five-day events that recruit new people to the ministry, inviting them to make a commitment to live drug free. The conferences also help develop leadership skills among the participants. These conferences usually are held at a central location in the sponsoring union conference.

To order a manual for the local church club or the leadership training manual, call Advent*Source* at (800) 328-0525.

How to Start a Local Youth To Youth Club
Step 1: Develop a Core Team for Planning and Leadership

This is the first step because this is the core group of people who will lead out in forming the club. The core team also will lead the program after it becomes organized.

Some of the essential characteristics of a successful core team are:

1. Youth and Adult involvement. The core team must include both youth and adults who enjoy youth.

2. **Proper Training.** It is imperative that core members understand the Youth to Youth model of prevention. Therefore, at least some of these core members must be youth and adults who have attended a prevention conference or have some form of peer prevention training.
3. **Be Role Models.** Both youth and adults need to be drug-free role models with a commitment to the drug-free message.
4. **Availability.** Members must have enough time to devote to the work of getting the group started and leading it.

Step 2: Select an Advisor or Sponsor

This advisor should serve on the core team, needs to be a part of all planning, and should be present at all group functions. Perhaps your group will need more than one advisor. The youth should design the programs, make the decisions, and solve problems while the adults facilitate, coach, and support them in these activities. This differs from the model where adults design the program, make the decisions, then invite the youth to participate, or the model where adults design the program but invite the youth to assist in leading it.

Experience in clubs has shown that although students run them, the groups that succeed have one or more strong, committed adult advisors. Selection of an adult advisor for the group begins with looking at adults who have attended a Youth peer prevention conference. Preferably, that person has been trained as adult staff at a conference and therefore understands the adult role in the Youth model.

Qualities of an effective adult sponsor:
- Committed to a genuine spiritual walk with Christ
- Liked by youth and adults
- Organized—follows up details
- Gets involved in the fun in an enthusiastic, positive way
- Encourages all to participate in decision-making
- Shows appreciation for youth accomplishments
- Facilitates—does not dominate
- Compassionate—doesn't shame or humiliate youth
- Not too busy with other programs—has real time for the club
- Has attended or soon will attend a training conference
- Has read or will read the manual
- Confidently willing to give his/her best

Adults are needed specifically to help youth with financial matters, safety, ethical, or legal concerns, and organizational details. However, the adult sponsor should always involve youth in the reasoning behind decisions made in these areas. The number of adult sponsors needed depends on the size of the club and how much responsibility each sponsor can handle. The average club would do well with two or three, but should always have at least one adult sponsor. These adults are also essential members of the core team or advisory board.

A commitment to drug-free living (including alcohol and tobacco) and a desire to work with young people are essential qualifications. Possibilities for advisors include teachers, school support staff, youth pastors, parents, counselors, or community service people. In addition, the core team also will probably want to identify a group of supportive adults who will be willing to serve as chaperons for large group events. These volunteers need the core team's appreciation for their work. Give them "warm fuzzies" and recognition.

Step 3: Begin Action Planning

Now that you have a core team and adult advisor(s) you are ready to lay the foundation for your group. Three things must be done in Step Three: (1) determine purpose, (2) develop goals and (3) create policy. Action Planning is a major leadership task that can be fun as well as challenging. The core team will undertake the initial phases such as determining purpose and setting goals. Although the group leaders may need to do some of the detailed work of planning, involving as many members as possible in deciding on priorities and activities helps build ownership within the entire group.

Determining Purpose. What are the needs in our community? What problems exist? What programs and services already exist to meet these needs? How will we fit into them? Answering these questions allows the core team to define a clear sense of purpose. After the core team has reached basic agreement, a statement of purpose should be written.

Developing Goals. Now that the purpose is clear, what do we want to accomplish? Some specific goals or objectives help the group to know where it is headed. These may be long-term objectives , such as for the entire year, or only short-term for a particular project or activity. Goal statements should be reviewed periodically by the core team and revised as needed. This helps confirm a sense of accomplishment when goals have been reached, and keeps the club headed in a definite direction.

Creating Policy. Some basic policies for the club need to be established. The philosophy of "Honor, Dignity, and Respect" should be the foundation for club policy. Specific policies should be developed for the following:
- Ground rules for club meetings and activities. The ground rules used for Family Groups can be applied to the entire club meeting.
- Use of pledge cards as a commitment tool.

Step 4: Determine Funding Sources

Financial resources needed for various basic items helpful to club success:
- Club identification (buttons, t-shirts, banners)
- Outreach presentation supplies (ribbons, handouts)
- Resource books
- Conference and/or training attendance
- Transportation to events sponsored by the club
- Newsletter printing and mailing

What will be the source of operating funds? There are several possibilities: government funds for health and social programs; private sponsorship, including churches; and business sponsorship from your local community. Funds also can be raised by activities sponsored by the local club, such as bake sales, special dinners or programs for which admission is charged, and many others.

Step 5: Determine Meeting Times

Spend some time thinking through the options for meeting time, place, and frequency. Finding the "perfect time" when everyone will find it convenient to attend regularly is impossible. Student schedules are affected by a variety of activities (which change throughout the school year). Priority needs to be given to the availability of the group advisor. Then consider the availability of the majority of the students. Some students will be able to come to club-sponsored events, but will be unable to attend regular meetings. Consider times for the entire club to meet as well as times for the core group to meet. If the large group meetings are less frequent than weekly, the core team probably will need to meet more often. Many core teams plan to meet after the club meeting to plan for the next one.

Step 6: Establish the Structure of the Club

The structure of the club meeting will facilitate achieving the purpose and goals of the group. The Youth prevention program can be summed up in three words: FUN, FAMILY, FOCUS. These three components need to be balanced in accordance with the purpose and goals for the program.

FUN is what you're going to present as positive alternatives that will recruit others for drug free living. Your club can be called "the Smile Factory" because it provides opportunity to play together and enjoy being Christians without the dangers of alcohol, tobacco, or other drugs. Since so many people think they must drink to have a good social time, the Youth club demonstrates that alcohol is unnecessary. Also, because smiles and humor were God's creation, having fun together enhances one's ability to grow spiritually. Fun is provided in many ways: social time during club meetings to visit, relax, enjoy refreshments; cooperative group games; social events sponsored by the club separate from regular meetings. Social events without alcohol or other drugs provide safe, enjoyable activities for club members. They demonstrate that it is possible to enjoy life without depending on chemical crutches. Therefore they provide exciting recruitment possibilities as well as the social outlet which every club member needs. Club members can join together in planning for these social events, then appoint a special committee to take care of the details.

FAMILY puts the emphasis on self-care and personal growth. Family group time should be built into each club meeting. Family groups should be led by youth who have either had special training in small group leadership, or have experience as a member of a group led by an experienced youth leader. Each group should have a co-leader who is an older, experienced youth or adult. A decision as to how to organize the Family Groups must be made. One way is to have an extended Family Group which is started at the beginning of the year and continues for several months with the same membership. This works best when the club membership stays the same over a period of time. But it doesn't accommodate new members very well. Some clubs have family groups which meet on a one-time basis, say at a club meeting or club event (camp out, retreat, etc.); in that way the membership varies from week to week. These clubs use the same ground rules, however, so that members become more and more trusting with one another and participate well in the Family Groups.

FOCUS brings youth together for a common purpose—positive environmental change and service to others in our community. Time will be needed in club meetings to develop plans, prepare materials, or rehearse presentations for outreach and service projects. The key here is to *involve everyone* in some way. Your club should seek to develop every member's potential, not just feature a few "star leaders." Plan your "Focus Time" to include everyone who has attended. Remember, however, that to lead out or be a pre-

senter on behalf of the club, the young person should have made a commitment to staying sober and clean (free of alcohol, tobacco, or other drugs). There are many ways you can have a positive effect on your school, church, and community to promote living without alcohol, tobacco, and other drugs. Do some group brainstorming to tap into the wealth of ideas in the brains of your members.

A successful group will consider the following:

Will the meeting be mostly for fun? Or for planning and practicing skits for a school assembly program (focus)? Or will there be a blend of fun, family, and focus at this meeting?

Step 7: Present Your Plans to Others

When the club's purpose, goals, and basic organization have been decided, the time has come to present the program to parents, teachers, churches, and other potential sponsoring organizations. Be certain that the presenter is familiar with the background and philosophy of Adventist Youth clubs. He or she will need to be able to answer questions intelligently and persuasively. A presentation should include the sharing of the program's purpose, goals, and policy. A sample of a classroom presentation or school assembly program, or a video tape of projected club activities would be beneficial as well. We have found poster displays of group photos and newspaper articles to be helpful in explaining the program to others. Discuss the appropriateness of group activities, music, and relationship of your club to other prevention programs. If the club has developed a newsletter as a communication tool within the group (see the next step), it would be helpful to mail it to parents as well as to sponsoring organizations.

Step 8. Communicate, Communicate, Communicate!

A crucial step in building your group is to determine how you intend to communicate. A newsletter is one of the most valuable means of doing this. If you aren't able to start the program with a newsletter, at least use a monthly calendar of events which can be produced by one of the youth members of the core team. Often a local business or civic club will be willing to sponsor the cost of printing and mailing a newsletter, if they are given recognition for this service to your club.

The newsletter should be written by the youth. It is a combination of what has been done and what is coming soon. Besides news, include regular features which appeal to a broad audience.

Some of these might be:

- "Warm fuzzies" to affirm and appreciate members and sponsors.
- Personal growth items (poems, essays, meditations).
- Drug information, especially new problems and products being pushed in the local area.
- Prevention program resources.

Invitations to participate in fun events or upcoming training sessions can be communicated through the newsletter. Highlighting achievements of members in areas outside yours generates positive celebrations within the club and group bonding and cooperation. Sponsors always like to see their contributions recognized. The newsletter is an ideal method for saying "thank you" and providing good publicity.

Newsletters also are useful recruiting devices. Always print more newsletters than you think you'll need. Distribute extras to prospective members, potential sponsors, etc. Keep a few in the club "archives" for anniversary celebrations in the future.

Be sure that your group is recognized for their work in the local community. Establish a working relationship with your local paper(s) and radio/TV stations so that reporters and photographers are notified in advance of your activities. This will help greatly in making sure they will be on the scene to report on the drug-free youth (that's you!) who are making a difference. Wherever possible, have a camera ready to use to document the success of your well-planned and highly successful group.

Step 9. Check up on Yourselves from Time to Time

Reviewing accomplishments and evaluating club strength should be done at least once a year, or more often. The purpose and goals need to be read again to discuss what progress has been made. Are any changes needed? Has the club organization been working? Some other aspects to consider in this evaluation are:

- Are the goals reflected in the activities of the club?
- How comprehensive is the club program?
- Are Fun, Family, and Focus all included?
- How effective are the adult advisors?
- What training is needed by the youth leaders?

Training is a constant need. Each club has different training requirements. Some or all of the following training areas may apply to your group: drug information, peer pressure resistance, outreach skills, and leadership development. As a core team, decide on what the training needs are and then investigate what resources are available in your community.

For Complete Details on Local Club Operations:

Get the manual *How to Make It Happen!* Available from Institute for the Prevention of Addictions, Berrien Springs, MI 49104-0211; (616) 471-3557; Fax (616) 471-6611.

Collegiate Adventists for Better Living (CABL)

Although primarily a college-based program, CABL members also become involved in community outreach projects such as blood drives and health screenings, alcohol and other drugs awareness drives in community schools, organizing fitness events, environmental protection projects and drug- free social activities.

For more information contact DeWitt Williams who directs health ministries for the North American Division, (301) 680-6733.

Pathfinder Clubs

The Pathfinder Clubs offer a health and fitness track for Friends through Guide levels. The track covers three areas: health principles, first aid/safety, and you can buy from your local Adventist Book Center or Advent*Source*, (800) 328-0525.

Young Pioneers

Young Pioneers is a component of the Adventist Youth Service Network or Youthnet. Young Pioneers is "youth working in teams to pioneer ministries in unentered areas and strengthen ministries in diminishing areas." The goal of the program is to have one Pioneers team (made up of two college-age youth working for 12 months mentoring two high school-age youth working for 2 months) in each of the conferences in North America. These young people can help with health screenings, drug intervention and stop-smoking programs, and other health ministries-related programs. For more information, contact Youthnet, (800) 331-2767.

Oratorical Contests

Oratorical contests are enjoying a comeback thanks largely to the efforts of NAD regional conferences and the Black Adventist Youth Directors Association. For example, Central States Conference Youth Director, sponsors annual contests which begin at the local level with children as young as three years old.

Resources Within the Seventh-day Adventist Church

Kids in the Kitchen VBS materials.

This program is for children ages 4-12. Instead of the usual VBS crafts, all crafts are edible because they are made in the kitchen. Other aspects of healthful living are included in the program. The program can be used in non-VBS settings too. There is a separate cookbook that can be used alone. Follow-up activities are suggested at the end of the program for adult evangelism opportunities such as fellowship dinners or vegetarian cooking classes. To order the cookbook, call The Health Connection (800) 548-8700.

Studies

Research studies which have been conducted by health professionals within the Adventist

Church often give insight into the needs of the youth in your church. Two are included at the end of this chapter.

The Daniel Diet

Beatrice Neall, former professor of Religion at Union College in Lincoln Nebraska, introduced a special health feature in her Daniel Class—The Daniel Diet. She urged her students to use The Daniel Diet at test time in order to perform well. Although not a scientific experiment, the 10-day health program outlined in Daniel 1 shows the students the disciplined life Daniel must have lived. Students who followed the Daniel Diet reported scoring higher than they normally would. Here is what is included:

- Eat no rich fatty foods or refined sugar.
- Eat a healthy breakfast.
- Consume only vegetables, fruits, whole grains, and nuts.
- Drink 6 to 8 glasses of water each day.
- Get 1/2 hour of outdoor exercise each day.
- Get at least seven hours of sleep each night.

The Daniel Diet also is a component of the Pathfinder Health and Temperance track.

Residential Homes for Troubled Teens
- Advent Home for boys
- Hilltop Home for girls
- Miracle Meadows
- Project Patch

Non-church Organizations and Resources for Youth Health Issues

AIDS National Information Clearinghouse, (800) 458-5231; M-F, 9 a.m.-7 p.m. EST. This Centers for Disease Control and Prevention line offers free publications as well as multiple copies for a fee, does literature searches, gives information about AIDS, drug clinical trials and offers treatment referrals. The Clearinghouse also publishes catalogs of materials for school-age children.

AIDS Hotline, (800) 342-2437; 24 hours, 7 days. Another CDCP service this hotline provides

AIDS-related information and education and answers questions about the disease, testing facilities and treatment. This is a crisis center and does answer personal concerns, although it does not provide counseling. Also check your local telephone directory or information for your state AIDS hotline.

SIDA (Spanish line) M-F, 8 a.m. to 2 a.m. EST, (800) 344-7432.

TDD (Hearing impaired) (800) 243-7889.

Al-Anon/Alateen: Al-Anon is a group meeting system for family members of alcoholics who are age 18 and over. Alateen is for family members of alcoholics, ages 12-18. National/ Worldwide meeting times M-F, 8 a.m. - 6 p.m. EST; (800) 344-2666. This line gives information about family groups. Al-Anon Family Group Head Quarters, Inc., World Service Office, M-F, 8 a.m. - 6 p.m. EST; (800) 356-9996 or (757) 563-1600; Fax (757) 563-1655. This office provides Al-Anon and Alateen materials and publications to the public.

Alcohol Treatment Referral Hotline, 24 hours, 7 days, (800) ALCOHOL or (800) 252-6465. This hotline provides referrals to local self-help groups and professional treatment centers for adolescents as well as adults. It also gives information on financial assistance.

Center for Science in the Public Interest, 1875 Connecticut Avenue, NW, Suite 300, Washington, DC 20009; (202) 332-9110. Conducts research and advocacy on alcohol marketing and policy as well as nutrition issues. This organization publishes the *Nutrition Action Health Letter* and *Kids Against Junk Food,* a videotape and teaching curriculum with text.

American Dietetics Association Consumer Information Hotline, (800) 366-1655; M-F, 9 a.m. to 4 p.m. CST; recorded nutrition information M-F 8 a.m.-8 p.m. CST. The ADA answers general questions and refers people to dietitians in their area for more specific advice. Some of their information about vegetarianism is sponsored by

Residential Care for Troubled Teens

Advent Home Youth Services. 900 County Road 950, Calhoun, TN 37309; (423) 336-5052; Fax (423) 339-5986. Staff: Blondel and Gloria Senior, Directors. Services: Residential care, schooling and counseling to 12-16 year old boys, grades 6-10. Started in 1985.

Child Guidance Home. P.O. Box 746, Bourbon, MO 65441; (573) 245-6271. Licensed residential group home. Ages 6-12 boys, grades 1-8. Staff: Al & Judy Jones. Services: Residential care, counseling, church school, work and recreational therapy. Started in 1989.

Hill Top Girls Home. P.O. Box 2153, Collegedale, TN 37315; (423) 236-5022; Ellen Crosby, Executive Director's home (423) 238-5472. Services: Girls 12-20.

Miracle Meadows School. Rt. 1, Box 289-B, Salem, WV 26426. Group Home (304) 782-3628; Fax (304) 782-3660. Staff: Bill and Gayle Clark, Directors (304) 659-3976. Services: Unlicensed residential care, schooling and counseling to 12-18 year old boys and girls, grades 1-12.

Project PATCH. 13455 SE 97th Avenue, Clackamas, OR 97015; (509) 653-8086; Fax (503) 653-8265. Staff: Tom Sanford, Director; Lynette Anderson, Director of Admissions. Services: Group home and counseling (at the Project PATCH Ranch in Garden Valley, ID) for 12-18 year old boys and girls.

Worthington Foods, and SDA health studies are cited.

Children of Alcoholics Foundation, (800) 359-2623; (212) 754-2623 in New York, M-F 9 a.m.-5 p.m. EST., COAF publishes a book of resources with products for children as well as adults. Three important resources: The Images Within, a three-session alcohol prevention program for ages 10-13 with posters, handouts and leaders guide; Kids Talking to Kids, a video with discussion guide for ages 9-13; The Feel Better Book with activity worksheets for grades 1-6; If You Think Your Parents Drink Too Much, a booklet for teens. This organization also offers referrals to meetings in the New York area.

Families Anonymous, (800) 736-9805, M-F, 10 a.m.-4 p.m. PST. This is a 12-step program for relatives and friends of drug abusers over the age of 13. The operator offers referrals to group meetings in your area as well as information packets for people who want to know more about the program before going.

Hazelden Publishing and Education, (800) 328-9000; M-F, 7 a.m.-10 p.m. CST. Hazelden publishes a variety of materials on addiction and other health related issues such as eating disorders, sexual abuse, HIV/AIDS, codependency, gambling, emotions. A K-12 Education catalog for individuals or for curriculum use is available as well as a general catalog.

Healthy Kids Resource Center, Alameda County Office of Education, 313 West Winton Avenue, Room 180, Hayward, CA 94544; (510) 670-4581; Fax (510) 670-4582. The Center assists schools in their effort to promote health literacy. Materials from the Center may be borrowed at no cost (except for return UPS charge) and include: videotapes, laser discs, curriculum guides, models and other visuals on such subjects as HIV/AIDS; family living; mental and emotional health; nutrition; physical fitness; ATOD; injury prevention and safety.

Just Say No International, (800) 258-2766; M-F, 8 a.m.-5 p.m. MST. Just Say No is a community based drug education club. Information, membership and publications are available for a fee. Also runs the Youth Power Program.

National Association for Children of Alcoholics (NACOA), (301) 468-0985; M-F 8:30 a.m.-5 p.m. EST. NACOA provides legislative advocacy, prevention, education and training for elementary schools. There is a membership fee. NACOA is also putting together a kit for kids, therapists, parents and teachers outside the school setting.

Minirth-Meier New Life Clinic, (800) 229-3000; M-F 8 a.m-5 p.m. CST. This is the number of the radio program for those wanting to speak on the air. You leave your number and they return your call. The Minirth-Meier New Life Clinics are located throughout the country. This organization is one of the largest mental health care providers in the U.S., a Christian organization dedicated to using Biblically based medically sound principles for problems ranging from addictions to eating disorders to marriage and family problems.

Minirth-Meier Crisis Line. (800) NEW LIFE; [(800) 639-5433]. Offers crisis counseling M-F, 9 a.m.-5 p.m. EST.

Minirth-Meier New Life Resources, (800) 266-5745; 24 hours, 7 days a week. This resource center offers tapes, books, videos and radio broadcasts covering the mental health field. One of their most popular resources is Drugproof Your Kids by Steve Arterburn (the ministry's founder). It comes in book, cassette and videotape form with leader's guide. A free resource catalog is also available.

National Clearinghouse for Alcohol and Drug Information (NCADI), P.O. Box 2345 Rockville, MD 20847-2345, (800) 729-6686. NCADI is a one-stop resource for federal alcohol, tobacco and other drug abuse (ATOD) prevention and awareness efforts. Resources for the Departments of Labor and Education, The National Institutes of Drug Abuse, Alcohol Abuse and Alcoholism, and the Center for Substance Abuse Treatment are all represented in a free catalog published by NCADI. Posters, bumper stickers, pamphlets, reports, video and audio cassettes, and curriculum materials are available—many of them for free. NCADI also offers a Prevention Materials database of over 8000 products from across the country. The offices at 11426-28 Rockville Pike in Rockville, Maryland, house a research library as well as Clearinghouse products. Both are open to the public from 9 a.m.-5 p.m. daily. Access to NCADI resources are also available on PREVline, an electronic communication system dedicated to exchanging ideas and information about ATOD. PREVline e-mail address: info@prevlin.health.org

(Access is available from almost anywhere in the world, 24 hours a day.)

Parents' Resource Institute for Drug Education (PRIDE), 100 Edgewood Avenue, Suite 1002, Atlanta, GA 30303; (404) 577-4500; M-F, 8:30 a.m.-5 p.m. EST. PRIDE offers drug prevention information and referral services both free and for a fee, publishes a catalog and a quarterly newsletter. They have also sponsored large annual youth conferences that have attracted guests such as former first lady Nancy Reagan.

The President's Council on Physical Fitness and Sports, 701 Pennsylvania Avenue, Suite 250, Washington, DC 20004; (202) 272-3431; Fax (202) 504-2064. Helping motivate children to become and stay physically active is one of the Council's highest priorities.

The Presidential Sports Award encourages individuals ages 6 and over to make a commitment to regular sports participation. With 68 sports and fitness categories available, it enables a person to make a personal commitment to fitness and earn a prestigious emblem and certificate.

The President's Challenge Physical Fitness Awards Program, the Council's largest program, is a fitness assessment for school-aged children that is administered by teachers and others who work with children (this is the program used in Pathfinders). The goal of the President's Challenge is to have all students be winners in fitness.

The Council also publishes *Get Fit*, a handbook for children ages 6-17, designed to help kids prepare for the President's Challenge; *10 Tips to Healthy Eating and Physical Activity for You*, a brochure for kids ages 9-15; *Kids in Action* a booklet for parents, teachers, and care-givers of preschool children which illustrates simple, fun physical activities for young children; and *Physical Activity and Fitness Research Digest*, which is specific to children and adolescents.

Vegetarian Awareness Network (VEGANET), P.O. Box 321, Knoxville, TN 37901; (800) USA-VEGE [234-8343], (800) EAT-VEGE [328-8343], Canada. This organization founded in 1980, is the originator and sponsor of Vegetarian Awareness Month, a nationwide event celebrated in October.

VEGANET offers free recipes, information, and a VEGE-KIT for local groups. They seem to have an unlimited source of materials for children about many different aspects of vegetarianism.

Vegetarian Education Network (VEN) P.O. Box 339, Oxford, PA, 19363-0339; (717) 529-8638; Fax (717) 529-3000; E-mail: HowOnEarth@aol.com. VEN publishes *How On Earth!* (HOE!), a quarterly magazine for and by youth who support compassionate, ecologically sound living. HOE promotes a vegan diet and publishes vegetarian recipes, nutrition advice from a registered dietitian and lifestyle information. The magazine is published by an almost all-volunteer force of teenagers and young adults. Those aged 13-24 are invited to submit articles, art work, poetry, personal essays, vegetarian recipes, photography, and advice "covering everything from current issues, to activism and boycotts, to dealing with parents and peers who just don't understand." VEN also publishes and distributes other resources for vegetarians, such as materials for promoting the vegetarian perspective in schools through educational materials and menu planners for school lunches. Call or write for a resource list.

The Vegetarian Resource Group (VRG), P.O. Box 1463, Baltimore, MD 21203; (410) 366-VEGE [8343]. The VRG is a nonprofit organization which educates the public about vegetarianism and the interrelated issues of health, nutrition, ecology, ethics and world hunger. They publish the bi-monthly Vegetarian Journal, which often prints articles about vegetarianism for children and teens. VRG also conducts polls such as the one published in their November/December 1995 issue on the eating habits of youth. They offer a student membership to the magazine for half-price. They publish other good resources for children and teens: Leprechaun Cake and Other Tales: A Vegetarian Story-Cookbook features over 40 healthy recipes; I Love Animals and Broccoli, and I Love Animals and Broccoli Shopping Basket, children's activity books; and The Soup to Nuts Natural Foods Coloring Book. In addition, each spring they conduct an essay contest for youth ages 8 through 18.

Vegetarian Times Magazine and The Vegetarian Times Bookshelf, P.O. Box 446, Mt. Morris, IL 60154; (800) 435-9610; e-mail: 74651.215@compuserve.com. The magazine prints articles about nutrition and cooking for children and teens as well as other vegetarian lifestyle issues. The Bookshelf offers books for children and teens, such as *Kids Can Cook; Cows are Vegetarians! A Book for Vegetarian Kids; A Teen's Guide to Going Vegetarian; Victor, The Vegetarian; and Foods From Mother Earth: A Basic Cookbook for Young Vegetarians (and Anybody Else)*.

The Need for Health Promotion with Youth

The following briefing paper prepared for the North American Division by the Institute for the Prevention of Addictions (IPA), as well as the article based on a research study that Loma Linda University did on AIDS among Adventist youth, indicates the need for health promotion. and Foods From Mother Earth: A Basic Cookbook for Young Vegetarians (and Anybody Else).

Briefing Paper on Substance Use Among Seventh-day Adventist Youth

*T*his concise summary of current knowledge and opinion relating to alcohol, tobacco, and other drug usage in North America by Seventh-day Adventist youth is designed to show the need for this issue to be a priority concern among church leadership at all levels. This briefing updates the one prepared in 1987 with additional data obtained following the Institute's national study of Adventist youth1. It draws from individual school studies and the 1988 Valuegenesis reports2 .

Youth in local churches

A national survey of the use of alcohol and other drugs by North American SDA youth ages 12-24 years was conducted in the summer of 1985, while these youth were in local churches 3. Some important findings were that 12 percent reported currently drinking alcohol and 8 percent were currently smoking tobacco. Use was highest among the older ages; 17 percent of college age youth reported present use. Baptism did not reduce involvement. However, attending an SDA school was protective; significantly less use occurred among SDA academy students than among SDA youth attending public high schools4.

Compared to national statistics on alcohol and other drug use by non-Adventists, these usage figures were encouraging. In 1985, drinking was reported by 67 percent of public high school non-SDA students compared to 15 percent by the same age SDA youth; 80 percent of all non-SDA college students reported drinking compared to 17 percent of the 18-24 year old SDA young adults5. But compared to Adventist values and expectations of abstinence, any use is distressing.

Adventist youth in SDA schools

The 1985-86 national prevalence study was further validated by a study on the 1986 SDA academy senior classes (9 academies) in one NAD union6. Drinking within the past 30 days was reported by 14 percent of the seniors. In this study, most of the drinking and drug use reported was casual experimentation. However, 7.7 percent of those reporting alcohol use had been drunk (5 or more drinks in a row) within the past two weeks. When SDA students do drink, their behavior does not differ much from non-SDA high school students. During 1988, a major study of students in SDA schools was undertaken by NAD Education known as the Valuegenesis Study. Questions included at-risk behaviors in the past year such as alcohol use (6 or more times) and marijuana use (once or more)7. Since these data were collected

Table 1

Alcohol and Marijuana Use Among SDA Youth

	Age Group	Alcohol Use	Marijuana Use
Junior High Students			
IPA Survey	12-13 year olds	4%	1%
Valuegenesis	7th, 8th graders	3%, 5%	4%, 6%
U.S. youth	similar age	8%, 16%	3%, 7%
High School Seniors			
Union-wide Survey	12th graders	13.5%	11.6%
Valuegenesis	12th graders	15%	11%
U.S. youth	similar age	54%	20%

Briefing Paper on Substance Use Among Seventh-day Adventist Youth

three years later, is there any evidence of shifts in incidence of use by SDA youth? Table 1 shows that there may be a trend towards increasing use of marijuana. Other evidence for increasing problems comes with comparisons between the 1985 IPA study findings on 18-24 year olds drinking and more recent studies. In 1985, 17 percent of youth enrolled in SDA colleges reported currently drinking. Four consecutive campus-wide studies of SDA collegiate youth on two separate campuses during 1989-1992 showed that 24-26 percent of students were drinking[8].

Table 2

First Use of Drugs by Non-Abstainers

	Academy X (1990)	Academy Y (1991)	Academy Seniors (1986)
Alcohol			
Use by grade 6	12.5%	9.9%	16.1%
Use by grade 8	48.4%	11.10%	11.6%
Tobacco			
Use by grade 6	34.1%	8.4%	16.7%
Use by grade 8	36.4%	6%	12.8%
Marijuana			
Use by grade 6	15.4%	.4%	2.7%
Use by grade 8	46.2%	2.5%	6.2%

When do students begin to drink or smoke?

Use begins earlier than most people believe as shown in Table 2. In the 1985-86 IPA study, 8 percent reported first using alcohol before age 10 (about 5th grade). By age 14 or 8th grade, 23 percent had tried alcohol and 22 percent had tried tobacco. The 1986 survey of SDA academy seniors showed that 27 percent had used alcohol by grade 8 or below. Two recent (1990, 1991) surveys of individual SDA academies emphasized that early use is a major problem9, Since the question related to *first use*, the responses for grade 6 and grade 8 must be summed. Therefore, while almost 28 percent of the seniors in the 1986 study had used alcohol before academy, at Academy "X" in 1990, more than 60 percent of the students reported starting to drink before they arrived at the academy. Prevention programs must be targeted to SDA elementary school children, preferably before the 6th grade, if later problems are to be avoided.

Why these problems?

Denial. As an abstinent faith community, lifetime Adventists know very little about the problems of chemical dependency. Parents, teachers, and pastors often do not recognize signs of trouble due to drugs when they are present, easily confusing them with adolescent behavior problems. In addition, the desire for a church, school, or home to "look good" is strong among Adventists who believe they should be a church "without spot or wrinkle." Denial creates many problems: ignorance, blurred perceptions, and comfort with focusing on evangelistic outreach rather than internal nurture of abstinence. Few SDA schools subscribe to SDA temperance magazines; in 1985, only 10 percent of the youth reported ever reading *Listen* or *The Winner* magazines, although the local church may sponsor several clubs of subscriptions for the local high school.

Silence. Believing that because we have an abstinence doctrine that alcohol and drug problems are infrequent among SDA youth, the church has been silent in recent years, just as the drug epidemic has hit North America. Data on adult Adventists suggest that only after more than 20 years membership were significant numbers (90 percent) practicing abstinence from alcohol10.

Prevention programs are extremely scarce in SDA elementary schools; only the availability of the Adventist Youth to Youth program has provided a partial remedy for SDA academies. Into this vacuum comes the increasingly high-profile, sophisticated advertising messages of the alcohol and tobacco industries, touting the pleasure, power, success, friendship, and romance to be obtained from using legal drugs, and implying they are harmless substances. Adventist youth are not invulnerable to these media messages.

Conclusions

Abstinence is more than a cultural attitude within the Adventist church. It has been the cornerstone of the Adventist health advantage. Few other lifestyle practices are as destructive of soul, body, and interpersonal relationships as chemical use and abuse. Significant and immediate attention to planting prevention programs in children's ministries and early school years is needed; maintenance and expansion of attractive alternatives such as Adventist Youth to Youth offers will be required to safeguard youth through the troubled waters of adolescence. And at all levels, the silence about the subject should be broken so denial can be eliminated.

References
1. Mutch, P.B., Dudley, R.L., Cruise, R.J. *A Study of Drug Usage Among Seventh-day Adventist Youth in North America.* Technical Report 86-3. Institute for the Prevention of Addictions, Andrews University. 1986.
2. Dudley, R.L., Mutch, P.B., and Cruise, R.J. "Religious factors and drug usage among Seventh-day Adventist youth in North America." *J. Scientific Study Religion* 26:218-233. 1987.
3. Johnston, L.D., O'Malley, P.M., Bachman, J.G. *Drug Use Among American High School Students, College Students, and Other Young Adults: National Trends Through 1985.* Univ. Michigan Institute for Social Research. Nat. Institute on Drug Abuse, 5600 Fishers Lane, Rockville, MD. 1986.
4. Guthrie, S., and Mutch, P.B. "Prevalence of alcohol use among Adventist academy seniors in a North American Union Conference." *Technical Report* 87-1. Institute for the Prevention of Addictions, Andrews University. 1987.
5. Benson, P.L., and Donahue, M. J. *Valuegenesis: Report 1: A Study of the Influence of Family, Church, and School on the Faith, Values and Commitment of Adventist Youth.* Minneapolis, MN: Search Institute. 1990.
6. Unpublished data, Institute for the Prevention of Addictions. 1991, 1992.
7. Mutch, P.B. "Substance use among academy students." Institute for the Prevention of Addictions, Andrews University. Unpublished data. 1990, 1991.
8. McBride, D.C., Mutch, P.B., Dudley, R.L., and Julian, A.G. "Substance use and correlates among adult Seventh-day Adventists in North America." *Technical Report* 89-2. Institute of Alcoholism and Drug Dependency, Andrews University, Berrien Springs, MI 49104. 1989.
9. *Ibid.*
10. Unpublished data, Institute for the Prevention of Addictions, Andrews University, Berrien Springs, MI. 1991, 1992.

This article is used with permission, Ministry Magazine, *July, 1996.*

AIDS and Adventist youth

Gary L. Hopkins,
Joyce W. Hopp,
Helen P. Hopp,
Christine Neish, and
Gayle Rhoads

An AIDS risk appraisal of students attending SDA high schools in the United States and Canada

Gary L. Hopkins, M.D., Dr.P.H., is coordinator of the evaluation research unit, School of Public Health, Loma Linda University, Loma Linda California; Joyce W. Hopp, Ph.D., M.P.H., R.N., is the dean of the School of Allied Health, Loma Linda University; Helen P. Hopp, Ph.D., is associate professor in the School of Public Health, Loma Linda University; Christine Neish, Ph.D.,M.P.H., R.N., is chair of the Department of Health Promotion and Education, School of Public Health, Loma Linda University; Gayle Rhoads, Ed.D., is the principal of Loma Linda Academy, Loma Linda, California.

The acquired immunodeficiency syndrome (AIDS) has become a major global threat. Worldwide, millions of persons have been diagnosed with and died of this dreaded disease. In the United States as of October 1995, a little over half million persons with AIDS were reported to the Centers for Disease Control and Prevention (CDC).

Clinically, overt AIDS represents only the end-stage manifestation of a prolonged infection with the human immunodeficiency virus (HIV). The CDC reported that 20 percent of the diagnosed cases of AIDS were in the age group of 20-29 years.[1] Since the period from the time of HIV infection to the development of AIDS is generally between eight and 10 years,[2] there is a high likelihood that adolescents are becoming *infected* with the HIV and are *diagnosed* with AIDS when they are no longer adolescents.[3]

Currently there is no known cure for AIDS, nor is there a vaccination to prevent HIV infection,4 although considerable research money has been directed toward this effort. Methods of preventing HIV transmission include abstinence from HIV risk behaviors such as IV drug use and avoidance of HIV-infected body fluids (semen, breast milk, blood, and vaginal fluid).

Seventh-day Adventist leaders recommend the maintenance of a monogamous sexual relationship between non-HIV-infected individuals in a marriage relationship as the most effective method for preventing HIV transmission. Until a cure is available, health education targeted at reducing AIDS risk behaviors will be a main method of preventing HIV transmission.

Christian schools typically advocate health standards that include (1) abstinence from dangerous substances, including tobacco, alcohol, and drugs, and (2) abstinence from sexual intercourse until marriage, along with other biblically based principles.

The Seventh-day Adventist Church sponsors 93 four-year high schools (academies) in North America. Four surveys of students in these high schools revealed that some adolescents practice sexual and drug behaviors that place them at risk for contracting or transmitting the HIV.[5] Because of the practice of such HIV risk behaviors, research is needed in the SDA high school population in order to determine the possible points of educational and behavioral intervention to address the potential problem of HIV/AIDS.

Current research
In 1995 the authors conducted research to describe the HIV/AIDS risk factors of a sample of students attending SDA high schools throughout the U.S. and Canada. This research was to assess students' AIDS-related attitudes, normative beliefs (perceptions of social pressure), and their perceived control regarding AIDS risk behaviors.

Questionnaire development
We constructed a questionnaire based on an extensive review of the professional health literature on AIDS and AIDS risk behavior specific to

the adolescent period of development. The purpose of this questionnaire was to measure accurately and identify determinants of behaviors that could place adolescents at risk for transmitting or contracting the HIV. The questionnaire was divided into four sections: (1) demographic characteristics of the respondents, (2) HIV/AIDS-related knowledge, (3) HIV/AIDS-related behaviors, and (4) intentions, attitudes, social pressures, and perceptions of control related to the HIV/AIDS risk behaviors of sexual intercourse and substance use.

Sample selection

Permission for the research was granted by Dr. Gil Plubell, director of the North American Division, Office of Education. The office of education also provided partial funding.

Application was then made to the Institutional Review Board (IRB) of Loma Linda University (LLU), under whose authority this research was conducted, for a review and acceptance of the research protocol. The functions of the IRB, as required by federal law, are to protect the subjects of research from emotional and/or physical harm and to assure that ethical research guidelines are followed. The IRB accepted the protocol proposal, but required that before students could answer the questionnaire it was necessary to obtain written consent from their parent(s).

Each of the 93 schools was mailed a box containing parental consent letters equal to its student enrollment. The schools applied mailing labels with the names and addresses of the parents of their high school students. The schools then mailed the letters. A total of 13,368. Parents who chose to allow their children to participate in this research signed and mailed a consent postcard to LLU. A total of 2,834 students were thus enrolled in the study. The students represented 85 of the 93 four-year high schools in the NAD.

Questionnaires were mailed to each of the participating schools with a list of the names of the students whose parents had granted consent. Each questionnaire was placed in a manila envelope with a letter to the student advising them as to the sensitive content of the questionnaire and guaranteeing that there would be no attempt to identify students by name.

Results

Response rate. A total of 1,765 completed questionnaires were returned, yielding a response rate of 62.46 percent of the 2,826 parental consents. Sixteen of the 85 schools did not administer a total of 1,061 questionnaires.

Demographics. The majority of the respondents attended boarding schools as compared to day schools (53.7 percent versus 46.3 percent). The median age of the respondents was 17, with an age distribution of between 12 and 19; 56.4 percent of the respondents were female; and 93.3 percent were SDA. The distribution of respondents by year in high school was fairly equal (24.1 percent freshmen, 24.0 percent sophomores, 27.9 percent juniors, and 24.0 percent seniors) with the modal year of enrollment reported as eleventh grade. A comparison of the ethnicity of the respondents with the total student population attending four-year high schools throughout the NAD revealed that in study sample White students were over represented (79.3 percent versus 58.0 percent) and all minorities were under represented.

Knowledge. Accurate knowledge regarding modes of HIV transmission was high. The average score was 90.92 percent.

Substance use. Regarding the use of substances, non-SDA students who attended SDA high schools were more experienced with the use of all substances. The differences in the rates of use of all of the substances were statistically significant.

Parents' use of substances. In order to determine whether or not an association existed between the students' reports of parental substance use and the students' rates of substance use, three questions were designed to measure this relationship. The students were asked if either of their parents or guardians smoked cigarettes, drank alcohol, or used marijuana. When at least one of the parents used either tobacco, alcohol, or marijuana, the rates of the students' use of all of the substances increased.

Sexual intercourse. Of the total sample, 16.3 percent reported having had sexual intercourse. Female students reported a lower rate of sexual intercourse (14.6 percent, N=144) when compared to males (16.2 percent, N-284). The median age at first sexual intercourse was 15 for both sexes. The mean age at first intercourse was 14.5 for males and 15 for females.

Parental and students' substance use behaviors and students' sexual experience. Substance use by parents and by students appeared to have a relationship with the students' past sexual experience. Students who used substances were shown to be the most sexually experienced (Table 1).

When students reported that they had a parent who also used a substance, the rate of sexual intercourse increased. The lowest rates of sexual experience were among students who had not previously used substances and whose parents, as reported by the students, also did not use substances.

Homosexual experience. Seventy-nine (4.6 percent, N=79) students reported sexual experience with someone of the same sex. The proportion of students with a history of a homosexual experience was higher in males than in females (5.0 percent, N-41 versus 4.2 percent, N-38).

Intentions to have sexual intercourse before marriage. The respondents were asked. "How likely is it that you will have sexual intercourse before marriage?" This question was followed by a seven-point *unlikely/likely* scale. The students who demonstrated a greater intention to have sexual intercourse before marriage were those who (1) were already sexually experienced, (2) were experienced with substances (i.e., drugs), (3) had a parent who used either tobacco, alcohol, or marijuana, and (4) were non-SDA.

Attitudes, social pressure, and perception of control toward sexual intercourse before marriage. Three separate questions were designed to measure the students' attitudes, perceptions of social pressure, and control regarding sexual intercourse before marriage. Each question was followed by a seven-point scale. The students who (1) were already sexually experienced, (2) were experienced with substances, (3) had a parent who used

either tobacco, alcohol, or marijuana, or (4) were non-SDA demonstrated attitudes and perceptions of social pressure more favorable toward engaging in sexual intercourse before marriage. These same four groups demonstrated a lower perception of control over sex before marriage.

Determinants of the behavior to have sexual intercourse before marriage. Using appropriate statistical tests, measurements were made to determine whether the students' attitudes, perception of social pressures, or perception of control best predicted their intentions to have sex before marriage. It was found that perceived control was the strongest predictor. Students who (1) were sexually experienced, (2) were experienced with substances, (3) had a parent who used either tobacco, alcohol, or marijuana, or (4) were non-SDA demonstrated a lower perception of control over sexual intercourse before marriage than those were otherwise.

Determinants of perceived control. The items that best predicted the students' perception of control over sexual intercourse before marriage were *encouragement from teachers and spiritual strength.*

Discussion

Substance use. Many students attending SDA four-year high schools across the North American Division practice substance-use behaviors that place them at risk for serious health problems, including transmitting or contracting the HIV. Although rates of substance use in SDA schools are typically lower than those in public schools, students who do use substances (including alcohol, tobacco, cocaine, and other drugs) are more likely to practice AIDS risk behaviors.[6]

Because of the association of substance use with AIDS risk behaviors, it is imperative that schools consider the future role of substance abuse counseling for adolescents.[7]

Parents have the most important role in influencing the lives of their children, and hence there is a need to counsel parents regarding their own use of substances. The present research demonstrated that parental use of tobacco, alcohol, or marijuana was significantly associated with their children's (1) use of drugs and (2) rate of sexual intercourse. This research demonstrates that parental use of substances may be a factor in the AIDS risk behaviors of their children. When students reported that their parents did not use tobacco, alcohol, or marijuana, and when the students themselves did not use any substances, the rate of sexual intercourse was only 3.5 percent.

One must remember, however, that the parental substance use was reported by the students and not by the parents themselves.

Sexual intercourse

Sexual intercourse, the key AIDS risk behavior, as reported in this research, was found to be moderately prevalent. The rate of intercourse for this sample was 16.4 percent for all students. SDA students were less likely to have been sexually active than non-SDA students (14.6 percent versus 37.1 percent). Though the prevalence of sexual intercourse in this sample of students attending SDA schools is lower than the rate of 53 percent in public schools, the students who begin their sexual experience as adolescents are more likely to have multiple sexual contacts, thereby increasing their likelihood of eventual contact with an individual who is HIV-infected.

SDA educational system

The SDA Church places a strong emphasis on Christian education. The North American Division has 1,050 schools, ranging from kindergarten through high school. Enrollment in the schools totaled 50,988 in the fall of the 1994-1995 school year. SDA schools are typically staffed by teachers who are members of the SDA Church.

The SDA Church holds a strong belief in the value of abstinence from premarital sex and from harmful substances including tobacco, alcohol, and addictive drugs. This research demonstrates that the strongest predictors of perceived control relating to sexual intercourse before marriage for those students who responded was *spiritual strength* and *encouragement from teachers.*

These findings reaffirm the belief that those who are chosen to teach in the SDA system should be committed to demonstrating Christian values not only in the classroom but also in all interactions with students. Those who work in the SDA school system need to have a sense of accountability regarding the seriousness of their roles in the schools. Administrators and school board members who are responsible for selecting teachers should carefully search for teachers who will make themselves available both in the classroom and outside the classroom to students for encouragement and counseling regarding issues such as substance use and pre-marital sexual intercourse.

Non-SDA students attending SDA schools

Until the last few years, North American Division policy has limited the number of non-SDA students admitted to the denomination's elementary and secondary schools. Schools serving grades K-6 were allowed 15 percent non-SDA students. Grades 7-12 were restricted to no more than 10 percent non-SDA. Those schools that admitted greater proportions of non-SDA students were designated "mission schools." In recent years local school boards have become increasingly ready to accept more non-SDA students. The driving force behind this philosophical shift seems to be that of financial necessity, although some explain the practice as part of the evangelical mission of the church.

Teachers and administrators quite universally report experiences with outstanding non-SDA students who contribute in a positive way to the Christian environment on campuses. There are undoubtedly outstanding non-SDA Christian young people enrolled in SDA schools. The current research, however, suggests that the church might be well served to review its policies regarding this issue.

Limitations in external validity

It is important to keep in mind some limitations of this data set. Although serious attempts were made to secure a representative sample of all students attending four-year SDA high schools throughout the U.S. and Canada, the responses collected represent (1) an over representation of White students, (2) only the responses of students whose parents or guardians consented to their students' participation, (3) a lack of representation of high school-age students who attended junior high schools, and (4) an under representation of students attending inner-city schools.

The need for continued research

During the process of contacting the 93 four-year high schools in the NAD and arranging the logistics of this research, it was clear that many parents and individuals in school administrative positions were skeptical of how such research could be of value to them. Commonly expressed fears were that reporting simple descriptive statistics regarding rates of sexual intercourse and substance use might place the SDA educational system in a bad light and serve as an embarrassment, while yielding little benefit to the schools and the students.

Useful conclusions drawn from this research were *not* that a certain proportion of SDA youth engaged in sexual behaviors or substance use, but were rather that SDA youth are not immune or exempt from engaging in behaviors that place them at risk for unintended pregnancy, sexually transmitted diseases including AIDS, and the legal and health consequences of substance use. Educators can now act by creatively designing strategies that, when implemented, may serve to reduce the consequences of the behaviors studied.

1 *HIV/AIDS Surveillance Report,* Part 7, No. 1 (Atlanta: Centers for Disease Control and Prevention, 1995).

2 V.L. Tucker and C.T. Cho, "AIDS and Adolescents: How Can You Help Them Reduce Their Risk?" *Postgraduate Medicine 89,* No 3 (1991): 49-53.

3 G.C. Zimet, D.L. Bunch, T.M. Anglin, R. Lazebnik, P. Williams, and D.P. Krowchuk, "Relationship of AIDS-related Attitudes to Sexual Behavior Changes in Adolescents," *Journal of Adolescent Health* 13, No. 6 (1992): 493-498.

4 H. Palacio, "Safer Sex," in P.T. Cohen, M.A. Sande, P.A. Volberding, eds., *The AIDS Knowledge Base* (Boston: Little, Brown, and Company, 1994).

5 See G. Ludescher, "AIDS-related Knowledge, Attitudes, and Behaviors in Adolescents Attending Seventh-day Adventist Schools in California: (doctoral dissertation, Loma Linda University, 1992); P.L. Benson and M.J. Donahue, *Valuegenesis: Report I: A Study of the Influence of Family, Church, and School on the Faith, Values, and Commitment of Adventist Youth* (Minneapolis: Search Institute, 1990); G.L. Hopkins, "AIDS-related Knowledge, Attitudes, and Behaviors of Twelfth-Grade Students at Loma Linda Academy" (unpublished manuscript, 1994); and D. Gray, "Human Immunodeficiency Virus and Acquired Immune Deficiency: Beliefs, Knowledge, and Behaviors of High School Students Attending Seventh-day Adventist Academies" (doctoral dissertation, Andrews University, 1994).

6 K.R. Miner, "Educating About HIV/AIDS," in P. Cortese and K. Middleton, eds., *The Comprehensive School Health Challenge: Promoting Health Through Education* (Santa Cruz, Calif.: ETR Associates, 1994), vol. 1, pp. 413-441.

7 M. Hochhauser, "AIDS and Chemical Dependency: Prevention Needs of Adolescents," *Journal of Psychoactive Drugs* 21, No. 4 (1989): 381-385.

11

Addiction Prevention and Recovery

History of the Work in Temperance and Addiction

From the beginning of Adventism, temperance has been an important part of its doctrinal teaching. Although generally "temperance" refers to the matter of alcoholic beverages, to Seventh-day Adventists it has a broader context.

Temperance, meaning self-control, is a spiritual foundation to the life restored and provided by the Holy Spirit (see Gal. 5:22, 23). Temperance pictures a life of victory over every harmful and defiling practice (see 1Cor. 9:24, 25). It causes the believer to have a distinct separation from the allurements of idolatry, lust, and pride (see 2 Cor. 6:14-18), making the body a living temple of dedication to God. Ellen White wrote in 1874: "Temperance alone is the foundation of all the graces that come from God, the foundation of all victories to be gained" (*Temperance*, p. 201). For contrast she wrote, "Intemperance lies at the foundation of all the evil in our world" (*Ibid.*, 165).

Alcohol, with its devastating effects on the individual and society, was early recognized by Seventh-day Adventists as opposed to the development of Christian experience and faith. Joseph Bates, one of the pioneers in modern Adventism, was the founder of a temperance society at Fairhaven, Maine, in 1827 and had given up alcohol and tobacco many years before his association with the development of the church. Other pioneers, such as James White and John Andrews, had never taken alcohol or tobacco. John Loughborough, who began smoking cigars on recommendation of his physician as a means to deaden the pain of a certain infection, discarded this habit on the eve of his conversion, throwing a partly smoked cigar into the river. Joseph Waggoner stopped smoking when he became a Seventh-day Adventist. Ellen White had her first vision on temperance in 1848. (*See Selected Messages*, bk. 3, pp. 272, 273.)

It appears that there was no special effort in the publications of the church to urge the Sabbath-keeping Adventists to discontinue the use of tobacco until late in 1853. Then on Oct. 15, 1855 in a general meeting of SDAs at Morristown, Vermont, the delegates voted, "That the use of Tobacco by any member, is a serious and bitter grief, and greatly lamented by the Church; and after such members have been labored with, and properly admonished, as long as duty seems to require, if they do not reform, the Church will then deem it their duty to withdraw from them the hand of fellowship." This attitude is essentially the current position of the church.

The use of alcoholic beverages by church members was never a major issue, since the anti-alcohol movement had well permeated most religious groups. The Seventh-day Adventists went further than most of the popular temperance groups, however, in making it clear that abstinence also included wine, hard cider, coffee, tea, and beverages containing caffeine.

Because of the impact of these destructive habits on society, the church was urged by Ellen White to "bear a clear, decided testimony against the use of intoxicating drinks and the use of tobacco" (Ms 82, 1900). So began the strong temperance work, focusing at first primarily on the prevention of these destructive habits and developing programs to break the additions.

Today the concept of "addictions" has broadened to include more than just tobacco and alcohol. Health ministries is concerned with *all forms of addiction*: chemical dependencies, gambling, sexual addiction, work addiction, compulsive eating disorders, compulsive spending, religious fanaticism, power mania, and co-dependency. Particularly, Adventists believe that the drug-free lifestyle is desirable and attainable. For that reason, the church promotes abstinence from alcohol, tobacco, and all addictive, mind-altering drugs.

This broader emphasis of the "temperance" work to include all addictive behavior has created a need for an organization within the church to spearhead this important work, and therefore the Institute for Prevention of Addictions (IPA) was established, and has become one of the most effective Adventist organizations engaged in addiction ministries.

Institute for Prevention of Addictions (IPA)

The Institute for Prevention of Addictions is housed at Andrews University in the School of Graduate Studies and is co-sponsored by the General Conference Health Ministries Department.

Mission

The mission of the Institute for Prevention of Addiction (IPA) is to combat chemical and other addictions particularly in connection with the Seventh-day Adventist denomination. It uses academic tools of research, innovation, and professional education to serve as a research and development resource unit for the world church with its various entities and institutions. Established in 1983 as the Institute of Alcoholism and Drug Dependencies (IADD), the IPA broadened its scope in 1995 to include other addictions.

Philosophy and Purpose

The purpose of the Institute is to combat various forms of addiction. This is best done through a wholistic approach to spiritual, physical, mental, emotional, and social wellness. The Institute promotes the creation, maintenance and expansion of personal lifestyles which encourage total wellness and commitment to a Higher Power. The use of the Twelve Steps of Recovery is encouraged as a practical, spiritually-based approach to addictive problems. Preventive strategies also nurture resistance to familial, cultural, and peer pressures for other addictions.

This philosophic framework is the foundation for the Institute's mission of discovery, innovation, and professional development through academic programs and services within a framework of a religious ethical system. The primary

service arena is the Seventh-day Adventist Church. However the Institute also seeks to serve and interface with other organizations, groups, and professionals who share its philosophy and seek to promote the benefits of a wellness-oriented drug-free lifestyle.

Organization

The Institute is governed by a board of directors containing representatives of the world headquarters of the Seventh-day Adventist Church, Andrews University, and concerned volunteers. It is administered by a director. Centers of program effort have been established to promote specialized mission objectives of the Institute: **Prevention, Education, Rehabilitation** and **Research**. Each center is chaired by a resident or adjunct faculty member who provides guidance and supervision to projects in that center.

The Institute does not offer academic degrees, but collaborates with other schools and colleges of Andrews University and provides continuing education. The faculty of the Institute is comprised of resident professors drawn from these academic units and adjunct professionals who are interested in aiding the Institute in achieving its objectives.

The Institute holds group memberships in various national prevention organizations and has participated in research and evaluation efforts at the national level. A list of publications by Institute staff as well as an order form for technical reports and manuals published by the Institute is available from the Institute office.

The Institute is funded by subsidies from the General Conference of Seventh-day Adventists and Andrews University, grants and contracts, and by donations from supporting patrons.

IPA Affiliations

The Institute affiliates with organizations which are in harmony with its philosophy and objectives, and holds group membership in a number of other organizations. Affiliated organizations are:

- The International Commission for Prevention of Alcoholism, a non political, non-sectarian body which serves as an educational organization for prevention as a Non-Governmental Organization (NGO) of the World Health Organization, United Nations, and its constituent national committees;

- The Association of Adventist Parents.
- Michigan Consortium on Substance Abuse Education, a consortium of institutions of higher education in Michigan which coordinate educational efforts for substance abuse services.
- Michiana Collegiate Consortium for Prevention.

Major Activities of IPA
1. Prevention

The Institute is engaged in several prevention activities and projects and is steadily seeking ways to expand the prevention initiative. The projects and activities are listed below:

- Adventist Youth To Youth (AY2Y) had it's beginning in 1988 and continues to function in the present as Youth Alive. It plans to continue expansion and maintenance.
- Collegiate prevention programs. FIPSE grants, U.S. Department of Education.
- Provides consultation on collegiate prevention programs in world divisions.
- Development of International Youth Leaders for Prevention: training in technology for peer prevention programs. 1992 Russia; 1993 Kansas City, KS; 1993 Baltic Republics; 1994 Far East.
- Leadership training mechanism: Achievers International.
- Positive Choices collegiate prevention program (Andrews University).
- *Man in the Mirror: A Workbook for Intercepting Violent Behavior Among Inner City Youths*

2. Education

- Training materials for development of Drug-Free-Schools; prepared for U.S. and adapted for international use. Includes policy development, curriculum scope and sequence, community involvement, and student assistance.

- Editorial services to Vibrant Life magazine, the official health outreach journal of the Seventh-day Adventist Church.
- Annual Summer School of Addictions, Andrews University.
- Professional training and continued education in "cutting edge" knowledge and skills.

3. Therapy & Rehabilitation

- Regeneration Seminar: Clergy training in ministry to chemically dependent persons and their families.
- Development of training tools.

4. Research & Evaluation

- Surveys of populations for prevalence and correlates of alcohol and drug use and consequences.
- Needs assessments for academies, school districts, counties, and regional planning commissions (high school youth, juvenile offenders, women). Surveys of populations in the World field.
- Motivational factors promoting abstinence; especially the role of Christian commitment.
- Meta-analysis of data on environmental change in college campuses; FIPSE Analysis grant.

Regeneration (Support Groups for Recovering Addicts)

The Christian organization called SDAxA (Seventh-day Adventists for the Extinction of Addiction) was started by Pastor Hal Gates, himself a recovering addict. This organization is the base of a network of support groups in Seventh-day Adventist churches for recovering addicts called Regeneration. Regeneration is a spiritual recovery program based on a Christ-centered approach to the Twelve Steps to Recovery developed and used by Alcoholics Anonymous.

Regeneration is an adjunct program to and does not take the place of such twelve-step self-help fellowships as Alcoholics Anonymous (AA), Narcotics Anonymous (NA), Al-Anon, Alateen, and Adult Children of Alcoholics (ACOA).\

Those who attend Regeneration are encouraged to continue their involvement in these groups.

For more information contact: Pastor Hal Gates, SDAxA Regeneration, 1172 Prospect Ave., Raymond, WA 98577 or call (360) 875-4189 or Washington Conference Health Department (425) 481-7171. For the Mid-Atlantic area, call Raye Scott, the regional coordinator, at the toll free number, (866) 447-3733.

Regeneration Credo

We are a fellowship seeking growth and deeper spiritual dimensions in our lives.

We know we can be honest about our shortcomings in an atmosphere of complete trust and confidentiality.

We believe in the regeneration of the whole person; physically, spiritually, socially, and mentally.

We believe in the regeneration of successful relationships at home as well as in the society in which we live.

We believe that God has a unique plan for our lives and wants us to live abundantly and joyously.

We believe that surrender to Christ can liberate us from the bondage of chemical dependency or similar obsessions that estrange us from God.

We believe in the power of prayer, both individual and corporate, and that our petitions will be answered through Christ.

We believe in the power of community, knowing that there is a strength and source of support in this fellowship that transcends anything attainable on an individual basis.

To provide information about addictions and train individuals to work with the Regeneration program in local churches, IPA, and health ministries in North America have worked in cooperation with Hal Gates in the development of a number of training resources.

• *The Regeneration Manual*

In a normal community one out of four families is affected by alcoholism or drug dependency. This fact alone, along with evangelism outreach, will bring you into contact with families troubled with this problem. Furthermore, many members are adversely affected by the use of alcohol or other drugs by others within their family circle. Others grew up in alcoholic homes and suffer the consequences of being an adult child of an alcoholic or addict. Thus chemical dependency or co-dependency among family members presents a continuing challenge to the health leader or member of the health team.

The *Regeneration Manual* is a resource guide for ministry with the chemically dependent, and is available at The Health Connection (800) 548-8700.

The purpose of this manual is to provide information and tools by which the health leader can deal appropriately and effectively with these problems. It includes a compilation of facts, articles, and guidelines which health leaders have found educational and helpful in their ministry. *The manual is not designed to make the health leader into a professional treatment counselor. Rather it is intended to provide a basic knowledge about the problems associated with addiction which these groups may bring to you in your capacity as their health leader.* The health leader frequently serves several important roles in meeting the needs of members who face a battle with this issue. Some of these are:

- Initial observation that a problem exists which is related to addictive chemicals.
- Connection by referral of member and the family to a professional therapist for assessment of problem and recommendations on problem solutions.
- Encouragement of participation in community Twelve-Step support fellowships—

Alcoholics Anonymous (AA), Narcotics Anonymous (NA), Al-Anon, and other groups.

- Spiritual support of the member and family during treatment and afterwards during recovery.
- Education of congregation about the nature of addiction and what actions are helpful or are unhelpful in helping a member and his/her family find recovery.
- Encouragement and legitimizing of congregational Christ-centered support groups for spiritual recovery based on the twelve steps of Alcoholics Anonymous.

• **The Regeneration Awareness Meetings** are held in local areas to acquaint church members and others with the Regeneration program. It is from this base that many choose to attend a support group, or encourage others to do so. To arrange for a Regeneration Awareness Meeting, contact SDAxA.

• **The Ministry to People with Addictive Behaviors core course** for those taking the NAD Lifestyle Specialist certification in addiction ministries. This is the core lecture series of 20 hours given over a three-day period at an official conference site. For information contact Advent*Source* (800) 328-0525.

• **The Regeneration Leadership Seminar** is a part of the NAD Lifestyle Certification program for training church members, health professionals and pastors for a leadership role in establishing a Regeneration chapter in a local church. The Regeneration Leadership Seminar is a one-day training workshop. For Lifestyle Certification purposes, Advent*Source* will maintain a master schedule of Regeneration Leadership Seminars, call (800) 328-0525.

• **The Regeneration Seminar for Pastors** (a six- to ten-hour training program to acquaint clergy with the Regeneration program and to help them be effective in a supportive role). This seminar is usually offered by professionals from

---

Lifestyle Specialist Certification in Addiction Ministries

Prerequisite: Attend a one-day Regeneration Awareness Meeting in your local area.

Requirements:

1. Attend the course, **Ministry to People with Addictive Behaviors**—a 20 hour core lecture series, held over a three-day period at an official conference site, using the *Regeneration Manual* as a textbook.

2. Attend any **"Celebration of Family Recovery."** Must have a certificate of attendance from organizers.

3. Attend six **A.A. Twelve Step meetings** in your local area.

4. Attend a one-day **Regeneration Leadership Seminar**.

5. Read and write at least a two-page outline of the following books:
   A. *Never Good Enough* by Carol Canon
   B. *Mind, Character, and Personality* by Ellen G. White (any three chapters).

Note: All of the above certification requirements must be completed within a three-year period. For more information contact Advent*Source*, the NAD Lifestyle Certification center (800) 328-0525.

Andrews University at the request of a conference office or union. If a pastor is working on the NAD Lifestyle Specialist certification in addiction ministries, the Regeneration Seminar for Pastors could be taken in lieu of the one-day Regeneration Leadership Seminar requirement.

The Seminar provides an introductory study of the nature of addiction with emphasis on spiritual aspects. The role of the pastor in intervention, referral, and support during recovery is stressed. The place of the church in nurturing the recovery of members and their families is also explained. At the conclusion of the seminar, the learner will:

- Recognize the nature of chemical dependency.
- Perceive the impact of co-dependency on the family.
- Recognize the steps to recovery.
- Note appropriate pastoral roles and actions.
- Identify steps for establishing church-based support systems.

The seminar is endorsed by the North American Division Ministerial Association. Seminar sponsors may be local or union conferences, or educational institutions.

The trainers for the seminar are individuals with experience in chemical dependency treatment and who have sensitivity for the role of the local pastor and chaplain. They have been trained in the standard seminar curriculum and have agreed to be available for scheduling through the Institute. A current roster of trainers is available upon request from the Institute.

Scheduling: The seminar is designed for some flexibility in time scheduling. Topics are covered most adequately with 10 clock-hour sessions, equivalent to 1 Continuing Education Unit (CEU). (Seminars can be offered in as little as 6

God, Help Me!

*H*al Gates, founder/director of the Regeneration recovery program for addicts, has experienced first hand the downward pull of drugs.

He was from a good family; a loved child who grew up in an atmosphere of stability. His father a postmaster; his mother a devout Christian who had sent him to a church school. He served as an air force medic and eventually graduated from law school and spent five years as a hard-driving attorney; a full partner in a successful Lincoln City, Oregon law firm.

Then, at 37, disillusioned, he left that life to live in the San Juan Islands as a recluse, where drinking became a way of life. Five years later he had lost everything—profession, home, family, money and self-esteem. Hal says, "I had lost my ability to deal with life, to cope with things. I just wanted to die."

One night when he was 43 years of age he hit the bottom, lying face down in a drunken stupor on the floor of a boat; his red beard in his own vomit.

When Hal awoke the next morning, the realization of the depths to which he'd fallen wrung from his lips a cry of despair, "God, help me!" Although he didn't realize exactly what he was saying, God heard and thus began the transformation of his life.

Hal recounts, "All of a sudden, something seemed to snap inside me, kind of like when you pull rubber to the point where it finally goes pop. And suddenly there was no more tension. I still had the sickness, the physical weakness, but there was no more emotional tension, no more inner conflict."

Normally after a binge, Hal would dry out for a couple of days and then start drinking again. This time, however, he'd lost his taste for alcohol. That was the end of his drinking.

"What was so beautiful to me was that God could completely, unequivocally, forgive me for all of the trash that I had done in my life and in other people's lives."

Hal gave the rest of his life to this forgiving God. Now, as a pastor, Attorney Gates is an advocate for God's law.

"I would say to anybody who has addictions of any sort, Let go and let God. Let go of trying to fulfill God's law yourself, and realize that Jesus Christ is the fulfillment of that law. Realize that when He's in your heart, when He's in your soul, when He's in your mind, when He's in your thoughts, then your life is going to serve the purpose you were created for—and this is to be full of the joy of God."

—Adapted from Maylan Schurch's article in *Signs of the Times*, Sept. 1995.

clock hours (0.6 CEU) by deleting certain topics and limiting discussion.) The most benefit will be obtained by providing the full time since most participants wish to discuss practical applications of the concepts presented.

Continuing Education: Up to 1 Continuing Education Unit (CEU) is approved on an on-going basis by the North American Division Center for Continuing Education in Ministry (CCEM).

Arranging a Seminar: Training is scheduled through the Institute for the Prevention of Addictions at Andrews University. Inquiries should be made to: Director, Institute for the Prevention of Addictions, Andrews University, Berrien Springs, MI 49104-0211, call (616) 471-3558; fax (616) 471-6611.

Cost of a Seminar: Costs include the travel and local maintenance expenses of the trainer and the cost of the textbook. No trainer honorarium is expected. The textbook is the *Regeneration Manual* available from The Health Connection (800) 548-8700. Bulk prices are available.

Why Pastors Benefit

Many pastors find working with addicts and their families to be a baffling and frustrating task. What they try doesn't seem to work, so they become discouraged. It's easier to work with people who don't have these problems. The overworked pastor has limits to how much counseling can be done. The pastor hasn't had special training, in most cases, for substance abuse issues. Some pastors admit to just ignoring alcohol or tobacco problems among their church members. This enables problems to get worse. The seminar is designed to address these very situations. It introduces pastors to the basic knowledge and appropriate skills for practical action. It prepares the pastor for those specific roles and actions which the pastor is best suited to take. These roles are not the same as those of the counselor, but they are vitally important:

- Educated, alert listener
- Referral linkage
- Supporter of addict and family during treatment

- Congregational educator
- Validator for church-based support groups

Many pastors also discover that the seminar provides insights which are personally valuable. Many helping professionals have had past experience with addiction problems or co-dependency. The seminar offers new and healthy ways of dealing with these issues which may have been repressed and denied.

Regeneration Seminar for Pastors Curriculum

Session 1—**Addiction and the Church Today***
Understanding the challenge of chemical dependency in the Adventist church. Why do we experience these problems? Who is affected?

Session 2—**What is Addiction?**
The nature of addiction as a chronic, degenerative, and fatal process. Exploration of the disease vs. sin models. Addiction possibilities. Understanding the process of addiction and the deterioration of spirituality.

Session 3—**Pastoral Awareness***
Basic drug information. Denial syndrome. Enabling. Dangers of stereotypic thinking. Addict attitudes toward religion and church. The role of the pastor.

Session 4—**The Burdened Family**
Stages of co-dependency. Enabling behaviors. Kids and drugs.

Session 5—**Adults with Addictive Personalities***
Roles and rules in dysfunctional families. Adults with addictive personalities. Help for adult children of addiction (ACOAs).

Session 6—**Getting Help**
Crisis action steps. Intervention. The pastor's role in connecting with help. The process of recovery.

Session 7—**Treatment and Aftercare***
Characteristics of effective treatment programs. Referral criteria. Relapse prevention.

Walk 2000: Taking a Stand Against Substance Abuse

On January 17, 1995, the General Conference Administrative Committee met and passed the following action:

"Voted, To authorize implementation of the program *Walk Around the World—2000 A.D.* This program mobilizes the Seventh-day Adventist youth to walk five miles or ten kilometers in support of a drug-free lifestyle. Friends and businesses will be requested to sponsor each mile or kilometer, and the money donated will be used to promote drug-free living."

For a kit of materials to help you organize *Walk Around the World—2000 A.D.* In your community, contact Advent*Source* (800) 328-0525.

Session 8—**Spiritual Steps to Recovery**
Understanding the Twelve Steps of Recovery. Self-help fellowships. The traditions of Alcoholics Anonymous and Alanon. Fifth Step ministry.

Session 9—**Congregational Support***
Ways a church can support spiritual recovery. Congregational education.

Session 10 — **Regeneration Fellowships**
Starting a self-help fellowship. Guidelines for group effectiveness. Potential for church growth and nurture. Summary of pastor's role.

* If the seminar is shortened, these sessions are omitted or abbreviated.

Association of Adventist Parents

Purpose:

The primary purpose of the Association of Adventist Parents shall be to inform and educate parents, youth, church members, and church leaders about the dangers of alcohol, tobacco, and other addictive behaviors; to promote, encourage, and assist in the formation of parent groups and a sense of community within the church; and to collaborate in appropriate activities with other parent groups and community efforts to prevent and intervene in alcohol and drug use by youth.

The main objective of these endeavors shall be to promote mental, emotional/social, physical, and spiritual well-being among all people, and to work to counteract those pressures which condone and promote addiction.

Emphasis also shall be placed on varied resources for recovery, including the personal experiences of those in process of recovery, and praise to God for the gift of continuing sobriety.

Rationale:

The use and abuse of both legal and illegal drugs in the Seventh-day Adventist church have reached challenging proportions. Such use has extended into many segments of our church community, bringing with it individual loss, spiritual degeneration, family disintegration, and disregard for law and authority.

With the ever younger age of alcohol and other drug users, even extending to elementary school children, we as parents feel that we must join forces to accomplish the changes necessary to ensure a drug-free environment for today's children and children yet to come.

Philosophy:

WE BELIEVE that a drug-free environment is necessary in the home, school, church, and community for the optimal and healthy growth of children who are the future of our church and society.

WE BELIEVE that all children have the right to grow up in a healthy, nurturing, drug-free family environment.

WE BELIEVE that in advocating such a drug-free life, we reject any educational or intervention program which advocates or condones the "responsible use" of addictive drugs.

WE BELIEVE in working with Adventist church leaders, educators, health professionals, and church and community groups to work with us in a nonjudgmental and productive manner to create positive change in our homes, our church, our schools, and our communities.

Guidelines for Celebrations of Family Recovery

(Revised Nov. 14, 1996)

1. These Celebrations are primarily for Seventh-day Adventists and people with Adventist backgrounds, and individuals seeking a Christian approach to recovery.
2. Consistent sponsor of the Celebrations is the Association of Adventist Parents. Other organizations, such as hospitals, schools, or conferences, are considered as co-sponsors, and need to be recognized for their participation.
3. If possible, it is desirable to co-sponsor the Celebration with a hospital or other health agency because of the health connotations of the event.
4. The holding of Celebrations in local churches or district areas is workable when qualified personnel are available and conditions are feasible.
5. The Celebration program follows the general format of the Twelve Steps of AA, and adheres to the Twelve Traditions, particularly anonymity.
6. Emphasis is on varied resources for recovery—personal experiences of victory, and praise to God for continuing sobriety.
7. Celebrations should be planned and conducted by a local committee headed by a person conversant with the purpose and plan of the Twelve Steps of AA and the Twelve Traditions of AA. This committee is also in charge of promotion and logistics.
8. Usual frequency of the Celebration is annual, however regular support group meetings are encouraged.
9. Registration fees are set in order to cover the expenses of the local Celebration.
10. Speakers and presenters should preferably be selected from the local area to minimize expense.
11. A kit of materials should be provided each registrant or family for continued information and inspiration.
12. Celebrations are held over the weekend, with registration and an opening meeting on Friday night, and the program continuing through Sabbath until Sunday noon. Light refreshments could be served Friday evening.
13. Open-speaker meetings feature recovering persons telling their stories of divine aid in their lives.
14. Specialized closed discussion groups should be arranged according to the needs of those attending, such as Al-Anon, ACOA, CODA, EA, NA, etc.
15. Workshops deal with various aspects of the Recovery process.
16. "Clean time" is celebrated with sobriety anniversaries at a Saturday night or Sunday morning token ceremony.
17. A Twelve-Step breakfast on Sunday morning encourages discussion of the Twelve Steps and is an occasion for social interchange and mutual inspiration.
18. The group conscience meeting at the close is for program evaluation and future planning.
19. The Celebration program should present the basic Twelve Steps not only as a recovery method, but also as a practical guide for everyday Christian living, based on fundamental Biblical principles.
20. Appropriate books and other literature should be on display during the Celebration, and be available for purchase Saturday night or Sunday.

(For more information contact Francis A. Soper, President of Association of Adventist Parents, Rt. 2, Box 368A, Stanley, VA 22851, (540) 778-5132 or Tom Neslund at the General Conference Health and Temperance Department (301) 680-6733.)

(For more information and brochures contact Francis A. Soper, President of Association of Adventist Parents, Rt. 2, Box 368A, Stanley, VA 22851, (540) 778-5132.

Celebrations of Family Recovery

The Celebration of Family Recovery is a program aimed at bringing a new dimension of hope to Adventists with dependency problems, and providing for them, their co-dependents, and

The Twelve Steps, Scripture, and Spirit of Prophecy

The Twelve Steps of AA	*Steps to Christ*
Surrender	
1. We admitted we were powerless over alcohol, that our lives had become unmanageable.	"The Sinner's Need of Christ."
2. We came to believe that a power greater than ourselves could restore us to sanity.	"Repentance."
3. We made a decision to turn our will and our lives over to the care of God as we understand Him.	"Confession."
Confession	
4. We made a searching and fearless moral inventory of ourselves.	"Confession."
5. We admitted to God, to ourselves, and to another human being the exact nature of our wrongs.	"Confession."
Repentance and Consecration	
6. We are entirely ready to have God remove all these defects of character.	"Consecration."
7. We humbly ask Him to remove all our shortcomings.	"Faith and Acceptance."
Reconciliation & Restoration	
8. We made a list of all persons we harmed and became willing to make amends to them all.	"The Test of Discipleship."
9. We made direct amends to such people wherever possible, except when to do so would injures them or others.	"Growing up into Christ."
Spiritual Growth	
10. We continue to take personal inventory and when we were wrong, promptly admitted it.	"The Work and the Life."
11. We sought, through prayer and meditation, to improve our conscious contact with God as we understand Him, praying only for knowledge of His will for us and the power to carry that out.	"A Knowledge of God," "The Privilege of Prayer," and "What to do with Doubt."
12. Having had a spiritual experience as the result of these steps, we tried to carry this message to alcoholics, and practice these principles in all our affairs.	"Rejoicing in the Lord."

families the assurance of continuing recovery. Established in 1985, Celebrations have been held in the Midwest, the Mid-Atlantic area, Southern California, the Pacific Northwest, New England, and elsewhere.

The principal sponsor of these Celebrations of Family Recovery, the Association of Adventist Parents (AAP), networks with other organizations such as conferences and hospitals.

The word of GOD is able to build you up...! Acts 20:32
Scripture is "Living and Powerful." Heb. 4:12

Biblical Comparisons

Rom. 7:18 NIV I know that nothing good lives in me, that is, in my sinful nature. For I have the desire to do what is good, but I cannot carry it out.

Isa. 41:10 NIV So do not fear, for I am with you; do not be dismayed, for I am your God. I will strengthen you and help you; I will uphold you with my righteous right hand.

Luke 9:23 NIV Then He said to them all: "If anyone would come after Me, he must deny himself and take up his cross daily and follow Me.

Lam. 3:40 NIV Let us examine our ways and test them, and let us return to the Lord.

James 5:16 NIV Therefore confess your sins to each other and pray for each other so that you may be healed. The prayer of a righteous man is powerful and effective.

Isa. 1:19 NIV If you are willing and obedient, you will eat the best from the land.

James 4:10 NIV Humble yourselves before the Lord, and He will lift you up.

Matthew 5:24 NIV Leave your gift there in front of the altar. First go and be reconciled to your brother, then come and offer your gift.

Luke 6:38 NIV Give, and it will be given to you. A good measure, pressed down, shaken together and running over, will be poured into your lap. For with the measure you use, it will be measured to you.

Rom. 12:3 NIV For by the grace given me I say to every one of you: Do not think of yourself more highly than you ought, but rather think of yourself with sober judgment, in accordance with the measure of faith God has given you.

Ps. 19:14 NIV May the words of my mouth and the meditations of my heart be pleasing in your sight, O Lord, my Rock and my Redeemer.

Gal. 6:1 NIV Brothers, if someone is caught in a sin, you who are spiritual should restore him gently, But watch yourself, or you also may be tempted.

The Celebration of Family Recovery is a weekend of mutual love, comfort, and unity for the purpose of exploring spiritual resources for recovery from addictions and dependencies, the sharing of personal experiences, strength, and hope, and for the gift of continuing sobriety.

It is Christ-centered, to focus on the constant need for divine power to return to normal, healthy life; and church-sponsored to encourage those in process of recovery to view the church as a healing, comforting and nurturing community, thus fulfilling the invitation of Christ, Himself, "Come unto Me, all ye that labor and are heavy laden, and I will give you rest" (Matthew 11:28).

During the weekend convention that follows the 12 steps of Alcoholics Anonymous, recovering persons share their stories of God's work in their lives, while workshops and closed discussions deal with various aspects of recovery. "Clean Time" is celebrated with sobriety anniversaries at a special Saturday night ceremony. A "12-Step Breakfast" and a group meeting for evaluations and future planning. concludes the weekend.

For more information about these Celebrations of Family Recovery, contact Francis Soper, president of the Association of Adventist Parents, Route 2, Box 368A, Stanley, VA 22851 or call (540) 778-5132 or DeWitt Williams at the NAD Health Ministries Department (301) 680-6733.

Finding Help for the Addict

Recovering from addiction is an extended process. The resources available differ according to the community, but the following stages seem necessary:

1. Intervention. Breaking the denial and delusion so that the addict agrees to receive help. This can be done through natural or "planned" crisis. Planned crisis or intervention is presenting reality to a person out of touch with it in a receivable way: objective, unequivocal, non-judgmental, and caring. It involves the "significant others" in a person's life. A trained counselor or therapist is recommended to assist the intervention team in preparing for the intervention.

Steps in Intervention:
- Conquer personal reluctance. Intervention is a profound act of caring. Breaks the "rule of silence."
- Gather the intervention team: persons with meaningful relationships to the addict and who are willing to risk those relationships in order to help.
- Gather the data about specific incidents. Prepare for treatment.
- Rehearse the intervention.
- Do the intervention. The addict must be sober and agree to listen. Team members share their letters or lists. Help is offered as the only option to maintaining the relationships.

2. Detoxification and Withdrawal. Removal of the drug from the addict's body, usually requiring medical management.

3. Treatment and Rehabilitation Program. The most successful programs are those which use a comprehensive approach including education, group therapy, and personal counseling. Traditional psychiatric methods do not seem to be effective unless mental illness is also present (dual diagnosis). A good program will include the family and be based on the Twelve Steps as a model for recovery. If this kind of help is not available the person can still benefit from long-term support systems.

4. Long-Term Support For Sobriety. Recovering people need support systems to share with others their experience, strength, and hope. The healing process takes place best in a support system such as that provided by Alcoholics Anonymous and similar groups which utilize the Twelve Steps of Recovery first developed by Alcoholics Anonymous.

Adventist Recovery Centers For Substance Abuse

Drug Alternative Program (DAP), Clifford and Freddie Harris, 11868 Arliss Drive, Grand Terrace, CA 92324; (909) 783-1094. Inpatient and outpatient support for drug and alcohol abuse. For clients 18 to 65 years of age.

Harding Hospital, 445 East Granville Road, Worthington, Ohio 43085; (614) 885- 5381. A full-service psychiatric hospital with special units for substance abuse, adolescents, adults and outpatient services.

Loma Linda Behavioral Medicine Center, 1710 Barton Road, Redlands, CA 92373; (800) 752-5999, 24-hour help line. Inpatient and outpatient chemical dependency recovery services for adults, adolescents and children.

New Day Center, a part of Hinsdale Hospital, 121 North Elm Street, Hinsdale, IL 60521; (630) 856-7700. Inpatient and outpatient services, with a two-year after care program for those 18 and over. The Living Resource Center offers apartments for night living for day-hospital patients.

New Life Health Institute, Beverly and David Sedlacek, 6676 Licking Rd. (Rt. 167), Pierpoint, Ohio 44082; (216) 577-1571. Inpatient and outpatient treatment for substance abuse and compulsive behaviors.

St. Helena Hospital and Health Center, 650 Sanitarium Road, Deer Park, CA 94576; (707) 963-6204. All levels of care for alcohol and drug dependency are provided for those 19 and older—out-patient, residential where patients stay in a licensed residential facility at night, and inpatient.

The Bridge, Paul and Carol Cannon, 1745 Logsdon Bowling Green, Kentucky 42101; (502) 777-1094. Inpatient recovery for codependency, with substance abuse, compulsive behavior, and alcoholic relapse services. For clients 18 years of age or older.

Signs of Drug Use

Changing patterns of performance, appearance, and behavior may signal use of drugs. The items in the first category listed below provide direct evidence of drug use; the items in the other categories offer signs that may indicate drug use. For this reason, adults should look for extreme

---

Serenity Prayer

God, grant me the serenity
to accept the things I cannot change.
The courage to change the things I can,
and the wisdom to know the difference.
Living one day at a time,
enjoying one moment at a time;
accepting hardship as a pathway to peace;
taking, as Jesus did,
This sinful world as it is,
not as I would have it;
trusting that You will make all things
right if I surrender to Your will;
so that I may be reasonably
happy in this life and supremely happy
with You forever in the next.

Amen

— Reinhold Niebuhr

---

changes in children's behavior, changes that together form a pattern associated with drug use.

Signs of Drugs and Drug Equipment
- Possession of drug-related equipment such as pipes, rolling papers, small decongestant bottles, or small butane torches.
- Possession of drug or evidence of drugs, peculiar plants, or butts, seeds, or leaves in ashtrays or clothing pockets.
- Odor of drugs, smell of incense or other "cover-up" scents.

Identification With Drug Culture
- Drug-related magazines, slogans on clothing and posters.
- Conversations and jokes that are preoccupied with drugs.
- Hostility in discussing drugs.
- Music which glorifies drugs.

Signs of Physical Deterioration
- Memory lapses, short attention span, difficulty in concentration.
- Poor physical coordination, slurred or incoherent speech.
- Unhealthy appearance, indifference to hygiene and grooming.
- Bloodshot eyes, dilated pupils.

Dramatic Changes In School Performance
- Distinct downward turn in student's grades—not just from C's to F's but from A's to B's and C's.
- Assignments not completed.
- Increased absenteeism or tardiness.

Changes In Behavior
- Chronic dishonesty (lying, stealing, cheating). Trouble with the police.
- Changes in friends, evasiveness in talking about new ones.
- Possession of large amounts of money.
- Increasing and inappropriate anger, hostility, irritability, secretiveness.
- Reduced motivation, energy, self-discipline, self-esteem.
- Diminished interest in extracurricular activities and hobbies.

—From "Schools Without Drugs," p 16. United States Department of Education, 1986.

(For a report on drugs and Seventh-day Adventist Youth, see Chapter 10.)

How To Effectively Confront An Addict
Goal: Getting the alcoholic or addict to admit he/she has a problem and agree that he/she needs help.

Essentials
1. Knowledge of the disease and of denial.
2. Facts about the person's use and consequent problems.
3. Belief that every drinking person knows at some level he/she has a problem and that he/she needs help and that it's alright to cajole him/her into getting help.
4. Understanding of the alcoholic's fear and panic when treatment is suggested.

5. Leverage (power)—knowing what's most important to that person and using it.

Counseling Techniques
1. Listening with an interpretive mind; showing kindness, gentleness, respectfulness, empathy, warmth, sincerity, honesty, and vulnerability; the ability to instill hope, and have a sense of humor.
2. Having enough courage, firmness, assertiveness, self-possession, specific information, and tough skin to interrupt denial and delusion.
3. Taking a risk: Once addiction is established, nothing else matters except getting help for the dependent person.
4. Surrendering: Once the counselor has presented his/her case, the counselor is powerless to control the results and must recognize that the disease will have to convince the victim if the counselor can't.

Simple Form for Self-Evaluation.
Ask if the person is drinking AND...
1. Has a family history of addiction.
2. Has had one or more blackouts (memory losses) in the last two years.
3. His/her significant others (family and close friends) are concerned about his/her drinking/drugging.
4. His/her personality has changed.
5. Has had more than one traffic ticket for driving while intoxicated.
6. Has a prior addiction to any other drug.
7. He/she drinks in an out-of-control fashion.
8. He/she is concerned about him/herself.

Answering "yes" to three or four out of the eight indicates a problem.

Seventh-Day Adventist Drug Needs Assessment Survey Tool
Why do a survey?
The first step toward developing a drug-free school is to assess the current status of the school with respect to student alcohol, tobacco, and other drug use and attitudes. Until recently, this has been an expensive process, feasible only for

larger schools. The Institute for the Prevention of Addictions, has used comprehensive needs assessment surveys to study the prevalence and correlates of Adventist youth in North America, Inter-America, and Africa, as well as provide contract assessment services to local public school systems. Now an inexpensive drug survey tool has been developed by the Institute with the cooperation of the Andrews University Center for Statistical Services for use with Adventist students, grades 7-12.

What is included?

The survey contains questions validated on national surveys by the University of Michigan High School Senior Survey. Special question features include inquiries into attitudes, practices, and factors which Adventist youth find motivational for choosing abstinence. Completed surveys are optically scanned and computer analyzed, with full protection for individual student anonymity.

The needs assessment service includes a full report, with data tabulations and graphs, presented to the contracting school. Schools may use the results to educate staff, the student body, parents and church members about the actual situation present at the time of the survey. Important insights into how students think about chemical substances will be gained.

How much does it cost?

Check with the institute for current costs. If the Institute staff make a personal presentation to the school community, travel expenses will be an additional cost.

How to order:

For detailed order information contact Institute for Prevention of Addictions, 8408 Westwood Drive, Andrews University, Berrien Springs, MI 49104-0211, E-mail: ipa@andrews.edu; CompuServe e-mail: 74532,350; (616) 471-3558; Fax (616) 471-6611.

Substance Use Among Seventh-day Adventist Youth

The Institute for the Prevention of Addictions prepared a briefing paper for the North American Conference on this subject. It is reprinted in Chapter 10 on Youth Ministries.

Further Reading and Study Bibliography
Chemical Addiction

Jerry Dunn. *God Is for the Alcoholic*. Revised ed. Chicago: Moody Press. 1986.

Vernon Johnson. *Everything You Need to Know About Chemical Dependence*. Minneapolis, MN: Johnson Institute. 1990.

Gerald May. *Addiction and Grace*. New York: Harper and Row Publishers, Inc., 1988.

Keith Miller. *Hope in the Fast Lane: A New Look at Faith in a Compulsive World*. San Francisco: Harper and Row Publishers, Inc., 1987.

Craig Nakken. *The Addictive Personality: Roots, Rituals, and Recovery*. Minneapolis: Hazelden Foundation, 1988.

Anderson Spickard and Barbara R. Thompson. *Dying for a Drink: What You Should Know About Alcoholism*. Waco, Texas: Word Books, 1985.

Substance Abuse Resource Guide—Faith Communities. Substance Abuse and Mental Health Services Administration 1997.

Other Addictions
Work:

Diane Fassel. *Working Ourselves to Death: The High Cost of Workaholism and the Rewards of Recovery*. San Francisco: Harper San Francisco. 1990.

Bryan E. Robinson. *Overdoing It: How to Slow Down and Take Care of Yourself*. Deerfield Beach, FL: Health Communications, 1992.

Relationships:

Anne Wilson Schaef. *Escape from Intimacy: The Pseudo-Relationship Addictions*, San Francisco, CA: Harper & Row, 1989.

Sex and Love:

Patrick Carnes. *Out of the Shadows: Understanding Sexual Addiction*. Minneapolis, MN: CompCare Pub., 1983.

Tobacco:

Karen Casey. *If Only I Could Quit: Recovering from Nicotine Addiction.* Center City, MN: Hazelden Foundation, 1987.

Linda Royer, *Taking Control*, Resources for Better Living, Inc. A self-help kit of instructive audio tapes to help overcome the habit of smoking or chewing tobacco. Contact (703) 477-9653.

Religion:

Alcohol, Tobacco, and Other Drug Abuse Challenges and Responses for Faith Leaders. Substance Abuse and Mental Health Services Administration, 1995.

Stephen Arterburn and Jack Felton. *Toxic Faith: Understanding and Overcoming Religious Addiction.* Nashville, TN:Thomas Nelson, Inc. 1991.

Carmen Renee Berry. *When Helping You Is Hurting Me: Escaping the Messiah Trap..* San Francisco: Harper San Francisco, 1988.

Recovery Devotional Bible. (NIV), Grand Rapids, MI: Zondervan, 1993.

Dr. James B. Richards. *Escape from Codependent Christianity.* Huntsville, AL: Impact Ministries Publications Dept. (205) 536-9402, 1996.

Peer Prevention:

Sharon Scott. *PPR: Peer Pressure Reversal.* Amherst, Massachusetts: Human Resource Development Press, 1985.

Parenting for Prevention:

Active Parenting is a widely respected training program used by Christian churches for teaching parenting skills. For more information, call 1-800-825-0060.

Ken Barum. *When Saying No Isn't Enough.* New York: Penguin/Signet Books. 1988.

Harriet W. Hodgson. *A Parents Survival Guide: How to Cope When Your Kid Is Using Drugs.* Hazelden Foundation, 1986.

Marsha Manatt. *Parents, Peers, and Pot II: Parents in Action* National Institute on Drug Abuse, 1983.

Gabriel G. Nahas. *Keep Off the Grass.* Revised edition. Oxford: Pergamon Press, 1979.

Beth Polson and Miller Newton. *Not My Kid.* New York: Arbor House. 1984.

J. M. Tobias. *Kids and Drugs: A Handbook for Parents and Professionals.* Annandale, Virginia: Panda Press, 1986.

David J. Wilmes. *Parenting for Prevention: How to Raise a Child to Say No to Alcohol and Drugs.* Minneapolis, MN: Johnson Institute. 1988.

School-Based Prevention:

Drug Prevention Curriculum. Office of Education, Research, and Improvement. United States Department of Education, 1988.

The P.A.C.T. Manual. North American Division of Education. 12501 Old Columbia Pike, Silver Spring, MD 20904. 1994.

What Works: Schools Without Drugs. United States Department of Education, 1986; (800) 624-0100.

Addiction:

Melody Beattie. *Codependent No More: How to Stop Controlling Others and Start Caring for Yourself.* Center City, MN: Hazelden Educational Materials, 1988.

Claudia Black. *It Will Never Happen to Me.* New York: Ballantine Books, 1981.

John Bradshaw. *Bradshaw: On the Family.* Deerfield Beach, FL: Health Communications, Inc.

Carol Cannon. *Never Good Enough.* Boise, ID: Pacific Press Publishing Association, 1993.

Anne Wilson Shaef and Diane Fassel. *The Addictive Organization.* San Francisco, CA: Harper and Row Publishers, Inc. 1988. ISBN 0-06-254841-7.

Abraham Twerski. *Addictive Thinking: Why Do We Lie to Ourselves? Why Do Others Believe Us?* Hazelden Educational Materials. 1990.

Jeff VanVonderen. *Tired of Trying to Measure Up.* Minneapolis, MN: Bethany House Publishers, 1989.

Intervention:

Toby R. Drews. *Getting Them Sober.* Vol. 1 & 2. Bridge Publishing, Inc., 1980, 1983.

Friends in Recovery. *The Twelve Steps for Christians.* PO Box 44, Curtis, WA 98538, (360) 245-3386, 1991.

Merle Fossum. *Catching Fire: Men's Renewal and Recovery Through Crisis.* Center City, MN: Hazelden Foundation, 1989.

Vernon E. Johnson. *Intervention: How to Help Someone Who Doesn't Want Help.* Johnson Institute Books, Minneapolis, MN. 1986.

Will Maloney. *Chemical Dependency Treatment Programs: A Guide to Referral*. Center City, MN: Hazelden Foundation, 1987.

Joy Miller. *Addictive Relationships: Recovering Your Boundaries*. Deerfield, FL: Health Communications, Inc., 1989.

Mary Ellen Pinkham. *How to Stop the One You Love from Drinking*. 1986. New York: G.P. Putnam's Sons. 1986.

Melody Beattie. *Codependent's Guide to the Twelve Steps*. New York: Prentice Hall Press. 1990.

Robert Hemfelt and Richard Fowler. *Serenity: A Companion for Twelve Step Recovery*. New Testament, Psalms, and Proverbs. Nashville, TN: Thomas Nelson Publishers, 1990.

Dale and Juanita Ryan. *Rooted in God's Love: Biblical Meditations for People in Recovery*. Downers Grove, IL: InterVarsity Press. 1992.

Relapse Prevention:

Tammy Bell. *Preventing Adolescent Relapse*. Independence, MO: Herald House. 1990.

Terence Gorski and Merlene Miller. *Staying Sober: A Guide for Relapse Prevention*. Independence, MO: Independence Press. 1986.

Adult Child Recovery:

Nancy Groom. *From Bondage to Bonding: Escaping Codependency, Embracing Biblical Love*. Colorado Springs, CO: NavPress, 1991.

Earnie Larsen. *Stage II Recovery: Life Beyond Addiction*. San Francisco, CA: Harper & Row. 1985.

Earnie Larsen. *Stage II Relationships: Love Beyond Addiction*. San Francisco, CA: Harper & Row. 1987.

Keith Miller. *A Hunger for Healing*. New York: Harper Collins, 1991.

Veronica Ray. *Design for Growth: Twelve Steps for Adult Children*. Minneapolis, MN: Hazelden Foundation. 1988.

Talk, Trust and Feel. New York: Ballantine Books. 1991.

Arlene Taylor. *Back to Basics: Timely Tips for Building Bona Fide Boundaries & Optimum Self-Esteem*. Teach Services, Inc. Brushton, NY. 1994.

Barry Weinhold. *Breaking Free of Addictive Family Relationships: Healing Your Own Inner Child*. Stillpoint Publishing. 1991.

Stanley D. Wilson. *Rising Above Shame: Healing Family Wounds to Self-Esteem*. Rockville, MD: Launch Press. 1991.

Congregational Education

Patricia Mutch and Winton Beaven. *Regeneration: A Video Course*. Ten modules (50 minutes each) with study guide for educating Adventist churches and their leaders on addiction and recovery. Available from The Health Connection.

Group Study Guides and Workbooks:

Hal Gates and others. *Regeneration Manual*. Silver Spring, MD: The Health Connection. Second Edition. 1994.

Keith Miller. *A Hunger for Healing Workbook*. New York: Harper Collins. 1992.

Ron Ross, *When I Grow Up...I Want to be an Adult*. 1201 Knoxville St., San Diego, CA 92110: Recovery Publications, Inc., 1990. A workbook for use in groups for adults who had dysfunctional childhoods.

Kolleen Neff and Jean Watkins. *The Tie that Binds: Shame and the Church*. A video and discussion guide from a Seventh-day Adventist perspective. Available from: Creative Horizons, 11665 W. Olympic Blvd., Suite #204, West Los Angeles, CA 90064.

Dale and Juanita Ryan. *Life Recovery Guides*. A series of Bible study and discussion guides on various recovery issues. Six studies per guide. Available from InterVarsity Press.

Leader's Materials:

Ron Halvorson and Valerie Deilgat. *Living Free: Making the Church a Safe Place for Recovery*. Also *Living Free: A Guide to Forming and Conducting a Recovery Ministry*. Valuable suggestions for organizing and leading recovery groups in Christian churches. 1201 Knoxville St., San Diego, CA 92110: Recovery Publications, Inc.

Steps. A quarterly publication for recovering Christians which has material for group discussion in each issue. Available by subscription from: National Association for Christian Recovery (NACR), P.O. Box 11095, Whittier, CA 90603.

Recommended Material Available From A.A. World Services, Inc. (Alcoholics Anonymous)
A.A. World Services, Inc.
Box 459
Grand Central Station
New York, NY 10163
(212) 870-3400

Books:
Twelve Steps and Twelve Traditions
The Big Book

Pamphlets:
"A Member's Eye View of Alcoholics Anonymous"
"How A.A. Members Cooperate With Other Community Efforts to Help Alcoholics"
"The A.A. Member"
"If You Are a Professional, A.A. Wants to Work With You"
"Problems Other Than Alcohol"
"Understanding Anonymity"
"Let's Be Friendly With Our Friends"
"Is A.A. for You?"
"A.A. in Treatment Centers"
"A.A. in Occupational Alcoholism Programs"
"A.A. As a Resource for the Medical Profession"

Guidelines:
For A.A. Members Employed in the Alcoholism Field
Forming Local Committees in Cooperation With the Professional Community
Public Information
Cooperating With Court, A.S.A.P., and Similar Programs

Toll-Free Information Sources
Federation of Parents for Drug-Free Youth (800) 554-5437

The Subtance Abuse and Mental Health Services Administration. National Clearinghouse for Alcohol and Drug Information See below (Agencies)

INTERNET: info@prevline.health.org

Parents' Resource Institute for (800) 241-9746
Drug Information tapes after 5:00 p.m.

Drug Education - PRIDE (404) 658-2548 in Georgia

U.S. Dept. of Education (800) 624-0100

Cocaine Helpline (800) COCAINE [262-2463]
24 hour information and referral service for treatment

National Institute on Drug Abuse (800) 662-4357

Associations
Addiction Research Foundation
Resources available in Canada.
33 Russell St.

Also: Canadian Centre on Substance Abuse, 112 Kent Str., Suite 480,
Toronto, Ontario Canada M5S 2S1
Ottawa, Ontario, Canada K1P 5P2;
(613) 235-4048
(416) 595-6144

Al-Anon Family Group Headquarters, Inc.
Alateen
1600 Corporate Lending Parkway
Virginia Beach, VA 23454-5617
(757) 563-1600 (8 am - 6 pm, EST)
E-mail: www@al-anon.org

American Lung Association
Write for catalog of materials on smoking prevention.
1740 Broadway
New York, NY 10019

Institute on Black Chemical Abuse
Catalog available.
Resource Center
2616 Nicollet Ave., South
Minneapolis, MN 55407
(612) 871-7878

National Families in Action
2296 Henderson Mill Road
Suite 300, Atlanta, GA 30345
(404) 934-6364

P.R.I.D.E.
Numerous resource publications for
parents and teachers.
(Parents Resource Institute Drug Educ)
Catalog available
Woodruff Bldg., Suite 1002
100 Edgewood Avenue
Atlanta, GA 30303
(800) 241-9746

Government Agencies
The Substance Abuse and Mental Health Services
Administration. National Clearinghouse for
Alcohol and Drug Information
P.O. Box 2345
Rockville, MD 20852 -2345
(800) 729-6686. Ask for the name of the RADAR
coordinator in your state. They have free loan
items and pamphlets available.

Also, can subscribe to *Prevention Pipeline*
published by NCADI for bimonthly updates.
These are *the answer people* for the nation. Call
them up!

Office on Smoking and Health
Smoking prevention information.
Technical Information Center
5600 Fishers Lane, Park Bldg., Room 116
Rockville, MD 20857
(301) 443-1690

Commercial Sources of Further Materials:
CampCare Publishers
2415 Annapolis Lane
Minneapolis, MN 55441
(800) 328-0330

Hazelden Educational Materials
Pleasant Valley Road
P.O. Box 176
Center City, MN 55012-0176
(800) 328-9000

Johnson Institute
7151 Metro Boulevard
Minneapolis, MN 55435-3425
(612) 944-0511

The Passage Group
1240 Johnson Ferry Place (Suite A-50)
Marietta, GA 30068
(800) 487-7743
www.passage group.com
Parent to Parent 2000
Parenting for Safe and Drug-Free Youth

Tools for Recovery
1201 Knoxville Street
San Diego, CA 92110
(619) 275-1350

Health Communications, Inc.
3201 SW 15th St.
Deerfield Beach, FL 33442
(800) 851-9100

12

AIDS Ministries

AIDS (Acquired Immunodeficiency Syndrome) is a chronic, wasting illness caused by the Human Immunodeficiency virus (HIV). It is almost always fatal and has reached epidemic proportions in most of the world including North America. AIDS was first recognized in 1981 as a cluster of unusual diseases in gay men and intravenous drug abusers. In retrospect, the first person with a documented case of AIDS died in 1959 in Manchester, England. The first United States case of AIDS, a St. Louis resident, died in 1968. By the late 1970's numerous cases were occurring in New York City, but were not recognized.

By 2000, Centers for Disease Control and Prevention (CDC) identified approximately 775,000 cases of AIDS in the United States with 320,000 deaths. CDC estimates that an additional 1,000,000 people are infected with HIV. This rapid spread of HIV has occurred during the past 20 years. Every year approximately 40,000 new HIV infections occur in the U.S. Nearly 9,000 HIV cases have been reported among children (ages 12 and under). The health care needs for HIV infected people overwhelm most families' resources. When HIV progresses to AIDS, the health care costs increase to a staggering amount per year.

Forty-nine thousand Canadian residents were living with HIV/AIDS by the end of 1999, according to data from the UNAIDS/WHO *Epidemiological Fact Sheet* published in 2000. There were 400 deaths in 1999.

As of December, 2000, the AIDS epidemic has been responsible for 448,600 deaths in the U.S. If the HIV epidemic continues to extend at the present rate, the epidemic will overwhelm the health care resources of the United States, even if a vaccine and a cure for HIV are developed. As the epidemic spreads, so will public fear, prejudice, discrimination and rejection.

World Health Organization Statistics on HIV/AIDS

At the end of 2000 an estimated:
36.1 million people were living with HIV/AIDS
34.7 million adults
  1.4 million children
      (70%) 25.3 million live in Sub Saharan Africa
      (16%) 5.8 millon live in South & Southeast Asia
      World-wide (Age Group 15-49)
      1% of adults are infected
      8.8% of adults in Africa are infected
      In 16 countries of Africa the HIV infection prevalence
          exceeds 10%. 47% of the 36.1 million adults
          living with HIV/AIDS are women.

New cases:
5.3 million *new* cases occured world-wide in 2000;
      —that is 15,000 each day. 95% of these are
          in developing countries.
      —of these, 6,500 cases were in young
          people aged 15-24 (5 per minute)

Deaths:
In 2000 alone 3 million died, including 500,000 children.
Cumulative to 2000 21.8 million
      —17.5 million adults
      —4.3 million children

Orphans:
13.2 million children had lost their mothers or both parents
      by the end of 1999.

A Challenge to the Church *by Charles Bradford*

My brothers and sisters, what good is it for someone to say that he has faith if his actions do not prove it? Can that faith save him? Suppose there are brothers or sisters who need clothes and don't have enough to eat. What good is there in your saying to them, "God bless you! Keep warm and eat well!" if you don't give them the necessities of life? "So it is with faith: if it is alone and includes no actions, then it is dead" (James 2:14-17 TEV).

The time has come for action. We Christians must lay aside every weight that inhibits us from effective ministry. The church must strip for action. What must we strip off? We need to get rid of wrong attitudes—negative attitudes, attitudes of superiority, attitudes of self-righteousness. We also need to get rid of fear and ignorance before the Church can engage in effective ministry to AIDS people. The Church must get rid of all of these soul-cramping attitudes.

First of all, we can become educated about AIDS. AIDS cannot be spread through casual contacts—hugs or handshakes. Touching an AIDS patient will not infect us, nor is AIDS contracted from such things as eating utensils or toilet seats. Let's lay aside this ignorance that keeps us from ministering to people.

All ministry begins on a personal level. Do something kind for the person with AIDS. Spend some time with him or her. Just listen. Allow him to express emotions. Be a friend. Offer to take your friend on an errand—a trip to the store, the bank, the doctor. There are so many things that Christians can do, all the way from a phone call, a brief note, or spending some quality time in talking about life and its meaning. Invite the person to church....

AIDS is the leprosy of our time. Deadly, incurable. The mere mention of this dread disease sends cold chills up and down the spine.

People ran from lepers in Jesus' day. But, when sending His disciples out to preach the gospel Jesus said, "Don't forget the lepers, those horrible smelly people. Cleanse the lepers!"

In this new millennium, Jesus' word is, minister to the people with AIDS. Yet in our self-centeredness and complacency we would rather exclude them from our worship. We must support the AIDS victims, not only with our prayers, but with our presence.

—Updated from two sermons preached by Dr. Charles Bradford when he was President of the North American Division, "Let's Get Down to Business," and "AIDS—What Jesus Said."

The vast majority of children born to HIV-positive women are not infected with HIV. Without therapy with zidovudine and other drugs as many as 35 percent are born infected but with therapy less than 10 percent become infected. The needs of these youngsters cannot be ignored. To do so would not only be lacking in compassion for the most vulnerable members of society; it also would invite a social catastrophe of the greatest magnitude. The fact is that the majority of women with AIDS are poor. For the children, then, the death of their mother can be the latest in a series of blows inflicted upon them by poverty and the AIDS epidemic.

The resources available for women with AIDS and their children are limited. "Once the mother with AIDS dies, any supports that she and her family had while she was alive are removed. So any support the children may have relied on are removed when they are the most vulnerable" (*New York Times*, December 23, 1992).

Alarmingly, the epidemic is spreading most rapidly in the nation's inner cities. Today's one million HIV-infected individuals will become ill and die in the decades ahead. This will present a huge challenge to the churches in America. Education in churches and in schools is needed to send a strong message regarding sexual integrity.

The risks must be shown, but we don't want to over-react out of unreasonable fear.

Today, almost every person knows at least one individual infected by HIV, or someone who has a family member who is infected. Thus, every church in the U.S. and Canada will ultimately have to address the issue. ASAP is one of several Christian models for ministry that can play a decisive role, emphasizing redemptive compassion for those infected and presenting a clear message of prevention for those not infected. Part of ASAP's work is to help churches develop AIDS policy statements so that when the question of AIDS ministry arises—as it will sooner rather than later—the congregation is ready.

Archbold Evangelical Mennonite Church in Archbold, Ohio, for example, adopted a written statement that supports children infected or affected by AIDS by offering foster care and adoption. The congregation faced the question of what to do when HIV-infected children appear at church and voted on this policy: "Should a parent or guardian of an HIV infected child desire fellowship at Archbold EMC, we shall seek to support them by providing nursery care that is age-appropriate."

Churches are becoming involved in this epidemic. Beyond Rejection Ministries, another ecumenical AIDS program, based in Long Beach, California, is directed by James Johnson, a lay Catholic, who became involved in AIDS work through counseling homosexuals. Beyond Rejection Ministries operates two shelters for people with AIDS and an AIDS "hotel" for homeless people with the disease.

The AIDS Interfaith Council, an association of clergy and laity, provides educational and service programs as well as congregational-based care to people with AIDS and their loved ones.

Dr. Robert R. Redfield, Jr., from the Walter Reed Army Institute of Research, challenges church members with these words: "It is time to reject the temptation of denial of the HIV/AIDS crisis; to reject false prophets who . . . preach prejudice; and to reject those who try to replace God as judge. *The time has come for the Christian community—members and leaders alike—to confront the epi-*

demic with the commitment that comes from Christ's example."

Needs in Your Community

As the numbers of those infected with HIV skyrockets, there will be a dramatic increase in the demand for home and hospice care. Hospices do not warehouse people. Community and family-based hospices provide care, some in houses, but usually in the patients' homes. This requires training of families and friends to provide care. As insurance and hospital costs soar, fewer will receive benefits. As homelessness among HIV-positive people increases, the only care they will receive is that provided by the community. Orphans, including adolescents whose mothers were chronically ill for several years before death, will increase. Most will come from Black and Hispanic populations because these groups have higher birthrates and because homosexuals have few children. Home care will be desperately needed and schooling will be a critical factor.

The world needs a church with Christ's compassion, ready to write a new chapter in *The Ministry of Healing* and add AIDS to the list in Matthew 25. The world needs a church that can simultaneously take strong stands on personal morality and social compassion. The world needs churches that are knowledgeable and trained in HIV prevention and ministry to People With AIDS (PWAs), as well as health ministries to provide health information for the prevention of AIDS and needed health services.

Principles for Ministry with People With AIDS (PWA)

Before initiating any ministry with people who are HIV-positive or have AIDS, there are a number of factors that must be taken into consideration.

To begin with there should be intensive individual and corporate self-examination. Initiating an AIDS ministry may require real courage. The threat to this type of ministry does not come from PWAs, the threat is from those who will oppose you from within your own community, perhaps even your own congregation. There may be both

Statement Concerning the HIV/AIDS Epidemic by the North American Division AIDS Committee

*I*n this second decade, the HIV/AIDS epidemic continues to afflict over one million adult men and women, children, adolescents, and young adults in North America. Lessons learned in the first ten years indicate that factual information and knowledge alone do not change behavior. Gaps still exist between the facts people possess about HIV/AIDS and what they actually do about it.

The Seventh-day Adventist Church upholds its position against the irresponsible use of drugs and narcotics, as well as fostering the belief that the beauty and intimacy of sexual relationships can only be maintained within marriage. Our mission is to build hope and encourage a new start by offering love, compassion, spiritual and emotional support to individuals and communities infected and affected by this disease.

The church will fulfill this mission by training the clergy and laity to respond to the AIDS crisis. Preventive education, decision making and coping skills will be taught. A positive, healthy, Adventist Christian lifestyle will be promoted. Individuals and communities will be empowered to lead health enhancing lives by providing a variety of education, medical, social, nurturing and financial services.

The officers of the North American Division also call attention to the necessity of all members of the Church being taught legitimate, proven, acceptable facts regarding HIV/AIDS. It seems that many individuals are attempting to build on the hysteria surrounding this illness. Unfounded claims are being made concerning the methods by which this disease is spread, as well as how non-health care professionals can care for AIDS patients safely. It is a great disservice to the population at large, as well as to AIDS patients, if extravagant hyperbole is used in the discussion pertaining to this disease. The epidemic is frightening enough, but to add innuendoes to it is unforgivable. It is imperative that books, printed materials, films, or lectures dealing with HIV/AIDS be founded in true science as well as accepted medical practice. (Some people apparently desire to use this epidemic to further their own ends.) We urge any leader to consult recognized AIDS authorities such as those recommended by NAD/ADRA office of AIDS or members of the North American Division AIDS committee prior to distributing or promoting materials, or engaging speakers dealing with this topic, in order to assure that what is about to be presented is factual. Church members who are unduly frightened and/or do not know what the facts are regarding HIV/AIDS may find it difficult, if not impossible, to receive the blessing God desires to give them through ministry to His hurting children who are suffering from this malady.

(See Appendix C, for "The Seventh-day Adventist Church and The AIDS Epidemic: Guidelines" voted at the Annual Council of the General Conference Executive Committee, October 1996.)

subtle and overt criticism. The strain on fellowship may intensify as people with HIV remain or become part of the corporate life of the congregation. People may want you to restrict the ministry to your home, to the hospital or hospice, anywhere away from the church. This spirit, not the spirit of Christ, clearly rejects PWAs. It requires unconditional courage to love unconditionally; to be with PWAs; to be with sick, wasted bodies, anguish, death, and grief; to be with young dying men the age of your son. In ministering to PWAs frequently you will be confronted with recurring illnesses. You will meet care providers who grow weary and frustrated as one acute illness blends into the next; loving, caring people who watch hopelessly as another human body loses its human beauty.

It is essential that you examine your willingness to be exposed to lifestyles that you find unfamiliar and often offensive. Many gay cultures and those of intravenous drug users are worlds away from a conservative Christian lifestyle. But God's people should not reveal one iota of condescension or self-righteousness. They need to follow the example of Jesus who loved and cared for those who did not know that their heavenly Father loved and cared about them, those whose behavior reflected rejection, those who needed to experience the love of their heavenly Father.

Your ministry group must examine your capacity to separate compassion from condoning the conduct by which a person was infected. Support of these persons does not endorse their conduct, rather, support says, "You are valuable and precious to your heavenly Father." We love and accept them because God loves and accepts them. It is for this reason that AIDS ministries challenge moral and theological understandings of God, personal Christian duty, and the value of persons. Christians ministering to PWAs must respond to the confusion of others who are not able to see in the PWA God's precious beloved child.

Christians preparing to minister to PWAs also must assess their reason for choosing this ministry. Has God called them to this ministry? Do all their reasons emerge from their commitment to Christ? If so, then serve by His Spirit. God will give you the courage and strength to do what He called you to do. God will give you the capacity to tolerate rapid change. God will give you the willingness to be inconvenienced and to sacrifice personal interests.

While initial overtures by Christians may be greeted with skepticism by PWAs accustomed to church rejection, a genuine interest and transparent compassion will soon change the picture. Overcoming this suspicion requires patience, loyalty and perseverance, but the suspicion will be overcome.

This type of ministry is unpredictable and defies scheduling. Christians investigating such a ministry must examine their available time. A certain amount of education and training is needed to work with AIDS. That is why the seminar, *A Call to Compassion*, has been developed and is one of the specialty courses that a person can take when working on a Lifestyle Certificate (See Chapter 22.) People must learn medical and physical facts. They must learn about the psychosocial aspects of the disease and about the emotional, social, economic, and relational losses associated with HIV and AIDS.

It is important to develop an understanding about how people touched by HIV feel: the homosexuals, intravenous drug users, their families and friends. Education and training should be sought in methods of pastoral care and ministry, as well as unskilled or semi-skilled nursing. This will involve continuing education. Even more, it will require humility and clarity of purpose found only in the Scriptures and on your knees.

Bible Principles for AIDS Ministry

In Luke 5:17-26 Jesus expresses compassion before the paralytic has opportunity to confess his sins. In fact, it was not the paralytic's faith that was honored, it was the faith of the four friends who brought him to Jesus. Despite the possibility that a sinful life caused his paralysis, Jesus responded proactively, forgiving the man's sins without waiting for confession. It clearly was this kind of behavior on the part of Jesus that caused the hypocritical indignation among the proper, religious folk standing around.

Note that Jesus addressed the spiritual brokenness and guilt before healing the paralysis. Jesus did not play down the guilt factor, He simply moved beyond the immediate physical situation to its root cause (guilt) and took the guilt away. The man was relieved of his guilt, making it possible for healing to occur. Jesus did not condemn; rather His love, acceptance, and hope made healing possible. This story provides a basis for a Christian approach to people with AIDS in today's world. We come not with condemnation, but with Christ's love, hope, and healing power. Even if there is no physical healing, Christ always brings inner healing to every sufferer.

John 3:16 portrays God's eternal work of salvation. The all-inclusiveness of this verse profoundly moves us. God loves unconditionally and universally. Can the Christian do less? God takes care of our past and gives us a future, this is the good news. God never excludes people from the Kingdom of God because of their past history. God forgives all. People are eternally lost, not because of their sins but because they refuse God's forgiveness. This ultimate tragedy comes when salvation is in our grasp but we refuse it.

The Scriptures indicate that God's love extends to the person with AIDS. No matter what history those suffering have, no matter how little they know of God's way, Christ died for them and His heart reaches out to them through His faithful followers. In the well-known story of the Good Samaritan (Luke 10:25-37), nothing is mentioned about the sufferer's race, nationality, moral state, or religious faith. All that is known is that he fell among thieves on a particularly dangerous section of the road to Jericho. Jesus redefined the term "neighbor" to represent any person who needs help, particularly help that we can provide. In this context, the person's need and that alone is what is important. Those who suffer from AIDS need our compassion. What we can do, Christ asks us to do for "neighbors" who are HIV-positive. The fact that they suffer and are in need is all that is necessary for God's children to reach out the hand of mercy and care.

Luke 4:18 records Jesus' inaugural sermon in His home church. In Luke's Gospel, this passage is the primary identification of the ministry of Jesus with the kingdom of God. In Jesus the kingdom is present, and it is person-oriented, not judgment-oriented. Love, acceptance and forgiveness take priority over judgment. This is consistent with God's historical pattern. (See Exodus 19:4; 20:1,2.) It is important to note that the kingdom of God is concerned with healing and its focus is on those who live on the margins of society.

The mission of Jesus includes a command for His followers to reach out to the modern "leper," the people on the edges of the community who carry HIV in their bodies; those who are dying with AIDS. Literally poverty-stricken by the economics of their health care and marginalized by the fear connected with AIDS, they are to be a special focus of Christ's mission.

Ellen White advises that Isaiah 58 is a passage that should be read often. It is basic to Adventism and to the ministry of compassion. It involves the incarnation of the gospel. This is not simply because the sufferers need it, but because it is our way of demonstrating God. To refuse to do this, or to do it poorly, is to perjure God. To reach out with healing and compassion to the poor, the oppressed, the hurting, and the sick, is to participate in God's redemptive project in this sin-sick world.

Can God bring healing to those who have been told that there is no cure known to medicine? Mark 16:17, 18 is a problematic passage for many Christians, particularly Seventh-day Adventists, but it is an integral part of Scripture, never having been revoked. Ellen White spoke of it as a sign of the true church and true disciples:

> When the Saviour said, "Go…. teach all nations," He also said, "These signs shall follow them that believe; In My name shall they cast out devils; they shall speak with new tongues; they shall take up serpents; and if they drink any deadly thing, it shall not hurt them; they shall lay hands on the sick, and they shall recover." The promise is as far-reaching as the commission. Not that all the gifts are imparted to each believer. The Spirit divides "to every person severally as He will…The promise is just as strong and trustworthy now as in the days of the apostles…This is the privilege of God's children, and faith should lay hold on all that it is possible to have as an endorsement of faith (*The Desire of Ages*, p. 823).

The gospel is to be presented, not as a lifeless theory, but as a living force to change the life. God desires that the receivers of His grace shall be witnesses to its power. Those whose course has been most offensive to Him He freely accepts; when they repent, He imparts to them His divine Spirit, places them in the highest positions of trust, and sends them forth…. (*The Desire of Ages*, p. 826).

Can we pray with faith for the healing of a terminal AIDS patient today? Of course, such prayer is appropriate. Those who minister with people who have AIDS must have the spiritual maturity to deal with the times when no physical healing results, but they also need to spend much time in prayer for those to whom they minister. Few ministries will be more spiritually demanding, few will come closer to the heart of the believer. (See Chapter 8.)

Developing an AIDS Ministry

Into a world fascinated with the notion of affliction's sinful cause, Jesus entered, giving attention to illness and affliction as opportunities to experience God's compassion and love. Into a world that judged some as sinners and made outcasts of others, Jesus came to forgive sin and cleanse the leper. In doing so, He gave a preview of God's kingdom where mercy and justice kiss each other.

Jesus redefined the meaning and activities of holiness. Holiness included entry into the lives of others. Holiness became an act of engagement, not a state of separation. In Jesus, holiness took on the suffering of others. Holiness associated with the meek, the lowly and despised. In Jesus, holiness' healing touch was the touch of inclusion and participation. The healing miracles of the New Testament present a Jesus who broke down barriers and took the kind of risks which challenge us today. Jesus risked unconditionally for the neighbor; risked without fear for His reputation; risked for the sake of the kingdom; risked His life and lost it, and rose again to reveal the promise of life eternal.

Preparing Your Church for an AIDS Ministry

1. Meet with Leaders. Hold special meetings with your church board, Sabbath School teachers, elders, deacons, and other church leaders to begin discussing the challenges HIV/AIDS puts before your congregation, and to begin putting together a plan to respond to the issue.

2. Plan Special Services. Plan several special services or Sabbath School sessions with HIV/AIDS panels comprised of members of the congregation interested in researching and presenting information. Panels can present: medical facts, education issues, legislation updates, ministry ideas and methods, etc. Choose participants who are in the health care, legal, education, or insurance professions, as well as concerned citizens who can address the issues from their perspectives.

3. Bring in Experts. Contact a ministry for people with HIV/AIDS (drug abusers, inner-city youth, or other communities in which HIV infection is prevalent) in your area. Invite them to present their ministry challenges and needs to your congregation. This could provide a special home missions or social concerns emphasis in a missions conference or service.

4. Emphasize the Problems. Plan a specific worship emphasis on those working in or touched by the epidemic: physicians and health-care workers, infected individuals and their families, HIV/AIDS-related ministries, etc.

5. Teach Youth. Plan special meetings with your church young people to help them understand HIV/AIDS, how it is transmitted, and their risks of contracting the virus. A variety of videos and materials are available for a teenage audience.

6. Inform and Educate. Plan information and education efforts to help members of the congregation understand that HIV/AIDS is a problem for all segments of society, that it is affecting many communities: sexually active teens, IV drug users, practicing homosexuals/bisexuals; spouses and children of HIV-infected individuals, and friends of those infected.

7. Pray. Make HIV/AIDS a regular matter for prayer among prayer chains, prayer circles, or other programs within your church. Begin to use examples related to HIV/AIDS in sermons and devotional settings to help members begin to see the epidemic as a part of the church's venue of concern and ministry.

8. Get Involved. Encourage members to participate in community education programs set up to recommend HIV/AIDS curricula for the schools and to help establish policy.

9. Talk about HIV/AIDS. Once people understand that your church is one willing to offer compassion and assistance, they will be able to come forward and discuss their needs related to the epidemic

Find Out What Your Community Is Doing for AIDS

1. Attend Conferences. Send representatives from your congregation to HIV/AIDS conferences and observe ministries already underway to brief church staff and leadership on ways your church can become involved.

2. Do Some Research. Find ministry opportunities related to HIV/AIDS, such as:

- Creating support groups for HIV-positive individuals and their families.
- Providing for practical needs of HIV-positive individuals, such as: food, transportation, household chores, etc.
- Providing housing for HIV-positive individuals no longer able to afford housing or to care for themselves.
- Providing housing for families of HIV-positive individuals hospitalized in your community.
- Offering companionship to those infected; in person or a telephone ministry conducted by those who are themselves house-bound.
- Encouraging members to provide foster or adoptive care for HIV positive children or children orphaned because their parents have died of HIV related diseases.
- Establishing a prayer ministry for individuals involved in the issue in the community and the nation.
- Encouraging members to provide volunteer service in existing community programs for HIV positive individuals and their families

3. Start an AIDS Ministry. Determine how these ministries can fit into existing church programs, and begin efforts to include HIV/AIDS as part of your church ministry outreach.

4. Raise Funds. Adopt a church-wide or special group project to raise funds for HIV/AIDS-related ministries. Projects could include: a walkathon, car wash, talent show, special offering, bake sale, craft sale, etc..

5. Organize Town Hall Meetings. Set up a community-wide meeting with other concerned churches to address questions related to HIV/AIDS and how it will affect both the community and its citizens.

Getting Started with Your Program

As you begin to build strategies for an AIDS ministry, there are a number of questions that must be asked. Many sincere Christians make a common mistake; they arrive at answers without ever having asked the correct questions. Do a "needs assessment." You might ask:

- What are the current AIDS trends in your community?
- What community attitudes toward people with AIDS prevail?
- What other ministries to PWAs are already in place?
- What community programs exist?
- Is another program needed or would it be a better use of time and money to support or cooperate with an existing program?
- What arrangements are there for testing and counseling?
- What is the public school curriculum on HIV/AIDS?
- Are there programs for needle exchange or for condom distribution?
- What needs do organizations who are working in your community fulfill?
- What needs are not being met?
- What about health and dental care, provision of medication, transportation, day care, child care, play and recreational therapy, housekeepers, laundry and house cleaning, ability to purchase food, food preparation?
- What other needs are present in your community relative to AIDS?
- What is being done for AIDS orphans?
- How many support groups exist for PWAs and/or their families?

- Are any churches now providing or planning in the future to offer healing services?
- What are the options for long-term health care?
- What are the available sources for home or hospice care?
- What nursing homes accept people with AIDS?
- What is the situation in your area regarding adolescent homelessness, with its attendant problems of drugs and prostitution?
- Is there a shelter for runaway teenagers?
- A hotline for them to call?
- What are the resources in your community that would enable you to minister effectively to PWA?
- Is any assistance available from such organizations as the county health department or human services agency, or local philanthropic institutions?

Many communities have good AIDS education and direct service resource people available. Find out who the people are in your area who are informed about AIDS and invite them to help your group with your planning. If there is an AIDS service organization in your town, it will have people to suggest. Check, also, with your county medical society, the local Red Cross chapter or the Visiting Nurse Association. Perhaps there are clergy or lay persons in your community who have AIDS training and experience in AIDS program development. Perhaps there is an interfaith committee that already coordinates the efforts of various churches to address the AIDS crisis. Reach out to these organizations. You probably will be able to find people with practical knowledge and experience who are happy to help you.

No matter how many members your congregation has or how large or small its budget might be, there are things you can do that will make a difference. You might be doing some of them already. Remember, people with AIDS have needs that are very similar to the needs of other people who have chronic or life-threatening illnesses.

For example:

1. PWAs may want to participate in a prayer group, a program of spiritual nurture, or be with people who understand the grieving process.
2. PWAs may like opportunities to tell their story about what it is like to be living with AIDS. PWAs and their loved ones are the most valuable resource persons your church or community can have when it comes to designing an appropriate, effective AIDS ministry. Help them collect their pictures in an album, their mementos in a scrapbook. Help them make audio tapes that describe the contents of their books, perhaps video tape the discussion of each important item. Encourage them to write out their story, or type it for them. Help them with their autobiography.
3. PWAs may feel abandoned or alone. Telephone calls and face-to-face visits are important. Call before visiting and discuss when to come and what to bring. Going out to dinner, to church, to a concert or a recreational event or just going to the mall can be welcome interludes and things PWAs look forward to doing with others.
4. PWAs will need help with basic tasks such as house cleaning, laundry, doing dishes, grocery shopping, picking up the mail or posting letters. These are tasks that need not take up a great deal of time, but that can be over-tiring to a person with AIDS.
5. Some PWAs require assistance keeping track of doctors' appointments and getting to and from the hospital, doctor's office or pharmacy. Often they need a person who will organize their medications by time and day, someone to put their pills in cups or medicine boxes, labeled by time and day.
6. Some PWAs need home-delivered meals which could be prepared by church members or in the church kitchen and delivered by volunteers.
7. Some PWAs need someone to be a financial advocate to provide help filling out and submitting medical and disability benefit forms,

as well as end-of-life planning, including the preparation of a will, instructions for a memorial service and/or funeral, and burial arrangements.

8. Some PWAs need someone to act as an intermediary to help with family reconciliation and to facilitate saying good-bye to loved ones.

9. Some PWAs are so weak as to require the simple bodily care (such as bathing, toilet needs, hair cutting and washing) that a friend can give.

10. A PWA may find himself or herself in need of legal advocates owing to housing or job discrimination, or denial of health care services.

Most important of all, people who have AIDS, their loved ones, family members, and care providers, know AIDS first hand. They can talk with your congregation about what it is like to be living with AIDS and to care for someone who has AIDS. Their stories and experiences are invaluable. These are the people who can tell you what their needs are and how your church might respond. Include these people from the outset as you become involved in AIDS ministries.

Do not be afraid of people who have AIDS, their care providers or loved ones. You cannot get AIDS by talking to, sitting beside, embracing, eating with, touching or praying with a person who has AIDS, or by letting that person use the facilities of your church or home. Of course, you need to be careful—this is important with any infectious disease, but don't let this stop you from helping others. It is through being in ministry with persons whose lives have been touched by AIDS that churches know anew what it means to be the Church following Jesus' example.

It is of the utmost importance that your pastor and church board members are involved in the AIDS education process. Without their support, little that you do will avail.

What an AIDS Program Can Do

Many different kinds of activities can be used to implement an AIDS program in your church.

Some examples include the following:

1. Volunteers can be recruited to provide the kinds of personal attention listed in the section above. If there are local AIDS service organizations already providing some of these services, coordinate with them.

2. In communities with many PWAs, your center or church can provide space, even telephone use and secretarial assistance, for local AIDS service organizations.

3. Use the church kitchen during the week for the preparation of meals to be delivered to PWAs; a specialized Meals on Wheels program.

4. Provide regular weekly congregate meals at the church for PWAs, their families and friends. Because many PWAs are interested in a healthful, vegetarian diet, the Adventist Church can provide particular expertise in this area.

5. Offer pastoral care and bereavement counseling. This may be part of the pastor's outreach to non-members, or lay pastoral volunteers can be trained for this ministry.

6. Develop respite programs for AIDS care providers. This might take the form of occasional volunteers or drop-off facilities where persons with AIDS can spend all or part of a day while their care provider is at work.

7. Organize recreational and cultural events that are open and comfortable for PWAs.

8. Develop programs for AIDS orphans. Eventually this must go beyond just volunteers visiting "border babies" in the hospital, but that is a good place to begin.

9. Work with foster care agencies to find prospective foster care placements for children or youth who have AIDS.

10. Open a day care program to serve the needs of children and families who are affected by AIDS.

11. Work with other groups in the community to provide AIDS prevention educational programs.

12. Coordinate with interfaith efforts to secure adequate housing, in-home care, skilled nursing care, hospice care, and other services that people with AIDS need.

13. Send one or two representatives to take the American Red Cross African-American HIV/AIDS Instructor Course. (Each person must complete the Instructor Candidate Training [ITC] prerequisite course first.) Then offer the first-aid training course in HIV/AIDS for your church members and community.

14. Participate in AIDS awareness events, such as the NAMES Project where a giant quilt is being made from panels memorializing the names of those who have died of AIDS.

The Needs of Women and Children

Women and children with AIDS may be a particular focus for you to explore as you build your ministry. Because large numbers of women and children have recently developed AIDS, this is a new area of need.

Find out how many such children and families are in your community and their needs.

- Are most of the children with HIV or AIDS living at home with their families?
- Are there children who have been left in area hospitals with no one to care about them?
- Are there children in need of foster or adoptive homes?
- Are there church members who would be willing to care for an HIV-infected child or assist a family by providing respite care or doing baby-sitting?
- What family-wide services are available in your community?
- Are there needs that are not being met?
- What advocacy is needed?

The siblings of children infected with HIV have special needs for friends, people to play with and support them. You might consider starting a support group for parents of children with HIV or AIDS. Here are some questions to consider:

- Do families in your community hide the infection status of family members? Why?
- How can your church respond?
- What child-centered programs could your church, perhaps together with other groups

in the community, develop for children with HIV or AIDS and other children?

- Are there any children who have special developmental delays for which early intervention strategies can be developed?
- Is HIV education being included in the health curriculum of the elementary and secondary schools in your town? Perhaps that can be supplemented through HIV/AIDS prevention programs and seminars at your church. What additional efforts need to be made to help the youth of your community avoid those behaviors that will put them at risk for infection?

What about prevention education for women? Find out the following:

- What prevention education and materials are available for women in your community?
- Are the materials culturally sensitive and in the women's first language?

Perhaps your health education center can become the women's HIV information center for your community. You could find many ways to cooperate with your church women's groups to support HIV prevention education for women in order to help protect their own health and avoid the possibility of mother-to-child HIV transmission. Find out:

- Are there women with HIV infection who are caring for children who are also infected?
- What outreach can your women's group or congregation make to them?

Maybe you can organize a volunteer team to "adopt" one or more of these families, visit regularly, provide respite care, help with household chores, and just spend time listening and being a friend.

Here are more considerations:

- Are children and families with HIV infection discriminated against in any way in your community?
- What attitude barriers exist that create negative responses to these families?

• Are there organizations for women of color or groups made up of clergy from minorities with whom you might collaborate to work with health professionals and child-care professionals to address the needs of children, women, and families of color? (This is particularly important if your community has significant numbers of immigrants.)

Adventist Resources

• **Information**: *AIDS Information.* Contact Dr. Bruce Moyer, Institute of World Missions, Andrews University, Berrien Springs, MI 49104; (616) 471-6532; Fax (616) 471-6252; CompuServe 74617,2465; Internet: bcmoyer@adrews.edu

• **Video**: *A Call to Compassion* is available from ADRA International by dialing (800) 931-ADRA [2372].

• **Manual**: *Compassion in a Time of AIDS*: A manual created especially for pastors and church leaders on how to minister to people with AIDS. Order from Advent*Source* (800) 328-0525.

Resource Organizations

• AIDS Action Council, 2033 M Street, Suite 802, Washington DC 20036; (202) 293-2886; Fax (202) 296-1292.

• AIDS Information Hotline, U.S. Public Health Service, Department of Health and Human Services, 5600 Fishers Lane, Rockville, MD 20857; (800) 342-AIDS.

World AIDS Day

*O*nce a year on December 1 people throughout the world come together in an organized manner to draw attention to the fight against AIDS. This effort is designed to encourage public support for development of prevention programs and to provide education and awareness on issues surrounding HIV/AIDS. The first World AIDS Day held on December 1, 1988 was proposed out of a meeting of the World Summit of Health Ministers for programs for AIDS prevention in London. It was suggested by the World Health Organization (WHO), an agency of the United States. Their focus was on encouraging governments, communities and individuals to talk about AIDS. In 1989 and 1990 the theme was Youth and Women, 1991 Sharing the Challenge, and in 1992 Community Commitment. In 1993 the theme was "Time to Act," which called for immediate measures to be taken by everyone to stop the spread of AIDS. In 1994 the theme was AIDS and the Family; in 1995, Shared Rights, Shared Responsibilities; and in 1996, One World, One Hope.

World AIDS Day provides an opportunity for individuals in churches to become involved not just on one day but throughout the year. Churches can become involved by

1. sponsoring a community seminar to provide information about HIV/AIDS,
2. having a special prayer service or candlelight service,
3. arranging a moment of silence on December 1, or the Saturday before and throughout the year for the struggle of AIDS,
4. holding your own World AIDS Day events,
5. distributing and encourage the wearing of red ribbons,
6. planning an AIDS walk or activity with another church or community organization,
7. having special AYS meetings.

For more information about World AIDS Day activities which differ each year, contact the American Association for World Health, 1129 20th Street, NW, Suite 400, Washington, D.C. 20036-3403, (202) 466-5883 or U.N. Health (212) 824-6643.

—Caroline Watkins

• American Foundation for AIDS Research, 5900 Wilshire Blvd., Second Floor, East Satellite, Los Angeles CA 90036; (213) 857-5900.

• American Social Health Association National AIDS Hotline, Box 13827, Research Triangle Park, NC 27709. Hotline, (800) 342-2437; Spanish hotline (800) 344-7432; deaf access/TDD (800) 243-7889.

• AIDS National Interfaith Network (ANIN), 110 Maryland Ave. NE, Rm. 504, Washington D.C. 20002; (202) 546-0807; Fax (202) 546-5103.

• The National Coalition of Hispanic Health and Human Services Organizations (COSSMHO), 1030 15th St., N.W., Suite 1053, Washington DC 20005; (202) 371-2100.

• Health Education Resource Organization, 101 West Reed St., Suite 825, Baltimore MD 21201; (410) 685-1180.

• National Minority AIDS Council, 300 Eye St., N.E., Suite 400, Washington, DC. 20002; (202) 544-1076; Fax (202) 544-0378.

• Pediatric AIDS Foundation, 2407 Wilshire Blvd., Suite 613, Santa Monica, CA 90403; (800) 552-0444.

Other Resource Materials

AIDS: A Guide for Hispanic Leadership from the National Coalition of Hispanic Health and Human Services Organizations (COSSMHO), Washington, DC.

AIDS: A Self-Care Manual from the Los Angeles AIDS Project, Santa Monica, CA: IBS Press, 1987.

AIDS: Ending an Epidemic. Do It Now Foundation, publication H105, 1988.

AIDS: Facts and Issues. New Brunswick, New Jersey: Rutgers University Press, 1986.

Beckham, Dixie, *When a Friend Has AIDS.* Diego Lopez, Luis Palacios-Jiminez, Vincent Patti and Michael Shernoff, New York: Chelsea Psychotherapy Associates, 1990.

Colman, Warren, *Understanding and Preventing AIDS.* Chicago: Children's Press, 1987.

Hitchens, Neal,*Fifty Things You Can Do About AIDS.* Los Angeles: Lowell House, 1992.

Kubler-Ross, Elizabeth, *AIDS-The Ultimate Challenge.* New York: Macmillan, 1987.

Latest Facts about AIDS a series of fact sheets from the American Red Cross and U.S. Public Health Service on topics such as "AIDS and Shooting Drugs," "AIDS and Your Job—Are There Risks?" and "Caring for the AIDS Patient at Home" (American Red Cross, 17th and D Streets NW, Washington, DC 20006).

Sunderland, Ronald H., and Earl E. Shelp, *AIDS: A Manual for Pastoral Care,* Philadelphia: The Westminster Press, 1987.

Sunderland, Ronald H., and Earl E. Shelp, *AIDS and the Church,* Philadelphia: The Westminster Press, 1986.

Surgeon General's Report on Acquired Immunodeficiency Syndrome, available from the U.S. Public Health Service, Department of Health and Human Services, 5600 Fishers Lane, Rockville MD 20857.

Volunteer Program Development Manual from the National Minority AIDS Council, Washington DC.

13

Mental Health Ministries

Look around your local church next Sabbath morning. Do you see anyone who has a child with special needs? Has anyone recently lost a child, or spouse, or job? Do you know anyone who is dealing with marital infidelity? Are there families whose relationships appear to be strained or unhappy? Does anyone appear to be anxious, dissatisfied with life, depressed, or isolated? Look at the best dressed; the worst dressed; the leadership; the uninvolved—are there any similarities? If you can answer yes to any of these questions, your church is made up of normal people who face normal challenges of everyday life. How people respond to these challenges often reveals their mental health and thus, their overall well-being.

Most people think of *physical* health when they hear the word "health." However, recent research about promoting health and preventing disease indicates that health is a state of total well-being. This broader definition of health includes well-being in physical, mental and emotional reactions, as well as the spiritual and social dimensions of the human experience. The various dimensions of health are important; just as different body parts perform specific functions that are important to the overall performance.

The first section of this chapter explores the concept of mental health and ways to assess and improve personal mental health, as well as outlining specific steps that you can take to enhance an existing program or launch a new initiative. The last section deals with the specific mental health issues of child abuse, domestic violence, eating disorders and suicide.

Your Role as Health Ministries Leader

At all levels of the Adventist church, there are human beings with needs. Besides the basic needs—something to eat, something to wear and somewhere to live—we humans have many men-

tal, social, emotional and spiritual needs that we try to meet. One of these needs, designed by the Creator, is the need to worship; to bond with something or someone that we believe can satisfy our soul's deepest needs. We want to belong; to feel safe; to feel loved and to have someone/something to love.

When these needs are not met in the ways we expect, we look for other people, places and/or things that we believe can satisfy those needs. Again, because of how we were created— to worship—we will go to extraordinary means to find something, or someone, or somewhere that feels safe for the physical, emotional and social parts of our being. In our search many of us go through life just on the edge of satisfaction, with only temporary inner peace. We would like to be whole, but we need tools and need guidance in using the tools. Some of us even need someone outside of ourselves to help us believe that we can be whole and victorious over forces that oppose our efforts to become whole.

As health ministries leader, you and the team of people who work with you have an awesome opportunity. Think of it: You can help people find the resources they need to become whole; to have their needs met or, to be content with *what* is. These resources include prayer; accurate information from reliable sources; social support; comfort, counsel and instruction from the Scriptures and sometimes, professional "people helpers" such as marriage and family counselors, social workers, pastoral counselors, clinical psychologists, psychiatrists and other licensed and/or certified professional counselors.

Sometimes our emotional needs may be related to spiritual needs as well. If so, your work will require a strong, steady connection with the Wonderful Counselor of Isaiah 9.6. ("For unto us a Child is born…. And His name will be called Wonderful, Counselor…") He alone has infinite wisdom and understanding of every situation. However, it is also part of His plan that we can be co-laborers with Him, assisting the Holy Spirit in bridging the gap between heaven and humanity.

What Is Mental Health Among Christians?

There are many definitions of mental health. Some describe mental health as the ability to negotiate life's challenges without experiencing undue dysfunction. Other authors refer to a mental health continuum, with mental illness at one end and psychological balance at the other end. Individuals with mental illness display symptoms that are identifiable and listed in the official manual of mental disorders that is published by the American Psychiatric Association. At the other end of the mental health continuum is a state of balance between psychological distress (for example, temporary times of depression or anxiety) and psychological well-being (for example, a sense of inner peace and true purpose). Most of us are somewhere along this continuum.

> "Great wisdom is needed in dealing with diseases caused through the mind. A sore, sick heart, a discouraged mind, needs mild treatment…. Sympathy and tact will often prove a greater benefit to the sick than will the most skillful treatment given in a cold indifferent way."
>
> —Ellen White, *The Ministry of Healing*, p. 244.

From a Christian perspective, mental health is a state of dynamic equilibrium where positive self-regard is developed through responsible interdependence with others and a vital relationship with God and characterized by the fruits of the spirit (love, joy, peace, longsuffering, kindness, goodness, faithfulness, gentleness, self-control [Gal. 5:22, 23]).

A person's mental health is largely subjective and determined by personal interpretation and perception. One individual develops a debilitating disease and faces an uncertain future with a joy that is an encouragement to others, while another in a similar circumstance gives up and suffers from bouts of depression and anger. How we see and interpret an experience, rather than the experience itself, seems to determine our well-being.

Most Christians deal with such mental health issues as occasional depression, perfectionism, issues around identity or fear on a fairly regular basis. Some have experienced abuse, codependency, hopelessness, and reluctance to forgive. Furthermore, because of the connection between our minds and our bodies, negative thoughts and attitudes may have led to physical illness and/or disease.

Ellen White describes the relationship between the mind and body as intimate: "Courage, hope, faith, sympathy, love, promote health and prolong life. A contented mind, a cheerful spirit, is health to the body and strength to the soul" (*The Ministry of Healing*, 1905, p. 241). The converse also is true: "Grief, anxiety, discontent, remorse, guilt, distrust, all tend to break down the life forces and to invite decay and death" (*Ibid.*).

Some associate the term "mental health" with attendants in white, hallways with locked doors, and the proverbial psychiatrist's couch, and therefore resist seeking help when they have an emotional problem they can't seem to solve. Sometimes people are reluctant to admit that they have problems because they believe that having problems is sinful. Others who admit to having a problem have been told that all they need to do is pray. Sometimes people pray for years about a certain person, situation, idea or goal, but their prayers seem unanswered.

As Christians the more healthy view of "mental health" is based on the assumption that because of sin we will have troubles and tribulation (John 16.33), but that we are never called upon to bear our trials alone. Also, there are God-ordained limits to what we have to experience (1 Cor. 10.13). Finally, we have this word of hope: "God never leads His children otherwise than they would choose to be led, if they could see the end from the beginning, and discern the glory of the purpose which they are fulfilling as coworkers with Him" (*The Desire of Ages*, pp. 224-225).

God has generously and lovingly offered Christians many additional resources for dealing with frustrations and challenges of everyday life. Prayer is at the top of the list. When we are "in tune" with divine wisdom, then we don't need to worry. We can trust God for healing, love and power. Prayer time is like a personal audience with the wonderful Counselor. He knows us intimately—the circumstances of our birth, our childhood, adulthood and eternity. He alone is capable of providing all we need to become whole persons. What appear to be "unanswered prayers" may actually be God leading in our lives.

Notwithstanding His divine wisdom and power, it also is part of God's loving plan to use people to help one another toward their ideals. Besides direct communion with Him, members also can share their burdens with trained, safe mental health professionals or other trusted individuals.

What Are Your Mental Health Strengths and Weaknesses?

*H*ere are some questions that can guide your thinking about strengths and weaknesses in your mental health. Take a few thoughtful minutes to write out your answers to the following questions. The answers will serve as a baseline from which you can observe changes in your mental attitudes, values and behaviors.

1. What is your definition of optimal mental health?
2. How mentally healthy do you think you are? What did you use to assess your mental health?
3. Describe some of the personal challenges that you have faced in the past 12 months? What coping strategies worked for you? Which ones did not work?
4. Which resources (people, books, Scriptures, etc.) were recommended to you? Which resources did you use? Which ones did you choose to disregard? Why?
5. Whom do you trust to share with or to direct you to help when you are in need?
6. What is your attitude toward seeking professional counseling from sources outside the Adventist Church? From sources within the Adventist Church?
7. What Scripture texts or stories do you rely on for:
   a. Maintaining positive mental health?
   b. Encouragement during troubled times?
   c. Counsel for decision-making?
   d. Building trust between you and God?

If you have never thought through answers to these kinds of questions, this exercise may open an exciting avenue of exploration. Did you discover any negative attitudes or some reluctance to look at some of these issues in your own life? If so, take heart. There probably are others just like you in your local congregation. Your own timidity/reluctance may help you to be even more compassionate toward your church family members.

If you have thought through answers to these questions, thank the Lord for the result of your prayers, therapy, struggles and victories. However, it may be helpful to try and remember how it was for you before you discovered God's wonderful plan for you. Perhaps you kept a journal; or maybe there is someone who guided you through a difficult period to some helpful resources. Talk to that person and find out what the person remembers about how it was before. Recollection can help you to understand how some members might respond or react to a church-sponsored initiative to improve mental health. The key is *compassion*.

We can consult God's Word for information, comfort, direction and healing. Combined with prayer, the words of Scripture can be trusted to give powerful, dependable advice and strength for managing life successfully.

Here are some of the positive and negative mental health issues that Christians face:

- Anxiety
- Courage
- Depression
- Hope
- Faith
- Anger
- Perfectionism
- Issues of identity (for example: low self-esteem, problems with the self)
- Guilt
- Codependency
- Fear
- An ungrateful spirit
- Bitterness, resentment
- Lack of forgiveness

"The Lord can do nothing toward the recovery of man until, convinced of his own weakness, and stripped of all self-sufficiency, he yields himself to the control of God…. From the soul that feels his need, nothing is withheld. He has unrestricted access to Him in whom all fullness dwells."

—*The Desire of Ages*, p. 300.

Steps to Developing and Enhancing Your Mental Health Program

Step 1: Building personal awareness about mental health issues

The first step in setting up an active, successful mental health component of your health ministries program is self-examination. Identifying and understanding your own attitudes, beliefs, values and behaviors can increase personal awareness that will eventually affect the mental health needs and interests of others in your church family.

How mentally healthy are you? Do you feel equipped to handle the challenges and difficulties of daily life? What role does your religion play in dealing with the frustrations of everyday life—frustrations like dealing with faulty appliances, congested traffic or handling small children? Is your spirituality a help or a hindrance? Different forms of religion have proven to be either positive (healthy) or negative (unhealthy) influences on mental health. For example, hundreds of cyanide-induced deaths in Guyana were associated with commitment to a religious leader, Jim Jones. On the other hand, Mother Teresa has inspired thousands with her message of social change through involvement in religious causes.

Step 2: Addressing your personal mental health issues

Why do we ignore physical symptoms that suggest actual problems? Why do we blame others for the unhappiness in our lives? What is the underlying reason for arguing about working conditions when the boss approaches us about tardiness? Personal examination can give us insight into the feelings that underlie the behaviors and attitudes we want to change.

The role of acceptance in mental health

The first step in addressing mental health issues, or changing any type of behavior, is to admit that there is a problem—such as depending on food, work, church activity or sex to medicate the pain of loneliness.

Many try to solve their problems with such pseudo-solutions such as academic or career success, material possessions, control, preoccupation with religious rules, and abusive behaviors to meet their own needs for love and/or belonging. When they discover one pseudo solution doesn't work, they often try another. Or they try the same ineffective solution again and again.

However, it's impossible to truly overcome negative mental health issues until you admit that (1) negative solutions are not working, and (2) your life has become unmanageable.

It's easy to "self-medicate" and get caught in the web of trying to overcome negative attitudes and/or behaviors on your own. Some people have to reach the "rock bottom" before they will admit defeat, and seek God's help, and the professional help they need.

In the process of growing psychologically more healthy, people often experience a spiritual awakening; a "new and improved" relationship with God. The inverse is also true. Improving one's relationship with God can improve mental health.

The role of confession in mental health

In addition to admitting to ones powerlessness to God, James 5:16 suggests that confessing faults to and praying for one another are prerequisites for healing.

Admitting wrongs to a trusted person and to God provides a sense of relief from the burdens (secrets) people often try to hide. Confession helps people accept their history and themselves as they are. It also helps them to receive the fulness of the love that God has always had for them. However frightening it may be to share ones wrongs with another person, this act of

A Personal Testimony

I wonder how many readers will decide to simply skip Step 2 after reading the first few paragraphs? My own experience of personal soul-searching led me to admit my self-defeating attitudes and behavior patterns to another human being. It was not easy—especially since one of my weaknesses was people-pleasing. (I thought that if I shared my negatives, people surely would not like me. I tried to manage people's impressions of me so that they only had positive information on which to base their opinions of me. What a lot of work that was!)

In spite of my fear, I moved ahead cautiously through the process of confession. I would like to say that I willingly and bravely embarked on the confession part of Step 2. However, the truth is that I went kicking and screaming, "I'm not OK but I'm not as bad as…" all the way to the confession setting.

What helped me most was the accepting, understanding response of the person I confessed to. From that person's example I was strengthened to believe that God would also respond with compassion to my emotional weaknesses. During those difficult times, this comforting passage from The *Desire of Ages* (p. 483) was revealed to me:

> "Through all our trials we have a never-failing Helper…. [He says] 'I have endured your sorrows, experienced your struggles, encountered your temptations. I know your tears, I also have wept. The grief that lies too deep to be breathed into any human ear, I know. Think not that you are desolate and forsaken, …The mountains shall depart, and the hills be removed, but My kindness shall not depart from thee, neither shall the covenant of My peace be removed, saith the Lord that hath mercy on thee.' Isaiah 54.10."

God has never disappointed my cautious efforts to address some of my mental health issues. I have felt humbled and reluctant to confess even the most seemingly innocent of wrongs. I feared the listener might be shocked or offended by my sharing. What actually happened instead was, I felt added support from other human beings—their prayers, cards of encouragement; a shared gem from the Bible; or sometimes a simple friendly message on our voice-mail. I might not have encountered these thoughtful love offerings if I had chosen to keep trying to hide my pain.

—*Donna Davis Cameron*

> "It is the duty of every person, for his own sake and for the sake of humanity, to inform himself in regard to the laws of life and conscientiously to obey them…. They should study the influence of the mind upon the body and of the body upon the mind, and the laws by which they are governed."
>
> —Ellen White, *Testimonies*, Vol. 3, p. 229.

courage and humility can free people from isolation and loneliness, but it must be done with sensitivity and common sense. An excellent guide to use is *The Twelve Steps for Christians*. (See Mental Health Resources at the end of this section.) This book gives suggestions about types of persons to share with: a pastor or trained women's ministry leader, a trusted friend, doctor or psychologist, a family member, or a member of a 12-step program. In any case confession of negative attitudes and destructive behaviors can be the bridge to recovery from self-defeating attitudes.

Find a group of supportive individuals Authors S. Arterburn and J. Felton write that, "If a person is to recover…it will be done with the assistance of a group of caring individuals. *It cannot be done alone*" (*Toxic Faith*, p. 284). The groups can provide support and accountability, both vital elements of the recovery process. If the first group you find does not meet your needs, keep looking. There is at least one group where you can experience acceptance and freedom to express emotions. Ask God to reveal it to you. Ask your friends or your pastor, but don't rest until you find it.

Arterburn and Felton conclude that "True love, the experience of unconditional positive regard, is an extremely healing force. The experience of true love from the group enables addicts to love themselves, God, and others" (*Ibid.*, p. 286). May you experience this true love—it is life-changing.

Step 3: Sharing mental health resources and information

Hopefully by now you and your team have started to notice human behavior in a new way. Maybe you are more aware of the positive and negative mental health issues (e.g., anger, faith, unforgiving spirits, perfectionism). Perhaps you have started reading some of the books listed in the Mental Health Resources at the end of this section. Or you have sought out a trusted counselor or friend. Some people may have decided to start sharing with God in a more intimate way.

Check out local community resources

Your next task is to discover resources that are available in your community. This includes organizations that can be found in the telephone directory—social service organizations, mental health services, psychologists' referral and information services, counselors, etc. These organizations and individuals, along with universities, schools, hospitals, work sites and health departments often have expertise, materials, and sometimes speakers to help local church leaders in their mental health education and awareness programs.

Just as you and your team began with a brief assessment of your personal mental health attitudes and practices, your team can provide opportunities for your church family to assess its current strengths and needs. This can be done, using a set of questions similar to those that appear in Step One of this chapter. Also, screening questionnaires obtainable from mental health professionals may be useful in determining the needs *and* interests of your local church members. Remember that there may be issues that need professional assistance. Be open and aware of these needs and have resources/contacts for referrals available.

Document all your activities, contacts, advice, questions, successes, failures.

A useful intermediate step in assessing the need for any educational effort is to study information about mental health trends within the denomination, as well as in the general population. If you need further information, call the Adventist PlusLine: (800) SDA-PLUS [732-7587].

Will any of these ideas work in your church?

Programs and services can be designed based on the perceived needs and interests of the church members. Health education programs that are a part of a comprehensive community plan usually are most effective. For example, most communities already offer a variety of mental health programs. Therefore your team may want to offer programs such as a stress seminar and then refer people with unresolved needs to existing mental health programs. By avoiding duplication you will use resources more efficiently.

Another consideration in planning programs for your local church audience is the cultural, economic and social context of church members' lives. An intricate web of factors influences the mental health of each person. Some of the many factors include the expectations of significant others in our lives, our hopes for ourselves, childhood experiences in our family of origin, our capabilities and talents, and our values. Since customs, unspoken rules of behavior and norms have such a subtle effect on us, it requires special attention to become aware of how they are affecting us. A church member with special expertise in cultural anthropology, sociology, or psychology may provide valuable insights on this aspect of planning a successful mental health program.

As you discover what works (and doesn't work) in your local setting, share this information with your conference health ministries director and other health ministries leaders. Help someone else.

Mental health informational presentations and seminars

There are two groups to whom you need to present mental health information. The first is your church through participation in various services. The second is the community through outreach programs. Here are ideas for meeting these needs:

Sample Mental Health Kickoff Program

To introduce your health ministries team, and formally announce its emphasis on mental health issues, you might choose to have a kickoff-type program. It could be on a Sunday afternoon, at the Adventist Youth (AY) hour, at a Friday night candlelight program, or Saturday night in connection with some other event like a church social. You can feature your planned activities for the upcoming month/quarter/year. Here is a suggested outline that you might use:

1. Provide a rationale for special emphasis on mental health issues in your local church.
2. Tell about your personal development in understanding mental health.
3. Share a song or two about issues that people in your congregation have faced (e.g., "Through It All," [Andre Crouch] or "He's Able," [Wintley Phipps]).
4. Role-play a few of the mental health issues that people face and have the audience identify the issue and their thoughts about how to address it.
5. Solicit ideas from the audience about topics of interest to them or what they are *not* interested in. (List audience ideas on a white or blackboard or flipchart. After most ideas are listed, prioritize them, using a straw-vote approach.)
6. Close with prayer in groups of two or three.

- Midweek prayer service series on positive and negative mental health issues and the development of a strong spiritual life as an anchor in the storms of life.
- Present special 1-5 minute informational messages during Sabbath School or before the church service; something like the health spots shown before the Net 96 meetings. Information can come from the following:

1. Play a *Got A Minute for Your Family?* radio spot by Dr. Kay Kuzma. Or obtain the scripts and read the spot yourself. If you want a longer presentation, obtain the five minute Family Matters columns to read. More than 600 of these scripts are available. Contact Family Matters, 1105 Big Creek Road, LaFollette, TN 37766; or via e-mail to kaykuzma@aol.com.

2. Use the Office of Minority Health Resource Center's "Infobits." These are 5-10 minutes features on mental health topics. Call (800) 444-6472 and allow 7-10 days for mailed responses.

3. Build a short presentation around an object lesson. This is one of the best ways for people to remember the point you want to make.

4. Print bulletin insert tips on mental health issues
   - Use fruits of the Spirit or other statements from The Ministry of Healing
   - Use quotes from articles or newspaper clippings.
   - Use Bible texts.

5. Conduct brief interviews with members or their associates about victories or revelations from real life. Good testimonies can be meaningful for both encouragement to cope and the strengthening of faith and members' relationship to Christ.

Seminar Presentations

Here are innovative titles for presentations or seminars in the mental health area. Since mental health overlaps with the family life area, you may want to co-sponsor these meetings.
- The High Price of Low Self-esteem
- Surviving the Pink Slip
- How to Handle Your Anger
- How to Make Bitterness Better
- How to Raise Your Child's Self-esteem
- Codependency: What it is and what it's not
- Free Guilt and Costly Shame
- How to Grow Gratitude
- Turning the Terrible into the Terrific
- Stress Bust-ers and Rest Must-ers
- Turning Distress into Success
- Making Your Family a Winning Team

TRY THIS!

A Mental Health Exhibit or Station at a Health Fair
You might feature the following:
- brochures
- video
- brief quiz (for example, "How Mentally Healthy Are You?")
- referral information for counseling services
- materials for school-age kids on abuse awareness
- placards or refrigerator magnets with Biblical promises
- magnets or cards with positive affirmations

Support groups

Support groups can meet on an ongoing weekly basis, or can meet for a specific period of time, such as six weeks to achieve a specific objective. Before choosing to start your support group check with the Mental Health, Social Welfare or Health Education Department of your local County Health Department or the local hospital for similar support groups in the area. Sometimes these groups need a facility to meet in and would consider meeting in your church. If you start a support group, let these organizations know so they can refer individuals to your group.

Step 4: Evaluating your mental health program

Often we think of evaluation as something to do at the end of something, such as the end of a project or the end of the day. However, in your health ministries program, you will evaluate your program periodically during its course.

The most important thing you can do to evaluate your program is *document all activities, con-*

tacts, programs, successes, criticism, compliments and efforts. Keep in mind that building awareness will be the primary goal. Thus, any change in the level of interest in mental health issues counts as success.

To justify budgets and activities in the mental health area you *can* document and track the following types of program effects:

1. Number of bulletin inserts and "infobits" over time
2. Number of support groups offered
3. Number of referrals to support groups in the church and/or community
4. Number of referrals to professional people-helpers
5. Requests for books, videos, tapes, etc.
6. Number of programs offered with special emphasis on mental health issues
7. Number of people who attended and/or participated in the session activities. (Use Person Visits (PV) counting each person at each presentation)
8. Written or verbal feedback received from participants
9. Number of conversations about mental health programs, issues, with members and leaders.

If you and your team meet weekly, or report to one person weekly, you can document much of the congregation's changing interests in mental health issues. Sometimes their inquiries or conversations will not be clearly distinguishable from general complaints or expression of concern about someone or something.

However, with daily guidance and prompting from the Holy Spirit you and your team can trust God to give the words to say, or not say, that will be "in a season to him that is weary" (Isaiah 50:4).

Types of Support Groups

- Parent groups (New parents, breast-feeding, general discipline, and child rearing issues, tough love for troubled teens, prayer groups for hurting parents)
- Groups for people with addictions or for the family of an addict
- Groups for eating behaviors
- Groups for women in multiple roles (single parents, working parents, adult caretakers)
- Prayer groups
- Death & dying support groups
- Panic/anxiety groups
- Depression or Bipolar (manic-depressive) support groups
- Career change, information and decision groups
- Divorce recovery groups
- Grief recovery groups

A Personal Challenge

Most of us are products of countless positive and negative influences and experiences. We did not become who we are overnight, and it is certain that we will not become our ideal overnight either. Be ready to evaluate your committee's effectiveness in small increments.

Look for increased awareness; for attitudes that slowly open to new ideas and ways of thinking. While doing so, expect great things—whether you see them or not. We have been told that "He has a use for [His people], and He is well pleased when they make the very highest demands upon Him, that they may glorify His name. They may expect large things if they have faith in His promises" (*The Desire of Ages*, p. 668).

Mental Health Resources

In order to heal the psychological damage caused by abuse, divorce, drugs, mental illness and/or AIDS there must be intervention, therapy, counseling, pastoral care and support groups. Although books, videos and other resource materials have their place, they alone *cannot* heal. Their most important role is to provide information and insight into critical mental health issues. Here are some of the best:

Arterburn, S. and Felton, J.,*Toxic Faith: Understanding and Overcoming Religious Addiction*. Nashville: Oliver-Nelson Books, 1991.

Beattie, Melody, *Codependent No More: How to Stop Controlling Others and Start Caring for Yourself*. New York: Harper and Row Publishers, Inc., 1987.

Cloud, H. and Townsend, J.,*Boundaries: When to Say YES; When to Say NO, to Take Control of Your Life*. Grand Rapids, MI: Zondervan Publishing House, 1992.

Cloud, H. and Townsend, J., *False Assumption: Relief from 12 "Christian" Beliefs That Can Drive You Crazy*. Grand Rapids, MI: Zondervan Publishing House, 1994.

Collins, Gary R., *How to Be a People Helper*. Wheaton, IL: Tyndale House Publishers, Inc., 1995.

When Is Professional Help Recommended?

*A*s your team works with various individuals, you may encounter attitudes and/or behaviors that require more skill or training than you have in the mental health area. How can you know when a problem requires professional counseling?

In the article "Good Counsel" pastor and counselor David Seamands says, that when the regular arenas of grace—prayer, church, support group—seem unable to help or appear insufficient alone, then professional help is recommended (*Today's Christian Woman*, May/June 1986, p. 48-53, 75). The article lists several symptoms that may signal the need for professional intervention: "loss of joy; apathy; uncontrolled crying jags, feeling out of control; inability to make simple decisions; belief that others are out to get you; ordinary behavior gone out of control, such as eating, drinking, cleaning rituals; difficulty dealing with a loss or a change; disruption of family or social relationships; a close friend or family member's suggestion that counseling might be beneficial" (*Ibid.*, p. 51). You should refer:

1. Those who can be helped more effectively by someone else, or a specialized community agency for their particular problem.
2. Those whose needs are beyond the help provided in a seminar, by books, videos and other resources, by information you have been able to provide in one or two private consultations, or by spiritual guidance and prayer.
3. Those who are severely depressed, suicidal, or whose needs require counseling or more intense therapy.
4. Those who need medical care or institutionalization.
5. Those who feel more comfortable talking to someone outside the church structure.

The following situations should immediately raise a "red flag" and be referred:
- Phobias: Irrational fears that are out of proportion or unrealistic.
- Compulsions: An irrational and repetitive impulse to perform some act that is extremely difficult to resist.
- Obsessions: Persistent ideas or thoughts that the individual recognizes as irrational but cannot get rid of.

Friends in Recovery, *The Twelve Steps for Christians: Based on Biblical Teachings*. San Diego: RPI Publishing, Inc., 1984.

Hemfelt, R. and Fowler, R., *Serenity: A Companion for Twelve Step Recovery*. Nashville: Thomas Nelson Publishers, 1990.

Hemfelt, R. and Minirth, F., and Meier, P., *Love is a Choice: Recovery for Codependent Relationships*. Nashville: Thomas Nelson Publishers, 1989.

Lutzer, Erwin W., *How to Say No to a Stubborn Habit—Even When You Feel Like Saying Yes*. Wheaton, IL: Victor Books, 1985.

Seamands, David A., *Healing for Damaged Emotions*. Wheaton, IL: Victor Books, 1991.

Sloat, Donald E., *The Dangers of Growing Up in a Christian Home*. Nashville: Thomas Nelson Inc., 1986.

Tan, Siang-Yang., *Lay Counseling: Equipping Christians for a Helping Ministry*. Grand Rapids, MI: Zondervan Publishing House, 1990.

- Anxiety: Generalized feelings of fear, apprehension or dread.
- Depression: Emotional state characterized by extreme dejection, gloomy ruminations, feelings of worthlessness, loss of hope, weight or sleep disturbances, or suicidal tendencies.
- Thought disorders: Absurd beliefs, bizarre perceptions with no basis in reality, severe paranoia, incoherent or rambling communications.
- Manic behavior: Out-of-control and uncharacteristic spending; tirelessness, racing thoughts, irritability, rash behavior.
- Personality disorders: Odd deviant, antisocial, cruel, or other noticeable "unhealthy" behavior. This is not just a one time act, but a characteristic of the person. May be abusive, controlling, involved in criminal activity, or have "no conscience."
- Eating disorders
- Abuse
- Sexual disorders

To whom do you refer?

Each church should develop a good referral file for the pastor, health professionals, or even the church secretary who may receive calls from those who recognize their need of professional counseling. Here are some types of professionals to refer to:

- **County Agencies:** Such resources as those for substance abuse treatment, emergency housing and food, child protective services, and various hotlines for suicide or abuse problems.
- **Marriage and Family Therapists:** These are licensed therapists who treat family and relational problems. This includes marriage counseling, child abuse, and child counseling.
- **Psychologists:** Only some psychologists are certified to treat clients.
  Clinical psychologists work with people suffering from psychological problems.
  Counseling psychologists counsel all types of psychological problems, including vocational problems
  School psychologists focus on academic difficulties, mainly with children at new schools.
- **Psychiatrists:** These are medical doctors who have additional training in mental health. They are able to prescribe medication. They are particularly helpful when dealing with severe depression and thought disorders.

How to Choose a Counselor

*F*inding a good counselor is much like finding a good physician, doctor, dentist, or auto mechanic. If you have no other sources, try the phone directory. Counselors (therapists) are listed in the yellow pages under such headings as psychologists, social workers, and marriage and family counselors. Psychiatrists are listed with physicians.

Your doctor, pastor, or a teacher may have suggestions. Keep in mind that they may not know which therapist would be best for you. Ask friends for their recommendations based upon personal experience. Also, most states maintain a list of certified counselors for referral purposes.

Once you have two or three names, do your homework. What professional associations does each counselor belong to? What are his or her educational background, professional training, and areas of specialty? Does the counselor have a license? Is there a sliding scale for fees? You can call the state bureau of licensing to see if the counselor has complaints filed against him or her. If you are looking for a therapist for a sexually abused child, check with your local child protective services, children and family services, or a mental health center.

Call and make an appointment for an interview. You need to know whether you can relate to the counselor and feel comfortable. Finding a Christian counselor may be important to you. It is important that you ask the therapist questions about his or her values and philosophy of helping. The right therapist can be very helpful.

Source: Wilma Hepker, *Adventist Review*, September 2, 1993, p. 18-20.

Dealing with Specific Mental Health Situations

The following health situations usually are addressed by Family Ministries in the local church. But because they also are major health issues, it is important that you have this information, and work together with the Family Ministries Leader to offer the services your church and community members need.

Take Heart for Those Who Have Been Abused

For those who have suffered child abuse in their past, especially sexual abuse, a woman's weekend called the **Take Heart Retreat** is offered at selected sites. It's an excellent way to promote healing. For information contact your Conference or Union Women's Ministries Director, or Take Heart Ministries, RR 1, Box 226, Red Lake Falls, MN 56750, (218) 253-2758. They will handle your inquiry in a confidential manner and make attendance as easy as possible.

Child Abuse

Sexual Abuse

Description: Incest, rape, sodomy, intercourse, molestation, lewd or lascivious acts upon a minor, penetration of the genital or anal opening with a foreign object, oral copulation, or psychological incest such as a parent or trusted adult showing a child a pornographic magazine, having a child pose for nude photographs in sexually suggestive poses, an adult caretaker masturbating in front of a child, inappropriate or suggestive sleeping arrangements, voyeurism (e.g., a father spying on a daughter while she undresses), or a parent making repeated seductive and suggestive remarks to a child.

Indicators: A child who expresses unusual or explicit knowledge of sexual behavior, or who tells you that they are experiencing abuse. (Sometimes complaints of pain in genital or anal areas when going to the bathroom may be a possible indication.)

Physical Abuse

Description: Willfully causing or permitting mental or physical cruelty toward children.

Indicators: Frequent bruises with an "accident" always given as the reason for them. In such cases the child may be protecting the parent. Also, observation or reports of willful cruelty, unusually severe or unjustifiable mental or physical suffering.

Neglect

Description: Children being subjected to unsafe or unsanitary living conditions.

Indicators: Knowledge of a young child being left alone for long periods of time, or living under health threatening or unsanitary conditions.

How You Can Help

1. *Offer loving concern and support to both the victim and the perpetrator.* Although you may experience some fear of the turbulence that reporting will create in the family and the church, it will almost always bring relief to all involved. The abuser often wants to get help, but may not know how to get it. The victim certainly is in need of being protected and cared for. Reporting, although it may be a painful process at times, actually begins the healing process for everyone involved.

2. *Stay involved.* Do not distance yourself from either the victim, the perpetrator, or their families. Model loving acceptance by staying involved with the families.

3. *Encourage treatment.* Sexual abuse impacts the entire family, and the Child Protective Agency will encourage the family to enter therapy. Be supportive of this. Your best help to the perpetrator is to refer him/her immediately to a qualified Sexual Abuse Therapist. The law will be more sympathetic if the abuser is in counseling.

4. *Do not investigate on your own.* The protocol used by Child Protective Agencies to investigate reports of abuse is specific and requires special training. Your attempts at investigating could result in liability for invasion of privacy or defamation of character. Provide support, make referrals, but don't go digging.

5. *After 2-3 weeks, check with the Child Protective Agency to see if they have followed up on your report.*

Resources

Your church should have a number of copies of the following booklets to give away:

- *Ministering to the Sexually Abused: A Guide for the Church Community*
- *My Child has been Sexually Abused: Help for Families*
- *Help for the Person who has been Sexually Abused*

(Available from Advent*Source* (800-328-0525) or your local Adventist Book Center.)

DOMESTIC VIOLENCE

Domestic violence includes all forms of violent behavior between people who live together. In most cases this takes the form of a man beating his wife or the woman he is living with. However, victims may also be male or elderly parents. Once started, abusive actions tend to increase in frequency and severity.

There is no "typical" victim. Violence occurs at all ages and all income levels, regardless of race, occupation or social status. Abused women commonly experience their first violence during pregnancy.

Indicators To Watch For

- Fear of a partner's temper.
- Over-compliance out of fear of hurting a partner's feelings, or fear of arousing temper.
- Decisions about activities or friends based on a partner's wants, or fear of the partner's reaction.
- The person has been hit, kicked, shoved, or sexually assaulted when the partner is angry or jealous.
- Apologizing to others for a partner's behavior when others have observed abusive acts.

How You Can Help

Your ability to help depends a great deal upon the willingness of the victim to be helped. Many keep returning to the abusive situation. You will be in a better position to help if they have come to you seeking help than if you became aware of the situation in some other way.

Mental Health Issues in the Bible and the Writings of Ellen White

Mental Health Issue	Bible	Ellen White's Books
Depression	*Feeling distressed?* Ps. 25:16-18 *Feeling disturbed?* Ps. 43:5 *Feeling isolated?* Rom. 8:38, 39	The weakest soul is more than a match (GC 530)* Trials are required of all (MH 470)
Anxiety	*Need sustaining power?* Ps. 55:22 *Feeling anxious?* Phil. 4:6	The power of prayer (SC 64)
Guilt	*God already knows ALL* Ps. 69:5 *The strength of God's "knowing" love* Eph. 2:1-5	God is patient with faults of His children (SC 21)
Fear	*God's plans for you* Jer. 29:10-14 *God's power to deliver* Ps. 34:4	Jesus calms the storm. If He has power over nature, what do we have to fear? (DA 333)
	The Lord goes before you. Deut. 31:8	Look away from self (MCP 480)
Anger	*Avoid plotting revenge* Prov. 24:29 *Human anger does not lead to holiness* James 1:19-21 *Take action against anger* Eph. 4:31	How to conquer anger (MCP 523)

Mental Health Issues in the Bible and the Writings of Ellen White

Identity Issues	*Feel forsaken by parents?* Ps. 27:10 *We may have all we need* 2 Cor. 9:8 *Your rightful place* Job 8:7 *On talking back to God* Rom. 9:21, 22	God is disappointed when we have a low estimate of ourselves (DA 669)
Perfectionism	*Aim for perfection* 2 Cor. 13:11	Aim high for God and to bless others (FCE 82)
Courage	*God gives us strength* Ps. 18:32, 39 *There are more with us than with them* 2 Chron. 32:7, 8	You can have courage in the Lord (MCP 464)
Hope	*Paul's prayer for us* Eph. 1:17-19	How to have hope (MCP 495)
Faith	*Trust precedes God's help,* Psalm 28:7 *Faith is the key* 1 John 5:4	Faith and acceptance (SC 32)
Sympathy	*The Lord longs to be gracious* Isa. 30:18 *Gently restore the wounded.* Gal. 6.1, 2	Jesus raised Lazarus from the dead (DA 524)

*Reference guide

DA	*The Desire of Ages*
FCE	*Fundamentals of Christian Education*
GC	*The Great Controversy*
MCP	*Mind, Character, and Personality*
MH	*The Ministry of Healing*
SC	*Steps to Christ*

Adventist Residential Care for Troubled Teens

Advent Home Youth Services. 900 County Road 950, Calhoun, TN 37309; (423) 336-5052; Fax (423) 339-5986. Staff: Blondel and Gloria Senior, Directors. Services: Residential care, schooling and counseling to 12-16 year old boys, grades 6-10. Started in 1985.

Child Guidance Home. P.O. Box 746, Bourbon, MO 65441; (573) 245-6271. Licensed residential group home. Ages 6-12 boys, grades 1-8. Staff: Al & Judy Jones. Services: Residential care, counseling, church school, work and recreational therapy. Started in 1989.

Hill Top Girls Home. P.O. Box 2153, Collegedale, TN 37315; (423) 236-5022; Ellen Crosby, Executive Director's home (423) 238-5472. Services: Girls 12-20.

Miracle Meadows School. Rt. 1, Box 289-B, Salem, WV 26426. Group Home (304) 782-3628; Fax (304) 782-3660. Staff: Bill and Gayle Clark, Directors (304) 659-3976. Services: Unlicensed residential care, schooling and counseling to 12-18 year old boys and girls, grades 1-12.

Project PATCH. 13455 SE 97th Avenue, Clackamas, OR 97015; (509) 653-8086; Fax (503) 653-8265. Staff: Tom Sanford, Director; Lynette Anderson, Director of Admissions. Services: Group home and counseling (at the Project PATCH Ranch in Garden Valley, ID) for 12-18 year old boys and girls.

Intervention of some kind is important, even if it is nothing more than letting the victim know there is a safe place to go if it is needed.

1. *Provide support for the victim.* Victims will need moral support, and in some cases, encouragement to get medical attention for any injuries they may have received. Do not encourage the myth that their partner will change, and they need to go back and stick it out. Your first concern is for the safety of the individual.

2. Put the victim in touch *with your local Adventist Community Services unit* or one of the other community agencies that deal with domestic violence. The agencies are set up to provide emergency shelter, counseling and other needed support.

3. *If necessary, help the victim to reach a safe place.* If the victim appears to be in immediate danger, encourage the person to call the police, or make the call yourself.

4. If you are able to do so, after the needs of the victim are cared for, *encourage the abuser to seek help.* Referrals are available through the same agencies that provide shelter. Continue to encourage and support the abuser's efforts to get help.

5. *Continue to maintain a supportive relationship with the individual and/or family.* The support of a loving church family can mean a great deal. Talk with community agency personnel about ways the church can provide assistance.

6. *Don't encourage a victim to return home as long as that person, domestic violence workers, or you have any reason to believe that the safety of the individual will be jeopardized by doing so.* Sending an individual back into an abusive situation will not save a marriage, or maintain the family unit; in fact it puts the victim at greater risk. The best way to save the family is to provide for the safety of those who need it, and get them professional help.

- 24 hour domestic violence hotline: (800) 752-SAFE [7233]. Also find local help numbers for battered women.

EATING DISORDERS

Identifying Anorexia Nervosa:

- Intensive fear of becoming fat which does not diminish as weight loss progresses.
- Claiming to feel fat even when emaciated.
- Weight loss of 20 percent or more of body weight with no known illness that would account for the loss.
- Moodiness, depression, and increasing social isolation.

Identifying Bulimia:

- Recurrent episodes of binge eating (consuming large amounts of food in a short period of time).

- Binging is usually done in secret and often involves large amounts of high calorie or sugary foods.
- Binging is usually followed by "purging," use of self-induced vomiting or laxatives to expel the just-eaten food.
- There may be frequent weight fluctuations in excess of 10 pounds, due to alternating binges and fasts.
- Fear of not being able to stop the binge-purge behavior.
- Because bulimics generally are ashamed of their behavior, episodes often are followed by depression and self-deprecating thoughts.

How You Can Help

1. *Provide support.* Individuals should not be made to feel guilty about what is happening, but encouraged to get treatment in order to get better. It is important for sufferers to know that they are not alone in facing this problem.
2. *Provide support for the family.* Family members need to be encouraged to see the problem as genuinely serious and in need of immediate attention. Encourage an attitude of support.
3. *Get the sufferer involved in a professional treatment program.* It is important to put the individual and the family in touch with a professional trained in eating disorders so the sufferer can be evaluated for treatment. Don't try to treat the problem yourself.
4. *If appropriate, take time to be involved* in the family/friend support groups offered by most treatment facilities.
5. Because the healing process often is painful for both the individual and the family, family members may have to be encouraged at times not to pull the individual out of treatment because of their own discomfort.

Should Abuse Be Reported?

- *Know the law.* You must report if you know of, or suspect, abuse or neglect. Your report is kept strictly confidential.
- *What about confidentiality in a counseling relationship with a church member?* There are three cases in which the law does not recognize confidentiality:
    1) when you learn that someone plans to harm or kill themselves;
    2) when you learn that they plan to harm or kill someone else; and
    3) when child abuse is taking place.
- *Keep your priorities straight.* The intent of the law is to protect the child. No matter who is involved in perpetrating the abuse (church elder, deacon, or pastoral staff member), you are responsible for protecting the minor from further abuse. This means reporting the suspected abuse to a Child Protective Agency, or call Child Abuse National Hotline, (800) 422-4453.

Why Do People Put Up With Abuse?

1. They believe the partner will change. This is reinforced by the fact that the abuser typically is apologetic and "good" between episodes.
2. They believe that they are somehow at fault, or "deserved" the abuse. Feelings of personal worthlessness are common.
3. Fear of a partner's acts toward children or themselves if they leave.
4. Tendency to be isolated, not knowing where to go, or who to turn to for help.
5. No money or safe place to go.
6. Feels that the partner is a good provider and/or parent and is reluctant to destroy the family unit.
7. Religious beliefs that they feel prohibit them from leaving.

SUICIDE

While a distinction can be made between an actual suicide, which is made by those who want to die, and an attempted suicide, which usually is carried out by those who want to live, both need to be taken quite seriously. Even if an attempt is only a desperate cry for help, many such attempts accidentally succeed.

Consider the Facts

- An estimated 10-15 percent of college students suffer from eating disorders. Most, but not all, are female. While eating disorders are most common among teenagers and young adults, they affect people in all age groups.
- People suffering from eating disorders are typically "good kids"; attractive, successful, perfectionists, and from homes where one or both parents are "professionals."
- Eating disorders are serious. They can lead to permanent organ damage and even death if not treated.

How You Can Help

1. *Involve another trained professional* in dealing with threats of or an attempted suicide. Don't try to deal with it on your own.

2. *Be supportive, accepting and nonjudgmental as you establish a relationship with the person.* Statements like, "You did the right thing by calling," or "I am glad you called," or "I think there is help available for you" may be useful things to communicate.

3. If your contact is by phone, do not pressure the person, but if you can *get the following information;* it may help to locate the individual if you need to.
   Name
   Telephone number
   Address from which the party is calling

4. *Do not promise confidentiality.* Most state laws require you to report those who threaten to take their own or someone else's life. You don't have to tell them this, however. You can assure them that you will do nothing to harm them.

5. *Listen.* Encourage the individual to share what has led him/her to this stage. Find out what is bothering the one threatening right now. Ask what he/she has done before to cope with such a situation. Don't challenge his/her feelings; help the person express and clarify them. If you can help the one threatening suicide to break up the overwhelming sense of helplessness he/she is feeling into smaller specific items, solutions and hope may be seen more easily.

6. *If you think a person who has contacted you may be contemplating suicide, but has not said so, ask.* Talking about it openly may relieve some of the trapped feelings the individual may have. He/she may be relieved to discover that you are willing to talk with him/her about it.

7. *Evaluate the situation.* It is important to know such things as: Do they have a plan to take their life? If so, how detailed is it? How lethal is it? Is the means available to do it? If the person has a detailed plan, and the means to carry it out, the risk is quite high. Are there friends or family the individual could turn to for understanding and support?

8. If the situation is critical, and the risk high, you may need to *take charge* of the situation if you can do so. If the gas has been turned on, have him/her turn it off. If the person has a loaded gun, have him/her unload it.If pills are involved, have him/her flush the pills down the toilet.

9. *Get the individual to commit to an appointment to see someone.* Let him/her know that you care, that you want to visit, that he/she is not alone, and get the person to a helping professional. Take the one you are helping there yourself if necessary.

10. *If necessary, you can call 911* or the para-medics. Inform them that the person has threatened suicide, and they will pick the person up and hold him/her for 72 hours for psychiatric evaluation.

UNWED/UNWANTED PREGNANCIES
How You Can Help

1. *Accept the reality of the situation with a supportive attitude of continuing love and acceptance toward the individual.* Whatever you may think or feel about the rightness or wrongness of what has happened, it is too late to change the situation now. What is needed is a "safe" place where she can get over fear and guilt and begin to sort out her options. The County Public Health Department provides assistance with pregnancy testing and counseling, as well as planned parenthood information. See the county listings in your phone book.

2. *Be aware of your own feelings about the situation.* Strong emotional feelings, especially if you are not willing to admit or face them, will get in the way of your ability to be of help. In some cases, referral might be appropriate.

3. *If the pregnancy is the result of rape or incest, get her involved with other helping professionals immediately.* Most communities have rape crisis centers that are there to help.

4. *Explore her support network.* Who are the people she will be able to turn to for support and help in making and carrying out her decisions: parents, family, friends, teachers, and others? Encourage her to see a physician immediately.

5. *If the girl is a minor, and has not done so already, encourage her to involve her parents.* After the initial shock, many parents are helpful and supportive. If appropriate, and safe spend some time exploring how she can tell them. Be willing to go along for moral support if she desires you to.

6. *If you feel able to do so, explore her options with her,* (keeping the baby, adoption, etc.). As far as possible, keep your suggestions about

---

Hungry for Healing

Drs. Ron and Nancy Rockey, formerly Family Life Directors of the Dakota Conference, are now working as an outreach ministry of Faith For Today. They give seminars and workshops that focus on how Satan uses hurtful situations during the formative years to cause psychological problems in adulthood, and how by understanding this process, and relying on God's power, healing can be found. For information on Ron and Nancy Rockey's schedule, their "Getting Personal" video seminar, or their audio seminars, contact Faith For Today at (805) 373-7683; Ron and Nancy's e-mail CompuServe address is 74532,644.

Warning Signs

People contemplating suicide often give signals of their intent. Such warning signs may include:

- Talking about, or "hinting at," taking their own life.
- Significant changes in personality, habits, school performance.
- Themes of death or depression in essays or art work.
- Loss of a close friend, especially through suicide, or another major loss.
- Making final arrangements—making a will, giving away possessions.
- Unplanned pregnancy.
- Long serious illness during which the person is very depressed.
- Previous attempts at suicide.

Statistics on Unwanted Pregnancies

Statistics suggest that about one-third of the female population will become pregnant before the age of twenty. While it appears that this number is somewhat lower within the Christian community, there are no clear statistics on the actual number of pregnancies and abortions within this group. Proportionately speaking, the statistics are somewhat higher among black female teenagers.

what you would do out of the conversation. She will need to come to her own decision. Whatever that decision is, be supportive and respect her choice. Community social services can be of help, both in supplying information and counseling.

7. *Encourage responsibility and the involvement of the father* (except in cases of rape or incest). Fathers often are left out and need to continue to be involved.
8. *Help the parents-to-be to sense they still are a part of the life of the church.*
9. *If her choice is to keep the baby, share information with her* on parenting and prenatal care classes available in your area.
10. *If appropriate, check with the local school district for special educational programs for teen mothers.*

14

Parish Nursing

Parish nursing is one of the most effective methods of health evangelism and wellness promotion today. It puts the church in the center of meeting the physical health needs as well as spiritual health needs of a community. Parish nurses see their role as helping people make a connection between their faith and their health.

Parish nursing is gaining acceptance around the country as it places the emphasis on enhancing self-care and preventive care as well as referring members of a congregation to appropriate resources.

What is a Parish Nurse?

The parish nurse is a registered nurse who has a personal relationship with God and practices nursing within a specific congregation for the purpose of assisting church members in attaining optimal mental, physical, and spiritual well-being. The parish nurse is in a unique position to promote health and healing within the church context. The term "healing" encompasses much more than simply curing physical ills. It connotes wholeness and harmony, balance with God, self, and others.

The parish nurse's primary role is to personify the church's interest in promoting health and healing. In order to accomplish this task, the nurse works with the ministerial staff on a part-time or full-time basis. Where an active health ministry already is in place, the addition of a parish nurse may serve to create an effective team that can enhance existing health services. Because churches are attempting to meet the needs of both their communities and their congregations, there is an increasing demand for parish nurses.

The parish nurse addresses the needs of the whole person. He/she does not perform hands-on nursing. Rather, the nurse identifies the needs of the congregation—physical, mental, social, and spiritual—and then takes action to achieve optimal health for the church member(s). The parish nurse's functions include but are not limited to:

- Health educator and counselor
- Reference source to community resources
- Coordinator of volunteers and support groups
- Interpreter of the relationship between faith and health facilitates healthcare referral and provides advocacy as needed.

The current trend in parish nursing is to combine the roles of healthcare and ministry. Interestingly, in early times the church treated the whole person. In modern times, however, treatment has been divided between health professionals and minister, with the former attending to the physical and the latter to the spiritual. The parish nurse program encourages churches to reunite health and ministry, thereby performing a wholistic health ministry for which there is no substitute. The program's mission statement reflects this goal: *To enable congregations to provide a church-based health ministry which is a ministry to the whole person—body, mind and spirit, and assist in the maintenance of health and wellness for church members and the community.*

The Adventist Health Parish Nurse understands the relationship between physical, emotional, social, and spiritual health; emphasizes interdenominational health partnership; operates a health ministry for the church members; develops the role of health ministries in response to the specific needs and priorities of each congregation; promotes preventive medicine, health promotion, and early detection of disease, and facilitates healthcare referral, providing advocacy as needed.

Background of Parish Nursing

Parish Nursing grew out of Granger Westberg's early experiments in providing a pastor/nurse/ physician team in several Chicago suburb Lutheran churches. The concept proved to be sound. In the elder age group they were able to reduce hospitalization 20 to 25 percent, with a

---

Obviously something special was underway at the Shiloh Temple Church: A banner fluttered on the side of the modest building in Bakersfield, California and the open door beckoned with the bustle of activity inside. Every fourth Monday of the month, the parish nursing program at this African-American church sponsors a clinic. Services include physical exams, prenatal care, nutrition, and health education which have attracted as many as 38 youngsters and their parents.

Shiloh Temple Church is part of San Joaquin Community Hospital's burgeoning parish nurse program. "This is a case of 'We're coming to you; you don't have to come to us, says'" Sandy Vigil, former parish nurse coordinator.

Sandy helped design programs to suit every situation—well-baby classes for new parents, educational seminars for the elderly, as well as programs about germs and hand washing for kids. "Parish nursing can help everybody in the church," she stated emphatically.

---

similar reduction in costs. Dr. Westberg discovered that having a nurse on the pastoral staff can enhance the church ministry at a reduced cost. He chose nursing over other disciplines because nurses are trained in both the scientific and behavioral worlds.

Different Types of Parish Nurses
1. Hospital/Agency Parish Nurse Coordinator
The hospital or agency Parish Nurse Coordinator, whose role is to promote and assist local churches with the development of the parish nurse program, is a Registered Nurse and staff member of a hospital or agency. The institution/agency has additional responsibilities for establishing peer support sessions with other parish nurses and pastoral staff with the aim of

providing and assisting with healthcare resources, encouraging and understanding the church parish nurse's questions, concerns and problems as they arise.

2. Church Parish Nurse Coordinator
The church parish nurse is a person with pastoral interests and clinical skills. The nurse coordinator must be currently licensed as a Registered Nurse with experience appropriate to the tasks, such as medical/surgical experience, some home healthcare activities, community education and operational organization skills. The church Parish Nurse Coordinator works with and requests assistance from the institutional/agency Parish Nurse Coordinator.

3. Parish Nurse Volunteer
The Parish Nurse Volunteer demonstrates clinical proficiency, a spiritual maturity which manifests itself as an empathic listener and is particularly adept at relating to young and old, rich and poor, males and females. The volunteer nurse works under the direction of the church Parish Nurse Coordinator.

Why is Parish Nursing Needed Today?
In the early church, healthcare was an integral part of church life. More than one-third of Jesus' teachings related to wholeness. However, with the rise of scientific thought, religion and medicine parted company. The physician became responsible for the human organism and clergy responsible for the human soul. Science and religion not only followed separate tracks, but in some cases they even became suspicious of each other.

Within the past century, renewed interest in the church's healthcare role and responsibility has emerged. Seventh-day Adventists, with their sanitariums turned into medical centers and their healthful life style education programs, are leaders in this movement. The Seventh-day Adventist health message with its concern for the healthy as well as the sick, has made major contributions to improving world health. These contributions are cause for rejoicing. And the basic message is as solid as ever.

However, with changing times and expanding needs, methods must be adapted. A ground swell is occurring in America in which churches are beginning to reclaim and herald wholeness (physical, mental, social, and spiritual well-being). One such evidence of this trend can be seen in the Parish Nurse program.

Numerous community-based organizations are seeking universal access to primary health-care services. Concerned with containing health cost, Congress, third-party payers, corporations, and others are calling for preventive health maintenance strategies.

The church is the one social institution uniquely structured to affect knowledge, faith, and physical dimensions of human behavior. More then 70 percent of this nation's citizens belong to a faith community, and more than 40 percent attend a worship service at least once a week. The local congregation is the fastest growing social institution in the not-for-profit sector. There are 10,000 more congregations of 2,000 or more members now than there were ten years ago, and they are serving all sectors of society. The health system in the United States is proving problematic in all areas—cost, quality, and accessibility. Many people do not have health insurance and many more are underinsured. Costs continue to skyrocket. One response to this crisis is to call people to a more active involvement in the promotion of their own health. The Parish Nurse program does that.

How did the Parish Nurse Concept Get Started in the Adventist Church?

The Adventist church has been involved in health ministries for more than 100 years, in large part due to the contributions of Ellen White. She wrote on numerous topics involving health education and lifestyle. Although her writings on smoking, vegetarianism and more were not based upon scientific research, their accuracy has been proven by modern-day science. With this historical backdrop in place, it becomes evident that parish nursing is but an expansion of a well-established ministry.

During the past century, a renewed interest in the church's role in healthcare emerged. It is up to individuals to practice prevention of disease. However, in order to do so effectively, health education needs to be provided. Currently, more than 50 percent of all health problems in the United States are caused by lifestyle and could be prevented if proper education were provided and lifestyle changes made. These numbers clearly demonstrate that more and better health education is needed. In response to this overwhelming need, Adventist Health established a Parish Nurse Coordinator. The program aims to provide a valuable and necessary service to both church and community members.

Established in 1994, it currently has regional Parish Nurse Coordinators in place. The goal of the program is for each facility/regional parish nurse to work with the Adventist Health coordinator located at the corporate office.

Since 1995, the Adventist HealthCare Community Health Partnering Program has worked with multiple faith groups and community organizations to develop health ministry programs. It has health Ministry/Parish Nurse Coordinators that represent Washington Adventist and Shady Grove Adventist Hospitals.

The Southern Union and other denominational entities have active Parish Nurse training programs in place with many nurses working in local churches. Most Adventist Health Systems, including Sunbelt in Florida Health are active in this field.

What is the Difference Between the Health Ministries Leader and a Parish Nurse?

Although in many churches the roles may be similar, the parish nurse works directly with the individuals within a congregation as a part of the health ministries/pastoral team. The parish nurse role is not so much outreach evangelism, as it is in-reach nurturing of church members.

Training to Become a Parish Nurse

For those wishing more information on parish nursing, including a training program, in the Western U.S. region write Maxine Blome, Parish Nurse Coordinator, Adventist Health, 2100 Douglas Boulevard, Roseville, CA 95661-9002 or call (916) 781-2000 or (916) 781-4691. In the Mid-

Atlantic region write Nancy Wallack, health Ministry Coordinator, Adventist HealthCare, 1801 Research Blvd., Suite 101, Rockville, MD 20850 or call (301) 315-3136 or (301) 315-3141. For those in other regions, please check chapter 17 for current addresses and phone numbers, or contact your local conference or Union health Ministries Department.

Individuals wishing to become parish nurses normally pay a fee for the six-unit training seminar offered by Adventist Health. Call the contact points indicated above for information for training in your area.

After having completed the brief training program, nurses begin their ministry in cooperation with their church and/or community as well as with the corporate representative at Adventist Health. As part of the program, the corporate staff meets with the regional coordinators to present suggestions and new materials. The regional coordinators then share what they have learned with the church parish nurses providing a much helpful network for all.

Program Models

Several models of parish nursing exist. Among these is the institutionally-based model which is the basis of Adventist Health's Parish Nurse Program. Within this model, a hospital's nursing service, outreach, home health agency or chaplain service recruits nurses and assigns them to work with a specific community, church or churches. The nurse is an employee of the hospital or employing agency.

A second model is composed of a free-standing church and a parish nurse without ties to the local hospital. This model often is found where the hospital is not located near the church and/or has no parish nursing coordinator. The nurse in this model may be paid by the church or may be a volunteer.

Most effective parish nurse programs have a health ministries committee or an advisory committee that establishes goals and mission for the program. The committee also may decide which projects and programs the church should pursue. Members of such a committee normally include

the parish nurse, ministers, health professionals and any other individuals interested in serving in the health ministry program.

The Role Of The Church Parish Nurse Coordinator

The church parish nurse works with the health ministries committee to foster the health and wellness of the members of the local congregation. It is essential to the success of the health ministries program that the parish nurse and the pastor work closely together, sharing information and making referrals to one another.

Parish Nursing Basic Services

There are five categories of services:

1. Health Educator Role

The role of health educator is often combined with that of the parish nurse coordinator in small churches. Large congregations may require additional personnel to assume the responsibilities of health education. This responsibility includes development and presentation of educational programs, which include not only group discussions or presentations, but written materials and video presentations.

The health educator instructs through a variety of formats, such as seminars, conferences, classes, workshops, discussion groups, individual sessions, home visits, newsletters, printed educational materials, bulletin boards, qualified guest speakers from the hospital speaker's bureau, and literature racks—targeting all age groups.

2. Personal Health Counselor Role

Health counseling may be done by the church Parish Nurse Coordinator, Parish Nurse volunteers, health educators or clinical specialists from the hospital/agency as arranged by the Parish Nurse Coordinator. Counseling may occur in a formal or informal manner in the home, hospital/agency, nursing home or church. In an effort to make the parishioners comfortable, the counselor must create an atmosphere of trust by sharing concerns, asking questions, discussing personal health problems, requesting healthcare related advocacy, learning health information, considering healthcare options, and accepting referrals for further assistance.

3. Healthcare Referral Liaison

This aspect of the Parish Nurse Coordinator is that of a referral agent who makes formal or informal recommendations of services within the church or community. The Parish Nurse Coordinator serves as the health liaison with church staff, members of the congregation, hospital program activities and services, as well as community resources and services.

4. Volunteers Training Role

This position consists of coordinating programs, both formal and informal, for volunteers so that they can carry out their ministries in an informed and effective manner.

5. Support Groups Development Role

This refers to the initiation of a group that is intended to provide help to the participants in dealing with a particular issue, i.e., grief, loss, care giving. This may mean that the Parish Nurse Coordinator leads the group, or provides a resource from the hospital/agency, church or community to facilitate the group's activity.

Other Services

Many new services have been added to the parish nurse program depending on the need. Parish nurses recently have begun holding blood pressure clinics once a month following church services. The clinics are open to both church and community members and are designed to attract many individuals who might not otherwise enter a church. To date, this service has been well received.

Computerized health appraisal programs also are provided by parish nurses. These programs utilize health questionnaires on blood pressure, cholesterol, lifestyle, and more to determine what healthcare is needed. If intervention is necessary, parish nurses offer advice or referrals as appropriate. The parish nurse program also holds wellness fairs.

> **I**n the burgeoning area of outpatient and aftercare, mainstream religions have created one of the most significant innovations in recent years, the parish nursing movement.
>
> Parish nurses are addressing what are widely regarded as the most costly unwieldy elements of any healthcare plan—geriatric medicine and long-term counseling.
>
> Could it be possible that the most innovative leadership in healthcare reform is coming from what is in the context of today's secular culture, a very unexpected place—the church!
>
> —*Maxine Blome*, Parish Nurse Coordinator, Adventist Health.

There are several special services the health ministries committee might choose to implement, such as:

- Welcome Baby program (available from Family Matters)
- Monthly blood pressure clinics
- Shut-in visitation program
- Community birthday parties for newborns or expectant mothers

Target Markets

The parish nurse program primarily targets churches located near healthcare facilities. The churches may represent many denominations, but in all cases parish nurses work with the church to share health information and the love of God.

Another target of the parish nurse program is churches that request help, especially those that have no parish nurse available through local hospitals. By filling this need, parish nurses demonstrate that Seventh-day Adventists love and care for people of all denominations. In order for these programs to be effective, the minister must be willing to work with the parish nurse to treat the whole individual.

Promotion

Parish nursing has been advertised through Seventh-day Adventist conferences, camp meetings and union papers. The program also has received attention at ministerial meetings.

Although awareness is increasing still more needs to be done to make the program more widely known.

Responsibilities of the Parish Nurse

- Work closely with the health ministries committee to develop and plan health ministries within the congregation.
- Meet regularly with the pastor to report on the activities of the health ministry and to share information about the ill in the congregation.
- Serve as a personal health counselor.
- With the health ministries committee members, plan and teach classes, secure guest speakers, coordinate support groups and special sessions on specific health topics.
- Provide regular health screening and monitoring.
- Work with the health ministries committee, promote health education through the church newsletter, bulletin and church services.
- Provide health referral information.
- Serve as a liaison between the congregation and the community resources.
- Maintain appropriate health ministry records.
- With the help of the health ministries committee, recruit and train volunteers to help with such areas of ministry as visiting the home bound, and those in hospitals.
- Attend the parish nurse meetings at the medical center and the quarterly meetings of all who are participating in the corporate network Parish Nurse Partnership, and join groups who promote parish nursing.

The program's advertising objective is to promote awareness of the parish nurse program among Adventist constituents. This primarily is accomplished by widespread distribution of brochures. However, advertising in Adventist Union papers provides an excellent promotional tool, as they are published throughout the United States. In addition to brochures and union paper ads, displays, pictures, and other materials can be made available.

Community Care Network

When parish nurses work with a liaison from the community hospital's Parish Nurse Coordinator, the hospital or agency provides health assessment tools, educational resources and coordinates networking among parish nurses and community health agencies. The liaison acts as a consultant and resource person and provides ongoing training and educational seminars. A nurses' support group meets on a monthly basis. Congregational health ministries needing assistance are given on-site consultations. By assessing congregational health needs and consulting the appropriate hospital staff, each parish nurse program can be custom designed to address the unique qualities of its congregation.

Although it may not provide substantial monetary rewards, parish nursing/health ministry has its own rewards. It is an excellent opportunity to share with members of other faiths what Seventh-day Adventists have known for years about obtaining and maintaining good health. Services such as blood pressure clinics, health screening and health education provided by the church are an excellent outreach. In these and other capacities, the parish nurse program is worthy of not only the investment of time and energy, but also the small but necessary monetary investment it takes for a church to serve as a true friend to its community.

Helpful Resources for Those Interested in Parish Nursing

For resources on parish nursing contact the National Parish Nursing Resource Center: (800) 556-5368. The following are some of their resources:

Books:
- Solari-Twaddell, Phyllis Ann, *Parish Nursing: Promoting Whole Person Health Within Faith Communities.*
- Westberg. Granger E., *Parish Nurse.* Parish Nursing Resource Center.
- Westberg-McNamara, Jill, *The Health Cabinet: How to Start a Wellness Committee in Your Church*, Parish Nurse Resource Center.

Manual:
- *Church Parish Nurse Resource Manual* developed by Adventist Health

Videos:
- *The Connecting Link*, Parish Nurse Resource Center.
- *Spiritual Ministry,* is by Chaplain Beulah Stevens from the Adventist Medical Center in Portland. It's available from Adventist Health, 2100 Douglas Blvd., Roseville, CA 95661-9002; (916) 781-4691.

15

Health Education Centers

In 1980, the Norwalk Seventh-day Adventist church, in the Los Angeles metropolis, had 340 members on its church books, but the actual attendance was less than half that figure. Five years later it had nearly tripled with up to 900 people attending services on a regular basis. What happened? It all has to do with following the blueprint for health evangelism in the cities. Here's the story:

In 1980, after the arrival of Pastor Dale Leamon and his wife, Yolanda, a group of church members studied and prayed that God would help them reach people in the surrounding communities.

"Several quotations from the Spirit of Prophecy gripped our minds as we prayed about impacting our community," Yolanda Leamon, a certified nurse-midwife, explained, such as… 'Centers of influence may be established in many places by the opening up of health food stores, hygienic restaurants, and treatment rooms' (*Testimonies*, vol 7, p. 234). 'Medical missionary work is the pioneer work of the gospel, the door through which the truth for this time is to find entrance to many homes…. A demonstration of the principles of health reform will do much toward removing prejudice against our evangelistic work' (*Evangelism*, pp. 513, 514). The formula was there—plain and simple," said Yolanda, "So we had to implement it.'"

In 1982 the Norwalk church members leased and remodeled a building and called it "Our Daily Bread Bakery." It featured whole-grain breads and wholesome health foods. (In 1993 it moved to a newly constructed city missions building, and a health food store, a deli-restaurant, and a Christian bookstore were added.)

Next the members started a health center that focused on lifestyle changes, health education, smoking cessation, weight and stress management, and a variety of other health-related programs.

Bits o' Heaven Day Care opened soon after, followed by the Mobile Health Van Ministry. Its free blood pressure checks, health screening, and health and spiritual literature created many interests for Bible studies and health classes and made the church well-known at the local shopping centers.

Next the Dorcas Closet opened and members began distributing clothing, furniture, toys, and household items.

Then the little congregation purchased a 20-acre ranch in the country and opened the Golden Hills Health Retreat following the Spirit of Prophecy counsel that "as far as possible, all who are seeking to recover health should place themselves amid country surroundings where they can have the benefits of outdoor life. Nature is God's physician" (*The Ministry of Healing*, p. 263).

An Update on the Leamons

Dale is currently the senior pastor of the Battle Creek Tabernacle and Yolanda is the Health Evangelism coordinator and owns and operates The Natural Childbirth and Gynecology Center, a freestanding birth center in Battle Creek, as part of her health ministry. In addition, they have developed a seminar using Hans Diehl's video tapes and have written a leader's manual. The Leamons are frequently asked to speak for camp meetings and retreats. If you are fortunate enough to hear them, you will become convinced that the Lord was right when He said there should be a vital link between the health work and the gospel. You can contact the Leamon's by calling: (616) 963-0368.

"It was really fun to see how God can bless, knock down prejudice, and lead people into the church. We just followed the formula," Leamon says. "We just followed the blueprint and the Lord blessed."

On the east coast, Gwen Foster, former health ministries director for Allegheny East Conference, is finding that God is blessing her special work in the cities.

"When I was graduating from Loma Linda School of Public Health in 1977, I met Nathan Pritikin, the famous health educator. I asked him how we could take his program to the inner cities. He said, 'You know how to do this! ...Start conditioning camps using the blueprint that your church already has.'"

The very next year Foster started conducting two-week live-in conditioning camps (Wellness camps, see chapter 28). "We used to have to advertise; now God opens doors and does the advertising for us. We have to turn people away because we can't handle any more," Foster reported.

Gwen Foster now serves under the Mayor of Philadelphia as the city' Health Czar. See chapter 2, section "Healthy Cities" for a brief report on what she is doing there with her "76 Tons of Fun" campaign.

The Foster Story Continues....

*G*wen Foster loves "city" work, but does the method work in the country?

There are nine regions in the Allegheny East Conference, each region has two people who serve as a health ministry team to coordinate, encourage and plan the health work for their area. One region has a small section that juts into the West Virginia mountains and for years people said nothing could be done there. It was dead.

Dr. Mamie Lindo and Sarah Wills, however, became impressed with the need to do something in a small hamlet in Martinsburg, West Virginia. Gwen began working with what she calls her "dynamic duo," and they went to the little church group in Martinsburg and certified *every member of the church* on the first level of the Lifestyle Certification program—a total of 20 people.

With these empowered people the next stop was the local hospital where the church members did health screening, using Wellsource materials developed by Don Hall. After that it was time to plan a town-wide Fitness for Life program.

When the hospital personnel asked Gwen how many she expected, she said 40. "To be truthful," Gwen said later, "The place was so small there didn't look to be 40 people in the whole hamlet. The hospital staff shook their heads, 'Impossible!'"

The Somner Ramer Memorial School, the first black school in the area, was made available for the meetings by Somner Ramer Memorial School Alumni Heritage, Inc., and the Berkeley County Board of Education. For 14 nights Gwen flew in from Boston to make the presentations to 62 people! The people were thrilled. They ended up with 14 Bible students, and one month later the church members, who were in the process of purchasing land, had a ground breaking ceremony for a church.

But the story is far from finished. The Methodist pastor of the most prominent church in the area where the cooking presentations were held, sat as an "observer" through the entire program. He was so impressed, he put what he was hearing into practice and his blood pressure went down 30 points. He is now a vegetarian and wants the program for the entire ecumenical ministerium—all the churches of the area.

Can anything come out of the mountains of West Virginia? We now know, following the blueprint for health evangelism, the answer is yes!

Centers in the Cities

As a means of relating church-sponsored health programs to community needs, community health education centers (sometimes called better living centers, health enhancement centers, or lifestyle centers) are ideal. Some of the reasons for operating such centers are:

1. Many people interested in health programs are prejudiced against attending programs in Adventist churches.
2. Such centers can be located in the hub of daytime activities and are easily accessible for evening programs. Window displays and other means of attracting attention can attract people who otherwise might not be aware of Adventist health programs.
3. Such centers create an image of Adventist concern for the community. In addition, the cooperation of community health agencies is often easier to obtain when the health education center is separate from the church.

Ellen White was given much instruction that is pertinent to operating such centers. Among her wealth of statements are these:

"It is God's design that our people should locate outside the cities, and from these outposts warn the cities, and raise in them memorials for God. There must be a force of influence in the cities, that the message of warning shall be heard" (*Evangelism*, p. 76).

"We must do more than we have done to reach the people of our cities. We are not to erect large buildings in the cities, but over and over again the light has been given me that we should establish in all our cities small plants which shall be centers of influence "(*Counsels on Health*, p. 481).

"Intemperance has filled our world, and medical missions should be established in every city. By this I do not mean that expensive institutions should be established, calling for a large outlay of means. These missions are to be conducted in such a way that they will not be a heavy drain on the cause; and their work is to prepare the way for the establishment of present truth. Medical missionary work should have its representative in every place in connection with the establishment of our churches" (*Medical Ministry*, p. 322).

There have been several notable attempts in developing such centers in recent years, but it's not always easy to put the instruction God has given into full operation.

What facilities does God tell us should be included in such centers? What kinds of programs should be featured? The health education centers should have the following components:

1. Health food store
2. Hygienic (health) restaurant
3. Treatment rooms
4. A room to have lectures and Bible study
5. A place for publications
6. The facility should be simple and non-expensive; not elaborate.

Examples of Health Education Centers
Pacific Health Education Center (PHEC)

One comprehensive non-profit health education center is the Pacific Health Education Center of Bakersfield, California, which was established with funds generated from the sale of a hospital. Dr. John Scharffenberg with a group of health professionals spent a number of years at the center shaping the program. Now students from around the world are trained in health evangelism by outstanding professionals in their field.

In addition PHEC operates House of Manna, a book center, health food store, and vegetarian delicatessen. One of PHEC's most popular services is the weekly Monday morning breakfast open to all, but provided as a complimentary service for those going through the HeartBeat screening, and the healthy noon meal they serve the second Sunday every month. These meals are served to exemplify their dietary recommendations of no dairy or animal products. The average attendance on Sunday is about 300 with more than 200 being non-Adventists.

The students attending PHEC cooperate with the center staff in presenting such features as: HeartBeat, weight control, diabetes, stop smoking, physical fitness, stress and family life, and both faculty and students work with churches wanting to provide cooking schools and health seminars. Hundred of non-Adventists have taken advantage of these programs and seminars that have enabled them to overcome tobacco addiction, control diabetes, control weight, and deal with other lifestyle problems.

In the first seven years that PHEC has been offering the three-month training program they have graduated 224students from 30 foreign countries. Their training prepares the students to adapt the health education center concept to the needs of the overseas communities they serve. One example of the success of this program is

Ellen White's Vision for Health Outreach

"Centers of influence may be established in many places by the opening up of **health food stores, hygienic restaurants, and treatment rooms**. Not all that needs to be done can be specified before a beginning is made. . . Plan to carry forward the work simply, sensibly, economically." —*Testimonies*, vol. 7, p. 234

"A place should be provided where treatment may be given for common ailments. The building might be inelegant and even rude, but it should be furnished with **facilities for giving simple treatments**. These, skillfully employed, would prove a blessing not only to our people, but to their neighbors, and might be the means of calling the attention of many to health principles." —*Testimonies*, vol. 6, p. 113

"In every city **a place should be provided where the slaves of evil habit may receive help to break the chains that bind them**. Strong drink is regarded by many as the only solace in trouble; but this need not be, if, instead of acting the part of the priest and Levite, professed Christians would follow the example of the good Samaritan." —*Temperance*, p. 127

"In every important place there should be **a depository for publications**. And some one who really appreciates the truth should manifest an interest to get these books into the hands of all who will read."—*Christian Service*, p. 154

"In connection with our city missions there should be **suitable rooms where those in whom an interest has been awakened can be gathered for instruction**. This necessary work is not to be carried on in such a meager way that an unfavorable impression will be made on the minds of the people. All that is done should bear favorable witness to the Author of truth, and should properly represent the sacredness and importance of the truths of the third angel's message."—*Counsels on Health*, p. 443

"**Hygienic restaurants** are to be established in the cities, and by them the message of temperance is to be proclaimed. Arrangements should be made to hold meetings in connection with our restaurants. Whenever possible, **let a room be provided where the patrons can be invited to lectures on the science of health and Christian temperance, where they can receive instruction on the preparation of wholesome food and on other important subjects**. In these meetings there should be prayer and singing and talks, not only on health and temperance topics, but also on other appropriate Bible subjects. As the people are taught how to preserve physical health, many opportunities will be found to sow the seeds of the gospel of the kingdom."—*Temperance*, p. 248

When workers in these centers cooperate with the Lord's will, He promises to give them success: "I have been instructed that little companies who have received a suitable training in evangelical and medical missionary lines should go forth to do the work to which Christ appointed His disciples. Let them labor as evangelists, scattering our publications, talking of the truth to those they meet, praying for the sick, and, if need be, treating them, not with drugs, but with nature's remedies, ever realizing their dependence on God. As they unite in the work of teaching and healing they will reap a rich harvest of souls."—*Counsels to Parents, Teachers, and Students*, p. 469

that in 1994 there were only 10 Seventh-day Adventist physicians and nurses in Havana. Two years later there were 40 Adventist Cuban medical professionals in Havana and 200 in Cuba, largely due to baptisms from the contacts made at health programs implemented by PHEC's trainees.

PHEC would enjoy training more students for the North American Division to meet the needs of the cities. But sometimes the news of a "steal of a deal" gets around foreign countries quicker than here in North America!

In addition to the medical evangelism programs, PHEC's faculty are developing new health programs, for example, DiaBeat, a screening program for diabetes, analogous to HeartBeat with blood test and computerized lifestyle recommendations for prevention or regression of diabetes. Keep the PHEC address and phone number handy because there is soon to be a set of videos available of a number of their seminars: Pacific Health Education Center, 5300 California Avenue, Suite 200, Bakersfield, CA 93309-1604 (888) 633-7432. Fax: (661) 633-5329.

Although Pacific Health Education Center is operated by a private non-profit organization, it performs a supportive role to the church. This is an example of what can be accomplished when medical institutions support the work of health evangelism.

Lifestyle Center of Benton

Until just a few years ago there was no appreciable SDA work in Benton, TN or in the surrounding Polk county. Dr. Al and Jane Sines, RN determined to do something about reaching that formerly dark county through the health message. They began with the purchase of an AM radio station that broadcasts Life Talk radio 24-hours daily, except for 3-hours they reserve for local programming for local news, a community calendar, and health talks.

By 2001, they, and those working with them, had a fully-paid-for conference-organized church of more than a hundred members functioning in Benton on their property. The most visible part of the property was used on which to build a truly magnificent and increasingly popular health, lifestyle and fitness center.

Health services are provided by a family practice physician. A dental and dental hygiene team focuses on preventive care. Exercise and weight management are a vital part of health care, so they provide a membership-based fitness center and provide weight training and conditioning equipment. A staff Dietitian counsels on steps to weight management. A staff Physical Therapist provides a variety of advanced technique treatments, including hydrotherapy.

The Vine Vegetarian restaurant serves bountiful and delicious vegan meals. The Vine Bakery not only provides wholesome bread products daily, but sells bulk supplies for healthy cooking and baking.

An 85-seat facility is the epicenter for ongoing classes presented by health and lifestyle professionals. Equipped with state-of-the-art audio and visual equipment to enhance the lifestyle and health lectures, they are able to present highly informative and interactive lectures that catch the interest and attention of participants.

The mayor, municipal judge, and other city officials have eaten in the restaurant and express great appreciation for the work being done there. The mayor's wife has requested Revelation studies and the banker's husband, who is retired has asked to join the Revelation study class because he "knows something awful is coming and wants to be on the right side."

For further information on the development of this model center and the programs being offered, contact Jane Sine at (423) 338-7777 during business hours Sundays through Thursdays.

Other Health Education Centers

Most health education centers are small, and many are written up in Chapter 19 as self-supporting health ministries. Other health education centers are started and operated by churches for as long as there is personnel to man them. This has been especially true with many restaurants, bakeries, and treatment programs. The greatest need for continuing health education centers that are following the blueprint, is trained, committed personnel who are willing and able to sacrifice for the Lord's work.

Roger Morton, now Director of Quality Life Seminars in Loma Linda, California was one such dedicated person who served for a time as director of the Better Living Center in Riverside, California. In a report to the faculty of the Loma Linda School of Public Health, he summarized the rationale behind these centers this way: "The basic philosophy of community approach on which the Better Living Center was developed is found in the detailed instruction given by God for health education within the institutional setting. Consequently our center was not primarily designed as a unit devoted to public evangelism. Every attempt was made to establish confidence in the Adventist philosophy of life and health and to portray God as the reference point in planning all activity."

The Riverside program was followed up by an evangelistic series in the nearby Arlington church. After one year of operation, ten had been baptized and the center had a list of 40 other persons who demonstrated specific interest in the spiritual phase of the Seventh-day Adventist message. One of the most popular features in the program was the weight control seminar which enrolled 145 people.

One non-Adventist woman drove more than eighty miles each night to attend the weight control seminar. She was thrilled that she had been able to reduce and keep her weight under control and expressed her opinion that this was a dramatic answer to the prayers that had been offered in her behalf.

Probably there would be more such centers if they could be truly self-supporting. It makes sense for hospitals and rural conditioning centers to sponsor city centers as a means of steering clients to less accessible localities. This has been the model for many self-supporting institutions. For example, for some years Wildwood Lifestyle Center in Georgia has sponsored the Country Life Natural Foods and Vegetarian Restaurant in Chattanooga, Tennessee. Besides the restaurant that is open for the lunch hour, and the health food and book store, the Country Life provides

evening health education seminars and physcians from Wildwood hold clinics and counseling sessions on a weekly basis. One unusual phase of the relationship between the restaurant center and the Wildwood Lifestyle program is that at least once during a guest's three-week stay at Wildwood they are taken by bus to the Natural Foods center in Chattanooga where they become familiar with the publications, health food supplies and are served a vegetarian meal in the restaurant.

The Uchee Pines Institute under the direction of Doctors Calvin and Agatha Thrash is operating a similar restaurant/health education center in Columbus, Georgia.

Community Services Centers

Some are confused about the difference between a health education center and an Adventist Community Services (ACS) center. In general, a health education center is a facility that specializes in health issues, while an ACS center is a multi-service agency which may include health programs.

For ACS today a "center" is not so much a building as it is an organization. ACS is the official agency of the church which has been recognized widely by government and non-governmental organizations in North America as representing the church's humanitarian interests outside the religious sector. As an "agency" it is not the same thing as a "department," nor is it an "institution." (Department and institution are the two most familiar organizational types in the Adventist Church.) As an agency, it collaborates with departments and institutions when they have programs they would like to project into the community.

An ACS agency has its own board, just like a church school does. Usually several churches co-sponsor an ACS center and have representatives on the board. The agency director is appointed by the board and accountable to the board. This is a different role from the local community service director or the local church health ministries leader.

Those ACS agencies that meet the highest standards of professional leadership, fund raising, program development and community relations can become ADRA Affiliates. But, many of these agencies do not use the name ACS or ADRA in their public operations. They may have a local name such as Good Neighbor House, Samaritan Center or Oasis Health Services. Some of the best health programs mentioned in this manual are run by ADRA Affiliate agencies. Most of the health programs given as examples in this manual are organized in a different way. ACS is an agency of the church with the mission of assisting the health ministries, as well as other departments, in achieving humanitarian objectives in the community.

For additional information on the guidelines for ACS agencies, see Ministries of Compassion which is available from Advent*Source* at (800) 328-0525.

Health Restuarants

Operating a vegetarian restaurant/and or bakery is one of the best ways there is to witness, and one of the most demanding to maintain. Once you begin food service, it's difficult to take time off unless you have a well-trained support staff.

There may be many "health" restaurants owned and operated by Seventh-day Adventists, but there is no association where names can be obtained. The Country Life restaurants, however, are a part of Outpost Centers, Inc. If you are interested in starting a food service ministry, contact the mangers of these organizations and benefit from their experience.

The Country Life name originated at Oak Haven where Ron Crary was working with the Country Life wholesale food distribution. When Ron went to New York, he started a Country Life restaurant that served noon meals, offered literature and provided health education and Bible study opportunity. His program, including the vegan diet and buffet method of food service, has become a model for other Country Life restaurants. If you happen to be doing some international traveling, you may want to visit one of the

Country Life restaurants located overseas.

Country Life restaurants in North America include:

Country Life Boston, (617) 951-2534, 200 High St. Boston, MA 02110

Country Life Chattanooga, (423) 622-2451, 3748 Ringgold Rd., Chattanooga, TN 37412

Country Life Columbus, (706) 323-9194, 1217 Eberhart Ave., Columbus, GA 31906

Country Life Keene, (603) 357-3975, 15 Roxbury, Keene, NH, 03431

Country Life Nashville, (615) 327-3695, 1917 Division St., Nashville, TN 37203

Schools of Health in Every Church

Here is the instruction:

"We have come to a time when every member of the church should take hold of medical missionary work. The world is a lazar house filled with victims of both physical and spiritual disease. Everywhere people are perishing for lack of a knowledge of the truths that have been committed to us. The members of the church are in need of an awakening, that they may realize their responsibility to impart these truths" (*Testimonies*, vol. 6, p. 62).

"Every church should be a training school for Christian workers. Its members should be taught how to give Bible readings, how to conduct and teach Sabbath-school classes, how best to help the poor and to care for the sick, how to work for the unconverted. There should be schools of health, cooking schools, and classes in various lines of Christian help work. There should not only be teaching, but actual work under experienced instructors. Let the teachers lead the way in working among the people, and others, uniting with them, will learn from their example. One example is worth more than many precepts" (*The Ministry of Healing*, p. 149).

Much of the city center work outlined in this chapter is being conducted by health professionals and ministers. Often church members excuse themselves from this kind of work because they feel limited by knowledge and experience. But their involvement is essential because of their unique ability to identify with people on their level and to offer love, sympathy, and support to those struggling with behavior change.

In every center and every program there should be built-in mechanisms and time for interaction between church members and the public. Bonds formed in this way will tend to lead people to attend the Seventh-day Adventist Church and to feel welcome because they already have friends there in whom they can confide and from whom they can receive ongoing help and support.

Nowadays, when competing community agencies are offering many of the same kinds of health and family programs and services that we are, one way Adventist programs can be unique is that we provide a voluntary staff of committed, loving church members eager to assist people in their struggle with behavior change. Accurate facts and quality presentations may attract people to our health programs, but only unselfish, loving interest on the part of church members will win people to Christ and His church.

16

The Adventist Health Network

Networking will empower you to get things done more effectively and efficiently. A network is a person-to-person or group-to-group connection.

In their book, *Networking: How to Enrich your Life and Get Things Done*, Donald Woods and Shirley Ormerod say, "Your network consists of all the people you know including those you do and do not enjoy, people from all walks of life, people you know extremely well, and those with whom you are only acquainted. Frequently, people underestimate the size of their networks."

Include in your network your relatives, coworkers, friends, acquaintances, fellow students of all the schools you have attended, members of your church, professional organizations and clubs, people you have met on vacation and workshops, and all the service people in your life.

The average person without realizing it, has a network consisting of 1,000 to 2,500 people. Most networks are expanding and contracting with life-changing circumstances. With proper planning and with clear-cut goals, your network can be connected to the networks of others.

Networking can help you reach anybody. Think: "I know somebody who knows somebody who knows the person I want to reach."

What Is Networking?

Networking is reaching out and joining hands with people with similar goals and similar interests to yours. Networking means, synergistic effect of networking means that instead of working alone, you add your strength to somebody else's strength. The one plus one can equal a hundred or a thousand. Networking is many hands making the load light. Networking is extending the sphere of your influence. Networking is what it's going to take to finish the Lord's work!

Networking Good Health

A number of years ago the Carter Center in Atlanta, Georgia, held a series of meetings in key cities to discuss how faith groups could become partners with health providers and social service agencies to close the healthcare gap and improve the health and well-being of the community. Through ongoing dialogue and by identifying opportunities for collaboration, their goal was to build national support for community health models in the churches.

Former president Jimmy Carter, speaking at that conference, said, "A religious community has the opportunity to be a key partner in a revolutionary breakthrough in health. The most exciting opportunity is not in finding high tech cures, but in discovering new ways of preventing disease and promoting wholeness.

These opportunities demand the full energies of religious organizations of all faiths. No matter what the outcome of the debate over healthcare reform, there will remain a major role for people of faith. Good health is born in community and sustained by community."

DeWitt Williams, who directs Health Ministries for North America, after attending the Carter Center's meeting in Baltimore, began networking with other churches in this concerted effort to make the church a community-based

Example of How Networking Works

Several years ago I attended a meeting of the American Council of Alcohol Problems. They wanted to pass the SAFE Bill (Sensible Advertising and Family Education). It was suggested that we contact President Bill Clinton. But nobody in the room knew President Clinton personally. One man said that he is a member of the Lions Club and that network included Rex Horne, President Clinton's pastor who could contact the president. It's amazing how one network can bridge to another network which can put you in touch with people you don't even know but need to know.

—DeWitt Williams

nonprofit organization dedicated to promoting preventive healthcare as a normal approach to health. It is essential that our churches become involved in this community work because many government-funded programs and programs funded by large foundations exist only during the duration of a grant. After a year or two when the funding runs out, the program is dismantled, the people go away and nothing more happens—and the community is left without needed services.

Churches are products of the community, and have permanence. Today's climate is ideal for networking between Seventh-day Adventist churches and with non-Seventh-day Adventist churches in delivering healthcare to the community.

Adventists do not have enough conference health ministries directors to finish the work. And many who have the responsibility for health ministries wear so many hats that it is difficult to give adequate attention to all the needs. In addition, many of them have not received training in health promotion work. *But by networking with qualified lay volunteers who are health professionals, much can be accomplished.*

Health Organizations, Workers, and Professionals within the Adventist Church

The Adventist church has at least eight types of health personnel that can be networked for maximum effectiveness in meeting health needs and spreading the health message. These are:

1. **Official Adventist Church Workers:** The health and temperance work, which is combined under the title "health ministries," has departments in the General Conference, the North American Division and other divisions worldwide, and the conferences. The individuals leading out in this work are paid church workers. At the base of this church structure is the local church and the church health ministries leader, who may or may not be a health professional and voluntarily gives leadership to the health evangelism work of a local congregation.

2. **Educational Institutions:** In North America, Loma Linda University, Florida Hospital's College of Health Sciences, and Kettering College of Medical Arts are schools devoted to training health professionals. Many Adventist institutions of higher learning offer training in nursing and other health professions. At least one, Southern Adventist University offers a specific course in health evangelism.

3. **Adventist Healthcare System:** The hospitals and healthcare institutions that are sponsored by the Seventh-day Adventist Church under the various Adventist health systems. (See Chapter 17 on Adventist Healthcare.)

4. **Self-Supporting Health Ministries:** These institutions are operated by Seventh-day Adventist members, but are not sponsored by the church. They belong to Adventist-laymens Services and Industries, Inc. (ASI) and some are loosely linked through Outposts Centers, Inc., an ASI umbrella organization that provides training and consultation to health institutions around the world. (See Chapter 19 on self-supporting health ministries.)

5. **Self-employed Health Education Professionals:** Individuals who have their

own businesses. They may offer screening and health education, produce materials, or work as paid consultants or speakers.

6. **Private Practice or Institutionally Employed Health Professionals,** such as physicians, nurses, physical therapists, and other health professionals (many of whom cooperate on a voluntary basis with evangelistic teams), pastors and the laity to promote health evangelism throughout the North American Division.

7. **Private, Adventist-owned Companies that Market Health-related Products.** Many of these organizations are ASI organizations who supply health resources for the church. Others offer services to industry, schools and other institutions.

8. **Health Media Ministries:** Any radio or television ministry that promotes the Adventist health message. This list would include television and radio satellite networks and stations, and the ministries that produce programming. (See Chapter 20.)

The challenge for the NAD is to encourage and support every aspect of the health work and to find ways to network these diverse groups or individuals to optimize the effectiveness of spreading the health message. In order to help accomplish this goal, NAD has established the Adventist Health Network (AHN).

Adventist Health Network (AHN)

Health ministries in the North American Division is actively developing networks of health professionals and interested volunteers in major metropolitan areas to conduct community-based health education programs. AHN mobilizes Adventist resources for this important area of ministry.

Reaching the Cities *A Profile of North America's Mission Field*

*M*ore than 100 years have passed since the Adventist Church first turned its mission attention to the large cities. Since then the cities have grown and merged into sprawling megacities. Yet statistics show that in North America our church growth has not kept pace with the growth of these cities. We still have our work cut out for us.

The challenge of reaching the cities' unreached peoples is almost overwhelming. Approximately 50 percent of all North Americans live in 36 metropolitan areas with populations of more than 1 million. But Jesus said that His church will be made up from every nation, tribe, language, and people. And that includes people in the cities.

To reach North America, we have much work to do; and as Ellen White predicted, that work is getting more difficult. The urgency of reaching the large cities is greater today than it was in 1909, when Ellen White told the General Conference session: "Behold the cities, and their need of the gospel! The need of earnest laborers among the multitudes of the cities has been kept before me for more than 10 years. Who are carrying a burden for the large cities? A few have felt the burden, but in comparison with the great need and the many opportunities but little attention has been given to this work.... Oh, that we might see the needs of these cities as God sees them!" (*Testimonies*, vol. 9, pp. 97-101).

Reaching the cities of North America is the task that is set before us. These are cities with high crime rates, homelessness, hunger, and low income families. They are also places where the Adventist Church has very little presence.

—Monte Sahlin, Assistant to the President, Columbia Union Conference

(AHN has been established to help meet this challenge to reach the cities.)

Examples of Area-wide Networks

Washington D. C. is divided by three conferences—Potomac, Chesapeake, and Allegheny East. Recently the church health ministries leaders from those conferences formed a citywide health network. Conference lines are not emphasized in order for all area churches to be linked together.

Alberta, Canada: Don King, Dr.P.H., former health ministries director for the Alberta Conference in Canada recruited volunteer district network leaders who served as associate conference health ministries directors. They were chosen on the recommendation of the pastors and local church health ministries leaders in that district. They were given a detailed job description. Besides the usual certificates of appreciation with the official seals of the conference on them, Don provided year-end tax-deductible receipts for the cost of their mileage. He also published a personal profile including photographs of these district leaders in the conference newsletter affirming the volunteers and letting them know how much they were appreciated.

The NAD provides some matching funds to local networks to help fund citywide advertising for Adventist health promotion activities. It also provides technical assistance in the development of the most effective health education programs.

The Adventist Health Network in many cities is headquartered in the Adventist Community Services (ACS) center. ACS directors are encouraged to provide their management, marketing and community relations skills for AHN. For purposes of government contacts, funding grants from corporations and foundations, and other inter-organizational relationships, the health network is a program affiliated with the ACS umbrella. Internal organizational arrangements may vary from place to place.

Organization and Structure of AHN

Each metropolitan or rural region Adventist Health Network is to be headed by an executive director and administrative committee from the area. The committee is made up of volunteers and the executive director should be given at least a modest stipend because of the hours demanded for a successful program. Each local network will develop along the following lines:

1. Recruit dedicated and gifted church members into health and temperance outreach ministries, and make provision for them to be certified as Lifestyle Consultants, Specialists and Trainers by providing or

gaining access to the necessary training. (See Chapter 22.)

2. Assist area churches, schools and church-related institutions to plan, market, implement and follow-up ongoing, coordinated health promotion activities that specifically meet local needs.

3. Develop a coordinated, widely-distributed calendar of health promotion events and services provided by Adventists and publish it two, three or four times a year. If possible, this should be a direct mail piece going to all the homes in the community. At least it must be mailed to all those who have had some contact with Adventist ministries, including the media ministries.

4. Coordinate the supply of health ministries resource materials to each church, school and institution. It is vital that they have the supplies needed for effective health ministries.

5. Facilitate and support the health promotion ministry of Seventh-day Adventist health professionals, and encourage some type of organization/convention that might bring these individuals together and harness their creativity and expertise for the purpose of advancing the gospel. All healthcare workers and personnel, including physicians, nurses, dietitians, and other professionals in allied health fields, should be identified and listed with pertinent information in a "talent

bank." Many conferences list these resource professionals in the conference directory.

6. Apply for, write and submit grant proposals offered by state, city and federal health organizations and other philanthropic organizations so that additional funds will be available to offer health services to the community.

A major effort has been launched to organize Adventist Health Networks in the largest metropolitan areas of North America. In those areas that have Adventist Community Services centers, these centers can function as a base of operations for the network.

Contact your local conference health ministries director for information on who to contact for the AHN in your area. If there is none, and you would like information on getting one started, contact your union.

Adventist Health Network (AHN)

Health ministries in the North American Division is actively developing networks of health professionals and interested volunteers in major metropolitan areas to conduct community-based health education programs. AHN mobilizes Adventist resources for this important area of ministry.

The NAD provides some matching funds to local networks to help fund citywide advertising for Adventist health promotion activities. It also provides technical assistance in the development of the most effective health education programs.

Elements of Successful Networking Among Churches

1. **Talent bank:** The Adventist church health network needs a talent bank which identifies every healthcare worker, all nurses, doctors, dentists, dietitians, and other health professionals in the area. Identify special skills, potential speakers and seminar presenters, and those with a special burden for health evangelism.

2. **Schedule of health activities for area churches:** Adventist churches sometimes act

Why Should Your City Form a Local AHN Chapter?

The advantages to becoming a recognized local chapter of AHN are numerous. Here are some of the benefits:

- Full logistical and professional advice, assistance, and support through an AHN agreement with Loma Linda University's School of Public Health.
- National networking of resources, information, and personnel with other AHN chapters and ADRA Affiliates.
- AHN/NAD assistance in organization and program development.
- Access to a national health and community services resource bank.
- Uniform and effective recognition of health education and community service efforts.
- Potential funding access in areas involved in Campaign for Community (an Ingathering alternative)
- Priority access for regional implementation of programs, such as the annual live, satellite HeartBeat program.

—Harry Krueger, AHN Project Director

as if they were jealous of neighboring Adventist churches, choosing not to print in their bulletin or make an announcement of a special program or service being offered in a "competing" church. This petty isolationism must be curbed if we are to offer to our church members and the public the health information and services they so desperately need. Many would drive miles to hear a certain speaker, or take part in a lecture series, *if they only knew about it.* There are not enough highly skilled professional presenters, nor

Can This Dream Come True?

I have a dream for the North American Division health work. May I share it with you?

It's a dream that all those people and institutions with differing ideologies and philosophies of health, but all with good motives to spread the health message, might begin working together in one united effort to finish the work.

Is that a pipe dream? A wish that defies rationality? An impossibility?

I hope not. I dream that...

- Adventist health education centers, self-supporting institutions, Adventist Community Services centers, hospitals, schools, and churches in a given area will work together and plan their marketing strategies and training together to reach a larger objective and maximumre sults.
- Each church will be open to promote the health evangelistic efforts of others.
- Churches will use the incredible talent and experience of workers in hospitals, health education centers not operated by the church, and self-supporting institutions for presentations and training of their members.
- Church leadership will encourage members who have lifestyle-related problems to attend a health education program, and if necessary a residential program, regardless of who puts it on, or where.
- Hospitals and churches will begin working together in a determined effort to place a parish nurse in each one of our churches.
- Local health professionals and self-supporting workers will be invited to official church health ministries meetings.
- Every member of the Seventh-day Adventist church who lives within driving distance of a self-supporting health institution will visit that organization and find out about their services,

enough money to pay for their services, for every church to have the same programs. With networking, we can meet the needs and maximize our efforts. Here's an example:

Before the Washington, D. C. Health Network was established, a woman called the NAD health ministries office and inquired, "I've heard that the Seventh-day Adventist Church does a stop-smoking program. When is the next one?"

In the Washington, D.C. area there were approximately 70 SDA churches at that time, but no one had any idea whom to call or where to direct this lady. Two churches might be doing a stop-smoking program simultaneously and then there are times when there aren't any.

Many times audiences for health seminars are small because the program is run on an irregular basis. By networking programs such as Breathe-Free™ (the stop-smoking program) or cooking schools, they can be offered six or seven times a year in different localities. When this happens doctors, schools, and friends will begin referring others to these programs.

With an area-wide networking schedule, every church can know what health programs are available at any other area church. Pastors and Health Ministry Leaders can promote health evangelism by encouraging their members to attend and tell the public that this is being offered in the area. No one can do it all. An active referral system is essential to maximize our health evangelism efforts.

3. **Training.** Many health ministries volunteers would do more if they were trained. By networking, training can be provided for a larger number of people, at a lower cost. Gwen

their dreams and their needs, and also learn how they can help advertise to their network of friends and neighbors the benefits of attending the programs offered there.

- Health professionals can bury the past, overlook differences in whether one should drink milk or how much fat is "healthy," and promote (or at least not criticize) the work of others who are trying to spread the health message.
- The health message presented by radio and television, either with programs on local stations, or via an Adventist radio or television satellite system, can be heard by every person in North America because churches have gone to the extra effort to sponsor these programs locally, or provide downlinks.
- Health ministries and community services will work together and wherever possible share facilities in order to meet people's health needs.
- Churches would support their local Adventist hospital health evangelism efforts and provide programming and church services that would meet the needs of those who are learning about the Adventist Lifestyle and interested in more, but are not ready for lectures criticizing their behavior.
- Adventist churches will become known as health education centers in their communities because of their efforts to network with other community health efforts.

I'm filled with excitement just thinking about these possibilities. And my list could be endless. Oh how much we could accomplish if we were truly working together with unselfish interests, not caring who got the credit or the baptisms.

I believe that with networking, my dreams can come true. Perhaps with men and women it is impossible, but we know that "with God all things are possible" Mark 10:27.

Let's work together and make these dreams come true!
—DeWitt S. Williams

Foster, Health Czar for the city of Philadelphia says, "Our people are excited about health. They're excited about the opportunity to train others in the church and reach out to the community with the knowledge they have learned."

To empower church members to provide effective health evangelism, the NAD has planned a major certification program called Lifestyle Certification (see Chapter 22). A wide variety of courses are offered through this program. But it will never work, unless churches network resources to bring this training to their area and if necessary commit travel funds to make it possible for their members to get the training when it is offered in another district or conference.

17

Adventist Hospitals

More lives are touched every day by Adventist hospitals and related health care services than by any other ministry of the Seventh-day Adventist Church. In communities across the United States and Canada, Adventist hospitals and nursing homes provide approximately 15,000 patient beds and serve nearly 8 million patient visits a year. This includes hospital admissions, emergency visits, outpatient services, home health visits and nursing home admissions.

While these numbers are impressive, a health care organization's influence extends far beyond direct patient care. Parish nursing contacts, hospice visits, chaplains' services, community education participants, as well as business contacts and partnerships add tens of thousands of lives that are touched by Adventist health care.

In addition, many thousands of physicians, employees and volunteers of other faiths help fulfill the health care mission by serving their communities through Adventist hospitals. It is safe to say that Adventist health care organizations in North America touch close to 10 million lives a year—nearly equal to the church's entire world membership.

Unforseen Growth

Clearly when the pioneers struggled to establish the first Adventist health centers more than 100 years ago, they could not have imagined the far-reaching influence their efforts would have today. As of 2002, the Seventh-day Adventist Church operates more than 500 health care organizations around the world, including nursing homes, clinics, dispensaries, hospitals and other facilities. With nearly 70 hospitals in the United States, Adventists are among the largest faith-based, not-for-profit health care providers in the country.

While nationalization of Canada's hospitals led to the closure of North York Branson Hospital

in 1997, the church continues to operate seven nursing homes located in six provinces. These facilities accommodate a total of 690 residents.

A Lifeline of Hope

The problem of runaway children receives relatively little notice, but one that has a devastating impact on the community served by Potomac Ridge Behavioral Health, a 170-bed freestanding psychiatric hospital operated by Adventist HealthCare, Rockville, Maryland. Developed to be more than a treatment facility, Potomac Ridge involves education and the proactive treatment of behavioral health problems.

Potomac Ridge joined forces with the Montgomery County Police Department in 1991 to develop a program to provide crisis intervention and ongoing treatment options for runaways and their families. Today it has grown into a community-based service involving many other county organizations, including public schools and the Department of Health and Human Services.

Called Operation Runaway, the program provides a toll-free number (1-800-204-8600) that anyone (a child, parent, or police) can call 24 hours a day to arrange for access to a licensed professional counselor. In addition, Operation Runaway organizes support groups that promote open communication among family members and ongoing conflict resolution.

—Robert E. Jepson, regional director of communications, Adventist HealthCare.

Historical Perspective

Shortly after the Seventh-day Adventist denomination formally organized in 1863, church founders recognized the close relationship of physical, emotional and spiritual well-being. In 1866, under the direction of James and Ellen White, Adventists opened a new kind of health center in Battle Creek, Michigan—one that treated disease, and also taught people how to prevent disease through nutrition, exercise and sanitation. It was a place where each person was valued as a creation of God, where caregivers created a positive healing environment.

Eventually, the Battle Creek Sanitarium and its famous physician and health educator, John Harvey Kellogg, M.D., gained international recognition. Guests at the San included the likes of J.C. Penney, Thomas Edison, Henry Ford, Amelia Earhart, Lowell Thomas, William Jennings Bryan, Dale Carnegie, C.W. Post and John D. Rockefeller.

However, the Battle Creek San was more than a health center for the rich and famous. Hundreds of young men and women trained here as medical missionaries. From Battle Creek they spread throughout North America and other parts of the world, inspired to share the Adventist message of health and healing.

During the late 1800s and early 1900s, Battle Creek graduates set up dozens of treatment rooms and small sanitariums specializing in hydrotherapy and massage. To meet the need for trained personnel, they opened schools of nursing—some of which continued until they were eventually transferred to collegiate programs.

While many of the early sanitariums were short-lived, some grew into large medical centers that are the flagships of Adventist health care today. Mrs. White was directly involved or strongly encouraged the establishment of many of these facilities. In fact, 12 U.S. hospitals in operation today were begun during her lifetime. These are Adventist Medical Center, Glendale Adventist Medical Center, Loma Linda University Medical Center, Paradise Valley Hospital, St. Helena Hospital, White Memorial Medical Center, Florida Hospital, Hinsdale Hospital, Washington Adventist Hospital, Park Ridge Hospital, Tennessee Christian Medical Center, and Walla Walla General Hospital.

Curing Loneliness One Loaf at a Time

*F*or many homebound seniors, loneliness is a way of life. Too often, loved ones are deceased, children seldom visit and the telephone rarely rings. Enter Sonora Community Hospital's Parish Nurse Program, which reaches out to congregations representing many faiths in California's Sierra Foothills.

After identifying loneliness as a real problem in a local Lutheran congregation, a volunteer parish nurse vowed to squeeze even more visits into her already busy schedule. Armed with a freshly baked loaf of bread, she knocked on the door of an elderly woman who was homebound following a massive stroke. When the door opened, she handed the still-warm bread to the eager resident, who immediately clutched the loaf to her chest and burst into tears.

"This is the nicest thing anyone has ever done for me," said the woman between sobs.

"Before getting involved in this ministry, I didn't realize how much even the simplest things are appreciated..." said the nurse of the revealing encounter. Following her initial visit, the parish nurse enlisted a fellow volunteer and together they "adopted" the no-longer lonely stroke victim. Their visits have taken them to her home as well as the hospital. But wherever they find her, she now feels supported and loved.

"We donít always have a cure," says Teresa Nelson, Parish Nurse coordinator. "But we always have healing."

—From an Adventist Health Community Benefits Report.

Training Center Established

The early growth of Adventist health care soon created a need for trained medical workers. To meet this need, a health center and school of nursing were founded in Loma Linda, California, in 1905. Four years later, the school of medicine enrolled its first class. Today, Loma Linda University is the premier educational center of the worldwide Seventh-day Adventist health system. It operates the second largest private school of medicine west of the Mississippi River. (See Chapter 18 on Loma Linda University.)

In the early 1900s, the new Loma Linda school provided a source of trained professionals to help expand Adventist health care overseas. While the church had begun sending medical missionaries overseas in the mid- to late 1800s, overseas medical work grew significantly after the school opened—almost to the exclusion of new hospitals in North America. In fact, only two U.S. hospitals in operation today began between 1915 (the year Ellen White died) and the close of World War II. These are Takoma Adventist Hospital, established in 1928, and Porter Adventist Hospital, established in 1930.

Meatless Fare

A physician approached Mike Gentry shortly after he arrived as president of Memorial Health Systems in Ormond Beach, Florida.

"I understand you guys are vegetarians," he said.

Not yet acquainted with the doctor, Gentry explained that about half of Adventists are vegetarians, and that, yes, he and his family were vegetarians.

"Great!" the doctor replied. "I'm a vegetarian, too. You must come to my house for dinner."

In the following months, the families of the new hospital president and this Hindu physician shared several meatless meals together.

—Provided by Jane Allen Quevedo

Community Hospitals

Post World War II brought dramatic changes to the health care industry and Adventist hospitals. Technological advances, new medicines, insurance and the availability of government funding offered new opportunities for the

Mended Hearts Find Hope and Faith Restored

*I*t never bothered Don to speak about trust, faith and reliance on God until the day his doctor said he had only six months to live.

"Suddenly the room grew so still I could hear the beat of my weakened heart," Don recalls. "I prayed for God to help me."

Fortunately, Chaplain Arunan at Hinsdale Hospital helped ease his mind and put things into perspective.

"He had a way of restoring our hope, and I felt my faith strengthening. By the time I headed for surgery, I knew everything would be okay," Don said later.

The chaplain was with the family after surgery and had an opportunity to pray with them. He was there again when time came for Don to go home. The two men said good-bye—but it would not be for long.

It seems the doctor was wrong about the six-months-to-live prognosis. As soon as Don was feeling up to it, he and his wife enrolled in a volunteer chaplains training program and began spending some of their time encouraging others—while strengthening their own faith at the same time.

—From Adventist Health System Mission Report.

Adventist church to meet the health care needs of many communities.

In some cases—such as Porter Adventist Hospital, Huguley Memorial Medical Center and Kettering Medical Center—individuals or families gave the funds to build Adventist hospitals. In other cases, Loma Linda graduates established small hospitals, which they later gave to the church. Examples include Feather River Hospital and Sonora Community Hospital. Many other communities found creative ways to raise money for hometown hospitals—from letter-writing campaigns and quilt raffles to street-corner solicitations.

Birth of Health Systems

The 1970s and 1980s brought changes in payment for health care and competition from large for-profit hospital corporations. This left many hospitals—including church-owned facilities—in difficult situations as stand-alone organizations. The formation of Adventist health systems provided corporate strength that the individual hospitals did not have. A number of community hospitals came into the Adventist system during those years, and some have become outstanding organizations, strongly committed to the mission of Adventist health care.

Today's consolidation of health care facilities is a continuation of the changes begun in the 1980s. Advances in medical science have brought increased costs, while payment for health care has been dramatically cut. As a result, health care organizations are developing relationships that enable them to provide their services cost-effectively. Again Adventist hospitals have the benefit of a rich history and a reputation for quality and service as they seek appropriate partners in this ever-changing environment.

Mission of Health, Healing and Hope

Although much has changed since the church's first sanitariums were established, today's Adventist hospitals remain focused on caring for the whole person. Each hospital and health system is guided by a mission. While the exact wording may vary from place to place, the aim is essentially the same—to follow Christ's example in meeting the physical, emotional and spiritual needs of their communities.

In addition to providing the technology, environment, and qualified health care personnel to meet physical needs, Adventist hospitals reach out in many other ways to minister to emotional and spiritual needs—from prayers offered at a patientís bedside to inspirational artwork and lit-

Historical Refund Still Remembered

*D*enver businessman Henry Porter had a bad cold one winter while he was staying near San Diego, California. Several years earlier he had gone to the Glendale Sanitarium with a similar condition. Although he tried to give his therapist a $1 tip, the young man would not take it.

Remembering his experience at the Glendale Sanitarium, Porter inquired as to whether there was a similar facility in San Diego. Someone told him about Paradise Valley Sanitarium in nearby National City. That winter both he and his wife patronized the sanitarium where they observed the spirit of service among the staff. Porter especially admired the kindness shown by a student nurse while caring for an old man with Parkinson's disease.

Sometime after returning to Denver, Porter received a 45-cent check from Paradise Valley Sanitarium with a letter explaining that his account had been overcharged. Porter returned the check, claiming it was he who owed a debt to the sanitarium staff, not the other way around.

Within weeks, Porter wrote another letter, which eventually led to his contributing the funds to build an Adventist hospital in Denver. Today's Porter Adventist Hospital opened in 1930, only a few months after the stock market crash of 1929. Copies of the famous 45-cent refund check and correspondence are on permanent display in the hospital—a silent reminder of the values on which Adventist health care is founded.

erature, and a wide variety of community programs.

Often it is the chaplain who touches lives in a most meaningful way in the health care setting. Working with various community clergy, and often with a team of trained volunteers, Adventist hospital chaplains are prepared to serve people of all faiths.

Adventist Chaplains Ministries (ACM)

The Seventh-day Adventist Church, through Adventist Chaplaincy Ministries (ACM), endorses chaplains for healthcare and other settings, including campus, corrections and the military. As church and healthcare organizations plan for ministry together, ACM can help you tap resources within various branches of chaplaincy. Many of these other chaplains have ministered in healthcare units in their respective settings, such as prisons or the military. All of them interface with the church and its mission in a variety of ways.

Today over 250 Seventh-day Adventist ministers serve full-time as chaplains in the North American Division. About 60% of them minister in healthcare facilities, but all of them are part of the healing and saving mission of the church. And ACM can help you identify which one(s) might be able to assist in the collaborative ministry of church and health-care organization.

Hospital Chaplains: An important resource for churches

Seventh-day Adventist healthcare organizations can be effective partners with the local church in its healing mission. Connecting with those institutions, however, may at times seem intimidating, particularly when the institution is large. While administrators and physicians can be approached and will welcome collaborating with the local church, the hospital chaplain can also serve as a connecting point. Most Adventist healthcare organizations employ ministers as chaplains, and they can be a link or liaison in the establishment of joint ministries. There are two reasons for this unique relationship:

1.*The chaplain walks in two worlds.* The Adventist healthcare institution is especially

Growing a Garden is a Healthy Experience

*I*magine a garden in an inner city neighborhood where local residents can dig their hands into the earth, pull weeds and harvest their own vegetables. That's what happened when a physician and a minister took over a vacant lot owned by White Memorial Medical Center.

Dr. Robert Krochmal, family practice resident, and Pastor Archie Tupas, director of the Los Angeles Development and Relief Agency (LADRA), a local affiliate of Adventist Community Services, thought a garden would help inspire a curiosity and respect for the natural world in a community surrounded by concrete and asphalt.

Many people became involved—physicians and hospital employees, school children, Adventist church groups and other local organizations. Many volunteer hours went into planting, weeding and harvesting the vegetables. For many of the neighborhood children, the garden offered their first opportunity to discover freshly grown vegetables. In addition, it provided a focal point for community beautification and offered a safe and inspiring environment for local residents.

"The basis of the garden is nurturing the local community. Gardens foster community spirit, cultural and artistic expression, and healthy environments by building bridges among groups," says Dr. Krochmal. "By creating gardens with their own hands, young people experience deeper understandings of nature and catch a glimpse of the Creator of all things."

—Written by staff of White Memorial Medical Center and published in Adventist Review, August 2001.

"user friendly" when approached through the chaplain's office. This is because he or she comes from the world of the church. Trained as a minister, and usually with several years of parish pastoral experience, the chaplain understands the needs of the local church and conference. However, the chaplain usually has additional training to do ministry in a clinical setting, and is a part of the healthcare team as well. In this dual role, he or she can be a key person to contact and enlist in the process of developing a partnering ministry, as well as being a doorway to tap other resources and relationships within the institution.

2. *The chaplain as a resource in ministry.* As the church plans for its healing ministry in the community, remember that Adventist chaplains often have talents and skills that can be employed to benefit both the congregation and community. Your local chaplain will be glad to participate in your program. While not every chaplain is expert in all of the services listed, here are some of the ways he or she may be able to help:

The Joy of Journeying Together *A Chaplain's Reflection*

by Charles Juanita Bartel
Shawnee Mission Medical Center, Shawnee Mission, Kansas

*T*he happiness that comes from seeing someone accept Christ as their personal Savior and Lord is an experience I will continue to savor. Not only am I able to be part of this experience in my work in the hospital, but it is also my joy as I work with people as an elder in the New Haven Seventh-day Adventist Church.

On Sabbath, August 19, 1995 I had the privilege of baptizing Donna at our church. Our friendship had started three years before when she and her husband John, already an Adventist, started coming to my Sabbath School class. Having recently moved to the Kansas City area, they were looking for a church to call home. Donna had never studied the Bible much and she and John realized that deep inside something was missing. Early in our relationship I sensed a depth to her young, yet growing relationship with Jesus. There was a hunger and thirst for God's Word. At first, Donna said that she started to attend for John and his children but in time she came to realize that she was coming for herself. At that point she asked the pastor and me for Bible studies, and I began to study with her.

From our respective backgrounds (mine, the hospital) we both were acquainted with the Twelve-Step recovery model, with its emphasis on placing trust in God. From that perspective we studied the Bible and the teachings of our church, acknowledging our powerlessness and leaning entirely on God. Many weeks we met in my office at the hospital. This was a time of joy for both of us. We both loved books, but the Holy Scriptures were the focus of our study. In time, Donna not only came to intellectually understand our beliefs, but she experienced an "advent" in her own life, the beginning of a new spiritual journey.

The day of her baptism Donna realized that she had only begun that journey and that it would continue each day for the rest of her life. My own heart was filled with joy as we rejoiced in God's redeeming love.

How grateful to God I am that He allows me to touch and be touched by others, and to share in their joyful journey in Christ. Whether in the hospital, or in the church, I sense his guiding in my ministry. I thank Him for the joy of sharing the spiritual journey with persons like Donna!

Edited by Martin W. Feldbush, D.Min., BCC, Associate Director, Adventist Chaplaincy Ministries, General Conference of Seventh-day Adventists.

- Local and/or regional planning councils for collaborative ministries.
- Preaching and Bible study groups in the local church.
- Supporting evangelistic programs with special features on health and spirituality.
- Participating in health-enhancement programs dealing with spiritual and emotional health.
- Involvement in health education programs for stress reduction, smoking cessation, as well as other programs.
- Family life education programs.
- Individual and family counseling.
- Facilitating support groups, for various needs such as grief, divorce, cancer, AIDS, and other health-related needs.
- Training programs for church members, particularly teaching interpersonal helping skills.
- Making contacts and building bridges to other community churches.

For more about how Seventh-day Adventist chaplains can assist you and your church or health-care organization in a collaborative ministry, contact your local hospital chaplain's office or Adventist Chaplaincy Ministries (ACM), an office of the General Conference that also serves the North American Division, 12501 Old Columbia Pike, Silver Spring, MD, 20904; phone (301) 680-6780; Fax (301) 680-6783; e-mail 74532.1614@CompuServe.com

Health networking is a great approach to getting work done. It creates partnerships and enables individuals and groups to cooperate in helping one another to be more effective. Creating a strong and viable Adventist Health Network (AHN) is a significant priority for the Seventh-day Adventist Church and NAD health ministries.

A Report from an Army Chaplain

Recently I returned from service at the US military base in Guantanamo Bay, Cuba, where we ministered to about 2500 emigrants from Haiti and our own military personnel. The Haitians had fled from their own country, leaving family and possessions behind, and had been picked up by the US Coast Guard. Their experience and courage reminded me of the trials through which we all must pass before Jesus returns.

Much of my work was helping to reunite Haitian families separated coming off the Coast Guard vessels. A great deal of my time was spent in conducting services and Bible studies. I was surprised to find so many Protestants among the predominantly Roman Catholic group. They were a religious people, hungry for the Word of God. In one camp we had services every night for two hours, so great was their desire to hear the Word.

About 150 Seventh-day Adventists in the group were organized and began Sabbath worship services in five of the seven camps. They actively shared their faith, and by the time I left Cuba 50 Haitians were baptized as Adventists. Today we all need an active faith in preparing others for the second coming of Christ.

—Chaplain Gary Losey, U.S. Army

Hospital Directory

The following hospitals in the United States are owned and/or managed by the various Adventist health systems as of January 2002. For updated information, see the health system websites at the end of this list.

CALIFORNIA

Central Valley General Hospital
1025 North Douty Street
Hanford, CA 93230
(559) 583-2100
www.hanfordhealth.com

Feather River Hospital
5974 Pentz Road
Paradise, CA 95969
(530) 877-9361
www.frhosp.org

Frank R. Howard Memorial Hospital
One Madrone Street
Willits, CA 95490
(707) 459-6801
www.howardhospital.com

Glendale Adventist Medical Center
1509 Wilson Terrace
Glendale, CA 91206-4007
(818) 409-8000
www.glendaleadventist.com

Hanford Community Medical Center
450 Greenfield Avenue
Hanford, CA 93230
(559) 582-9000
www.hanfordhealth.com

Loma Linda Community Medical Center
25333 Barton Road
Loma Linda, CA 92354
(909) 799-3315
www.llu.edu

Loma Linda University Children's Hospital
11234 Anderson Street
Loma Linda, CA 92354
(909) 558-8000
www.llu.edu

Loma Linda University Medical Center
11234 Anderson Street
Loma Linda, CA 92354
(909) 824-4302
www.llu.edu

Paradise Valley Hospital
2400 East Fourth Street
National City, CA 91950-2099
(619) 470-4321
www.paradisevalleyhospital.org

Redbud Community Hospital
18th Avenue and Highway 53
Clearlake, CA 95422
(707) 995-5820
www.adventisthealth.org

St. Helena Hospital
650 Sanitarium Road
Deer Park, CA 94576
(707) 963-3611
www.sthelenahospital.org

San Joaquin Community Hospital
2615 Eye Street
Bakersfield, CA 93301
(661) 395-3000
www.sanjoaquinhospital.org

Selma Community Hospital
1141 Rose Avenue
Selma, CA 92662
(559) 891-1000
www.adventisthealth.org

Hospital Directory

Simi Valley Hospital
2975 North Sycamore Drive
Simi Valley, CA 93065
(805) 527-2462
www.simivalleyhospital.com

Sonora Community Hospital
One South Forest Road
Sonora, CA 95370
(209) 532-3161
www.SonoraCommunityHospital.org

South Coast Medical Center
31872 Coast Highway
Laguna Beach, CA 92651
(949) 499-1311
www.southcoastmedcenter.com

Ukiah Valley Medical Center
275 Hospital Drive
Ukiah, CA 95482
(707) 462-3111
www.uvmc.org

White Memorial Medical Center
1720 Cesar E. Chavez Avenue
Los Angeles, CA 90033
(323) 268-5000
www.whitememorial.com

COLORADO
Avista Adventist Hospital
100 Health Park Drive
Louisville, CO 80027
(303) 673-1000
www.avistahosp.org

Littleton Adventist Hospital
7700 South Broadway
Littleton, CO 80122
(303) 730-8900
www.littletonhosp.org

Porter Adventist Hospital
2525 South Downing Street
Denver, CO 80210
(303) 778-5252
www.porterhosp.org

FLORIDA
East Pasco Medical Center
7050 Gall Boulevard
Zephyrhills, FL 33541
(813) 788-0411
www.epmc.com

Florida Hospital Orlando
601 E. Rollins Street
Orlando, FL 32803
(407) 896-6611
www.flhosp.org

Florida Hospital Altamonte
601 E. Altamonte Drive
Altamonte Springs, FL 32701
(407) 830-4321
www.flhosp.org

Florida Hospital Apopka
201 N. Park Avenue
Apopka, FL 32703
(407) 889-1000
www.flhosp.org

Florida Hospital Celebration Health
400 Celebration Place
Celebration, FL 34747
(407) 303-4000
www.celebrationhealth.com

Florida Hospital Deland
701 West Plymouth Avenue
Deland, FL 32720
(904) 734-3320
www.fhdeland.org

Hospital Directory

Florida Hospital East Orlando
7727 Lake Underhill Drive
Orlando, FL 32822
(407) 277-8110
www.flhosp.org

Florida Hospital Fish Memorial
1055 Saxon Boulevard
Orange City, FL 32763
(904) 851-5000
www.fhfishmemorial.org

Florida Hospital Heartland Medical Center
4200 Sun ëN Lake Boulevard
Sebring, FL 33872
(863) 314-4466
www.flhosp-heartland.org

Florida Hospital Kissimmee
200 Hilda Street
Kissimmee, FL 34741-2302
(407) 846-4343
www.flhosp.org

Florida Hospital Lake Placid
1210 US Highway 27, North
Lake Placid, FL 33852
(863) 465-3777
www.flhosp-heartland.org

Florida Hospital Waterman
201 North Eustis Street
Eustis, FL 32726
(352) 589-3333
www.fhwat.org

Florida Hospital Wauchula
533 West Carlton Street
Wauchula, FL 33873
(863) 773-3101
www.flhosp-heartland.org

Memorial Hospital-Flagler
Moody Boulevard
Bunnell, FL 32110
(904) 437-2211
www.memorial-health.com

Memorial Hospital-Ormond Beach
875 Sterthaus Avenue
Ormond Beach, FL 32174
(904) 676-6000
www.memorial-health.com

Memorial Hospital-Peninsula
264 South Atlantic Avenue
Ormond Beach, FL 32176
(904) 672-4161
www.memorial-health.com

Winter Park Memorial Hospital
200 N. Lakemont Avenue
Winter Park, FL 32792
(407) 646-7000
www.winterparkhospital.com

GEORGIA
Emory-Adventist Hospital
3949 S. Cobb Drive
Smyrna, GA 30080
(770) 434-0710
www.adventisthealthsystem.com

Gordon Hospital
1035 Red Bud Road
Calhoun, GA 30701
(706) 629-2895
www.adventisthealthsystem.com

Hospital Directory

HAWAII
Castle Medical Center
640 Ulukahiki Street
Kailua, HI 96734
(808) 263-5500
www.castlemed.com

North Hawaii Community Hospital
67-1125 Mamalahoa Highway
Kamuela, HI 96743
(808) 885-4444
www.planet-hawaii.com/nhch

ILLINOIS
GlenOaks Hospital
701 Winthrop Avenue
Glendale Heights, IL 60139
(630) 545-8000
www.keepingyouwell.com

Hinsdale Hospital
120 North Oak Street
Hinsdale, IL 60521-3890
(630) 856-9000
www.keepingyouwell.com

La Grange Memorial Hospital
5101 South Willow Springs Road
La Grange, IL 60525
(708) 352-1200
www.keepingyouwell.com

KANSAS
Shawnee Mission Medical Center
9100 W. 74th Street
Shawnee Mission, KS 66204
(913) 676-2000
www.saint-lukes.org

KENTUCKY
Manchester Memorial Hospital
401 Memorial Drive
Manchester, KY 40962
(606) 598-5104
www.adventisthealthsystem.com

MARYLAND
Kessler-Adventist Rehabilitation Hospital
9909 Medical Center Drive
Rockville, MD 20850
(240) 864-600
Potomac Ridge Behavioral Health
14901 Broschart Road
Rockville, MD 20850
(301) 251-4500
www.potomacridge.com

Shady Grove Adventist Hospital
9901 Medical Center Drive
Rockville, MD 20850
(301) 279-6000
www.adventisthealthcare.com

Washington Adventist Hospital
7600 Carroll Avenue
Takoma Park, MD 20912
(301) 891-7600
www.adventisthealthcare.com

NEW JERSEY
Hackettstown Community Hospital
651 Willow Grove Street
Hackettstown, NJ 07840-1798
(908) 852-5100
www.hch.org

Hopsital Directory

NORTH CAROLINA
Park Ridge Hospital
Naples Road
P.O. Box 1569
Fletcher, NC 28732
(828) 684-8501
www.adventisthealthsystem.com

OHIO
Charles F. Kettering Memorial Hospital
3535 Southern Boulevard
Kettering, OH 45429
(937) 298-4331
www.kmcnetwork.org

Grandview Hospital
405 W. Grand Avenue
Dayton, OH 45405
(937) 226-3200
www.kmcnetwork.org/gvhsvh

Southview Hospital
1997 Miamisburg-Centerville Road
Dayton, OH 45459
(937) 439-6000
www.kmcnetwork.org/gvhsvh

Sycamore Hospital
2150 Leiter Road
Miamisburg, OH 45342
(937) 866-0551
www.kmcnetwork.org/sycamore

OREGON
Adventist Medical Center
10123 S.E. Market Street
Portland, OR 97216
(503) 257-2500
www.adventisthealthnw.com

Tillamook County General Hospital
1000 Third Street
Tillamook, OR 97141
(503) 842-4444
www.tcgh.com

TENNESSEE
Jellico Community Hospital
188 Hospital Lane
Jellico, TN 37762
(423) 784-7252
www.jellicohospital.com

Takoma Adventist Hospital
401 Takoma Avenue
Greeneville, TN 37743
(423) 639-3151
www.takoma.org

Tennessee Christian Medical Center
500 Hospital Drive
Madison, TN 37115
(615) 865-2373
www.tcmconline.com

Tennessee Christian Medical Center-Portland
105 Redbud Drive
Portland, TN 37148
(615) 325-7301
www.tcmconline.com

TEXAS
Central Texas Medical Center
1301 Wonder World Drive
San Marcos, TX 78666
(800) 730-0061
www.ctmc.org

Hopsital Directory

Huguley Memorial Medical Center
11801 S. Freeway
P.O. Box 6337
Fort Worth, TX 76028
(817) 293-9110
www.huguley.org

Metroplex Hospital
2201 South Clear Creek Road
Killeen, TX 76542
(254) 526-7523
www.mplex.org

Rollins-Brook Community Hospital
608 North Key Avenue
Lampasas, TX 76550
(512) 556-3682
www.mplex.org

WASHINGTON
Walla Walla General Hospital
1025 South Second Avenue
Walla Walla, WA 99362
(509) 525-0480
www.wwgh.com

WISCONSIN
Chippewa Valley Hospital
1220 Third Avenue West
Durand, WI 54736
(715) 672-4211
www.keepingyouwell.com

For More Information
Adventist Health
2100 Douglas Boulevard
P.O. Box 619002
Roseville, CA 95661-9002
(916) 781-2000
www.adventisthealth.org

Adventist HealthCare
1801 Research Boulevard, Suite 300
Rockville, MD 20850
(301) 315-3030
www.adventisthealthcare.com

Adventist Health System
111 North Orlando Avenue
Winter Park, FL 32789
(407) 647-4400
www.adventisthealthsystem.com

18

Loma Linda University and the School of Public Health

God Prepares the Way for Loma Linda University

In *Legacy,* a fascinating book about the heritage of Loma Linda University, Richard Schaefer tells the story of how God led in the establishment of medical missionary training at Loma Linda.

By the turn of the century, Seventh-day Adventists had established twenty-six sanitariums and treatment rooms in the United States and abroad. Under added appeals by Mrs. White, in 1904 and 1905 they established three more sanitariums in Southern California: in Glendale, Paradise Valley, and Loma Linda.

In her home near St. Helena, California, Ellen White had predicted in 1902 that "unoccupied properties" would soon become available in Southern California; properties that could be purchased "far below the original cost" and used as sanitariums. "For months," she wrote, "the Lord has given me instruction that He is preparing the way for our people to obtain possession, at little cost, of properties on which there are buildings that can be utilized in our work."

The Paradise Valley facility (now the Paradise Valley Hospital) represented an investment of $25,000. It was offered to the Seventh-day Adventist church for $12,000. In 1904 it was purchased for $4,000—"far below the original cost," just as Ellen White had predicted. The Glendale Hotel (which became the Glendale Adventist Medical Center) represented an investment of $50,000. It was offered to Seventh-day Adventists for $26,000. In 1904 it was purchased for only $12,000—"far below the original cost."

Though to all appearances it seemed financially impossible, even foolhardy, Ellen White instructed John Burden, manager of the St. Helena Sanitarium (now St. Helena Hospital and Health Center) near San Francisco, to look between Riverside, San Bernardino, and Redlands

for this third property which she had seen in vision. In March 1894, Burden found seventy-six acres of property four miles from Redlands that matched her description, and inquired about the price. He learned that the facilities on the property had been built in the 1880s by land speculators, or "boomers," as those who built boom towns in the West were called. The speculators had named the proposed resort community Mound City. But they went bankrupt, then sold out to a group of eighty physicians and forty businessmen from Los Angeles who wanted to develop Mound City into a health resort. The new owners renamed the property "Loma Linda" ("Hill Beautiful") and invested over $155,000 in new buildings, redecorating, furnishings, and other improvements. But their effort failed and the stockholders were desperate.

For months Loma Linda was deserted except for a caretaker and grazing sheep. People in the surrounding community nicknamed the hill "Lonesome Linda." Burden was told that the $155,000 property could be purchased for $110,000. But $110,000 was out of the question. He left.

Mrs. White urged him to return. This time the price was lowered to $85,000. Still, $85,000 might as well have been $85,000,000. The fourteen hundred church members in Southern California were already supporting a large building program of new churches and health institutions. And church headquarters—the General Conference of Seventh-day Adventists in Washington, D. C.—had just established a "no-debt policy" and could not help finance any new institutions. When Burden told Ellen White the new price, she said that someday thousands of people would be moving into the area and Loma Linda would become not only a center of medical and spiritual healing but also "an important educational center" to prepare medical missionaries.

How were these ideals to be realized? In 1905 Ellen White's 541-page book, *The Ministry of Healing*, was published. It revealed Christ as the true Gospel Medical Missionary and outlined how to follow in His footsteps: A school should be built to provide practical experience in Gospel medical missionary work. Mrs. White urged Burden to return to Loma Linda a third time. This time Burden asked whether the owners were really serious about selling Loma Linda and what would be the bottom dollar they would accept. They said they would settle for $40,000. Although the sum still seemed astronomical. Burden inspected the property more closely. He found that it included thirty-one acres of grain land; twenty-two acres of alfalfa, vegetable gardens, an apricot orchard and a barn; and a twenty-three-acre terraced hill covered with orchards, gardens, beautifully landscaped lawns, scores of tall shade trees and pepper trees filled with canaries, a profusion of flowers and ornamental shrubs, carriage drives, and over a mile of gracefully curving concrete walks. On the summit of the hill were several cottages, a large recreation hall, and a four-story, sixty-four-room frame hotel. The buildings, in excellent condition, were lighted with electricity and heated with steam. Water was piped through the premises from a large artesian well. The property also included $12,000 to $15,000 worth of equipment and supplies that had never been used. Burden decided to purchase the land and buildings.

The terms were $5,000 down and, within the next few months, three monthly payments of $5,000 each—the first half of the purchase price. The remaining $20,000 was to be paid at the end of three years. On Friday afternoon, May 26, 1905, lawyers came to sign the contract of sale. Because it was nearing sunset that Friday evening and "the Sabbath," was about to begin, Burden and the few church members with him decided to postpone the signing of the papers until Monday.

On Sunday, May 28, Burden received a telegram from G. W. Reaser, president of the Southern California Conference, who at the time was in Washington, D.C. It said, "Developments here warrant advising do not make deposit on sanitarium." It is not difficult to understand the directive since it seemed certain that there would be no funds available to make either the deposit or the payments. But, at Mrs. White's urging, and with her assurance that the Lord would provide, on Monday Burden paid $1,000 borrowed on his personal note to secure an option to buy Loma Linda. This $1,000 was to be forfeited if the down payment or monthly payments could not be made.

Two weeks later, on Monday morning, June 12, 1905, Mrs. White came to Loma Linda for the first time. As she was taken on an inspection tour she said repeatedly that she recognized it as the very place she had seen in vision nearly two years before (in the fall of 1903 and also on October 10, 1901). She sat down in the parlor and spoke of the educational work that was to be carried forward in Loma Linda. Encouraged by Burden's example, local Adventists contributed another $4,000 to complete the June 15 down payment, though none had any idea how they would meet the July payment—another $5,000—due in one month.

On the day the July payment was due, the conference committee members met with Burden in Los Angeles in emergency session. Not only did they not have the $5,000, but they did not have one dollar of it. Some of them were critical of Burden. Creditors were knocking at the door, ready to foreclose. The situation was tense. Burden's only assurance was faith in a statement by Mrs. White that money would come from unexpected sources.

Someone suggested that they wait for the morning mail. Soon they heard the postman walking up the stairs. In the mail was a letter from Atlantic City, New Jersey, written by a women unknown to anyone on the committee. Accompanying her letter the 3,000 miles across the continent was a draft for $5,000, the exact amount needed on that deadline day—and it had been mailed weeks in advance. Just as Ellen White had predicted, money came from an "unexpected source."

One who had been critical of Burden came to him and said, "It seems that the Lord is in this matter."

"Surely He is," Burden replied, "and He will carry it through to victory."

That is exactly what happened. Unlooked-for funds from various persons enabled them to pay for the property in less than six months, thus gaining an additional discount of $1,100. The final purchase price was $38,900—"far below the original cost."

In November of 1905, the Loma Linda Sanitarium and School of Nursing opened. During the first few weeks, the thirty-five Sanitarium employees, including physicians and nurses, learned that patient revenue ($16 to $25 per week per patient—which included medical care, meals, treatments twice a day, and a room) was not sufficient to meet the payroll. With strong faith to offset their deepening poverty, they cheerfully offered to work for room and board until the patronage increased. That winter there were only forty patients. But by June 30, 1906, Sanitarium accounts were over $1,000 in the black.

The Loma Linda College of Evangelists opened on September 20, 1906 offering four courses: Collegiate, Nurses, Gospel Workers, and a three-year Evangelistic-medical course that included standard medical school classwork plus Bible classes…. (Richard A. Schaefer, *Legacy: Daring to Care*. Loma Linda, CA 92354 (P.O. Box 1500): Legacy Publishing Association, 1995, pp. 157-161. (Note: This is an excellent book on the development of the Adventist health message and medical training. It will make you proud of your heritage!).

That was the beginning. In order to provide clinical experience for the medical students, facilities were opened in Los Angeles in October, 1913. In 1951 the School of Dentistry began. Then in 1961 the College of Medical Evangelists—then a consortium of several colleges, schools, and professional curricula—became Loma Linda University, with the Schools of Medicine and Nursing still offering part of their training in Los Angeles. In 1962 the trustees voted to consolidate the two campuses in Loma Linda, making it necessary to build a hospital/teaching/research facility—the Loma Linda University Medical Center.

The Vision Fulfilled

Loma Linda University, the Loma Linda University Medical Center and Children's Hospital is now the home of one of the largest private schools of medicine in the western United States, and by 2001, 8635 physicians have graduated since records began to be kept in 1914.

In addition to the advanced degrees offered by the Schools of Medicine, Nursing, Dentistry, and Religion, Loma Linda University offers master's and doctoral degrees through its Graduate School, the School of Public Health and the School of Allied Health Professions. The School of Public Health now offers an undergraduate degree in public health. Training is now available in physical therapy, occupational therapy, medical technology, medical radiography, radiation technology, radiation therapy technology, health information administration, health education, nutrition and dietetics, respiratory therapy, speech-language pathology and audiology, cytotechnology, cardiovascular technology, cardiovascular perfusion technology, emergency medical care, nuclear medicine technology, and medical sonography.

Loma Linda University Medical Center (LLUMC) is licensed for 798 beds and is the only state-designated, level 1, regional trauma center for the four Inland Counties of Southern California. Therefore, it provides the highest level of care available for patients in more than one-fourth of California. The Loma Linda University 244-bed Children's Hospital is the Inland Empire's largest and most comprehensive hospital dedicated exclusively to children. It is also the only level three (the highest level) regional perinatal program for premature/sick babies. Its 84-bed neonatal intensive care unit is one of the largest in the world. The institution has received as many as 14 helicopter flights in one day because of the intensity of the care it delivers. Loma Linda is indeed on the cutting edge of medicine. (See Chapter 17). Here are just a few ways Loma Linda University is known throughout the world.

Proton Treatment Center

In 1990, after almost 20 years of research, LLUMC opened the world's first hospital-based Proton Treatment Center for the treatment of cancer and other diseases. This $85 million facility produces 250 million electron-volts of energy. The equipment alone weighs 400 tons and stands three stories high. In 1971 Dr. James M. Slater, director of radiation medicine, recognized the need to focus a beam inside the body, and assembled a team to explore the possibilities of the proton accelerator. Protons are subatomic, positively charged particles, found in the nuclei of atoms. As they go through a patient's body and stop at a point called the Bragg Peak, they release most of their energy. By focusing the Bragg Peak on a patient's tumor, the deadly radiation causes most of its damage to the tumor. The superior controllability of the proton beam has allowed for the delivery of higher radiation doses than is possible with conventional radiation and promises, therefore, better results.

On December 1, 1994, Loma Linda University Medical Center signed a five-year Memorandum of Agreement to establish formal scientific collaboration with NASA's Office of Life and Microgravity Sciences Applications. NASA administrator, Daniel S. Goldin, said that the Loma Linda facility was the only place on earth where NASA could do everything it needs to do to learn how to protect its astronauts and their electronics from the dangers of positively charged particles in space. In 1997 research began in the NASA-sponsored LLU radiation medicine radiobiology laboratories.

By 2001, more than 6000 patients had been treated with protons since1994 when the facility became fully operational. In 2001, more than140 patients were being treated each day. Proton radiation therapy has become established as one of the standard treatment options for prostate cancer. Recently a new process is being developed to modify the proton beam therapy system by adding a new "scanning" technique. This non-invasive proton option will enhance the treatment of breast cancer while minimizing side effects.

Pallidotomy for Parkinson's Disease

A patient from Rochester, New York, shuffles into Loma Linda with one-inch steps and walks normally out of pallidotomy surgery. A young Adventist arrives from Brazil, bobbing and waving from the waist up, arms flailing uncontrollably. His wife walks 10 paces ahead. Following a stereotactic pallidotomy for Parkinson's disease, the couple walks out of Loma Linda side by side, thanks to the research and the refinement of neurosurgical techniques by Robert P. Iacono, M.D. who has taught senior neurosurgeons from across the US and Canada how to perform the delicate surgery.

The Infant Heart Transplant Program

The first baby in history to undergo heart transplant surgery was an infant in Brooklyn, New York. The baby lived 6 1/2 hours. The second was in London, England. She lived 18 days after surgery. The third baby was Baby Fae at Loma Linda University Medical Center. With the heart of a baboon, since no human heart was available, she lived 20 1/2 days. And so began the incredible story of Dr. Leonard Bailey and the infant heart transplant program.

On November 20, 1985, Baby Moses (not his real name) at just four days old became the youngest person in the world to undergo successful heart transplantation. Since that time the team has performed heart transplants on more than 300 babies. Of the 208 babies under six months of age, 75 percent are alive. For nine years the youngest patient in the world to undergo successful heart transplantation and thrive was delivered by cesarean section at the age of 3 hours. Paul Gabriel Bailey Holc, a Canadian, is affectionately known as "The Incredible Holc." The record is now held by a baby at Florida Hospital who was one hour old.

Osteoporosis Research Center

Osteoporosis, an age-related disease, is one of the deadliest diseases among the elderly, and the most common of all metabolic bone diseases, characterized by an abnormal loss of calcium and phosphorus from the bones.

In the four years before coming to Loma Linda for treatment, Carolyn Tarter had lost 4 inches in height. She was in constant pain from osteoporosis, spending most of her days lying on the floor. At age 69, she was pessimistic about her chances for ever leading a normal life again. Then Carolyn learned about the Loma Linda Osteoporosis Research Center. Two months after treatment began, which included medication, diet and exercise, she was walking every day without constant pain. After six months, Carolyn had resumed her former daily household routines, traveled extensively, and even managed to enjoy Disneyland with her grandchildren. Now she says she is physically active, working out regularly at a fitness center, and able to do everything she did before her symptoms became severe, thanks to the work of Dr. David J. Baylink at Loma Linda.

International Outreach Programs

Loma Linda probably has sent out more medically trained missionaries than any other training institution in North America. In addition, approximately 50 percent of the faculty have served in some type of mission service. Members of the faculty are committed to missionary work.

The **Loma Linda Overseas Heart Surgery Team**, periodically gives of their expertise and time to travel to such countries as Nepal, Saudi Arabia, Pakistan, or Greece performing hundreds of open-heart surgeries, leaving behind not only mended hearts and all their sophisticated medical equipment, but also national heart surgery teams who now have the training to do these surgeries on their own. In 1974 and 1975 the team made two trips to South Vietnam. During their total stay of more than 10 weeks, the team operated on 103 patients—leaving the country only eight week before the fall of the South Vietnamese government.

The team has since worked in North Korea and other countries. They witness not only to their patients and families, but also to the highest government officials, and perhaps the most skilled medical professionals in these different countries—individuals who could not be reached in any other way.

From the Heart of a Loma Linda University Trained Medical Evangelist

"Few life events on earth exceed the realization of love, the miracle of conception or the emotion of birthing. Babies are naturally embraced by home, by reflection of what can be, and by promises to keep; that is, unless the heart within a baby's breast is so poorly developed that life cannot go on. I have been driven by the notion that heart disease should not end the promise of a newborn infant. Heart transplantation restores the hopes and dreams surrounding the babies and, hence, ranks right up there with the best of life events on earth.

"Every time we look into the eyes of those little babies who have new hearts in them, we're convinced we're on the right track. When a baby dies, it just doesn't seem fair. Death never seems quite fair. But to begin your life with death...is a terrible tragedy...."

—Leonard L. Bailey, M.D.
Dr. Bailey is the beloved physician who performed the first successful infant heart transplant in the world, and has given life to hundreds of others.

Then there are the physicians, nurses and dentists who donated their time to sail on the 71-foot catamaran, **CanvasBack**, that traveled through the Islands of Micronesia meeting medical needs. Others join the **aviation teams** and **caravans** of dentists, nurses, physicians and students who travel into remote parts of Mexico to meet medical needs. The list could go on and on.

In recent years, LLU has been one of the strong moving agents in the formation of Adventist Health International (AHI) that has adopted the overwhelming project of helping Adventist hospitals in the third-world overcome conditions that threaten their existence. Why attempt the seemingly impossible? "If the medical need still exists," says Richard Hart, MD, DrPH, President of AHI and chancellor of LLU, "Then our Biblical commission to teach, preach, and heal is still valid. Loss of our international commitment would undermine what this church is all about and what LLU has come to embody."

Certainly Ellen White's turn-of-the-century vision about Loma Linda becoming a major training center for medical evangelists has been fulfilled.

The School of Public Health

The training of health education professionals has been the primary focus of the School of Public Health (SPH). Physicians, nurses, dietitians, physical therapists, and many other health professionals obtain degrees in Public Health in addition to their own specialty in order to have skills and expertise in preventive medicine and health education. Many pastors, after reading what Ellen White has said about the importance of combining the gospel ministry with the health message, have come to the School of Public Health for additional training to be better equipped as medical evangelists.

The School of Public Health had its beginning with the organization in 1948 of the School of Tropical and Preventive Medicine, the purpose of which was to provide a base for research and teaching. After its reorganization in 1961, the Division of Public Health and Tropical Medicine began to offer Master's programs through the Graduate School. Harold N. Mozar, M.D., was the director from 1948-1964; Mervyn G. Hardinge, M.D., Ph.D., Dr.P.H., became the director of the Division of Public Health in 1964.

The establishment of a School of Public Health was authorized in 1964, and plans were made for faculty and facilities to meet the requirements of the Committee on Professional Education of the American Public Health Association. Dr. Hardinge became the dean in July, 1967. In October, 1970, the name of the school was changed to the School of Health. Authorization was given to offer work leading to the degrees of Master of Public Health and Master of Science in Public Health.

In 1972, the School was authorized to offer the Doctor of Health Sciences degree. Subsequently the Doctor of Public Health degree was authorized with the first Dr.P.H. in epidemiology being granted in 1980. Students were first admitted to the Dr.P.H. program in health education in 1981 and to the Dr.P.H. program in nutrition in 1987. The Doctor of Health Science degree program was restructured to a Dr.P.H. in preventive care in 1991.

In the fall of 1979, the School was approved to begin a preventive medicine residency and an occupational medicine residency. An M.P.H. degree in a selected area is an integral part of the residency program.

The original name, School of Public Health, was readopted in 1987. In 1991, the School was reorganized to include the Center for Health Promotion and the Preventive Medicine Faculty Practice. The School provides the services of the Department of Preventive Medicine for the School of Medicine.

Dr. Hardinge served as dean until 1976. He was followed by James M. Crawford, D.D.S., M.P.H. from 1977 to 1980 and again from 1983 to 1986; Andrew P. Haynal, M.D., M.P.H. served from 1980 to 1983, and Edwin H. Krick, M.D., M.P.H. from 1986 to 1990. Richard H. Hart, M.D., Dr.P.H. became dean in 1990 and served until 2001. Patricia K. Johnston, DrPH. M.S., R.D., became Dean in 2001.

The instructional, research, and service programs within the School are organized and administered by six academic departments and three centers. The academic departments are Environmental and Occupational Health, Epidemiology and Biostatistics, Health Administration, Health Promotion and Education, International Health, and Nutrition. The three centers are the Center for Health Promotion (CHP), the Center for Health Research (CHR), and the Center for Health and Development (CHD). In 2000 the SPH established an Office in Public Health Practice.

Center for Health Promotion (CHP)

A large spectrum of programs are offered by CHP, including weight management, executive health, stress management, smoking cessation, nutrition, exercise, and alcohol and drug dependency. Group sessions, individual counseling, and health assessment are conducted in the community or in corporate settings. CHP serves more than 10,000 clients per year and is a major training center for students. Specifically they offer:

- Profile Plus: Comprehensive health evaluations by a multidisciplinary health team.

Evaluations include: physical, sigmoidoscopy, hearing, vision, glaucoma screening, pulmonary function test, treadmill test, blood test, body composition and a nutrition evaluation.

- Health and Risk Evaluations: These services are available throughout Southern California. (909) 558-4940.
- International Travel Clinic: Provides the full range of vaccinations necessary for travel, as currently recommended by the Centers for Disease Control and Prevention

Working in No-man's Land

*H*is day might start out as fairly routine—rise with the sun since there is no regular source of electricity, worship with the compound staff of 10 to 15 workers, eat breakfast, plan the next outing to a remote village clinic, or take inventory of the latest medical shipment from the United Nations headquarters in Nairobi, Kenya.

However, his day could just as easily include a mad dash to the bomb shelter as a government plane makes a bombing run on a nearby rebel position, taking cover as bullets whiz through the trees, over his head, or heading for the Ugandan border if government forces mount a major assault on the region.

Steve Cooper, who is finishing his MPH degree in the School of Public Health's international health program, has lived in a war zone since he arrived in south Sudan in 1994 when he was asked by ADRA to direct an emergency vaccination and health-care project. South Sudan is "in a corner." This region is occupied by a nomadic population of approximately 150,000 people, who have their own tribal skirmishes, and is cut off from the rest of the world because of a civil war that has been raging for half a century.

Mr. Cooper and his team are developing an entire community structure from scratch in an attempt to make the local population self-reliant. Already 35 to 40 local people have been medically trained in "Mango College" (held in a Mango grove) and sent out to villages.

The project involves a veterinarian component because the cattle and goat herds provide a livelihood for the tribes and are their main food source. Disease among the livestock can prove to be a major threat to the population.

Steve Cooper has set up a solar-power-based system which allows them to operate two-way radios, a necessity in south Sudan. He has also found a way to use his laptop computer and keeps in regular contact with LLU.

The dangers, challenges, and inconveniences are all part of life for him. So are the rewards of helping people in a forgotten corner of the world.

Steve Cooper is an example of just one of thousands who have been sent out from Loma Linda University as "medical evangelists" to the world.

(This profile is adapted from an article in SCOPE, the Loma Linda University alumni journal, Autumn, 1996.

- Weight Management: Four different programs currently are offered:
  Optifast: A 26-week, medically supervised program for individuals with 50 or more pounds to lose.
  The Better Weigh: A 10-week program for those who want to improve their health and weight through exercise, food choices, and a new understanding of the psychology of eating.
  Women & Food: A 12-week group program for women who struggle with food, eating issues, and constant dieting. The focus is breaking the compulsive and emotional eating patterns and improving self-worth and health, rather than merely dieting.
  Child & Adolescent Weight Management: Group sessions for children eight to 18, plus individual sessions with a dietitian and psychotherapist.

For more information on the Center of Health Promotion services call: (909) 558-4594.

Loma Linda University Speakers Bureau

Many of the faculty and staff at Loma Linda University are available to give presentations and training for churches and communities. For the Speakers Bureau Directory contact the Office of University Relations at (909) 824-4526.

Center for Health Research (CHR)

The Center for Health Research opened in 1990 and reflects the School's growing involvement in public health research. The School is active in research projects involving preventive medicine epidemiology, health education, nutrition, and other aspects of public health. Most notably, it has directed the Adventist Health Study, internationally recognized as a path-breaking project in health research. CHR administers a research endowment fund and provides technical support for faculty projects in the School. It provides consultation to researchers throughout the University and surrounding community. (See Chapter 23 on research.)

Center for Health and Development (CHD)

The newest center in the School, the Center for Health and Development, coordinates and directs service and community development programs in the School that have a cross-cultural emphasis. It started the Students for International Missions Service (SIMS) providing short-term mission opportunities around the world as well as in local communities for students and faculty. It also started the Social Action Community Health System (SACHS) which operates medical and dental clinics in the surrounding area for persons who cannot afford adequate healthcare. This provides a valuable community service through which students gain experience and understanding. The Center also assists faculty in arranging international consulting projects with a variety of organizations and works with the World Health Organization and in primary healthcare projects.

Majors

Majors are offered in the following areas: biostatistics, environmental and occupational health, epidemiology, health administration, health education, international health, maternal and child health, nutrition, preventive care, and the generalist program. For the details of these majors and specific departmental offerings, please contact the SPH.

Illustrative of the majors, degrees, and collaborative programs available are those offered by the Department of Health Education:
Bachelor of Science in Public Health
Master of Public Health Degree
Majors: Health Education and Maternal and Child Health
Doctor of Public Heath Degree Majors: Health Education and Preventive Care
Conjoint/Collaborative Programs (Dual Degrees with the Graduate School

Certified Health Education Specialist (C.H.E.S.)

The National Commission for Health Education Credentialing, Inc. (NCHEC) has established a process by which academically prepared and experienced individuals may be certified as health education specialists (C.H.E.S.). Qualified individuals may apply to sit for an examination and, if successful, may add the letters C.H.E.S. to their list of degrees, licenses, registrations, and credentials.

This competency-based examination is given annually, usually in mid-October, at sites located throughout the United States. Two sites, New York, New York and **Loma Linda, California, make the examination available on Sunday** instead of Saturday. NCHEC may be contacted for information at its national headquarters at: 9944 Marcon Boulevard, Suite 310 Allentown, PA 18103, (610) 264-8200; Fax (800) 813-0727; e-mail: cogs101w@wonder.em.edc.gov

The Commission offers two routes to apply for certification:

Option A Eligibility: for those with academic qualifications, only.

Persons are eligible to apply if they have both of the following:

* A bachelor's, master's, or doctoral degree from an accredited institution.
* An official transcript that clearly shows a major in health education, community health education, public health education, school health education, or other health education program.
  OR they must have:
* An official transcript that reflects 25 semester hours or 37 quarter hours of course work with specific preparation in addressing the following seven responsibilities:
  1. Assess individual and community needs for health education.
  2. Plan effective health education programs.
  3. Implement health education programs.
  4. Evaluate the effectiveness of health education programs.
  5. Coordinate the provision of health education services.
  6. Act as a resource person in health education.
  7. Communicate health and health education needs, concerns and resources.

Option B Eligibility: Takes into consideration academic qualifications and experience.

Persons are eligible to sit for the examination if they:

* Have a bachelor's, master's, or doctoral degree from an accredited institution of higher learning; AND
* Have 15 semester hours or 22 quarter hours of course work in health education that addresses the seven responsibilities and competencies mentioned above; AND
* Have at least five years of continuous full-time employment in health education/health promotion positions.

Application fees vary according to the application date. (From $215-250) Certification must also be renewed annually for a fee of $25. Every five years CHES certified individuals must recertify demonstrating that they have acquired 75 continuing education units (CEU) during the five years and paying a fee of $75.

An excellent place to obtain approximately 25 continuing education units each year is at the Loma Linda School of Public Health Annual Convention, "**Healthy People**." (See write-up Healthy People.)

Healthy People: The School of Public Health Annual Convention

One of the most exciting training opportunities offered at the School of Public Health is their annual **Healthy People** convention that takes place during the last four days of the School of Medicine's Alumni Postgraduate Convention (APC), which falls during the last of February or first of March.

During this time world-recognized leaders in their field and Loma Linda University faculty present the latest information in health education, preventive medicine, and public health. Regardless of your background or training, you will enjoy these helpful workshops and seminars, and come away inspired and better prepared for medical evangelist work. Approximately 25 hours of continuing education units are offered each year for a very reasonable fee. Attending Healthy People is a great way to stay current in your field, and an inexpensive way to obtain the continuing education units you need to keep your C.H.E.S. certification current. For information call the School of Public Health at (909) 558-4595 or (800) 854-5661.

Approximately 1/3 of the off-campus graduates were in international settings. The courses are taught in person by faculty from the School of Public Health—not via teleconferencing or video/audio tape. They are taught in a condensed 3 to 5-day format as part of a 10-week quarter during which students prepare assignments, study in depth daily, and take proctored exams. The degree may be completed in four years by attending one course per quarter (four courses are offered at each site per year). Students may accelerate the process by attending several sites. Faculty are available for consultation throughout the course of study and provide feedback via mail, telephone, FAX, e-mail, and in person.

A large number of the health ministries directors and leaders across North America received their training through the off-campus program. The student is not required to spend time on campus in Loma Linda. Rather, the instructor comes to the students in the various locations. Some start their degree program in the off-campus program and then transfer to the Loma Linda campus to get the specialized advanced degree that they want. The off-campus program has been an important service for the training of health promotion professionals within the church. To learn which majors are available and for more information about the program call the SPH at (800) 854-5661.

Off-campus Program

Through its off-campus program, the School of Public Health was a pioneer in bringing graduate education in public health to health professionals who could not leave their place of employment for full-time education. Courses have been offered in Canada, the Far East, Inter-America, as well as several sites in the United States. The first off-campus class graduated in 1978 and perhaps 25 percent of the graduates from the School of Public Health have received their public health degrees through this program.

19

Self-Supporting Health Institutions

The Gospel commission commands, "Go ye into all the world, and preach the gospel to every creature" (Mark 16:15), and Matthew 10:8 declares, "Heal the sick." Matthew 28:19 commands, "Go ye therefore, and teach all nations.... Teaching them to observe all things whatsoever I have commanded you: and lo, I am with you alway, even unto the end of the world."

Based on this commission, all church members should be active medical missionaries. Yet, it is impossible for the church to hire everyone. Some must work as medical missionaries on a self-supporting basis.

One could argue that Enoch, Noah and Abraham were the original self-supporting Adventist-laymen Services and Industries (ASI) workers—sharing the gospel in their place of work. Jesus had no church organization behind Him. And Paul was an obvious self-supporter—tent maker, soul winner, and character builder. No wonder Ellen White writes of him, "It was as a self-supporting missionary that the apostle Paul labored in spreading the knowledge of Christ throughout the world" and further, "In many places self-supporting missionaries can work successfully ...many today, if imbued with the same spirit of self-sacrifice could do a good work in a similar way" (*The Ministry of Healing*, p. 154).

Throughout most of Christian history, pioneer workers went forward in faith trusting God to provide. As a church structure grew, workers were given salaries, and the work came under the control of budgets, personnel committees, and administrators, so it could progress systematically.

Although there are many benefits to being a part of the "organized" work, there are also some disadvantages. For example, it's easy to become dependent on the financial resources of the larger institution, rather than on God for your "daily bread." As long as the money is available, there is no problem. But should the funds be withdrawn, such as in financially difficult times, the work could falter or cease.

Self-supporting workers who are independent of the financial structure of the church, have the freedom to plan their work according to their own understanding of the Bible and the Spirit of Prophecy guidelines. If the work is small, it is much less vulnerable to economic depression, and governmental control.

History of the Self-Supporting Work

Within the Seventh-day Adventist church, the idea of self-supporting work can be traced to a comment David Paulson, M.D. made to Edward A. Sutherland (first President of Walla Walla College, president of Battle Creek College when it moved to Berrien Springs, and first president of Emmanuel Missionary College) as they were discussing the need for educational opportunities for needy students at the turn of the century. Dr. Paulson said, "If I were in your place I would establish a school whose doors would swing open to any young man or woman of worthy character who is willing to work. You ought to have a large tract of land and provide facilities for student self-support." Sutherland, who from the writings of Ellen White and of the Oberlin system had become an educational reformer, was impressed.

In 1904 Sutherland and P. T. Magan, under conviction that they should work directly for the people of the Southern mountains, resigned their posts at Emmanuel Missionary College and went to Nashville, planning to proceed to the mountains of east Tennessee or the Carolinas to find a site for their school. Informed of their plans, Ellen White, who repeatedly had published appeals for denominational work in the South and who was in Nashville at the time, told Magan and Sutherland that they should locate the school within a few miles of Nashville. Mrs. White invited the two men to go with her son, Edson, and a group on a trip up the Cumberland River in the boat, Morning Star. When the engine broke down a few miles from Nashville, opposite an old, half-worn-out plantation, Mrs. White went ashore with W. O. Palmer and looked at the old Nelson farm. Returning to the boat, she told the men that she believed this to be the place on which God would have them establish a school.

The farm was purchased and Sutherland began a self-supporting school (later to become known as Madison College) to train home and foreign missionary teachers who were sent out as self-supporting workers. Nearly 40 small outpost schools and centers were started from Madison. These "units" included schools and sanitariums located on farms, also vegetarian cafeterias and treatment rooms in several large cities of the South—Nashville, Knoxville, Louisville, Memphis, Birmingham, and Asheville. Usually when a unit was established, it led to the formation of a company or church.

And so began what has become known as the "self-supporting work." Some units have now become known for their educational programs—like Little Creek School and Sanitarium in Knoxville (now Heritage Academy in Crossville), Laurelbrook School and Sanitarium in Dayton, Tennessee, and Pine Forest Academy and Sanitarium-Hospital in Chunky, Mississippi. Others, like Wildwood Sanitarium and Institute and Eden Valley Institute, now operate lifestyle centers and have become known for a strong preventive medicine training programs.

The Self-Supporting Health Work Today

Carefully following Ellen White's counsel over the years has led some self-supporting institutions into considerable experience with natural remedies. Because drugs are not very effective for treating influenza, colds, coughs, and simple seasonal afflictions, to name a few; self-supporting institutions view a plant-based diet, exercise, and hydrotherapy as important remedies. Self-supporting work specializes in prevention.

Most self-supporting workers live sacrificially in order to serve humanity full time. They don't believe in debt or partnerships with non-Adventist hospitals or institutions. Their strong convictions are what lead them to be self-supporters. Nevertheless, self-supporting institutions, following the blueprint of medical evangelism outlined by Ellen White, are growing rapidly around the world. They have something unique and substantial to offer the church, society, and humanity.

One of the tenets of these institutions is to closely follow the counsel of Ellen White concerning education and health. While many of the educational institutions are now under the umbrella of The Layman Foundation, many of the health programs operate under Outpost Centers, Inc. (OCI). OCI is a spin off from Wildwood Lifestyle Center and Hospital, and now is responsible for approximately 100 facilities in 38 countries of the world including lifestyle centers, mission stations and the Country Life Restaurants.

The lifestyle centers featured in this chapter are members of Adventist-laymen Services and Industries (ASI). ASI organizations, although operated independent of church stipends and funding, are highly supportive of the Seventh-day Adventist organization and its leadership, and perform an important role in keeping the preventive Adventist lifestyle health work alive in North America. Thousands are brought into the church through the activities of the ASI members and its annual meetings provide an impetus for soul-winning and spiritual rejuvenation. The member entities are now called "supporting" ministries because of their unquestioned loyalty to the Church.

How Can Self-Supporting Workers Help the Local Church?

First, each self-supporting institution has health professionals who are capable communicators of the health message. These resource people can be valuable for consultation, presentations, and the training of local church members to use simple remedies for the prevention and treatment of certain diseases, and to learn to cook without animal products.

Churches, even small ones, can afford mileage and simple expenses that will make it

Christian Care Ministry Endorses Self-supporting Health Institutions

*O*ne Christian organization that has recognized the value of the Adventist lifestyle and approach to preventive medicine as found in various self-supporting health institutions is Christian Care Ministry, a not-for-profit organization where Christians share the medical costs of other Christians. Their members' monthly fees are kept at a minimum because only those individuals with a healthy lifestyle, no current medical problem and not overweight are allowed into the program.

While regular insurance companies do not reimburse for health conditioning programs that help people learn a healthy lifestyle, Christian Care Ministry encourages those members with medical problems caused by an unhealthy lifestyle to attend such facilities as Weimar, Uchee Pines, Wildwood or Poland Spring, and reimburses them for their expenses. Here is a testimony of one of their members:

At age 65, I thought I knew a lot more about health than most having been a distributor for a quality producer of organic source vitamins and minerals. Although I took my vitamins and minerals religiously, I was on several medications for hypertension. My weight, although not grossly out of line, was far from ideal. A physician at the Uchee Pines Lifestyle Institute told me there was no reason with lifestyle changes that I couldn't go off medications and have the added benefit of having higher energy levels and feel much better. I decided to consider some permanent changes.

I set up a 21 day schedule to give the concept of no animal products, eight glasses of water and eight hours of sleep a day an honest try. I became narcotic free for the first time in 45 years when I dropped coffee and iced tea.

My new lifestyle included fruits, vegetables, legumes, nuts, and grains in quantities which totally satisfied my hunger. I noticed very soon I was losing weight while eating all I desired. To date, I've lost 20 pounds, started exercising every day for at least 30 minutes using brisk walking techniques, and my resting heart rate went from 80 to 68 and continues to fall. Under doctor's supervision, I began dropping my blood pressure medications and the outlook is that I expect to be free of medications in the next 30 days. Hallelujah!

I had one added blessing. For the last 20 years, I have had an open draining osteomyelitis in my left leg as a result of being hit by a truck. A variety of creams, solutions, baths, wrappings, and other treatments were used to stop the drainage. Since my lifestyle changes, the drainage stopped completely 45 days ago. Praise the Lord!

The net result is this; at 65 I have energy levels I haven't experienced in at least 20 years, my mental focus is much better, I get much more accomplished in a day, I no longer have the mid-afternoon energy slump, I sleep much better, and I feel great.

—Rev. Bert Weis

possible for experienced responsible health leaders or a small team from a self-supporting institution to come to their churches to advance the health work.

Second, there are many Seventh-day Adventist church members who could benefit from a residential lifestyle program to control hypertension, arthritis or diabetes, to prevent heart disease, or for weight control. Self-supporting institutions usually offer these valuable programs for significantly less than commercial centers. In addition, church members will enjoy a Christian atmosphere, and will be strengthened spiritually by attending these programs.

If there is a self-supporting program near your church, you should visit the program and become acquainted with the resources of that facility. If there is not one near you, write for brochures from each of the centers mentioned in this chapter. There is a wide difference in services and costs. Some church members may want to plan a vacation around attending a residential program and wouldn't mind the travel.

Self-supporting Health Institutions

The following health institutions offer a variety of health education, live-in lifestyle programs, training programs, week-long in-service "camp meetings," publications, and other resources to meet health needs through lifestyle change.

Black Hills Health and Education Center

Box 19
Hermosa, SD 57744
(800) 658-5433; (605) 255-4101; Fax (605) 255-4687

Black Hills is located about 20 miles south of Rapid City, South Dakota in the "Banana Belt" of the Black Hills. Nearby attractions include: Mount Rushmore, Custer State Park, the Badlands, a number of caves, Reptile Gardens, Bear Country, the tourist town of Keystone, the Needles, Sylvan Lake, and more.

It was founded on about 400 acres of strikingly beautiful foothill terrain in 1979 by a small group of individuals which included an educator, a nurse, and several physicians. In February 1997 their Wellness Lodge was completed, which accommodates 22 health guests as well as treatment areas for hydrotherapy and massage.

Black Hills offers a live-in lifestyle and wellness program with a therapeutic plant-based diet and hydrotherapy. They follow the eight natural remedies (nutrition, exercise, water, sunlight, temperance [self-control], air, rest and trust in divine power). There is a training program for students wanting to learn about natural remedies and offer simple treatments, and a newsletter which is published periodically.

The health center is the home of the Mission College of Evangelism. Carol Torres is president and Pastor Louis Torres is dean. Under their direction , the college's strong emphasis is on medical evangelism. For information on the courses available, call (800) 658-5433 or (605) 255-4101; fax (605) 255-4687 or write Mission College, Box 19, Hermosa, SD 57744.

Desert Springs Therapy Center

66705 East 6th Street
Desert Hot Springs, California 92240
(619) 329-5066 or 251-6205; Fax (619) 251-6206

Desert Springs Therapy Center is a small, family-sized physical therapy center founded by Charles Thomas Ph.D., teaching healthful living and treating guests with physical therapy needs.

Dr. Charles Thomas, professor emeritus of Loma Linda University School of Health has been teaching simple remedies for common illnesses for the past 40 years. Dr. Thomas has traveled around the world lecturing to healthcare professionals and lay people.

He directs and co-teaches the New Life Style Program, State Certified therapeutic Massage and Home Health Aids courses and Hydrotherapy programs he founded more than 16 years ago.

People with weight problems, high blood pressure, diabetes, heart disorders, stress and numerous other disabilities, find the individually tailored programs most helpful.

Eden Valley Lifestyle Center

6263 North County Rd. 29
Loveland, CO 80538-9598
(970) 667-1770; Fax (970) 663-7072; Business office (970) 667-0809; Lifestyle center (800) 637-WELL [9355] or (970) 669-7730; Fax (907) 667-1742

Eden Valley is located in a quiet valley in the foothills of the Rocky Mountains, with 550 acres of forested mountains, meadows, and farmland, and is known throughout the area for its agricultural program. Eden Valley was originally established to train for and promote mission work, and that continues to be their primary focus. They support several mission stations and projects worldwide. Visitors are always welcome and tours of the facilities may be arranged.

The Lifestyle Center offers a complete lifestyle approach to wellness, using hydrotherapy, massage, exercise, nutrition and cooking classes, trust in God, and natural remedies. This is an 18-day program. There are 8 (double occupancy) guest rooms available.

The **World Missions Training Course** is a 11-month commitment starting in January with the goal of actually placing graduates in mission outposts worldwide. They train at Eden Valley Institute with classroom study and practical hands-on experience. Students receive training in felt-needs seminars in the community, such as stress seminars, and cooking schools, with evangelistic reaping campaigns held twice a year.

Students also have quality classes in Bible, practical health science (massage, hydrotherapy lifestyle counseling, herbal and natural remedies, etc.), agriculture, construction, and other skills necessary for the mission field. The students will be prepared for mission work—both in foreign mission fields, and in the United States in dark counties, and in city missions.

The **Eden Valley Country Store** offers wholesome, reasonably-priced health foods. Most items are available in bulk or individual packages. For information call (970) 669-4867.

The **Lifestyle Village** is a retirement center licensed for 16 residents. It provides a beautiful country environment with the best homegrown organic foods served in the cafeteria for residents and guests.

The **Eden Valley Lay Missions Convention** is held late in September or early in October each year, featuring mission speakers and lay involvement from around the world. Their quarterly newsletter is called, *Faith Ventures.*

Lifestyle Center of America
Route 1, Box 4001
Sulphur, OK 73086
(405) 580-2327; (800) 596-5480; Fax (405) 993-3902
www.lifestylecenter.com
e-mail: life@brightok.net

Lifestyle Center of America is a $12 million world-class care provider established to help people from all walks of life attain the best health possible. Located on 1,700 acres in the beautiful Arbuckle Mountains of Southern Oklahoma overlooking Lake Arbuckle, the Center provides an ideal setting for individuals to focus on their health. Just two hours north of Dallas/Ft. Worth, the facility is offering help and hope to individuals around the globe.

The Center's approach to good health starts at the very foundation of many modern day diseases and illnesses—lifestyle habits. Diabetes, hypertension, heart disease, over weight, and stress-related illness are typically caused by the way we live our daily lives. Lifestyle Center of America offers powerful, proven methods that help individuals prevent, improve or even reverse these chronic diseases. In addition, the Center provides outstanding success for those who are wanting to quit smoking. The Center's approach through medical evaluation, diet, exercise, stress reduction, health lectures, massage, hydrotherapy and Christian counseling offers dramatic life-changing results and a better way of living.

An experienced and caring group of healthcare specialists work closely together to help individuals achieve their personal health goals. The Center's staff includes physicians, nurses, dietitian, exercise physiologist, health educators, physical therapist, preventive care specialist, massage and hydrotherapists, and food service professionals.

The Center offers three different physician-supervised residential programs that are tailored to meet an individual's specific health need. These residential programs follow each other every month begining with a 19-day, then a 12-day, and a 7-day program that help guests see dramatic health improvements during their short stay. More importantly, however, they provide practical hands-on experiences for individuals to take back home for continued success.

The Lifestyle Center of America also provides a popular one-day get acquainted program and extensive corporate physicals. Businesses, churches, and other groups also can take advantage of the personalized one- to three-day wellness retreats provided by the Center.

The Center is a division of The Ardmore Institute of Health and is a nonprofit organization operated by Seventh-day Adventists as a business rather than what is usually considered a "self-supporting" ministry. It was developed from a trust by the late Otey Johnson, M.D., a graduate of Loma Linda University who worked in the oil business instead of medicine, and was a longtime resident of Ardmore, Oklahoma.

M.E.E.T. Ministries and Our Home Health Center
480 Neely Lane
Huntington, TN 38344
(731) 986-3518; Fax (731) 986-0582; Hours: 9-5 p.m. CST

Our Home Health Center is the answer to those who need the small home like atmosphere that is conducive to the restoration of physical and spiritual health. They operate a small health sanitarium and offer a 10 day and 19 day live-in conditioning program based on the natural remedies.

M.E.E.T. Ministries is (Missionary Education and Evangelistic Training) the founding organization. It offers a three month training program for medical missionaries and weekend lectures on health education for the community. They publish and distribute gospel and health literature and a newsletter. They also manufacture and distribute health products. Thomas Jackson is the founder and director along with his wife, LaVerne Jackson.

Pacific Health Education Center
(See Chapter 15 for a complete description.)

Poland Spring Health Institute
226 Schellinger Road
Poland Spring, ME 04274-6134
(207) 998-2894; Fax (207) 998-2164
web site: www.pshi.org
e-mail: pshi226@aol.com

Poland Spring was founded more than two decades ago and is under the direction of Ulla Hansen. This large estate in a beautiful country setting has horses, many miles of paths through the woods, and several small ponds. It is within walking distance of Range State Park.

The Instituteis a residential lifestyle center for patients with heart conditions, diabetes, and weight management. They do hydrotherapy and massage and offer health education in the natural remedies and diet. There are five guest rooms, that can accommodate up to 10 guests who stay from one to three weeks.

Poland Spring is also a massage training school for students around the world who stay four and one-half months from January to May.

Uchee Pines Institute
30 Uchee Pines Road
Seale, AL 36875-5702
(334) 855-4764; or 4781; Fax (334) 855-4780
web site: www.ucheepines.org

Fifteen miles southwest of Columbus, Georgia, in rural Alabama, Uchee Pines Lifestyle Center offers a warm and friendly alternative approach to health recovery. The facility is situated on 200 acres of quiet woodland, offering the senses rest while healing takes place in the body. Also known as Anvwodi (Cherokee for "get well place"), the center invites guests to rediscover the natural rhythms of their bodies through the eight natural remedies spelled out in the acronym **STEWARDS.** We can best be stewards of our bodies by understanding and utilizing **S**unshine, **T**rust, **E**xercise, **W**ater, **A**ir, **R**est, **D**iet, and **S**elf-control. There are wooded trails to hike, gardens to tend, flowers to nurture; all waiting to aid in the business of health recovery.

Anvwodi's major offerings are 21-day lifestyle programs which include a physical exam, blood chemistry profiles, regular physician consultations, personalized treatments by a lifestyle counselor, health lectures, natural remedy and cooking classes, and delicious vegetarian diets designed for the individual patient. Each program is customized to address each patient's major goals (e.g., weight loss, smoking cessation, blood pressure or diabetes control, chronic disease management, or other lifestyle changes.) Uchee Pines also offers twice yearly Simple Remedies and Preventive Medicine Seminars, one held in the beautiful southern early spring, the other in the early fall after the heat of summer is past. These seminars offer hands-on training in simple remedies, insightful lectures on the major health concerns facing us today, and a special spiritual message brought by a guest speaker.

Two student programs are also offered. The Lifestyle Educator course begins the middle of August and lasts 9 months. It is designed for the individual who has recognized a personal need to make meaningful, permanent changes in the life in order to be used of God in medical missionary service. The Lifestyle Counselor course begins the end of August and lasts 12 months. This course is for students who wish to understand the natural treatment of disease more thoroughly and to receive experience in patient care. Both courses offer a comprehensive curriculum in a work-study environment calculated to quickly, thoroughly, and inexpensively prepare a person for service.

Uchee Pines Institute was founded by Calvin and Agatha Thrash, both M.D.'s and devout Christians. They have co-authored numerous books on natural remedies and preventive medicine. They, combined with a team of Seventh-day Adventist Christian lay persons and physicians, specialize in the natural methods of healing for the uplifting of humanity. Their goal is that each person coming to Uchee Pines may have health of body, soul, and mind and will return home to teach others the good things God has done for him.

Dr. Agatha Thrash is available to speak at camp meetings. Uchee Pines also makes available health teams to present Health Emphasis Weekends which cover the laws of health, chronic diseases, simple remedies, and healthful cooking.

Brochures for any of the programs mentioned may be obtained by writing or calling the institute. Books by Drs. Thrash are available from NewLifestyle Books (334) 855-4708 or (800) 542-5695; Fax (334) 855-3952; or from your local Adventist Book Center.

Weimar Institute
20601 W Paoli Lane, P.O. Box 486
Weimar, California 95736
(530) 637-4111; (800) 525-9192; Fax (530) 637-4408
e-mail: communications@weimar.org
web sites: www.weimar.org/ www. newstart.com/ www. reversingdiabetes,org

Weimar Institute, home and founder of the NEWSTART® Lifestyle Program, is a 500 acre campus-like facility located between Sacramento and Lake Tahoe. It is idyllically situated in the Sierra foothills, amid the pines. Academy and college students are trained on the Weimar campus, plus it is known for its health education center and conditioning program, and its beautiful guest facilities. People come from around the world to strengthen their immune systems and reverse the effects of diabetes, heart disease, high cholesterol, arthritis, allergies, high blood pressure, and obesity.

This unique residential facility offers a physician-operated medical clinic that provides a comprehensive program for improving overall physical, emotional and spiritual health. Since 1978 the purpose of this wellness center has been to heal and educate.

The NEWSTART® Lifestyle Program includes research-based, medically-directed lifestyle intervention programs addressing those health concerns that respond favorably to the program. Beside comprehensive diet and exercise the healing modalities used include massage and hydrotherapy (water) treatments, informative educational seminars and lectures, cooking classes, outings and field trips, stretching and exercise classes, plus 12 miles of natural trails for walking, hiking, exploring and relaxation, and most of all a dedicated support staff of health professionals.

"Reversing Diabetes," an intensive three-day seminar held across North America at respected Christian conference centers presents scientific evidence that is clearly explained by experienced Christian physicians. It demonstrates that simple lifestyle choices can eliminate or dramatically reduce the need for insulin or oral medication.

If you can't enjoy the benefits of attending programs on the Weimar Institute campus, the Institute can send the basics of NEWSTART® to you in a variety of selected Physicians lectures available on Videos or cassette tapes.

Weimar provides a wide range of helpful health education materials, books (including a NEWSTART® cookbook being used in Buckingham Palace), audio cassettes, and video programs. Call (800) 525-9192 for a catalog or to place an order.

The cookbook and weight control program has been ranked by the Physicians Committee for Responsible Medicine in Washington, DC as among the top two weight loss programs in the United States.

Wildwood Lifestyle Center and Hospital
P.O. Box 129
Wildwood GA 30757
(706) 820-1493; (800) 634-WELL [9355]; Fax 706-820-1474
web site: www.tagnet.org/wildwood

Wildwood is nestled in the rolling, wooded hills of Northern Georgia, near Chattanooga, Tennessee. It was founded in 1942 by William D. Frazee. Hundreds of students have received their training for self-supporting work at Wildwood and have started similar programs throughout the world.

Treatment is provided for such health problems as overweight, smoking, emphysema, heart disease, high blood pressure, arthritis, stress, diabetes, depression, hypoglycemia, and allergies. Residential programs are offered for10-days and/or 17-days, depending on the need.

The Wildwood Lifestyle Educator Course offers students six months of a variety of medical, spiritual, and practical classes with experience in a lab setting that is balanced by a daily work program that aims to prepare them to fill a special place in community evangelism, local church outreach, or in a self-supporting sanitarium or restaurant. Student qualifications include: spiritual maturity, dedication to serving as medical missionaries, and being 21 years of age or older, with a high school diploma or the equivalent.

The Wildwood Lifestyle Center, a duly registered school with the State of Georgia Department of Education, may grant certificates. Upon the successful completion of the Lifestyle Educator Course, a student receives the following certificates: (1) a lifestyle educator certificate, (2) a massage therapist certificate, (3) a hydrotherapy certificate, and (4) a certificate for CPR, from the American Heart Association.

A second course is offered called the Health Ministry course designed to further train the students to be teachers of health and Bible subjects. This 18-month course follows the Lifestyle Educator Course. An annual long-weekend training program each October is called "Seminar in Physiology and Medicine," for medical professionals and interested lay persons.

Wildwood has a well-stocked natural foods and book store. Wildwood's regularly published newsletter is *Wildwood Today*. For many years the Lifestyle Center has published a much-appreciated *Journal of Health and Healing* that provides reliable, well-documented health information that is significant in preparing our body temples for maximum health and ministry.

A Testimony for God's Natural Laws

*S*omething was wrong, very wrong. Despite a definite diagnosis and appropriate medication Audrey Watts wasn't feeling better, instead the joint pain, stiffness and muscle weakness now involved her hands and arms as well as her legs. The pains were increasingly incapacitating, leaving her wheelchair bound and unable to do even the simplest household duties.

Her husband pastored at a lifestyle center so she knew "the health rules," and she followed many of them. Her doctors said they didn't matter. Lifestyle changes probably wouldn't help her condition anyway.

As a last desperate resort after long years of suffering, Audrey checked herself into the Weimar Lifestyle Center's three-week live-in program. There she ate a diet free of refined oils, high fat foods and refined sugar. She was served an abundance of fresh and unrefined plant foods. Her daily routine included several hydrotherapy treatments, physical exercise and spiritual renewal. By the end of three weeks, Audrey was feeling better than she had in years. She was able to move with less pain, even exercise some.

At home she put the principles she had learned into practice. Concentrating on actually living all eight of the natural remedies, she reordered her life to eliminate stressful activities, prepared only natural, unrefined foods, exercised daily outdoors in the fresh air and sunshine, conscientiously drank adequate amounts of water and continued with hydrotherapy and massage treatments. For her, temperance meant not overdoing it, learning to relax and getting adequate rest as well as good quality sleep. Daily she renewed her walk with Jesus and her trust in God.

Day by day she had less stiffness and pain. A year later she was off medication, symptom free, and holding an undemanding job. Her painful symptoms creep up if she slips back into her old health destroying habits, but God's natural remedies continually work a miracle in her life.

There's no doubt in Audrey's mind, or mine, about the truth of this statement, "The laws of nature are divine…. only in obedience to them can health be recovered or preserved" (*The Ministry of Healing*, p 113).

—Dawna Sawatzky

From: *Energized!* One-a-day devotionals for body, mind and soul. An excellent resource for introducing others to the Adventist lifestyle. Hagerstown, MD: Review and Herald Publishing Association, 1997. Used by Permission.

20

Health Media Ministries

Communication is key in spreading the gospel and the health message. When Jesus admonished his disciples to "go ye therefore and teach all nations" he was stressing the importance of communicating a lifesaving message. As Christians living in modern times we are fortunateto have access to technology that can take a message and disseminate it to millions of people around the world. Seventh-day Adventists have a growing radio and television network that is spreading the gospel and in many cases, the health message. Are you acquainted with the health programming that is currently provided? Is your community able to tune into a Seventh-day Adventist radio or television station? As you plan what you and your church can do to share the health message in your local area you will want to carefully consider the possibilities of radio and television ministry.

Have you considered starting a health radio program?

In today's radio programming climate, producers must consider that audiences have changed over the last few years. The latest programs are much shorter in length than older programs. Research has shown that listeners respond more favorably to good information being disseminated in shorter frames to accommodate their busy schedules. Radio stations across the United States are more likely to accept 1 or 2 minute features on a free PSA (Public Service Announcement) basis than longer programs. It's difficult to get a 5 minute feature on a free basis, and almost impossible to be given free air time for a 15 or 30 minute format, unless it fits a specific need for a local radio station. For example, many local stations are interested in a live call-in health program, or a program that would feature local health professionals in an interview-type program. Before starting this type of program be sure you consider the discipline and subject matter it takes to produce a program on a regular basis.

Many radio productions offer long features once a week and short features throughout the week, that often are extracted from the longer program. This gives the radio station program directors the opportunity to choose the format that suits their individual stations. Daily programming runs M-F, with weekly programming generally reserved for weekend use.

Here are some things to consider if you are starting your own health program:

1. Are you interested in a local program or would you like to syndicate to other stations? Many start out locally by filling a specific need, and when they have established a proven track record begin syndicating.

2. If you are interested in syndication, consider the following:
   - It costs money. The more stations you are on the more expense.
   - If your program airs free (such as a short spot) you cannot ask for funding over the air. Focus on the Family (and other similar programs) has two versions of their program: one that doesn't "sell" products or ask for funding for stations that play the program free, and one for which they pay for time and have the freedom to solicit funds. Also, you may have to pay for the air time if you want a specific time—such as drive time. There is more low cost or free time available in the middle of the night. This is not a bad time. Audience members who are listening at 2 a.m. are often quite susceptible to change and ready to hear the message of health and salvation.
   - Radio stations prefer state of the art production, which now means CDs. It is no longer expensive to burn now

with a CD-burner attached to a computer. You can create a CD for the cost of buying a blank CD

- Because syndicators who are most successful in gaining stations, are those who have a number of productions that are similar in format to yours (but different content areas) they are contacting stations on a daily basis. Self-syndication is possible, but you must know what you're doing, and be willing to advertise in the National Religious Broadcasters (NRB) publications and make contacts.

What about sponsoring a health program on your local station?

Sponsoring an already produced program is easier, costs less, and takes less time than trying to produce your own.

If you have the budget you can pay air time and have an already produced radio program aired on your local station. Most stations will not charge you for this comment, "This program was brought to you by your local Seventh-day Adventist Church." If you want to advertise your local health programs, commercial stations will sell you advertising time. Most non-profit stations will announce an up-coming program, but it may not air at the time your paid program is airing.

If your budget is small, encourage your station to play a free spot, such as "LifeLines" and pay for a 10 second or longer announcement to air right before or after the program so listeners will associate the good health information they are getting with your church.

Adventist Produced Health Radio Programming

- *Got a Minute for Your Family?*

If your are interested in one-minute mental health spots, Family Matters, with Dr. Kay Kuzma as host, produces a radio spot called, *Got a Minute for Your Family?* For information, contact Family Matters, 1105 Big Creek Road, LaFollette, TN 37766; or e-mail to kaykuzma@aol.com,

- *Health for Today*

Produced by Victoria Miller at WOCG-FM, the Oakwood College station, *Health for Today* is a fifteen-minute interview-type format with one or two public service announcement (PSAs) breaks per program (which can be used for commercial sponsors) that airs Friday nights at 8:30 p.m. Victoria Miller, the station's general manager, interviews featured physician, Dr. William Hicks, a specialist in Internal Medicine from Huntsville, Alabama, and other guest health professionals. WOCG is currently considering the possibility of offering shorter formats of the program for syndication. If you are interested in sponsoring this program on your local Christian radio station contact WOCG at (205) 726-7418. The program is well received and has been on WOCG for four years. Being locally produced helps to fulfill the station's public service requirements.

If you are considering producing a similar radio program, Miller suggests that having various guest consultants makes it more attractive to busy professionals and lends credibility and a wide variety of subject matter to your program.

- *Health Week*

Health Week is a production of KGTS in College Place, Washington, which houses the studios for Positive Life Radio, a satellite network that serves several Adventist radio stations. This five-minute program that features new developments in the medical field and research findings airs twice a week on the satellite network. The source for most of their stories come from news service releases based on leading medical journals. The feature is not available for syndication because it focuses on current news, but it is an idea that others could use to produce a health feature for their local radio stations.

- *The New Way of Life*

A 15-minute daily radio program produced by The Quiet Hour speaks to the needs of busy people everywhere. Each program consists of an interview with a lifestyle health authority who covers topics directed toward helping listeners live a longer and quality filled life. Also included

Use Lifelines to Promote Wellness & Improve Quality of Life!

*7*he Seventh-day Adventist Church's North American Division has created a new radio program called Lifelines. For its premiere, compact discs with ten 90-second shows were submitted to 700 U.S.-based Christian and mainstream radio stations to be used as public service announcements (non-paid programming).

According to partnering producers Vibrant Life magazine, North American Division Communication and Health Ministries, and Loma Linda University Medical Center, Lifelines was designed to provide radio listeners with practical tips about a variety of topics, including disease prevention, physical, mental, and spiritual wellness, and the eight principles of health, all to raise quality of life.

The program is hosted by Elmar Sakala, M.D., M.P.H., a teaching and practicing physician at Loma Linda University Medical Center in Southern California, who wants to see Americans live longer and fuller lives.

At the end of each program, listeners are offered the opportunity to call or visit a web site (www.vibrantlife.org) to get more information about healthy living. Those inquiries will be handled by Larry Becker, editor of Vibrant Life magazine and a vice president at the Review and Herald Publishing Association. The name Lifelines comes from the most popular section of his bimonthly magazine, available in Barnes and Noble bookstores, on newsstands, and by subscription.

In addition to targeting radio stations, producers plan to make the program available to local church Health Ministries directors and pastors who wish to personally place the programs on community radio stations.

Before producing additional programs, project partners plan to send three direct mailings to radio stations in 2002. TRANSDA, the Church's media booking agency, will monitor station usage and listener response.

To receive a Lifelines radio program packet, call 800-790-5433.

—Celeste Ryan, assistant director of communication for media relations at the North American Division, served as producer for the Lifelines radio project.

is a story, or testimony of dramatic life changing consequences, and a message of inspiration from the Word of God. *The New Way of Life* was one of the unfulfilled dreams of Pastor J. L. Tucker, the founder of The Quiet Hour, and is now being hosted by, Laura Hertel.

If you would like to sponsor this program on your local station, contact Jackie Tucker, The Quiet Hour, 630 Brookside, Box 3000, Redlands, California 92373-1500, Tel: (909) 793 2588.

• *Lifestyle Magazine* is also available in a radio format with limited current coverage in the United States and Canada, over the Adventist Radio Network member stations. Contact: Curt Dolinsky Lifestyle Magazine, 101 West Cochran Street, Simi Valley, California 93065, Tel: (888) 840-0062. (See a more complete description of Lifestyle Magazine under TV.)

• *Three Angels Broadcasting Network (3ABN)* also has expanded into radio format. The Abundant Living TV program, Abundant Living, is available in 15-minute segments. Two other 15-minute offerings prepared only for radio are Barbara Kerr's Taste of Health program and Your Health News with Ri´se Rafferty which focuses mainly on nutrition. Several other TV offerings are now available in 30-minute formats: Health for a Lifetime, Help Yourself to Health, Homeschool of Health, and Wonderfully Made. Contact 3ABN at (800) 752-3ABN to order.

Other Health-related Radio Programs

There are a number of public service health radio programs which have no particular Christian orientation. One of the most widely syndicated is Karen's Kitchen, a daily, 60-second radio feature, presented by the American Institute for Cancer Research, and is available free of charge to radio stations. These programs are provided monthly (22 original spots each month) on a ready for broadcast CD. The shows attempt to help listeners learn about good health in an entertaining way by including music, humor, sound effects and interesting information. The educational information is presented by a registered dietitian on behalf of the American Institute for Cancer Research and airs on 27,000 stations. Contact information: Karen Owens, Producer, Karen's Kitchen, 2409 Nido Aguila, Alpine, CA 91901; (619) 445-4496.

Have you considered starting a radio downlink station in your community?

Two radio programming services currently available on satellite are owned and operated by Seventh-day Adventist organizations. These can be helpful on at least two levels: 1) they will audition programs for possible inclusion on their satellite service, and 2) they can significantly cut the cost of starting and operating a local Adventist radio station. A satellite delivered format frees the small staff of a local station to spend more time building contacts in the community. Because most of the on-air work is being done by the satellite programming service, the local station can concentrate on developing local programming.

Positive Life Radio

Positive Life Radio provides an inspirational music format for radio stations across the country. A combined effort of Walla Walla College and the Upper Columbia Conference, this service is targeted towards adults aged 35-54. For more information contact: Chris Gilberth, Network Manager, (509) 527-2991, or reach them at their NRB award-winning web site: www.plr.org.

Life Talk Radio

Life Talk Radio is a 24-hour programming service which is seeking to develop an increasing number of SDA-sponsored radio talk programs. It is affiliated with the Adventist Media Center and provides a traditional music and talk format. For more information contact: Ken Veal, General Manager (423) 884-2800.

Both Positive Life Radio and Life Talk Radio are currently using a KU-band satellite uplink system that requires a special downlink receiver for decoding. The downlink equipment cost is approximately $3,500. Creating a radio format that will attract listeners and make a significant positive impact on the community requires careful planning. Both satellite radio programming services listed above are happy to discuss the potential of radio broadcasting in any area.

Health Ministry Programs For Television

If you are mature enough to remember waking up to the sounds of the National Anthem on your television, you've probably noticed the major changes in the medium. The invention of cable has birthed hundreds of stations with continuous additions, and 24-hour programming. Talking back to the set has taken on new meaning, as adults and children participate in the technological advance known as interactive television and at the same time government is attempting to provide parents with more control over what their kids watch. Amidst the racy programming of commercial and cable television, health programs have managed to find a niche.

Lifestyle Magazine is an award winning half-hour talk show produced by Faith For Today Television, a Seventh-day Adventist ministry headquartered at the Adventist Media Center in Simi Valley, California. Hosts Dan Matthews and Clifton Davis combine wit and charm with the humor and expertise of down-to-earth medical experts. Each show taped in front of a studio audience, offers a close look at a specific health topic with guest celebrities, authors, specialists and every day citizens. The program focuses on all dimensions of healthful living-mental, emotional and spiritual, as well as physical.

NAD Adventist Radio Stations

*T*he following is a list of Adventist owned and operated radio stations in North America. They will be able to give you the criteria for producing a radio program for their station. It is important that you have a written proposal before taking on this venture.

KACS FM
2401 NE Kresky, Suite B
Chehalis, WA 98532
(360) 740-9436

KADV FM
Modesto Adventist Academy
2031 Academy Place
Ceres, California 95307
(209) 537-1201

KARM FM
Visalia SDA Church
1300 S. Woodland Drive
Visalia, California 93277
(559) 627-5276

KCSH FM
Life Talk Radio Network
P.M.B. 222 West 6th Ave.
Ellensburg, WA 98926

KEEH FM
P.O. Box 19039
Spokane, WA 99219
(509) 456-4870

KGTS FM
Walla Walla College
204 S. College Avenue
College Place, Washington
99324
(509) 527-2991

KJCR FM
Southwestern Adventist College
200 N. College Drive
Keene, Texas 76059
(817) 556-4788

KNDL FM
PO Box 89
Angwin, CA 94508
(707) 965-7141

KPLW FM
606 N. Western Ave.
Wenatchee, WA 98801
(509) 665-6641

KSDA FM
290 Chalan Palasyo, Agana
Hgts.
Guam 96919

KSGN FM
11498 Pierce Street
Riverside, California 92505
(909) 687-5746

KSOH FM
Life Talk Radio Network
402 E. Yakima Avenue, Suite
1320
Yakima, Washington 98901
(509) 248-HOPE (4673)

KSVA FM
PO Box 2378
Corales, NM 87048
(505) 890-0800

KTSY FM
Life Talk Radio Network
16115 S, Montana Avenue
Caldwell, Idaho 83605
(208) 459-5879

KUDU FM
Life Talk Radio Network
PO Box 719
Tok, AK 99780

KWLR FM
Life Talk Radio Network
PO Box 13197
Maumelle, AR 72113
(501) 912-9700

KYPL FM
3205 River Road
Yakima, WA 98801
(509) 457-0725

VOAR AM
P.O.Box 2520
Mount Pearl, Newfoundland
Canada AIN 4M7
(709) 745-8627

WAUS FM
Andrews University
Berrien Springs, Michigan
49104
(616) 471-3400

WBIN AM
PO Box 617
Benton, TN 37123
(423) 338-2864

WBLC AM
4787 Browder Hollow Rd.
Lenoir City, TN 37771
(865) 096-5332

WDNX FM
3730 Lonesome Pine Rd.
Rt. 2, Savannah, TN 38372
(901) 924-9236

WGTS FM
7600 Flower Avenue
Takoma Park, MD 20912
(301) 891-4200

WJYC FM
5733 Dutch Hollow Rd.
Aurora, Indiana 47001
(513) 564-8807

WOCG FM
Oakwood College
Huntsville, Alabama 35896
(256) 726-7418

WSGM FM
PO Box 1269
Tracy City, TN 37387
(931) 592-7777

WSMC FM
Southern Adventist University
P.O. Box 870
Collegedale, Tennessee 37315
(423) 238-2905

WSOH FM
PO Box 209
Vonore, TN 37885
(812) 246-0200

Lifestyle Magazine, which began airing in 1985, can now be seen nationally in more than 85 markets and is broadcast on cable stations in almost every major city in the United State and Canada. It airs on the Hallmark Channel, the American Independent Network, the Armed Forces TV Network, Trinity Broadcasting Network, and Vision TV Network in Canada, among many others. The program airs daily or weekly on stations either on a barter basis, as a public service or as a paid program.

For more information on Lifestyle Magazine, Contact: Curt Dolinsky Lifestyle Magazine, 101 West Cochran Street, Simi Valley, California 93065, Tel: (888) 840-0062.

Video Productions That Can Be Used for TV

Let's Eat! For Strength, a Sure Word production, is a professionally produced 23-episode video-series designed for health education and life enrichment. The Let's Eat! series is designed to educate the public about the principles of lifestyle and diet in their relation to disease prevention. The facts are clearly and simply presented using 3-D animation, graphs and other eye-catching, attention holding devices. Recipes presented on each program are simple and cost-saving. The 10 one-hour VHS videos, covering topics ranging from social drinking to the dangers of dieting, are available for purchase.

Dane Griffin, a professional videographer and Vicki Griffin, Nutrition Counselor and Health Ministries Director for the Michigan Conference, attempt to provide information with a spiritual emphasis. These programs are co-hosted by medical professionals who discuss the scientific validation of lifestyle factors in disease prevention in an easy-to-understand manner. Contact Vicki Griffin, PO Box 19009, Lansing MI 48901 (517) 485-2226; E-mail: vgriffin@misda.org

HeartBeat 2000 is a redesigned, revitalized take off of the HeartBeat program started more than 20 years ago by Dr. John Scharffenberg with the support of the School of Public Health at Loma Linda University. HeartBeat 2000 is available by special videos to any church, community service center or other organization desiring to participate. Program participants have the results and recommendations from laboratory evaluations done on their blood as well as lifestyle questionnaires to help them make lifestyle changes.

Opportunity for live interaction between sites and coronary care experts and participants will be featured as well as a thorough discussion of questionnaire and lab results. This program is an annual media event which occurs in February, which is "Heart Month." It allows thousands of people in communities across the land that would never set foot in an Adventist-sponsored event otherwise to receive life-changing information. Contact: Pacific Health Education, 5300 California Avenue, Suite 200, Bakersfield, CA. 93309; (661) 633-5300.

Adventist Communications Network (ACN)

ACN is a resource for local churches—a linkage that uses satellite technology to bring together and improve communication within the Seventh-day Adventist Church in North America. In short, ACN links local churches with resources for ministry. Here are some of the benefits to the local church:

- ACN provides training events for church leaders, pastors, and members.
- ACN links evangelistic meetings to all churches who wish to participate and minister to their communities.
- ACN provides outreach seminars on health, family life, and spiritual topics for local churches to invite members of their communities to participate.
- ACN makes it possible for local church members and leaders to participate in major events (General Conference Session, ASI Convention, Year-end Meetings, Annual Council).
- ACN delivers news and mission reports and other inspirational and informational reports for use in local churches on Sabbath or during mid-week meetings.

To be placed on the mailing list, and for more information about how your church can participate in ACN events, call (800) ACN-1119 [226-1119] or (301) 680-6315.

Three Angels Broadcasting Network (3ABN)

Three Angels Broadcasting Network offers a wide variety of Christian programming 24 hours a day designed for the home viewer. Believing a healthy mind promotes a healthy spiritual life, 3ABN considers health programming to be of particular importance. Programs are designed to bring the viewers important information on medical and lifestyle issues such as cancer prevention, diabetes and heart disease.

A stop smoking clinic hosted by Dr. Arthur Weaver runs regularly for those who wish to break their addiction to nicotine. Other programs deal with issues such as drug and alcohol recovery. Vegetarian cooking programs feature recipes showing viewers how to cook with less added fat, salt and sugar. The following are a sample of the health programs available on 3ABN. Contact 3ABN (800-752-3ABN) to order VHS tapes of the following programs for home or church use, or TV quality tapes for broadcast on local stations.

- *Abundant Living:* Hosted by Curtis and Paula Eakins. Presents vegetarian cooking and other health and lifestyle topics.
- **Body and Spirit:** with Dick Nunez, exercise physiologist. This is an exercise program designed for body building to prevent and treat musculo-skeletal problems of all age groups.
- *Cooking by the Book:* This series, hosted by Marcella Lynch, shows how to prepare delicious vegetarian cuisine.
- *Food for Thought:* A second series by Marcella Lynch features many favorite dishes in vegetarian cuisine
- *Health for a Lifetime:* A variety of popular health lecturers present lifestyle topics
- *Help Yourself to Health,* hosted by Dr. Agatha Thrash of the Uchee Pines Institute, in a 30-minute format examines home remedies and healthful living as preventive medicine. Dr. Thrash deals with subjects from strengthening our immune system to grief recovery.
- *Homeschool of Health,* is a 30-minute program dealing with health remedies and preventive medicine. The program also deals

---

Is 3ABN an effective soul winning tool?

Yes! 3ABN reaches the world via satellite and their network of downlink stations. For example, in the area covered by our Salem, IL, downlink the pastor reported that there were more than 30 baptisms in the past few years. At the time of his report he was studying with nearly 20 more that became interested in Adventists through watching 3ABN. For information on how you can see 3ABN in your local community, contact 3ABN at (800) 752-3ABN [3226].

—Karl Leukert

---

with the philosophy of health. It is a variety health program with speakers and lecturers on everything from spiritual health and physical exercise to lifestyle therapy and the effects of alcohol.

- *Wonderfully Made,* features a variety of guests that deal with many health issues, as well as educational issues about the body.

If a local church is interested in promoting health evangelism in their community, building a downlink or getting 3ABN added to cable is one of the best things it can do. Many times, people who would never step foot in a church or health education center will watch the health programs on 3ABN. If a downlink cannot be built and the local cable station will not air 3ABN, individuals or churches can get free copies of the 3ABN video catalog and order tapes for their lending library. TV quality tapes of the above television programs aired on 3ABN, and Lifestyle Magazine, are available for local cable stations. Many times these stations are interested in health programming, if your church would supply them with TV quality tapes.

The highest honor granted to man is the honor of serving as the dwelling place of the Spirit of the Most High God through whom the light of His love might shine out into a dark and hurting world. The gift of "the health message" was given to the church in order to establish these living temples as brilliant beacons of light scattered among the masses of mankind, enlightening the far corners of the earth with the message of God's unfathomable love.

At 3ABN we have not taken this honor lightly. From the beginning, the health message has been given a prominent place in our program format. It is our goal to provide a broad range of health programs touching upon all aspects of life from disease prevention to therapeutic intervention. On 3ABN for example, you may learn how to reduce your risk of cancer and heart disease, experience a seminar on family relationships, join in a program to stop smoking or learn strategies for optimizing your dietary intake for health. Through it all, the transforming power of God's love is promoted as the effective agent through which lifestyle change takes place.

Presented wisely and with love, the health message is truly the right arm of the gospel and an effective entree into the hearts of men, women and children. Why not make your house of worship a house of light and healing in your community?

—Walter Thompson, M.D., Chairman of the Board of Directors, 3ABN

Have You Ever Considered Starting Your Own TV Station?

That's what Carlos Pardeiro and a concerned group of Seventh-day Adventists and community leaders decided to do in Springdale, Arkansas, when they got tired of the violence, permissiveness and immorality seen on regular TV. As Springdale's first full-power TV station in Adventist hands, the programming offered on Safe TVTM is designed to reach the secular world for Christ by uplifting God, family, and country.

Now on the Sky Angel satellite they have become known across America as the Safe TV channel. One of the most effective aspects is that, because of their programming style, they are able to reach into the homes of people from all walks of life, social status, and religious views.

They have produced a number of health related television programs, which are also available in VHS format to be used in seminars, or for health ministries leaders. Broadcast quality tapes also are available to place these programs on local cable television stations.

These video seminars include the following:
* *Stop Smoking.* Art Weaver, M.D., has helped tens of thousands to break this addiction. This video is a recent stop smoking clinic he held in the greater Detroit area. Five 1-hour sessions.
* *Divorce Recovery.* Pastor Dan Smith, himself a victim of divorce, through personal experience and the Bible offers healing insights. Four 1-hour sessions. Ideal for small group study.
* *Home Remedies and Hydrotherapy.* Dr. Charles Thomas, Ph.D., well-known physical therapist, joins James Brackett to give step-by-step, safe use of simple home treatments, massage, and water treatments to effectively prevent and treat many health programs. Eight 30-minute sessions.
* *Family Wellness.* John and Millie Youngburg, family life specialists. help struggling and breaking families find healing and strength. Fourteen 30-minute sessions.
* *Peripheral Vascular Disease.* Duane Bietz, M.D., heart and blood vessel surgeon and TV

media news commentator talks about preventing and treating diseases of the blood vessels. Two 30-minute sessions.

- *Weight Control.* John Scharffenberg, M.D., former Medical Director of Pacific Health Education Center presents this scientific approach to weight management. Four 30-minute sessions.
- *Wellness Seminar.* Melvin Beltz, M.D., Medical consultant for the Black Hills Wellness Center, presents the basics for an efficient health-promoting life. Thirteen 30-minute sessions.

- *In the Fullness of Health.* Dr. David DeRose and Dr. Neil Nedley share information on a variety of health subjects. Eleven 30-minute sessions.
- *Natural Lifestyle Cooking.* Videos, participant workbook and organizational manual, for Net '96 with Mark and Teeny Finley, is timeless material. The five 60 minute (plus) sessions include: Homemade breadmaking made easy; Making breakfast a better meal; Planning a balanced menu; Adequate protein inexpensively; The advantages of a vegetarian diet; and Simple, healthful desserts.

For more information on KSBN, or to order health videos: contact Carlos Pardeiro, Creation Enterprises International, P.O. Box 274, Siloam Springs, AR 72761; (501) 524-9891; or call KSBN TV 57 at (501) 361-2900.

The Story of How One Person Found Christ Through the Health Message

Rebecca Clark had watched a Christian channel for some time (not 3ABN) and was impressed with the health-related programs. At that time, she was having many health problems and was sure that the answers were in the Bible. As she watched for about a year, she changed her diet and her problems disappeared.

Then her family moved and she figured it was OK to return to her old diet. Very slowly, the health problems began to return. At her new home, she started looking for the program again but couldn't find it. She did, however discover a channel (3ABN) that not only had nutrition shows about a vegetarian diet, they also talked about the Sabbath. This excited her very much because she thought that she was the only one in the world that believed that the seventh day was the Sabbath. Over the next few years, she was convinced of all of the truths she had been hearing.

Today Rebecca and her five daughters are members of the Seventh-day Adventist church. She says, "I appreciate 3ABN and the programs they telecast. They have made a big difference in my life. If I had not watched the programs they have on nutrition, I would not have found this Sabbath-keeping church.".

Religious Broadcasting Satellite Networks

American Christian TV System (ACTS)
6350 West Freeway
Fort W orth, Texas 76150
Programming: Julia Hollers
(817) 737-3241

Christian Broadcasting Network (CBN)
Pat Robertson's TV Network
(also owns the Family Channel)
700 CBN Center
Virginia Beach, VA 23463
Attn: Linda Freeman
(804) 424-7777

Faith & Values Network
National Interfaith Cable Coalition, Inc.
74 Trinity Place
New York, NY 10006
Programming: Jeffrey Weber (212-964-1663
x 122)
(212) 964-1663 x 126
(Also includes Vision Interfaith
Satellite Network

Lesea Broadcasting Network
P.O. Box 12
South Bend, IN 46624
Chairman: Lester Sumrall
(219) 287-6518

Three Angels Broadcasting Network (3ABN)
20802 Neal Davis Rd.
Thompsonville, IL 62890
Chairman of the Board of Directors: Walter
        Thompson, M.D.
(800) 752-3ABN [3226].

Tri-State Christian Television
P.O. Box 1010
Marion, Il 62959
President: Garth Coonce
(618) 997-9333

Trinity Broadcasting Network (TBN)
2442 Michelle Drive
Tustin, CA 92680
Programming: John Huff
(714) 665-2136.

Community Television

In 1979 the Federal Communications Commission (FCC) access ruling resulted in what we know today as "Cable Access Channels." These channels, sometimes tagged "the people's television," allow individuals and groups to gain access to the nation's most popular entertainment and information-processing medium. Access to the cable television station allows small groups a sense of identity and provides them with a channel of communication to the larger community. It allows special interest groups the ability to reinforce their common interest and relate their purpose to others.

The common bond of these access usergroups might be age, ethnic background, political cause, intellectual interest or hobby. Creating viable access programming involves helping community groups and other organizations integrate television communication into their own quite specific activities and interests. Minority groups, readers of Tolstoy, model railroad club members, and a myriad of special interest groups who want to be on television. Health ministries directors are no exception.

21

Health Ministries Resources

Although a comprehensive list cannot be published here, the following are some of the most helpful resources for those practicing health ministries. Contact health agencies and other education programs in your area to discover resources most conveniently available to you.

Call the *Adventist PlusLine* for general information such as resources to meet a specific health need, hotline, speakers, or other information. Call (800) SDA-PLUS [732-7587].

There are two major NAD product distribution centers. *The Health Connection* is the official health ministries resource center. **Advent**Source provides leadership resources for local church leaders in North America and handles most community service materials. Because many churches combine community service and health ministries at the local level, both resource centers may be of help in finding the resources you need.

The church's publishing houses, Review and Herald and Pacific Press, publish a variety of books, cookbooks, and other materials on health and health-related issues, all of which are available through Adventist Book Centers. Call (800) 765-6055 to obtain a catalog or shop online at www.adventistbookcenter.com

Adventist Health Resource Centers
The Health Connection

The official Seventh-day Adventist health ministries resource center is located at the Review and Herald Publishing Association, 55 West Oak Ridge Drive, Hagerstown, MD 21740; (800) 548-8700; (301) 790-9735 or fax (301) 790-9733. Visit The Health Connection on the Internet at: www.healthconnection.org E-mail at: sales@healthconnection.org

This will be your primary source for health education products. If they do not have something, they will be able to refer you to other sources.

Two types of materials are distributed through The Health Connection: 1) Materials produced by the Seventh-day Adventist Church. 2) The best materials from other vendors that support the drug-free message of the church in a way acceptable to public schools.

Because The Health Connection has a dual role of serving the health promotion needs of the church *and* promoting a drug-free message to public schools, two different catalogs are produced. Be sure to ask for the one that best meets your needs.

1. The Health Connection Wellness Catalog (Adventist Edition). This is the one you'll want to ask for in order to get products for children and adults with a spiritual or Adventist basis. Categories of materials include: exhibit backdrop with coordinated handout pamphlets, Breathe Free™ and stop smoking materials, Power Point® presentations and videos, lifestyle videos/slides, nutrition and health books, pamphlets, and videos, the *Regeneration Manual*, and seminars. It is important *when requesting a catalog to specify that you want the catalog for Seventh-day Adventists* or you may miss out on the most valuable materials for your program.

2. Basic Health Connection Drug-prevention Catalog that is acceptable for public schools and government programs. If you work for a public school or government agency you can promote the use of materials from The Health Connection because everything in the basic catalog will be acceptable. Anyone from your school or agency who requests a catalog will automatically get the basic catalog. Because The Health Connection enjoys the reputation of being one of the best sources of drug and violence prevention material, church members who are professionals in these fields can confidently introduce their schools, hospitals, and government agencies to *The Health Connection* Catalog.

The Health Connection and the Adventist Book Center

Your local Adventist Book Center (ABC) can provide any of the products in The Health Connection or Advent*Source* catalogs upon request. The Health Connection and Advent*Source* products are inventoried by some ABC's so you can order from the most convenient place.

The Health Connection works closely with the School of Public Health at Loma Linda University (and others) in developing new health promotion materials and serving the needs of the students and graduates of that institution. For example, the *Stress Beyond Coping* six-session seminar was developed cooperatively with the School of Public Health. New products from other sources are being added continually. That's why it is important for you to have a current catalog, or call about new products. *The Health Connection Wellness Catalog (Adventist Edition* is revised as often as quarterly and the *Basic Health Connection Drug-prevention Catalog* is revised annually.

Advent*Source*

This is your source for Adventist-produced leadership materials. Advent*Source* handles all questions for Lifestyle Certification and training materials. They are the source for community service and family life/mental health seminar materials. New products are continually being developed. If you are on their mailing list you will be kept up to date. Advent*Source* is located at 5040 Prescott, Lincoln, Nebraska, 68506. Call for a catalog: (800) 328-0525; (402) 486-2519; Fax (402) 486-2572; www.adventsource.org.

Concerned Communications

Concerned Communications is an Adventist-owned publisher that develops materials and seminars for church growth, health education, and family life, as well as provides community advertising assistance and consultant and training services in how to develop an effective, needs-based seminar outreach program. Some of their seminars includes an Instructor Kit and Participant Worktexts with 5 in a pack, and overhead transparencies for the seminar sessions.

Concerned Communication also has books promoting the Adventist Lifestyle. Contact Seminars Unlimited for the Concerned Communications catalog or orders: P.O. Box 66, Keene. (800) 982-3344 or (817) 541-3643.

Institute for Prevention of Addictions

Andrews University is the location for this information and training resource center that conducts research and provides specialized resource materials for clergy and teachers, as well as training and consultant services. The institute provides ten days of specialized training for local activists each summer, as well as training for pastors and lay persons in working with the Regeneration program for recovery from addictions. (Training in Addiction Ministries is one of the specialty areas for the Lifestyle Certification Specialist.) For information on issues relating to addictions, contact the Institute at Andrews University, Berrien Springs, Michigan 49104-0211; (616) 471-3558; fax (616) 471-6611. (For a description of their work and services, see Chapter 11.)

The School of Public Health at Loma Linda University (LLU)

The LLU School of Public Health has been designated as a "collaborating center" by the World Health Organization (WHO). LLU has been charged primarily with helping to set up and evaluate public health programs and primary health-care services around the world. The school also provides numerous materials, training and consultant services for local community health programs in North America.

For a catalog of materials and schedule of special events, including the Healthy People alumni convention contact the School of Public Health, Loma Linda University, Loma Linda, California 92350; (800) 854-5661; (909) 558-4595 or

(909) 558-4300. For the LLU faculty Speakers ureau Directory, call (909) 558-4526. (See Chapter 18 for a more complete description of programs and services.)

Other Resource Organizations
Lifestyle Magazine (A Production of Faith for Today Television)

Dan Matthews and Clifton Davis host the 30-minute television series Lifestyle Magazine. (See Chapter 20.) Other resources include:

• **Lifenet 2000:** 25 short health segments that were featured during the Net 96 meetings on 2 VHS videos. These come with an outline/synopsis of all the health presentations, and a quiz of all the material covered.

• **Lifestyle Home Seminars** are home study courses that are excellent for group discussion groups, or to just acquaint individuals with various health topics. Lifestyle Magazine uses these as resource materials for those who write to them, but churches can purchase these booklets in bulk for special prices. Here's what is available:

- *Binding the Wounds* by Drs. Ron and Nancy Rockey. A family series .
- *Keys to Wellness* by Jim Wood. The health benefits of nutrition, exercise, water, sunlight freedom from drugs, fresh air, rest, and trust in divine power.
- *Nutrition* by Dr. David Nieman, former professor at Loma Linda University. An authoritative guide to improving your lifestyle through good nutrition.
- *Marriage* by Bonnie Blum, marriage counselor, designed to help husbands and wives develop the skills that make marriage fulfilling.
- *Parenting* by Kay Kuzma, child development specialist and President of Family Matters. Information for effective parenting.
- *Friendship.* Targeted to meet the needs of singles of all age.

To order materials from Lifestyle Magazine, write Box 320, Newbury Park, CA 91319; (888) 940-0062; Fax (805) 522-2144.

Self-Supporting Institutions

Almost all of the self-supporting institutions with a strong health outreach have a bookstore and/or health food store that carries excellent products. In addition, most institutions publish their own cookbooks, audio or video productions and other health education materials. (See Chapter 19 for more information.)

Sure Word Productions

This organization founded by Dane and Vicki Griffin produces award winning nutrition videos and books. For more information contact Vicki Griffin at P.O. Box 19009, Lansing, MI 48901; (517) 485-2226; E-mail: vgriffin@misda.org. (See Chapter 9 on Nutrition Ministries for greater detail on the video productions.)

Quality Life Seminars

Quality Life offers pre-evangelistic community seminars on stopping smoking; coping with stress, anxiety, and depression; wealth creation and preservation; and forgiveness. These unique seminars prepared by Roger Morton, who has held several denominational teaching and departmental positions are not produced or offered anywhere else. For more information contact: Quality Life Seminars, Loma Linda, CA 92350, PO Box 946, (888) 357-2341)

The Quiet Hour

Not only does The Quiet Hour produce a daily 15-minute radio feature with a health component and sponsor many overseas health evangelism programs, but they offer health products to their listeners. Ask for their catalog: P.O. Box 3000, Redlands, CA 92373; (909) 793-2588; Fax (909) 793-3082.

Total Life Creations

Fred Hardinge, Dr.P.H., a well-known health educator, organized Total Life Creations to continue developing valuable health education materials—a work that his father, Dr. Mervyn Hardinge, began. Here is what is currently available:

- **Fatigue Busters®: How to Survive Fatigue in the 90's.** This 46-minute video, showing the importance of sleep, is beautifully done, and makes a strong impact on the viewer.
- The complete **Hardinge Lifestyle Series** available in video (some available also in Spanish).

Total Life Creations, P.O. Box 19039, Spokane, WA 99219; (800) 283-6040; (509) 838-3791; Fax (509) 838-4882; e-mail fredh@uccsda.org.com (Note: The Hardinge Videos also are available through The Health Connection.)

Universal Class

Randy Horning's organization, Universal Class, offers a number of interesting health products, including the Fatigue Buster video produced by Total Life Creations, and Dr. Mervyn Hardinge's health education video productions.

Also available is the book, *Comfort for the Day,* a padded, gold-leaf edged, embossed book designed especially for the grief-stricken individual over the loss of a loved one. It contains 32 messages of comfort and journals a response to the thoughts presented, including helpful ways of coping. This book, authored by an Adventist, has been sold by the thousands to hospital chaplains and churches. Universal Class is located at 300 Cold Springs Road, Angwin, CA 94508-9984; (800) 827-9445; (707) 965-3654 or Fax (707) 965-0919.

LifeLong Health

LifeLong Health ™ is an Adventist-owned, non-profit organization that offers the following tools and training for community outreach programs:

- **HealthAwareness Series:** This series provides quick and simple, paper and pencil self-scored and computer-scored health appraisals on a variety of important health topics. These are perfect for health fairs, seminars and community health outreach activities from your church or organization, included are: Health Age, Your Stress Profile, Your Heart Risk Profile, How Health is Your Lifestyle, ?, A Health Weight, Osteoporosis Risk, Diabetes Risk, ?.

- **Eight Weeks to Wellness** is the first of several Life style change programs, Fitness for Life being the most recent (see chapter 22 for the relationship of these programs to the Lifestyle Certification Level 2 program.)
- **WellAssured® Guides to Better Health:** These "guides" are instructional materials for health classes. Materials include a notebook for participants, an instructor's guide, and overhead transparencies for usually 6 instructional sessions, includes 21 key health topics in the series.

For information, and orders, contact: LifeLong Health (503) 557-9545; (800) 862-4395; Fax (503) 557-9568. Web site: www.life-longhealth.org. E-mail: Info@ lifelonghealth;org, or write PO Box 569, Clackamas, OR 97015.

- **Conference-Wide Weekend Training Programs—How to Run an Effective Health Ministry in your Church and Community**

Other Health Resources

Lifestyle Certification Manuals and Materials

Contact AdventSource and The Health Connection for information on Lifestyle Certification and the packaged materials for Level 1 and for many of the seminar manuals and other materials for level 2. (See chapter 22 for up-to-date information.)

Nutrition Materials and Cooking Schools

The Health Connection works closely with the General Conference Nutrition Council to be sure that the materials it carries meet the approval of the leading nutrition authorities in the church. Thirty top nutritionists serving on the Nutrition Council prepare Position Statements which address current controversial nutrition issues such as dietary fat, herbs and herbal teas, vitamin B 12 supplements, the use of caffeine, vitamin and mineral supplements, and trans-fatty acids in margarine. These position statements are published and distributed by The Health Connection along with the Vegetarian Food Guide Pyramid Poster, also developed by The Nutrition Council.

Because cooking schools are an Adventist tradition, The Health Connection provides cooking

Meet Don Hall, the Source of Wellsource

*D*on Hall, DrPH, CHES, was a minister who loved the sciences. During his pastoral internship, Don became convinced that God's blueprint of combining the Gospel with the health ministry was what he should do. At the same time he heard about Dr. Mervyn Hardinge's Doctor of Health Science program at the newly developed School of Health—a degree that would equip pastors and other non-health professionals to work in the area of prevention. Suddenly Don knew what he must do.

Don applied to his conference to be allowed to take the program. At first his request was denied, but later it was reversed and Don became one of the first students to finish his doctoral degree in Health Science. He later earned the Dr.P.H. degree.

For eight years Don worked as the Health and Temperance Director of the Upper Columbia Conference. To aid him in the screening of individuals in the various health education programs, he began to develop computer-based screening tools. He simply bought himself a computer, learned how it operated and began to write programs.

Word began to spread that Don had computer-based screening tools that would greatly simplify the screening process allowing the health educator to be more specific in helping individuals with lifestyle changes. Soon requests from around the world began to flood his office. At first he merely ran off the various programs he had designed and shared them with others. But the heavy demand forced him to a fork in his career path. Should he continue with his work at the conference office, or should he work full time developing these screening tools that would enable health educators world-wide to be more effective? God seemed to be calling him to the latter. So he, and his wife Phyllis, stepped out and began the family business called Wellsource® which saves corporations thousands of dollars in health costs.

Now Don and Phyllis not only run marathons together, they work together. She carries the business end of their organization, and he the development and marketing responsibilities. Their company, based in Clackamas, Oregon, has some 40 employees, servicing over 2000 industries using their wellness screening and training programs, and more than 700 hospitals and managed care groups, *and it's growing.*

Now that his business with industry and medical groups is well established, Don is turning once again to his first love—health ministry—and is developing a line of products for churches and other community organizations available through the non profit organization, LifeLong Health.

Wellsource® has developed numerous health appraisals that form a part of prevention systems used in employee wellness programs by corporations, government agencies, hospitals, and universities. It also offers support through the Internet and by telephone consultation.

Don Hall began LifeLong Health™ as a non-profit corporation that provides tools and training for effctive health outreach used by chuches, universities, public health agencies that train health leaders and community workers.

And what do Don and Phyllis do in their spare time? Well, if you looked carefully you might have seen them running the Los Angeles marathon—they run a number of marathons each year. Don was the founder of Loma Linda Lopers when he was a student at Loma Linda—a group of runners that has now grown to more than 1000! Their family also loves to travel, and each year they plan something special. In 1996 it was spending a month in China and climbing on Mt. Everest! Their son, David, has his M.P.H. and is a physician in occupational medicine at Loma Linda, and their daughter, Heather, is an attorney in Portland.

There are many ways to be a health minister. Don has chosen the path less traveled and in doing so is a key support to front line health-ministry workers.

school more fun, including gorgeous food posters to set the mood, pamphlets for handouts, and Power Point® presentations, tabletop displays of the amount of hidden fat, sugar, and salt in processed foods, and games that teach nutrition facts. There is so much to choose from you can easily design a program that's right for your personality and the needs of your community

Health Fairs and Screening

Public events are an important way to communicate to your community the health promotion services offered by your church. (See chapter 24 for guidelines on health fairs and exhibits.)

Seminar Packages

The Health Connection also makes available a number of programs developed outside the church which help our churches meet various cutting-edge concerns of the community. If your church has been stuck in a rut, doing the same programs year after year, The Health Connection can help you redesign and liven up your standard programs to meet the current felt needs of your community.

Youth Programs

Public schools of necessity have discovered the value of training youth for service. Many responsibilities that were previously carried by parents and churches have defaulted to the public schools. To meet this crushing burden, some of the best professionals have packaged their helping skills in training programs to help teens learn to help their peers handle specific problems like peer pressure, drugs, grief, suicidal tendencies, and family problems. Youth programs available from The Health Connection help youth plan and execute their own community service projects.

Children's Materials

The Health Connection is your source for thousands of health education materials for children. You can start a full puppet ministry, and even get a puppet stage from The Health Connection. Also available are the Vacation Bible School materials called Jesus' Kids in the Kitchen (see sidebar).

Training in Health Education

Home Study International offers health-related, college-level correspondence courses. Contact Home Study International, P.O. Box 4437, Silver Spring, MD 20914-4437; (800) 782-4769; (301) 680-6570; Fax (301) 680-5157.

Loma Linda University, School of Public Health offers graduate programs in public health. (See Chapter 18.)

Pacific Health Education Center offers practical training in health education. (See Chapter 15.)

Self-Supporting Institutions: Almost all of the health related self-supporting institutions offer live-in training programs for students wanting to learn the basics of health promotion and how to operate a health education center on a self-supporting basis. In addition, most offer annual week-long seminars or "camp meetings" where they offer their alumni and others update courses on health and wellness. These are excellent training programs. (See Chapter 19 for contact numbers.)

Southern Adventist University Executive Wellness Training: SAU offers the only Seventh-day Adventist B. S. Degree in Corporate/Community Wellness Management, and the only corporate wellness program in Tennessee. The Ball State Wellness graduate program which is the number one program in the nation has accepted all of the SAU students that apply. Some of the specialty courses that are offered are: Care and Prevention of Athletic Injuries, Method/Materials of Health Promotion, Current Issues in Health, Foundations of Nutrition, and Conditioning. SAU also produces a monthly health newsletter called Wellness Pointers. For more information contact the Physical Education, and Recreation Department, Southern Adventist University, P.O. Box 370, Collegedale, TN 37315; (423) 238-2852.

SAU also offers a 3-hour class in Health Evangelism through the School of Religion.

Weimar Institute offers academy and college undergraduate courses and a degree in religion with an emphasis in health. This is an excellent training institution for students wanting experience in health evangelism because there is an emphasis on the application of academic learning. Contact Weimar Institute, P.O. Box 486, Weimar, CA 95736-0486; (800) 525-9192 or (916) 637-4111.

Church Produced Health Magazines and Newsletters

There are three official health and temperance magazines published by the church: *Vibrant Life, Listen,* and *The Winner.* (For pricing and order information on these publications, call your local Adventist Book Center at (800) 765-6955; *Listen* and *The Winner* can also be ordered through The Health Connection, (800) 548-8700.)

Vibrant Life (The official outreach health journal of the Adventist Church)

The church has been blessed with a wealth of information on health, and the proof of our willingness to share that valuable information has always been *Vibrant Life* magazine. Formerly called *Life and Health,* it shows readers that there's a better way to live. Just the advice on nutrition and fitness can revolutionize a person's life. Readers discover simple ways to avoid disease. They enjoy wholesome, delicious recipes.

Vibrant Life doesn't shy away from emphasizing the connection between faith in God and personal well-being. This magazine leads people to a better life in more ways than one. (A one-year subscription includes six bi-monthly issues. Bulk rates are available for churches.)

There are also special issues of the magazine that can either be purchased individually or in bulk for health programs. In addition, *Vibrant Life* publishes the *Health Planner,* which is an excellent give away at fairs and health seminars.

Listen (magazine for teens)

Statistics prove that drug education works, and *Listen* is the most highly-respected drug education magazine in the United States. Adventists can be proud of this magazine that grabs the attention of teens with cover personalities like Kristi Yamaguchi, Darrell Green, Wayne Gretzky and Steve Young.

Kids in the Kitchen

Many parents would just as soon shoo the kids out of the kitchen, but Judi Rogers, Marketing and Sales Representative for the Review and Herald, thinks the kitchen is a great place for kids. In fact, it's the best place to begin their training for a healthy lifestyle.

That's why Judi wrote the original "Jesus' Kids in the Kitchen" VBS program which is based on the eight principles of health. The Review and Herald recently published her first children's book called, *Fun with Kids in the Kitchen Cookbook,* which contains more than 50 kid-tested recipes and other kitchen craft ideas.

Judi's interests in kid's health is bigger than just the kitchen, as she writes the "Kid's Body Shop Page" for Vibrant Life magazine which focuses on good health habits, drug awareness and fitness for kids, in addition to serving as the coordinator of the Children's Resource Center and travels extensively conducting leadership training workshops for children's ministries.

Listen still features true stories that communicate the horrors of drug use. But it also takes the positive approach of suggesting interesting hobbies and sporting activities as drug-free ways to enjoy life.

Listen leads teens to make a serious, personal decision to avoid alcohol, tobacco and other drugs and gives them a clean shot at a happy and successful future. (A one-year subscription includes 12 issues.)

The Winner (For children grades 4 to 6)

The earlier you start drug education, the better. *The Winner* starts at grade four. It's really the most fun a kid can have and still call it drug education. It's loaded with stories told from a kid's-eye view, plus puzzles, games, and riddles. Some of the stories build self-esteem so that kids are equipped with the confidence, as well as good reasons, to say "NO" to drugs. (Nine issues delivered monthly September through May.)

Special Magazine Issues on Health
- AIDS (Message magazine)
- Drugs Close to Home (Message magazine)
- Violence (Message magazine)
- Special health issue of the Adventist Review

Get Acquainted with the SDA Periodical Index

If you're looking for information about health or successful health programs going on across the country, you'll want to get acquainted with the annual *SDA Periodical Index*. Every article that has been published in a Seventh-day Adventist publication is referenced in this index. It's available at college libraries, and through the Internet.

Health topics listed in the Index include: Healing (around the world), Healing in the Bible, Health Education (around the world), Health evangelism (around the world), Health fairs, Health promotion, Health screening, Healthful living, Heart disease. And these were only some of the health items listed under "H"!

Newsletters

HealthWorks is published by the NAD Health Ministries Department every two months. If you are not receiving the newsletter call AdventSource (800) 328-0525 and ask to be put on the mailing list. If you are the health min-

istries leader for your church, your copy will be sent to your church. If you are not the Health Ministries leader and would like to subscribe, contact AdventSource.

Nutrition Update is a compilation of the latest, up-to-date research in the area of nutrition and nutrition's effect on lifestyle. There is a small fee. For information or to subscribe contact the General Conference Health Ministries Department, 12501 Old Columbia Pike, Silver Spring, MD 20904; (301) 680-6702.

Health Newsletters Published by Seventh-day Adventists

Better Health: It's originator, Dr. Jackson Saxon has passed away, but his son, David Saxon, M.D. produces this monthly newsletter for the general public. This is an interpretive health newsletter that emphasizes self-help and preventive health-care. He distributes it to any conference wishing a copy and gives them permission to duplicate it and give it to the churches. It has been very well received. It can be accessed at www.gccsda.com.

FastFacts: A monthly health/nutrition update from the producers of "Let's Eat! For Strength" with Dane and Vicki Griffin. The newsletter is creatively written and tastefully designed. FastFacts is distributed by TEACH Services, Inc. Rt. 1, Box 182, Brushton, NY 19916-9738, through your local ABC, or call (800) 367-1844; (518) 358-2125.

HealthLine: A newsletter sponsored by Lifestyle Medicine Institute in cooperation with The Quite Hour. Edited by Hans Diehl. For more information contact: Better Health, P O Box 1761, Loma Linda, CA 92354; (909) 825-1888.

Helping One Another: quarterly newsletter featuring health topics and the vegan diet, edited by John Reinhold. This informative letter is sent to the members of the Christian Care Ministry Medi-Share program. Members help meet the medical needs of other Christians by paying a monthly fee. This program is for families who are living a healthy lifestyle in lieu of more expensive insurance plans. For copies of the newsletter and to inquire about the Medi-Share program call

(800) 374-2562, or write The Christian Care Ministry, P.O. Box 1779, Melbourne, FL 32902-1779.

The Rilenco Report, a quarterly newsletter written by Richard Neil, M.D., M.P.H., for the general public about health trends, stress, corporate wellness, and general health issues. Contact The Rilenco Report at 1743 Orange Tree Lane, Redlands, CA 92374 or call (909) 396-3877.

Wellness Pointers: Published monthly by Southern Adventist University Wellness Program for Employees. An excellent well-written short newsletter on all types of health related issues. Each newsletter has a special focus and can be ordered by writing, Southern Adventist University Corporate Wellness Program, P.O. Box 370, Collegedale, TN 37315, or by calling (423) 238-2852.

Note: Most of the self-supporting health-related institutions publish a health newsletter. (For contact information see Chapter 19.)

Other Health-related Newsletters

Journal of Health and Healing
Another health journal that promotes the Adventist lifestyle that you should know about published by Wildwood Sanitarium, Inc., and edited by Dr. Marjorie V. Baldwin, is The Journal of Health and Healing. Published quarterly; this journal contains vital and well-documented health information. Order from P.O. Box 109, Wildwood, GA 30757-0109 or call (800) 834-9355.

The following newsletters, although having current information on health, do not necessarily promote the Adventist lifestyle and should be carefully screened.

A Grain of Salt contains innovative news about good salt, natural food, and other health-related issues; published quarterly by Celtic Ocean International, Inc. D.B.A., The Grain and Salt Society, 273 Fairway Drive, Ashville, NC 28805; (800) TOP SALT [867-7258]; www.celtic@seasalt.com

CMDS HealthWise is a special edition of Today's Christian Doctor and published six times each year. To use this magazine as an outreach tool with patients, remove the CMDS (Christian

---

> ### Price List for Special Health Issues
> ### Call your local ABC to order:
> ### (800) 765-6955
>
> *   1-9 copies, ea. $1.00; 10-99 ea. $0.75; 100-999 ea. $0.55; 1,000 or more ea. $0.40
> ** 1 copy $2.25; 2-5 copies ea. $1.95; 6-99 ea. $1.25; 100-999 ea. $1.00; 1,000 or more $0.75
> *** 1 copy $2.50; 2-5 copies ea. $1.95; 6-99 ea. $1.25; 100-999 ea. $1.00; 1,000 or more $1.00

Medical and Dental Society) News pages at the center, then leave CMDS HealthWise in your waiting room. Physician can receive a complimentary one year subscription upon request. It contains excellent mainstream medical information but accepts meat as one of the major food groups. Contact CMDS, P.O. Box 5, Bristol, TN 37627-0005; (423) 844-7000 or (800) 804-0658; Fax (423) 844-1005.

Consumer Reports on Health is an excellent source of monthly information published by the Consumer Union. Contact: P.O. Box 52148, Boulder, CO 80321-2148.

John Hopkins Medical Letter: Health After 50 is published monthly. P.O. Box 420179, Palm Coast, FL 32142; (904) 446-4675.

Harvard Health Letter is published monthly from the Harvard Medical School. For subscriptions contact P.O. Box 420300 Palm Coast, FL 32142-0300; (617) 432-1485. Also, available is the *Harvard Women's Health Watch* and *Health Gazette* (Dr. Alexander Grant's Digest of Medical Facts and News) is published 10 times a year. P.O. Box 1786, Indianapolis, IN 46206, Fax (317) 253-8582.

Hope HealthLetter a monthly newsletter produced by The Hope Heart Institute, 528 18th Ave. Seattle, WA 98122 (206) 328-8600. For subscriptions contact the International Health Awareness Center, Inc. 350 East Michigan Ave., Suite 301, Kalamazoo, MI 49007-3851; (616) 343-0770; Fax (616) 343-6260. (You might want to inquire about other Hope Heart Institute publications like the newsletter, HealthyBites.)

Mayo Clinic Health Letter is published monthly. Subscribers receive three eight-page Medical Essays and a Five-Year Cumulative Index. Contact Mayo Clinic Health Letter, Subscription Services, P.O. Box 53889, Boulder, CO 80322-3889. For a free copy of their current index, call (800) 291-1128. For customer service call (800) 333-9037.

Mind/Body Health Newsletter is published quarterly. For subscription information contact: The Center for Health Sciences c/o ISHK Book Services, P.O. Box 381069, Cambridge, MA 02238-1069; (800) 222-4745.

PennState Sports Medicine Newsletter. Published monthly. Contact: P.O. Box 3073, Langhorne, PA 19047-9377; (215) 788-8424. Physician Magazine is published by Focus on the Family and deals with issues that confront today's Christian physician (FREE). Order by calling (800) A-FAMILY[232-6459]; (719) 531-5181 or write Focus on the Family, 8605 Explorer Dr., Colorado Springs, CO 80920.

The Edell Health Letter is published 10 times a year by Hippocrates Partners, 301 Howard St., Suite 1800, San Francisco, CA 94105. For subscriptions contact The Edell Health Letter, P.O. Box 57812, Boulder, CO 80322-7812; (800) 456-0958.

TopHealth is published 10 times a year by Dreyfuss Hunt, Inc., 443 Western Ave, Boston, MA 02135; (617) 254-5000.

Total Wellness: Becoming a total person is published monthly by Rutherford Publishing, Inc., P.O. Box 8853, Waco, TX 76714; (800) 815-2323.

University of California at Berkeley Wellness Letter is a monthly publication that offers professionally sound medical information. P.O. Box 420148, Palm Coast, FL 32142; (904) 445-6414.

(See Chapter 9 for nutrition newsletters.)

Internet Resources

In addition to the above resources, there is a great deal of free information available via the Internet. Access to the Internet, a collection of thousands of computer networks, gives millions of people from around the world the means to share and exchange information for a fairly inexpensive rate. Internet users have access to electronic mail (e-mail); subject matter discussion groups, long-distance computing; the Web, the most popular and fastest-growing part of the Internet, which allows users to access both graphical and text-based information from a number of databases. The prevention community needs to take advantage of the innovative tools that the Web and Internet represent.

The National Clearinghouse for Alcohol and Drug Information (NCADI) is using the Web to disseminate information provided by the federal government on the topics of alcohol and other drug issues. Their Web site (or home page) is http://www.health.org. Why should you access NCADI's Web site? With a click of the mouse homepage users can:

- Learn about NCADI, the world's largest resource for substance abuse prevention information.
- Find resources and referrals, including publications, Internet links, and telephone numbers to help individuals overcome substance abuse problems.
- Search for publications by topic, audience, or series, or order items instantly from the online catalog rather than wait the 6-8 weeks customarily expected for postal delivery.
- Access the most recent research, surveys, and statistics.
- Take part in forums with other people interested in substance abuse prevention and learn about the latest news, trends, and opportunities for collaboration in the field.
- Access related Internet links.

Thousands of organizations are putting out vital health information over the Web. Unfortunately, no list can be exhaustive because the Internet is constantly growing and changing, but we have provided what we have available. Since the *Directory of National Help Lines* also includes Internet addresses and is updated annually, it provides an easy, inexpensive way to keep up-to-date.

Information Resources Available Via e-mail

WellnessWise Electronic Journal (WEJ): A health newsletter published by Dr. David DeRose, from Life Center of America, is mailed free to all subscribers biweekly. For free subscriptions request from: docderose@aol.com or drderose@brightok.net

Note: Back issues of WEJ are available at several sites in cyberspace. Some of the more popular sites are as follows:

(1) http://fermi.jhuapl.edu/wej/
(2) http://www.glasscity.net/~tolsda/wej/
(3) http://www.social.com/health/news.html

International Health News: Health@pinc.com

List Services (Also accessible only via e-mail.)

Notes on subscribing to a list service: To subscribe to a particular mailing list, send the following message:

To: LISTSERV@LISTSERV.NET
Subject: < Blank
Body: sub listname full_name

The command "sub" stands for "subscriber," and "listname" is the name of a valid list below such as "FOOD-NET." The option, "full_name" refers to your full name and does not need to be given. A few samples illustrate:

- FOOD-NET Exchange of Information Relative Food Safety & Nutrition
- LONGEVITY: Longevity List
- MEDNEWS: Health Network Newsletter
- NUTEPI: Nutritional epidemiology
- PUBLIC-HEALTH: Issues in U.S. Public Health
List of Listservs:http://tele.net/LISTSERV

Newsgroups: (Usenet groups)
- sci.med
- misc.health.alternative
- sci.environment

Where to Start on the Web: Lists, Search tools, directories, etc.

The Good Health Web: The Good Health Web. Wellness wise is posted at http://www.

social.com/health/news.html. (Features among other things, a list of over 1000 health-related organizations in the US and how to reach them (phone, fax, e-mail, etc.)

Global Health Net work (GHNet)
http://www.pitt.edu/HOME/GHNet/GHNet.html

Econet: Web site directing to resources of environmental interest: Environmental resources directory http://www.econet.apc.org/econet/en.issues.html energy resources: http://www.igc.apc.org/energy/

University of Virginia's list of environmental resources: http://ecosys.drdr.virginia.edu/Envirlists.html

Health Websites (Includes sites of general health interest as well as resources for health professionals)

Country Life Natural Food/ Oak Haven Inc.

Country Life Natural Foods is a distributor, both wholesale and retail, of bulk and packaged natural foods, and is a division of Oak Haven, Inc., and ASI organization located in Pullman, Michigan.

They also teach cooking schools and hold health seminars both on campus and assist local churches within a 100-mile radius in Southeast Michigan.

Anyone who wants to start a health food ministry is invited to join them, or come and learn from them. You can write Country Life Natural Foods/Oak Haven at P.O. Box 489, Pullman, MI 49450-0489; (616) 236-5011; Fax (616) 236-8357.

Note: sub pages and files are shown as words after a slash (/). If you enter them as part of the address, you will probably get where you want to go. However, some sites take exception to this, so if you get a"directory/file does not exist", try lopping off the address before one (or more) of the slashes. Then use the hypertext links to travel to where you wanted to go.

- American Heart Association (AHA): email - inquire@amhrt.org:
- American Heart Association Homepage : http://www.amhrt.org/features a searchable information file with material relevant to heart disease and its prevention. Also includes: AHA 1995 Heart and Stroke Guide: http://www.amhrt.org/heartg/aa00.htm
- AHA Scientific Publishing (journals on line): http://www.at-home.com/amhrt/
- The American Heart Association publishes five major journals as well as other types of scientific publications. Circulation: http://www.at-home. com/amhrt/CIRC/issues.html
- Arteriosclerosis Current and Prior Issues: http://www.at home.com/amhrt/ARTER/issues.html
- Hypertension: Current and Prior Issues: http://www.at home.com/amhrt/HYPER/issues.html Circulation Research and Stroke also available—has references and table of contents
- American Medical Association Publishing Home Page http://www.ama-assn.org/scipubs/pubhome.htm This site is where you'll find the Web editions of:
  - Journal of the American Medical Association
  - Archives of Surgery
  - American Medical News
  - Archives of General Psychiatry
  - Archives of Ophthalmology
  - Archives of Pediatrics
  - Archives of Neurology
  - Archives of Otolaryngology
  - Archives of Dermatology
  - Archives of Family Medicine
  - Physician Recruitment Advertising

- Press Releases
- Archives of Internal Medicine
- Weekly News Announcements
- Archives Journal Club - Women's Health

- Cancer News: http://cancer.med.upenn.edu/cancer_news/index.html
- Center for Food Safety and Applied nutrition: http://vm.cfsan.fda.gov/list.html for example: has information on food additives and chemical contaminants: http://vm.cfsan.fda.gov/lrd/foodadd.html
- Centers for Disease Control (CDC) Home Page: http://www.cdc.gov/
- CDC National AIDS Clearinghouse Web Server: http://cdcnac.aspensys.com:86/
- Complementary Medicine: http://galen.med.virginia.edu/pjb3s/ComplementaryHomePage.html
- Cornell University Agriculture: http://www.mannlib.cornell.edu/ examples: meat animals agricultural statistics: gopher://usda.mannlib.cornell.edu:70/00/data sets/livestock/95907/sb907-hi.txt
- Current Journal of the National Cancer Institute issues available on-line: http://wwwicic.nci.nih.gov/jnci_issues.html
- DOE Technical Information Service (TIS): http://venus.hyperk.com
- Duke Occupational and Enviromental Medicine: http://occ-env-med.mc.duke.edu/oem or http://dmi-www.mc.duke.edu/cfm/occ&env/index.html
- Duke University Department of Community and Family Medicine: http://dmi-www.mc.duke.edu/cfm/cfmhome.html
- Duke University Medical Informatics: http://dmi-www.mc.duke.edu/
- Enviro-Health: http://www.niehs.nih.gov
- EnviroLink Network: http://envirolink.org/
- Environ-health Clearinghouse: http://web.fie.com/web/fed/ehs/text/nhsteh01.htm

- Environmental Medicine:
  http://www.pic.net/~enviromd
- FDA home page (Food and Drug Administration):
  http://vm.cfsan.fda.gov/index.html
- Foodnet: http://food-net.fic.ca
- Health Information Resources: Toll-FreeNumbers for Health Information:
  http://nhic-nt.health.org/htmlgen/html-gen. exe/Tollfree?Descriptor='800'
- icd-9-cm site:
  ftp://ftp.cdc.gov/pub/Health_Statistics /NCHS/Publications/ICD9-CM
- JAMA - HIV Site: http://www.amaassn. org/special/hiv/hivhome.htm
- Martindale's Health Science Guide '95:
  http://ssssci.lib.uci.edu/martindale/HSGui de.html
- Medical Matrix Guide to Internet Medical Resources:http://kuhttp.cc.ukans.edu/cwis / units/medcntr/Lee/HOMEPAGE.HTML
- The Medical Reporter:
  http://www.dash.com/netro/nwx/tmr/tmr .html
- MMWR Mortality and Morbidity Weekly Report: http://www.crawford.com/ cdc/mmwr/mmwr.html
- Mosby Publishing:
  http://www.mosby.com
- National Center for Health Statistics:
  http://www.cdc.gov/nchswww/nchshome. htm. Get vital statistics on youth and smoking, contraception, births and deaths, etc.
- National Health Information Center, U.S. Department of Health and Human Services: NHIC Home Page National Health Information Center:
  http://nhicnt.health.org/
- National Highway Traffic Safety Administration:
  http://www.nhtsa.dot.gov/
- National Institute of Mental Health Gopher:
  gopher://gopher.nimh.nih.gov/
- National Institutes of Health (NIH) home page: http://www.nih.gov/home.html has sections devoted to health information: includes Cancer and AIDs databases as well

as access to NIH consensus documents, news and events, etc. related gopher site (for those without Web access): gopher:// gopher.nih.gov:70/11/clin
- National Safety Council:
  http://www.nsc.org/nsc
- NIOSH Agricultural Health and Safety Centers:
  http://wwwoem.ucdavis.edu/www/niosh/ niosh.html
- NIOSH National Institute for Occupational Safety and Health: http://www.cdc.gov/ niosh/ homepage.hmtl or http://iadss1. niosh.cdc.gov/
- NursingNet: http://www.communique.net/ nursgnt/
- OncoLink: http://cancer.med.upenn.edu/
- OSHA (Occupational Safety and Health) Home Page: http://www.osha.gov/
- Patient Education Web Site: http://www. cyberport.net/mmg/homepage. html
- Pharmaceutical Information Network:
  http://pharminfo.com/
- Poisons Information Database:
  http://biomed.nus.sg:80/PID/PID.html
- SCIENCE Magazine On-Line:
  http://sciencemag.aaas.org/science/ home/browse.html
- University of South Carolina Preventive medicine:
  http://www.prevmed.scarolina.edu/ designed for their residency—but has links to interesting articles and a wealth of information
- Virtual Hospital Home Page: University of Iowa site that gives access to
  - American Family Physician
  - Morbidity and Mortality Weekly Report
  - Physician Assistant Newsletter
  - RX Update
- Radiology Journals, etc. (For example you can get patient handouts from the American Family Physician Journal) http://vh.radiolo-gy.uiowa.edu/
- Your health daily from the NY times syndicate: http://nytsyn.com/medic/

Other Valuable Websites

- ATT 800 directory:
  http://www.tollfree.att.net/dir800/
- Library of Congress Marvel:
  http://marvel.loc.gov
- Government Documents (US):
  http://thorplus.lib.purdue.edu/gpo/ or
  http://ssdc.ucsd.edu/gpo/
- Government Printing Office:
  http://www.access.gpo.gov/su
  ocs/index.html
- Federal Information Exchange:
  http://www.fie.com/
- Federal Register:
  http://www.counterpoint.com
- Federal Register searching:
  http://www.istech.com/tore-fr.html
- FedWorld: http://www.fedworld.gov
- List of all Newspapers on the Web:
  http://www.infi.net/naa/hot.html#News
- New York Times fax:
  http://nytimesfax.com/
- National Public Radio: http://www.npr.org/
- On line newspapers:
  http://www.mediainfo.com/edpub/e-
  papers.home.page.html
- SDA Periodical Index: A helpful resource for
  articles on Adventist Lifestyle, or health
  evangelism activities of various churches
  that have been published in SDA publications. This index is available at Seventh-day
  Adventist libraries connected with colleges
  and universities, or you can access it via the
  Internet:
  http://www.andrews.edu/library
- Zip code directory:
  http://www.mit.edu:8001/geo

Where to find other resources in this manual

This handbook lists many resources. You can find the Adventist Retirement and Care Facilities in Appendix F and Chapter 17; Adventist Speakers on Health are in Appendix D; Books on Adventist Lifestyle are listed in Appendix E; Hotlines and Helplines are in Appendix G; Published research and articles on Adventist Lifestyle can be found in Chapter 23; and for resources on specific health issues see the chapters on those topics.

22

Lifestyle Certification

The Lifestyle Certification program has been designed to empower you to answer the cry of millions who need improved health and wellness. Public and private agencies are asking churches to step into the battle against AIDS, heart disease, high blood pressure, cancer, drug abuse, mental illness, and other diseases. This program had its birth in Allegheny East Conference. Gwen Foster, former health ministries director for the conference, had great success with it for the last ten years. We are happy Allegheny East has agreed to share this successful program with the North American Division. We now offer you this outstanding certification program.

Many people are unaware of their personal health needs. Others, while aware, need to be reminded and helped to pursue a healthy lifestyle. The Lifestyle Certificate courses are short, yet informative, and designed to equip and train you to help hurting people.

Hopefully, the end result will be that enough individuals in your church will be trained for service in different health areas so that a variety of seminars can be presented in your community on a regular basis. When this happens your health ministry will win respect and referrals, not only from health professionals, but also from church members, relatives and friends.

If the seminars have a strong follow-up program involving participants in support groups and other opportunities for spiritual growth and fellowship, many will want to know more about Adventist beliefs.

There are three levels of certification:

Level 1: Lifestyle Consultant

The requirements for completion cover the basic aspects of health education. When you are finished, you will know how to take personal responsibility for your health and how to share simple health principles with your church and family.

Level 2: Lifestyle Specialist

On completion of Level 2 you will have the knowledge and expertise you need to engage in a specialized ministry of prevention and health promotion in church and community. The ideal would be to have at least four trainers for each level 2 category in each union conference.

Level 3: Lifestyle Trainer

The third level will enable you to better communicate instruction in healthy lifestyles to people in your church and community. To more adequately serve as a qualified instructor, you will learn how to (1) facilitate level 2 classes; (2) network with community health leaders and organizations, (3) advertise and use media facilities, (4) acquire public speaking skills, and (5) learn how to be a more effective teacher.

Instructions for Completing the Certification Process

*Please consult the Health Ministries web page (www.nadadventist.org/hm-certification) for the latest requirements—at the time of this writing, many changes were being discussed.

The materials recommended for Lifestyle Certification may be purchased from the following sources:

Advent*Source*
5040 Prescott Avenue
Lincoln, NE 68506
(800) 328-0525
Fax (402) 486-2572
e-mail: service@adventsource.org
web site: www.adventsource.org

Note: Advent*Source*, the NAD Adventist health ministries certification center, will handle your questions concerning certification and carry all certification materials, except the actual health education seminar materials which are available at The Health Connection.

The Health Connection
55 West Oak Ridge Dr.
Hagerstown, MD 21740
(800) 548-8700
Outside the USA, call (301) 790-9735
Fax (888) 294-8405
web site: www.healthconnection.org
e-mail: sales@healthconnection.org

The Health Connection is your source for health information, materials, seminars and supplies.

Your local Adventist Book Center (ABC)

If there is no Adventist Book Center near you call (800) 765-6955. The ABC only will sell. It cannot give counsel or advice. The best source of information should be your local conference Health Ministries Director.

Now let's take a closer look at what's involved in each level of the Lifestyle Certification program. As you do, prayerfully consider where God needs you to minister, and what training you should have to do a more noble work for Him and for humanity.

Level 1: Lifestyle Consultant

- To develop and maintain a personal healthy lifestyle that harmonizes with the Biblical principles that govern the total person— physical, mental, social, and spiritual.
- To be qualified to assist in minor emergency situations.

Requirement 1: In order to receive certification for Level 1 complete the required courses and other assignments in a time period of three (3) years or less. Any course work older than three years does not qualify for certification. Health professionals having received equivalent training in some or all Level 1 areas need to submit a statement to Health Ministries Certification, 5040 Prescott, Lincoln, NE 68506

Requirement 2: After all four courses are completed, send copies of proof of completion certificates to Health Ministries Certification, 5040

Prescott, Lincoln, NE 68506. Retain a copy for your records. You should receive your Level 1: Lifestyle Consultant certificate within four to six weeks.

PLEASE DO NOT SEND ITEMS COURSE BY COURSE. WAIT UNTIL ALL REQUIREMENTS FOR LEVEL 1 ARE COMPLETED AND THEN SUBMIT THEM AT ONE TIME

Lifestyle Consultants Receive training in the following areas:
- Basic Principles of Health Evangelism
- Cardiopulmonary Resuscitation and Emergency Cardiac Care (CPR)
- First Aid
  (It has been suggested that CPR & First Aid be made a level II specialty and removed from level l).
- Philosophy of Healthy Living
- Understanding of how to teach the Laws of Health
- Developing a Personal Mission Statement

Level 1: Develops the Following Skills
- Understand the basic principles of health evangelism
- Define health from a Biblical perspective.
- Identify the eight natural principles of health and be able to share them with others.
- Learn the Ten Laws of Life and Health (Georgia-Cumberland Conference program).
- Be qualified to render first aid in minor emergencies.
- Be qualified to administer CPR.
- Articulate your philosophy of healthy living.
- Develop a personal mission statement.

Lifestyle Consultant Courses
Level 1 Develops the Following Skills
Lifestyle Consultant Courses
Course #1: Basic Principles of Health Evangelism
Materials needed:
- *The Ministry of Healing* (by Ellen White)
- *The Ministry of Healing Study Guide*
- *Search video*
- *The Search Study Guide*

- *Adventist HealthStyle* (by David Neiman)
- *Adventist HealthStyle Study Guide*

A package containing all the books and study guides you will need to complete this course is available at Advent*Source*: It is also available at The Health Connection.

This course can be conducted with a local church group or as a self study project.

- Read the book, *The Ministry of Healing*.
- Complete *The Ministry of Healing Study Guide*.
- View the Search video and complete the *Search Study Guide*.
- Read *Adventist HealthStyle*.
- Complete the *Adventist HealthStyle Study Guide*.
- Return the completed three study guides to Health Ministries Certification, 5040 Prescott, Lincoln, NE 68506. *(Do not send until all requirements for Level 1 certification are completed.)*

Level 2: Cardiopulmonary Resuscitation (CPR) and Emergency Cardiac Care

To fulfill this certification requirement, you must hold a current valid card from the American Heart Association, Red Cross, local hospital or other recognized organization. To receive credit, send a photocopy of your certificate/card to Health Ministries Certification, 5040 Prescott Avenue, Lincoln, NE 68506. *(Do not send until all requirements for Level 1 certification are completed.)*

Course #3: First Aid

To fulfill this certification requirement, you must hold a current valid card from the American Heart Association, Red Cross, local hospital or other recognized organization. To receive credit, send a photocopy of your certificate/card to Health Ministries Certification, 5040 Prescott, Lincoln, NE 68506. *(Do not send until all requirements for Level 1 certification are completed.)*

Course #4: Philosophy of Healthy Living

This course can be conducted with a local church group or as a self study project.

Materials needed:
- *Dynamic Living* by Aileen Ludington and Hans Diehl and the *Dynamic Living Workbook*

Requirements:
- Read the book, *Dynamic Living*
- Complete the *Dynamic Living Workbook.*
- Create a Personal Mission Statement (see instructions below)
- Send a photocopy of "Test Your Knowledge" in the Dynamic Living Workbook and your Personal Mission Statement to Health Ministries Certification, 5040 Prescott, Lincoln, NE 68506

(Do not send until all requirements for Level 1 certification are completed.)

Alternate Level 1 Certification Program

The North American Division also has approved the Level 1 Certification course prepared by the Georgia-Cumberland Conference. The structure is indicated in the box below. Rather than the four courses listed above, this program is divided into two training sections–A and B.

Some of the materials listed above under course requirements have been substituted by the following:

- *The Ministry of Health and Healing* manual produced by the NAD.
- *Take 10* book authored by Leo Van Dolson on the laws of life and health outlined by Ellen White (Not the same as the 8 natural remedies). Available from The Health Connection (Catalogue # 47010, being adapted to supplement The *12 Celebrations* presentations).
- A participant's syllabus entitled Health Ministries in the Finishing of the Work also available from The Health Connection (catalogue #47020).

Level 1 and 2 Health Certification Programs for the Georgia-Cumberland Conference

The Level 1 Certification program prepared by the Georgia-Cumberland Conference in consultation with and the approval of the North American Division is an entry-level course based on the study of the concepts and methods of creative witnessing opportunities. It takes advantage of the current interest in preventive lifestyle practices. The objective of the materials presented is to lead church members to decide to follow a more abundant way of life and to lead men and women within the church and community to Christ through a health emphasis. The course provides church health leaders, and others who may be interested in certification, with practical ways to utilize their talents and to involve members of their churches in health ministries.

Level 1 training now has been divided into two separate training sessions:

Section A–This 10-hour seminar provides a completion card that is the first step in receiving a 3-year certificate that authorizes participants to conduct the Level 1 training program in their local area as a means of training local church members in health evangelism.

Section B–Practical application and home-study of the section A principles that provides a 3-year certificate upon completion. This certificate qualifies participants to conduct the Level 1 certification program anywhere they might be invited to do so in the Georgia-Cumberland conference.

Level 2 certification trains those enrolled to conduct specialized health programs, such as: Breath-Free stop smoking programs, stress control seminars, cooking classes and schools, etc., anywhere in the conference. It is a requirement (unless waived by the conference) to take Level 1 training, which lays the foundation, before taking the Level 2 specialized programs.

For further information contact E. W. Dempsey, Adult Health Ministries Director of the Georgia Cumberland Conference (Phone number: 1-800-567-1844, ext. 332).

What is a Personal Mission Statement?

A Personal Mission Statement is as much a discovery as it is a creation. It can inspire you and provide direction and guidance for your life. It is not static. It grows as you grow and as your lifestyle roles change. The basic elements of a personal mission statement are:

1. What you want to be.
   - What character strengths you want to have
   - What qualities you want to develop
2. What you want to do.
   - What you want to accomplish
   - What contributions you want to make

Write your Personal Mission Statement by completing the following work sheets.

Step 1: Identify an Influential Person

Identify an individual who has highly influenced your life. Think about how this individual has influenced you. This person may be a parent, work associate, friend, family member or neighbor. Answer the following questions, keeping in mind your own personal goals.

Creating a Personal Mission Statement

My name is: Date:

Here is how I would describe myself:

Identify an Influential Person

The person's name:

Which qualities do I most admire in this person?
(The characteristics you admire in this individual constitute your values.)

-

-

-

Define what you want to be, and do

- I'd like to be:

- I'd like to do:

Define your life roles

Role #1:
How I want to be described:

Role #2:
How I want to be described:

Role #3:
How I want to be described:

Role #4:
How I want to be described:

Role #5:
How I want to be described:

Role #6:
How I want to be described:

Role #7:
How I want to be described:

Step 2: Define what you want to be, and do.

Step 3: Define your life roles.

You live your life in terms of roles—not in the sense of role-playing but in the sense of authentic roles you have chosen to fill. You have roles at work, in the family, in the community, and other areas of your life. These roles become a natural framework that give order to what you want to do and to be.

You may define your family position as "family member." Or, you may choose to divide it into more specific roles, such as "wife" and "mother" or "husband" and "father."

Some areas such as your professional life, may involve several roles. For example, you may have responsibilities in administration, in marketing, in personnel, and in long-range planning, all simultaneously.

- Define up to seven life roles and write these below.
- Next, project yourself forward in time and write a brief statement of how you would most like to be described in that particular role.

Note: By identifying your life roles, you will gain perspective and balance. By writing these descriptive statements, you will begin to visualize your highest self. You will also identify the core principles and values by which you desire to live.

Step 4: Creating a Personal Mission Statement

Now write your own Mission Statement below. Including the following:
- Your values
- What you want to be
- What you want to do, considering your life roles

Now that you have finished all your requirements:

Mail copies of all your requirements to your Local conference Health Ministries Director or Conference President (Note: The papers you sub-mit will not be returned to you.) You will receive your certification in 4-6 weeks.

Congratulations! May God bless your achievement.

Level 2: Lifestyle Specialist
Purpose of a Lifestyle Specialist

To become a competent and skilled health promotion specialist in one or more of the following areas. Specialist courses require from 25 to 40 hours of class work, reading and/or home-work. The basic texts may change, or other texts may be substituted by instructors. Other supplemental material may be required.

Instructions for Certification

Step 1: Certificates of completion will be issued at the end of each Specialist course completed(by the presenter). Make arrangements in advance with the instructor to insure that the course and the instructor has been approved by NAD Health Ministries department and that the certificate will be available at the end of the course.

Step 2: After completing the requirement for a Level 2 Specialist course send your report to Health Ministries Certification, 5040 Prescott, Lincoln, NE 68506. Retain a copy for your records.

Specialists Receive Training in One or More of the Following Areas

1. Fitness for Life
2. Stress Management
3. Addiction/Regeneration
4. Principles of smoking cessation (Breathe-Free)
5. Eight Weeks to Wellness
6. Vegetarian Cuisine Instructor
7. Emergency Care (CPR & First Aid)
8. Van Ministry
9. Diabetes Mastery
10. Grief Recovery
11. Hydro Therapy (Natural Remedies)
12. Parish Nursing
13. HeartBeat

Your Personal Mission Statement

• Your values (Refer to Step 1)

• What you want to be (Refer to Step 2)

• What you want to do, considering your life roles (Refer to Step 2 & 3)

Requirements for Lifestyle Specialist Certification

Requirement 1: Completion of the Lifestyle Consultant Certification program: Level 1 (or the equivalent basic health training).

Requirement 2: Complete course work for one or more of the Specialist courses from the following list. These are not self-study courses.

Lifestyle Specialist Courses

The following courses are available on a periodic basis. Consult your Local conference Health Ministries Director or Conference President for information on the time and place of the course you want to take. All materials, unless indicated, are available from Advent*Source* or The Health Connection:

Course #1: Fitness for Life

This course prepares the seminar facilitator to lead participants through a successful exercise fitness program utilizing the materials and scripts from Wellsource, Inc.

Course #2: Stress Management

The latest techniques for controlling stress and hypertension and the onset of disease, stages of burnout, and techniques of relaxation. *Stress Beyond Coping* package, includes instructor's manual, workbook, Power-Point presentations or overheads, and a video series. (The Health Connection)

Course #3: Addiction Ministries (Regeneration Seminar)

The course will teach pastoral and church leaders how to minister to the chemically dependent and their families. It includes how to start a Twelve Step group and guidelines for effective leadership in this area. Basic text: *Regeneration Manual*. (Health Connection) (For certification requirements, see Chapter 11.)

Course #4: Principles of Smoking Cessation (Breathe Free™)

Thirty hours of class work are required to complete this course. The revised Breathe Free™

The Plan to Stop Smoking prepares the student to organize and conduct a stop smoking clinic for interested participants. Basic text: *Breathe Free™ Manual*. (The Health Connection)

Course #5: Eight Weeks to Wellness

Motivates participants to make two lifestyle changes they select from the following topics:
Week 1–Developing a Healthy Lifestyle
Week 2–Becoming More Physically Active
Week 3–Low Saturated Fat/Cholesterol
Week 4–Eating Enough Fiber
Week 5–Achieving/Maintaining a Healthy Weight
Week 6–Dealing With Dependencies
Week 7–Coping With Stress
Week 8–Preventive Exams and Safety

Eight Power Point presentations are included in the package available through The Health Connection.

Course #6: Vegetarian Cuisine Instructor (VCI)

The requirements for this course are completed by attending a 30-hour seminar on vegetarian nutrition. Practical ideas for meal planning, menu selection and food preparation are provided for in-reach to new members, updating of regular members and public outreach. Basic text: *Vegetarian Cuisine Instructor Manual*. (The Health Connection)

Course #7: Emergency Care

Must complete CPR and First Aid and hold a current valid card from the American Heart Association, Red Cross, local hospital or other recognized organization.

Course #8: Van Ministry

Participants will lean how to start and successfully run a vital community health ministry in their church or conference.

Course #9: Diabetes Mastery

Participants will learn how to operate a church-or community-based diabetes program. The emphasis will be on lifestyle and other non-drug therapies such as diet, exercise, and group support. (Note: Limited to health professionals).

Lifestyle Certification Record

Level 1: Lifestyle Consultant
Course Title

___ 1. Basic Principles of Health Evangelism . . . . Date: _____

___ 2. Cardiopulmonary Resuscitation (CPR) . . . . Date: _____

___ 3. First Aid . . . . Date: _____

___ 4. Philosophy of Healthy Living . . . . Date: _____

___ 5. Describe equivalent training for any of the above: _____

_____

_____

Level 2: Lifestyle Specialist
Course Title

___ 1. Fitness for Life . . . . Date: _____

___ 2. Stress Management . . . . Date: _____

___ 3. Addiction/Regeneration . . . . .Date: _____

___ 4. Principles of smoking cessation (Breath-Free) . . . . .Date: _____

___ 5. Eight Weeks to Wellness . . . . Date: _____

___ 6. Vegetarian Cuisine Instructor . . . . Date: _____

___ 7. Emergency Care (CPR & First Aid) . . . . .Date: _____

___ 8. Van Ministry . . . . Date: _____

___ 9. Diabetes Mastery . . . . Date: _____

___ 10. Grief Recovery . . . . Date: _____

___ 11. Hydro Therapy (Natural Remedies) .Date: _____

___ 12. Parish Nursing . . . . Date: _____

___ 13. HeartBeat . . . . .Date: _____

Lifestyle Certification Record

Level 3: Lifestyle Trainer

___1. How to Create and Present Great Seminars . . . . Date: _____

Describe Apprenticeship 1:

Location: _____ Number of hours: _____ Date: _____

Evaluated by: _____

Title: _____

Describe Apprenticeship 2:

Location: _____ Number of hours: _____ Date: _____

Evaluated by: _____

Title: _____

Keep a record for your files. You will receive the Lifestyle Certificate in 4 to 6 weeks.

When you have completed all LifeStyle Certification requirements for each level:

1. Sent all documentation of proof of completion to your local Conference Health Ministries Director or to Health Ministries Certification, 5040 Prescott Avenue, Lincoln, NE 68506. Retain a copy for your records.

2. Begin to use the skills that you have acquired. Remember: *If you don't use them, you will lose them!*

Here is a wonderful promise to help keep you focused on the importance of health evangelism. "Is not this the kind of fasting I have chosen; to loose the chains of injustice and untie the cords of the yoke, to set the oppressed free and break every yoke? Is it not to share your food with the hungry and to provide the poor wanderer with shelter-when you see the naked, to clothe him, and not to turn away from your own flesh and blood? Then your light will break forth like the dawn, and your healing will quickly appear" (Isaiah 58:6, 7, 8 NIV).

Course #10:Grief Recovery

This seminar will teach the dynamics of both grief and loss recovery. You will learn the stages of grief, a basic understanding of the process of recovery, how to cope with anger, and how to put your life back together. You will gain the skills to conduct either grief or loss (suicide, death, divorce, etc.) recovery in your church or community.

Course #11: Natural Remedies/Home Health Care

How to strengthen the immune system through the use of natural remedies and treatments. Physiology of disease and why natural remedies are effective. Learn the basics of hydrotherapy, use of charcoal and many other practical home treatments. For current information on this course contact the NAD Health Department at (301) 680-6733.

Course #12:Parish Nursing

(Note this course is limited to registered nurses) Participants will learn how to meet the needs of the whole person in the church and in the community. Participants will learn how to provide advocacy, make referrals, coordinate volunteers and support groups, and interpret the relationship between faith and health facilities.

Course #13: HeartBeat

This seminar teaches the participant to organize a community outreach program that evaluates coronary risk, blood pressure, nutrition profile, exercise profile and other health risk factors. It can be used to generate interest in nutrition cooking schools, smoking cessation plans, weight control programs, physical fitness and stress management seminars. Updated and revised 1996. Basic text: HeartBeat Manual from Pacific Health Education Center, 5300 California Ave., Suite 200, Bakersfield, CA 93309; (805) 633-5300; Fax (805) 633-0108.

It is a significant achievement to become certified as a Lifestyle Specialist. *Congratulations!*

Level 3: Lifestyle Trainer

Purpose of a Lifestyle Trainer

To develop skills to present effective lifestyle seminars.

Requirements

Requirement 1: Complete Level 1 (or the equivalent) and at least one (1) specialty course in Level 2 (or the equivalent). A physician, nurse or other health professional with special training in one of the 13 areas listed under Level 2 certification, who wants to learn how to be a more effective presenter is eligible for Level 3 certification.

Requirement 2: Complete "How to Create and Present Great Seminars" and two apprenticeships.

Make arrangements in advance with the instructor to insure that a certificate of completion will be available.

Lifestyle Training Courses

Course: How to Create and Present Great Seminars

This seminar will teach general preparation and presentation skills to the individual who desires to train others.

Apprenticeship:

The participant will prepare and conduct two seminars under the direction of the conference or NAD Health Ministries director or his/her designate.

Record Keeping

It's important that you keep an accurate record of the certification courses that you have taken and the dates, along with the certificates of completion you receive. The following should be filled out and submitted with your final request for Lifestyle Trainers Certification.

23

Research on Seventh-day Adventists and Health

For years health educators have promoted the healthy lifestyle that God presented to Ellen White. They were convinced it made a difference. But what kind of difference? Researchers at Loma Linda University in the 1950's decided to subject their fellow church members to scientific evaluation to see if this way of life promoted health as it claimed to do.

The story of this research is a fascinating one. Now forty years later, with almost 250 published papers on the subject, the evidence is in. *Yes, living the Adventist Lifestyle does make a difference.* Early reports based on a three year follow-up suggested that there was a 6.7 year difference between Adventist men and California men in general. Later analysis on the Adventist mortality study found that Adventist men live an average of 81.2 years or 7.3 years more than the average California male. Adventist women live an average of 83.9 years—4.4 years more than the average California female.

Vegetarian Adventist men surviving to age 30, Dr. Gary Fraser, principal investigator of the Adventist Health Study and professor of epidemiology and biostatistics at LLU, tells us have a life expectancy of 83.3 years and vegetarian SDA women 95.7 years–a remarkable addition of 9.5 and 6.1 years as compared to the life expectancies of other Californians.

Studies on Adventists in other countries, such as the Netherlands, Norway, and Poland have confirmed these findings. As word of these amazing findings have spread throughout the scientific community through numerous publications, and the presentation of papers at professional meetings, it has impacted fellow researchers and government officials. After one presentation by the late Dr. Roland Phillips, then director of the Adventist Health Study, a scientist commented, "It appears that the best insurance that one can take out today is to follow the lifestyle of Adventists."

In 1980, Sidney Katz, a Canadian official, reviewed the data on the benefits of the Adventist lifestyle. He said, "I've got some advice on how to improve the health of Canadians and, at the same time, lop billions of dollars off our annual health costs. I think we should study the lifestyle of adherents of the Seventh-day Adventist Church and then explore ways and means of persuading the public to emulate the Adventists in at least some ways."

When the U.S. Congress was adopting dietary guidelines for the nation, the Senate Select Committee utilized findings on Adventists, among others, to come up with the guidelines.

Dr. T. Oberlin of Harvard University stated, "Such an increase in life expectancy at these adult ages is greater than all of the gains in life expectancy made in the past 60 years in this country as a result of all the advances in medical skills and knowledge, plus innumerable improvements of the environment in which man lives."

Now, many scientists when discussing the results of Adventist studies, refer to the beneficial effects of the Adventist lifestyle as the "Adventist Advantage."

Even though it has been found that Adventists live healthier and longer, not all Adventists adhere to all of the principles with the same intensity. In fact, in a 1990 survey conducted by Survey Research Services of Loma Linda University, it was found many Adventists had harmful health habits that they wanted to change, such as getting too little exercise (69 percent), drinking too little water (42 percent), coping with too much stress (31 percent), and eating between meals (29 percent).

About 56 percent of the members felt that they were overweight, with about 8 percent of these indicating they were considerably overweight. Unfortunately, only 44 percent of those who believed they were overweight were trying to correct the problem.

Interesting Findings from Research on Adventists

In 1978 Drs. Roland Phillips and Frank Lemon reported:

- Coronary heart disease mortality among California SDAs was 60 percent that of California nonsmokers.
- About 1/3 fewer coronary heart disease deaths occurred in male Adventist vegetarians than in SDA non-vegetarians.
- For every disease looked at, deaths of Adventists were less than what was expected among the general California population.

The figures mean, for example, that for every 100 Californians who died from coronary heart disease, only 55 of a similar-aged SDA control group would die—almost half the number. However, Dr. Fraser warns, "Many of these findings were not confirmed in the later, and methodologically superior Adventist Health Study. Remember that the old study could look at only fatal events–a serious restriction." So we should be cautious about using these familiar older reports.

On November 11, 1986 a headline in the New York Times read, "Adventists Are Gold Mine For Research On Disease." The article by Jane E.

Cause of Death:	Californians	SDA
bronchitis & emphysema	100	32
coronary heart disease	100	55
diabetes	100	55
all cancer	100	59
breast cancer	100	72
lung cancer	100	20
large bowel cancer	100	68
leukemia	100	62

From: Adventist Health Study pamphlet based on Adventist Mortality Study data, Loma Linda University, School of Public Health, 1970.

Brody was based on an interview with Dr. David Snowden, who was the director of the Adventist Health Study at the time. The following are some of the findings that he reported.

- The Adventist study was the first to show a dose-response relationship between eating meat and disease. The more years people are meat-eaters and the more meat they consume each week, the greater is their risk of dying from heart disease and diabetes.
- Consumption of animal products in general is strongly related to an increased risk of prostate cancer but, on the other hand, no link was found to breast cancer in women.
- Exercise seems to protect against fatal coronary heart disease, especially among former smokers and current meat-eaters. But relatively little added benefit from exercise is seen for vegetarians and nonsmokers. (One explanation is that vegetarians and non-smokers may already have such "clean" coronary arteries that no effect is discernible from any further widening of these vessels that may be induced by exercise.)

Epidemiologic Studies of Adventists

Dr. Gary Fraser, the present director of the on-going Adventist Health Study at Loma Linda, summarized the current research on Seventh-day Adventists in his 2001 article in the Autumn issue of Scope, The Loma Linda University Alumni Journal. This article is reprinted in this chapter with permission.

From a statistical point of view, ten years looks pretty good. But individually, when a person is looking at adding one or more hopefully healthy years to his or her life, *that is significant.* In other words, why go for ten years, if with a few lifestyle changes you could live an average of twelve years longer?

The story is told of a boy walking along the beach throwing beached starfish back into the water. Watching for a while, a man finally walked up to him and asked, "Why are you doing that? There are thousands of beached starfish—you can't save them all."

Continued on page 294.

The Adventist lifestyle

WHY IS THE WORLD SO INTERESTED IN THE DIETARY AND OTHER LIFESTYLE CHOICES OF ADVENTISTS?

Many Seventh-day Adventists may not be aware that their lifestyles have been the subject of much discussion and scrutiny by the scientific community for close to half a century.

"Although Adventists have long been convinced of the benefits of their special lifestyle," said Gary E. Fraser, MD, PhD, principal investigator of the Adventist Health Study, in a recent interview, "it was not until the early 1950s that the first scientific studies were conducted to document the validity of this belief."

The Framingham Heart Study, also in its infancy during 1950s, attracted a great deal of attention as medical scientists became increasingly interested in the relationship between dietary fats and blood cholesterol.

"Consequently, Adventists became an attractive group in which to test these theories," Dr. Fraser explains, "particularly those associating diet and the absence of cigarette smoking with risk of both cardiovascular disease and cancer."

Gary E. Fraser, MD, PhD, principal investigator of the Adventist Health Study and professor of epidemiology and biostatistics, stocks up on fruits, vegetables, and nuts which he discovered are protective against coronary heart disease and cancer.

The absence of smoking and alcohol use—two factors which often overshadow the findings with many other epidemiological studies—together with the interest most Adventists have regarding dietary habits, make them an ideal population for such longitudinal studies.

The first large-scale epidemiological study funded by federal sources and conducted at Loma Linda came to be known as the Adventist Mortality Study. Principal investigators Frank Lemon, MD, and Richard T. Walden, MD, sent questionnaires to 47,866 California Adventists who completed the first brief section.

Subsequently, Drs. Lemon and Walden sent American Cancer Society questionnaires to a subset of 27,530 subjects from 1958 to 1965. Of these, 22,940 subjects ages 35 and older were included in the study. Informal follow-ups continued into 1985.

The Adventist Health Study, which began in 1973 with funding from the National Cancer Institute, was led by investigators Roland Phillips, MD, DrPH, and Jan Kuzma, PhD.

From 1973 to 1976, two questionnaires were developed and tested for use in the upcoming study. The first questionnaire, primarily a census instrument, was to be completed by heads of the households. A database of 63,530 California Adventist households was created. Out of 36,805 household responses, 59,081 individuals over the age of 25 were identified.

In 1976, a lifestyle questionnaire was mailed to the same group which had received the census document. Of the 43,537 white non-Hispanic individuals contacted, 34,192 returned the lifestyle questionnaire. Of the 3,475 black subjects receiving the questionnaire, 1,739 individuals responded.

"The study looked at the relationships between diet, cigarette smoking, and risk of cancer among California Adventists," Dr. Fraser points out. "Scientists continued to collect data for both fatal and non-fatal events from this population through 1982, with a subsequent follow-up of deaths only through 1988."

In 1980, Dr. Fraser received funding from the National Heart, Lung, and Blood Institute, and later from the National Institute on Aging, to conduct a variety of demographic studies using the large data bank in place at Loma Linda University.

This group of studies starting in 1973, according to Dr. Fraser, makes up what has become known internationally as the Adventist Health Study.

"We have just received funding to develop a larger cohort study both of black and white Adventists across the United States," Dr. Fraser reports. "This will take advantage of what has already been learned, utilizing new methods and technologies to help answer an increasing list of questions associating diet—or other aspects of lifestyle—with risk of chronic disease."

Dr. Fraser and his colleagues have been notified by the National Institutes of Health that funding for the next phase of the Adventist Health Study has been approved. Over the next four years, 125,000 Seventh-day Adventists will be enrolled through their local churches and asked to fill out a lifestyle questionnaire.

In addition to preparing for the upcoming study, Dr. Fraser is putting together a book that will be published by the Oxford University Press and will chronicle the various studies of Adventists over the years, including those conducted by the Adventist Health Study researchers.

"We're working on the final chapter," Dr. Fraser reveals. "We hope to have the book published within a year."

Design and findings of the Adventist Mortality Study (1958 to 1985)

Drs. Walden and Lemon set about in 1958 to study all California Seventh-day Adventists. Church membership rolls existed but did not include any demographic information—even one's age.

Using the mailing list of one of the weekly Church papers, they mailed five copies of their questionnaire to each household, requesting that the head of the household enroll all Adventist members living there.

Three repeat mailings were sent to those who did not respond. A representative in each of the 341 Adventist churches was also asked to make public announcements during services, as well as distribute additional questionnaires.

With this methodology, 47,866 individuals were enrolled. It soon became evident, however, that some of those registered included inactive or unavailable church members.

"The researchers asked church clerks and pastors to provide an independent count of active members that included 91 percent of the total membership," Dr. Fraser details. "Using this amended count as a denominator, study investigators estimated that 88 percent of active and 'available' members had been enrolled."

Dr. Fraser has been in front of the cameras and microphones a number of times through the years as various findings have come to light and caught the interest of the media. As recent as July 9, 2001, he spoke with reporters regarding findings that California Adventists live longer than their non-Adventist neighbors—close to 10 years longer for Adventist vegetarian men.

Dr. Fraser adds, "This level of participation is quite remarkable for a study of this magnitude, but that's part of what makes the Adventist population such an ideal group for dietary and lifestyle research."

The questionnaire, according to Dr. Fraser, was extremely brief by present standards and asked about gender, date and place of birth, length of Church membership, race, marital status, occupational and residential history, and a general statement regarding personal health.

"The intention was to calculate mortality rates according to levels of some of the above demographic variables," Dr. Fraser suggests. "These were then compared to similar findings for other Californians."

In 1960, 21,380 of the original enrollees, as well as an additional 6,150 Adventists not previously enrolled—all over 29 years of age—volunteered to complete a second four-page questionnaire that this time included diet and many other variables.

With the assistance of E. C. Hammond, MD, who was concurrently conducting his own study of 1 million individuals from the general population known as the American Cancer Society Prospective Study, Drs. Walden and Lemon embarked on this second study of 27,530 Adventists from 198 congregations in California. Volunteers from each congregation were responsible for enrolling 10 to 20 local adult members from five households.

During the period from 1960 to 1965, these volunteers also agreed to report any deaths in their congregations, since a major objective of the study was to report death rates in Adventists, and another was to discover whether Adventists with varying health habits experienced different rates of mortality among themselves.

Church clerks were also asked to help report all fatalities in the church membership between 1958 and 1965, as well as enough information to identify the subjects in California Department of Public Health death records. This enabled Drs. Walden and Lemon and their fellow researchers to determine the immediate and underlying causes of death.

A less formal follow-up from 1966 to 1985 ascertained the vital status of study subjects by computer linkage with the California state death tapes. It was found in a later substudy that 93 percent of the deaths were actually detected by this means. Adjustments were also made for the 3 to 6 percent of deaths estimated to have occurred outside of California.

The Adventist Mortality Study found that, for every 100 California non-Adventist men who died of cancer at a particular age, only 60 California Adventist men died at that same age. Similarly, for every 100 non-Adventist women, 76 Adventist women died at the same age of cancer.

Death from coronary heart disease (CHD) among California Adventist men at

The Adventist lifestyle

a particular age was 34 percent below that of their non-Adventist counterparts; for Adventist women, the number was 2 percent below their non-Adventist neighbors.

The Adventist Health Study: methodology and findings (1974 to 1988)

Beginning in 1974 and continuing into the early 1980s, data was collected through a series of questionnaires that made up what has come to be known as the Adventist Health Study. Drs. Phillips and Kuzma led out in the original study, with Dr. Fraser first becoming involved in 1980 and ultimately taking over as the principal investigator. The data has provided a wealth of findings that have attracted worldwide attention—the most recent being findings shared at a news conference on July 9, 2001.

"What has made the Adventist Health Study so valuable is the inclusion of much greater detail than the Adventist Mortality Study," Dr. Fraser reasons. "Typically, when we consider conducting a major epidemiological study, we have certain questions that we hope to answer; however, our findings often suggest a host of new questions for future studies."

In addition to more extensive lifestyle questions, the main Adventist Health Study questionnaire contained 55 questions regarding the frequency of consumption of certain foods.

"The food frequency method is usually considered the only practical way to assess diet by questionnaire in thousands of subjects," conveys Dr. Fraser. "In the Adventist Health Study, questions simply required subjects to nominate one of eight frequencies of consumption for each of the 55 foods."

---

1. What ONE type of bread do you use most of the time? *Mark only the one type used most frequently.*

White (enriched or unenriched) - - - - - - → ☐
100% whole wheat or whole grain - - - - - → ☐
Sprouted wheat or wheatberry - - - - - - - → ☐
Other (rye, cracked wheat, pumpernickel, soy, etc.) - - - - - - - - - → ☐

2. Mark the box which comes closest to how often you use each food when you are following your usual routine. *Be sure to mark in the correct column and mark "never" if never used.*

a. Eggs (except those used in recipes) - (a)
b. Cheese (except cottage cheese) - - - - (b)
c. Meat, poultry, or fish - - - - - - - - - - - (c)
d. Sweets and desserts - - - - - - - - - - - - (d)

	d	c	b	a
CURRENT USE: Never - - - - - - - - - - - - -	☐	☐	☐	☐
Less than once/month -	☐	☐	☐	☐
1-2 times per month - - -	☐	☐	☐	☐
1-2 times per week - - - -	☐	☐	☐	☐
3-4 times per week - - - -	☐	☐	☐	☐
5-6 times per week - - - -	☐	☐	☐	☐
Once per day - - - - - - - -	☐	☐	☐	☐
More than once/day - - -	☐	☐	☐	☐

3. Mark the box which comes closest to how frequently you NOW use each food or beverage when following your usual routine. *Be sure to mark in the correct column and mark "never" for foods you never use. You should make 11 marks for this page.*

a. Low fat (2%) milk - - - - - - - - - - - - - (a)
b. Nonfat (skim) milk - - - - - - - - - - - - (b)
c. Soymilk - (c)

	c	b	a
CURRENT USE: Never or almost never -	☐	☐	☐
Less than once per week	☐	☐	☐
Several times per week -	☐	☐	☐
Once per day - - - - - - - -	☐	☐	☐
2-3 times per day - - - - -	☐	☐	☐
4-5 times per day - - - - -	☐	☐	☐
Over 5 times per day - -	☐	☐	☐

Above are three examples of questions included in the main Adventist Health Study questionnaire that subjects were asked to complete.

The Adventist lifestyle

Frequencies ranged from "rarely or never" to "more than six times daily" (see examples of questions on page 19).

For most variables in the census and lifestyle questionnaires, the rate of missing data was between 4 and 7 percent. There did not appear to be a higher rate of missing data for "sensitive" variables among Adventists, such as pork consumption, cigarette smoking, or alcohol use.

"Thus, the investigators believe that the population responded as accurately to these variables as any others," states Dr. Fraser. "Nevertheless, with this potential sensitivity in mind, the investigators gave much effort to assuring study subjects of the anonymity of their responses."

The design of the Adventist Health Study also included methodology for measuring both fatal and non-fatal disease events among the study population—an important advance over the original Adventist Mortality Study.

Upon completing the lifestyle questionnaire, the non-Hispanic white population was first followed for six years until December of 1982. All new or incident events of cancer and coronary heart disease were documented. The same population was then followed until 1983 to document fatalities only, as well as obtain death certificates for those who were deceased.

Black Adventists were followed through 1985 for fatalities only, but death certificates were not obtained which would have revealed the cause of death.

From 1976 to 1982, annual questionnaires were sent to the non-Hispanic white population asking whether they had been hospitalized and, if so, where. The response rate to the annual questionnaires consistently exceeded 90 percent. The final and most important contact in early 1993 yielded a response rate of 99.5 percent.

Adventist Health Study investigators used information from the annual questionnaires to guide field representatives who collected details of the hospitalizations, visiting each California hospital named by any subject and reviewing each medical chart.

Any mention of cancer, tumor, neoplasm, or malignancy, as well as myocardial infarction (heart attack), coronary thrombosis, cardiac arrest, myocardial ischemia, coronary insufficiency, coronary angiography, or heart catheterization resulted in portions of the charts, medical and nursing history, and electrocardiographs being microfilmed, and cardiac enzyme results being abstracted to coding forms.

"Field representatives visited 698 hospitals in California," Dr. Fraser attests. "We also contacted 960 out-of-state hospitals by mail for those study participants hospitalized outside California who had moved or were on vacation."

Fatal events which occurred outside the hospital were found through local church records, responses to a questionnaire by next of kin, and by computerized matching with the California state death tapes.

"As 15 percent or so of our population moved out of state," Dr. Fraser adds, "computerized matching with the National Death Index was also used to find deaths out of state beginning in 1979, when this service became available."

The research methodology of both the Adventist Mortality Study and Adventist Health Study have withstood the scrutiny of numerous peer-reviewed journals. To date, various findings from the mortality study have been published in 39 peer-reviewed journals, while the number of similar publications for the Adventist Health Study stands at 43.

What are the key findings of the Adventist Health Study? For coronary heart disease, the data for Adventists was compared with data from a study of non-Adventists conducted at Stanford University from 1975 to 1985—remarkably concurrent with the Adventist Health Study.

"We found that Adventists had one half the risk of coronary heart disease as their Stanford study counterparts," Dr. Fraser confirms. "We only compared data for subjects up to the age of 75 because that was the upper age limit for data collected by the Stanford study."

It was also found that Adventists ages 60 or younger experienced a 60 to 70 percent reduction in risk, while those over 60 years of age experienced a 20 to 30 percent risk reduction.

"To be sure that our findings were credible," Dr. Fraser grants, "we looked at traditional risk factors in relation to heart disease rates, factors such as exercise, obesity, high blood pressure, and diabetes—the findings for Adventists were consistent with those of other population studies."

Findings relating to diet—the "strength of the study" in Dr. Fraser's opinion—showed that vegetarian Adventists had a

Cancer site	Standardized incidence ratio	95% confidence interval
Colon	0.78	0.62–0.98
Stomach	0.66	0.39–1.12
Bladder	0.55	0.36–0.86
Lymphoma	1.62	1.14–2.31
Leukemia	0.79	0.48–1.29
Lung	0.30	0.19–0.47
Pancreas*	0.68	0.41–1.14
Breast	0.87	0.68–1.12
Ovary*	1.14	0.63–2.07
Uterus*	1.33	0.86–2.04
Prostate*	1.12	0.90–1.39
All smoking related	0.46	0.36–0.58
All sites	0.77	0.70–0.85

Invasive only

A recent comparison of cancer incidence in California Adventists 75 years of age and older with similar-aged subjects from the Los Angeles County and Oakland Bay Area tumor registries (1976 to 1982) yielded the findings above, showing that in a number of cases California Adventists enjoyed protection from certain cancers.

The Adventist lifestyle

David Shavlik, MSPH, demonstrates how questionnaires from a projected 125,000 new study subjects will be fed through the NCS 5000i, a scanner/reader manufactured by National Computer Systems. The first phase of the new Adventist Health Study will take four years to complete and will involve Adventists across the United States.

significantly lower risk for both fatal and nonfatal heart attacks as compared to nonvegetarian Adventists. The protection was greater for men, with nonvegetarians having twice the risk. For women, similar risks were evident for nonvegetarian young and middle-age subjects.

In 1992, the "Nut Study" garnered worldwide media attention when the findings were published in the *Archives of Internal Medicine*. Dr. Fraser and his colleagues discovered a relationship between consuming nuts five or more times a week and having half the risk for a fatal or nonfatal heart attack—evident for both men and women. This has subsequently been confirmed by several large studies of non-Adventists.

Whole grain bread versus white bread provided approximately a 25 percent reduction in the risk of a fatal or nonfatal heart attack. Consumption of red meat, in particular, greatly increased the risk of certain cancers according to Dr. Fraser.

"We found that Adventists who avoided eating meat had 50 to 60 percent the risk of developing colon cancer as their meat-eating counterparts," notes Dr. Fraser. "Meat eaters, when they added beans to their diet, experienced some protection from colon cancer due to the beans."

Dr. Fraser and his fellow researchers were careful to factor in all of the other possible reasons for their findings, probably pointing to meat consumption alone as the culprit. For prostate cancer, vegetarian California Adventists had

approximately 50 percent of the risk. For ovarian cancer, meat eaters were two times more at risk. Meat eaters were also at a 50 percent higher risk of developing bladder cancer.

On the flip side, fruit was shown to be protective against lung, prostate, ovarian, and pancreatic cancers, with a reduced risk of up to 75 percent.

Tomatoes were protective against both prostate and ovarian cancer, providing a 43 percent risk reduction for prostate and a 60 percent reduced risk for ovarian.

Soy milk, consumed more than once a day, provided up to an 80 percent reduction in the risk for prostate cancer.

Longevity study

As recent as July 9, 2001, findings from the Adventist Health Study were still making the news.

In an article, titled "Ten years of life: is it a matter of choice?" and published in the July 9 issue of the *Archives of Internal Medicine*, Dr. Fraser and his research team were able to establish a connection between certain lifestyle characteristics and increased life expectancy.

"California Adventists appear to be the longest-lived population that has yet been described in a formal way," Dr. Fraser said during a news conference held on the Loma Linda University campus. "The expected ages at death for those already surviving to age 30 is 81.2 years in men and 83.9 years in women." He continued, "This corresponds to an extra 7.3 years in

men and 4.4 years in women, when compared to other Californians."

Vegetarian Adventist men surviving to age 30, observes Dr. Fraser, have a life expectancy of 83.3 years and vegetarian women 85.7 years—a remarkable addition of 9.5 and 6.1 years respectively as compared to the life expectancies of other Californians.

"Our results, looking at five common behaviors individually or all together, directly estimate effects on life expectancy," he indicates. The behavioral factors included a vegetarian diet, eating a handful of nuts five or more days a week, vigorous and regular exercise, smoking history, and body mass (based on body mass index or BMI).

"Although the higher risk combination was quite uncommon in Adventists," Dr. Fraser clarifies, "it is much more common in the general population, as most people are nonvegetarian, eat nuts infrequently, and obesity is very common."

Each factor—being vegetarian, a nonsmoker, regular exerciser, nut eater, and non-obese—adds between 1.25 and 2.75 years of life, with nut consumption and exercise having slightly stronger effects.

"Our results strongly suggest that there is real potential for other Americans to also extend their life expectancy by 5 to 10 years with relatively simple behavioral choices," Dr. Fraser concludes.

The next phase of research

The National Institutes of Health has given word that it will fund the next phase of the Adventist Health Study. Pilot studies are already underway to test the newest questionnaire.

Plans have been set to enroll 125,000 Seventh-day Adventists across the United States over the next four years.

A number of questions raised by the previous studies will be covered in this latest venture.

"I think we've proven the benefits of the Adventist lifestyle," Dr. Fraser insists. "Perhaps some of our neighbors can benefit from what we've learned."

This article is a reprint used with permission, *Scope Magazine*, Autumn, 2001.

"No," said the boy, "But what I do will make a difference to this one!"

Helping others live up to all the knowledge we have been given about the health message will make a difference to individuals. And it's our job to share this message and give them a chance to live longer—and healthier.

Bibliography of Health-related Studies Among Seventh-day Adventists.

The findings from research on Adventists are fascinating and convincing— *There is an Adventist Advantage.*

Although much can be learned by reading a summary of the research findings as given in this chapter, reading the original sources can be extremely instructive.

As of May 24, 2001 the bibliography of health-related research studies among Seventh-day Adventists includes 302 articles. This bibliography is being continually updated at the Center for Health Research (CHR) at the Loma Linda University School of Public Health. For your convenience, the Center for Health Research has given permission for this list to be published here. To receive an up-dated list in the future, you can either write to the Center for Health Research, Loma Linda University, Loma Linda, CA 92350 or call: (909) 824-4753.

BIBLIOGRAPHY OF HEALTH-RELATED RESEARCH STUDIES AMONG SEVENTH-DAY ADVENTISTS UPDATED: May 24, 2001

1. Hardinge MG, Stare FJ: Nutritional studies of vegetarians. I. Nutritional, physical, and laboratory studies. Am J Clin Nutr 1954; 2:73-82.
2. Hardinge MG, Stare FJ: Nutritional studies of vegetarians. II. Dietary and serum levels of cholesterol. Am J Clin Nutr 1954; 2:83-88.
3. Hardinge MG, Chambers AC, Crooks H, Stare FJ: Nutritional studies of vegetarians. III. Dietary levels of fiber. Am J Clin Nutr 1958; 6:523-525.
4. Wynder EL, Lemon FR: Cancer, coronary artery disease, and smoking: A preliminary report on differences in incidence between Seventh-day Adventists and others. Calif Med 1958; 89:267-272.
5. Downs RA, Dunn MM, Richie EL: Report of dental findings of Seventh-day Adventists as compared to comparable students in other schools. Bull Amer Assoc Pub Health Dent 1958; 18:19-21.

6. Wynder EL, Lemon FR, Bross IJ: Cancer and coronary artery disease among Seventh-day Adventists. Cancer 1959; 12:1016-1028.
7. Donnelly CJ: A comparative study of caries experience in Adventists and other children. Public Health Rep 1961; 76:209-212.
8. Hardinge MG, Crooks H, Stare FJ: Nutritional studies of vegetarians. IV. Dietary fatty acids and serum cholesterol levels. Am J Clin Nutr 1962; 10:516-524.
9. Dysinger PW, Lemon FR, Crenshaw GL, Walden RT: Pulmonary emphysema in a non-smoking population. Dis Chest 1963; 43:17-2
10. 10. Larsson E, Webb AT: Cancer survey: Experiences in mass screening of cervical smears. Obstet Gynecol 1963; 22:630-635.
11. Hardinge MG, Crooks H. Non-Flesh Dietaries. I. Historical Background. J Am Dietet Assoc 1963; 43:545-9.
12. Hardinge MG, Crooks H. Non-Flesh Dietaries. II. Scientific Literature. J Am Dietet Assoc 1963; 43:550-8.
13. Hardinge MG, Crooks H. Non-Flesh Dietaries. III. Adequate and Inadequate. J Am Dietet Assoc 1963; 45:537-42.
14. Walden RT, Shaefer LE, Lemon FR, Sunshine A, Wynder EL: Effect of environment on the serum cholesterol-triglyceride distribution among Seventh-day Adventists. Am J Med 1964; 36:269-276.
15. Lemon FR, Walden RT, Woods RW: Cancer of the lung and mouth in Seventh-day Adventists: A preliminary report on a population study. Cancer 1964; 17:486-497.
16. Wynder EL, Lemon FR, Mantel N: Epidemiology of persistent cough. Am Rev Resp Dis 1965; 91:679-700.
17. Hardinge MG, Crooks H, Stare FJ: Nutritional studies of vegetarians. V. Proteins and essential amino acids. J Am Diet Assoc 1966; 48:25-28.
18. Lemon FR, Walden RT: Death from respiratory system disease among Seventh-day Adventist men. JAMA 1966; 198-117-126.
19. Glass RL, Hayden J: Dental Caries in Seventh-day Adventist Children. J Dent Child 1966; 33:22-23.
20. Holmes CB, Quade D, Collier D. Comparative study of nine variables for Seventh-day Adventist and non-Adventist teenagers. J Dent Res1967;46(4):650-5.

21. Marsh AG, Ford DL, Christensen DK. Metabolic Response of Adolescent Girls to a Lacto-Ovo-Vegetarian Diet. J Am Diet Assn 1967; 51:441-6.

22. Mozar HN, Farag SA, Andren HE, Peters JR: The mental health of Seventh-day Adventists. Med Arts Sci 1967; 21:59-66.

23. West RO, Hayes OB: Diet and serum cholesterol levels: A comparison between vegetarians and nonvegetarians in a Seventh-day Adventist group. Am J Clin Nutr 1968; 21:853-862.

24. Amundsen W. Experience of the Seventh-day Adventist Church in North America. Am Ann Deaf 1968;113(4):896-7.

25. Lemon FR, Kuzma JW: A biologic cost of smoking: Decreased life expectancy. Arch Environ Health 1969; 18:950-955.

26. Cohen CA, Hudson AR, Clausen JL, Knelson JH: Respiratory symptoms, spirometry, and oxidant air pollution in nonsmoking adults. Am Rev Respir Dis 1972; 105:251-261.

27. Starr P. Hypercholesterolemia in School Children: A Preliminary Report. Amer J Clin Path 1971;56:515-22.

28. Dysinger PW: Traffic accidents and human ecology. Med Arts and Sciences 1972; 26:27-41.

29. Kuzma JW, Dysinger PW, Strutz P, Abbey D: Nonfatal traffic accidents in relation to biographical, psychological, and religious factors. Accid Anal Prev 1973; 5:55-65.

30. Armstrong BK, Davis RE, Nicol DJ, Van Merwyk AJ, Larwood CJ: Hematological, vitamin B12, and folate studies on Seventh-day Adventist vegetarians. Am J Clin Nutr 1974; 27:712-718.

31. Phillips RL: Role of lifestyle and dietary habits in risk of cancer among Seventh-day Adventists. Cancer Res 1975; 35(Suppl):3513-3522.

32. Ruys J, Hickie JB: Serum cholesterol and triglyceride levels in Australian adolescent vegetarians. Br Med J 1976; 2:87.

33. Phillips RL, Kuzma JW: Estimating major nutrient intake from self-administered food frequency questionnaires. (Abstract) Am J Epidemiol 1976; 104:354-355.

34. Taylor CB, Allen ES, Mikkelson B, Ho K: Serum cholesterol levels of Seventh-day Adventists. Arterial Wall 1976; 3:175-179.

35. Walker AR. Colon cancer and diet, with special reference to intakes of fat and fiber. Am J Clin Nutr 1976;29(12): 1417-26.

36. Phillips RL, Kuzma JW: Rationale and method for an epidemiologic study of cancer among Seventh-day Adventists. Natl Cancer Inst Monogr 1977; 47:107-112.

37. Armstrong B, Van Merwyk AJ, Coates H: Blood pressure in Seventh-day Adventist vegetarians. Am J Epidemiol 1977; 105:444-449.

38. Goldberg MJ, Smith JW, Nichols RL: Comparison of the fecal microflora of Seventh-day Adventists with individuals consuming a general diet: Implications concerning colonic carcinoma. Ann Surg 1977; 186:97-100.

39. Finegold SM, Sutter VL, Sugihara PT, Elder HA, Lehmann SM, Phillips RL: Fecal microbial flora in Seventh-day Adventist populations and control subjects. Am J Clin Nutr 1977; 30:1781-1792.

40. Phillips RL, Lemon FR, Beeson WL, Kuzma JW: Coronary heart disease mortality among Seventh-day Adventists with differing dietary habits: A preliminary report. Am J Clin Nutr 1978; 32(Suppl):S191-S198.

41. MacDonald IA, Webb GR, Mahony DE: Fecal hydroxysteroid dehydrogenase activities in vegetarian Seventh-day Adventists, control subjects, and bowel cancer patients. Am J Clin Nutr 1978; 31(Suppl):S233-S238.

42. Finegold SM, Sutter VL: Fecal flora in different populations, with special reference to diet. Am J Clin Nutr 1978; 31(Suppl):S116-S122.

43. Simons LA, Gibson JC, Paino C, Hosking M, Bullock J, Trim J: The influence of a wide range of absorbed cholesterol on plasma cholesterol levels in man. Am J Clin Nutr 1978; 31:1334-1339.

44. Trahms CM, Larson LD, Worthington BS (int. by Monsen ER): Dietary intakes and growth of Seventh-day Adventist preschool children. (Abstract) Am J Clin Nutr 1978; 31:720.

45. Webster IW, Rawson GK: Health status of Seventh-day Adventists. Med J Aust 1979; 1:417-420.

46. Berkel J: The Clean Life: Some Aspects of Nutritional and Health Status of Seventh-day Adventists in the Netherlands. Amsterdam, Netherlands, 1979, Drukkerij Insulinde.

47. Smith S, Shultz T, Ross J, Leklem J: Nutrition and cancer attitudes and knowledge of Seventh-day Adventists. (Abstract) Fed Proc 1979; 38:713.

48. Enstrom JE: Cancer mortality among low-risk populations. CA--A Cancer Journal for Clinicians 1979; 29:352-361.

49. Armstrong B, Clarke H, Martin C, Ward W, Norman N, Masarei J: Urinary sodium and blood pressure in vegetarians. Am J Clin Nutr 1979;32:2472-6.

50. Simons L, Gibson J, Jones A, Bain, D: Health Status of Seventh-day Adventists. (Letter to the Editor) The Med J of Australia 1979; 2:148.

51. Bachrach S, Fisher J, Parks JS. An outbreak of vitamin D deficiency rickets in a susceptible population. Pediatrics 1979;64(6):871-7.

52. Gori GB. Dietary and nutritional implications in the multifactorial etiology of certain prevalent human cancers. Cancer 1979;43(5 Suppl):2151-61.

53. Marsh AG, Sanchez TV, Mickelsen O, Keiser J, Mayor G: Cortical bone density of adult lacto-ovo-vegetarian and omnivorous women. J Am Diet Assoc 1980; 76:148-151.

54. Phillips RL: Cancer among Seventh-day Adventists. J Environ Pathol Toxicol 1980; 3:157-169.

55. Phillips RL, Kuzma JW, Lotz TM: Cancer mortality among comparable members versus non-members of the Seventh-day Adventist church. In: Cancer Incidence in Defined Populations (Banbury Report 4; Cairns J, Lyon JL, Skolnick M, eds). New York, 1980, Cold Spring Harbor Laboratory. pp. 93-108.

56. Phillips RL, Garfinkel L, Kuzma JW, Beeson WL, Lotz TL, Brin B: Mortality among California Seventh-day Adventists for selected cancer sites. JNCI 1980; 65:1097-1107.

57. Phillips RL, Kuzma JW, Beeson WL, Lotz T: Influence of selection versus lifestyle on risk of fatal cancer and cardiovascular disease among Seventh-day Adventists. Am J Epidemiol 1980; 112:296-314.

58. Reddy BS, Sharma C, Darby L, Laakso K, Wynder EL: Metabolic epidemiology of large bowel cancer. Fecal mutagens in high- and low-risk population for colon cancer: A preliminary report. Mutat Res 1980; 72:511-522.

59. Reddy BS, Sharma C, Wynder E: Fecal factors which modify the formation of fecal co-mutagens in high- and low-risk population for colon cancer. Cancer Letters 1980; 10:123-132.

60. Kondo AT: Belief systems and health status. Ph.D. Dissertation, University of Texas at Galveston, 1980. (Available from University Microfilms International, Ann Arbor, Michigan).

61. Harris RD, Phillips RL, Williams PM, Kuzma JW, Fraser GE: The child-adolescent blood pressure study: I. Distribution of blood pressure levels in Seventh-day Adventist (SDA) and non-SDA children. Am J Public Health 1981; 71:1342-1349.

62. Fraser GE, Swannell RJ: Diet and serum cholesterol in Seventh-day Adventists: A cross-sectional study showing significant relationships. J Chron Dis 1981; 34:487-501.

63. Insel PM, Fraser GE, Phillips RL, Williams PM: Psychosocial factors and blood pressure in children. J Psychosom Res 1981; 25:505-511.

64. Kuzma JW, Beeson WL: The relationship of lifestyle characteristics to mortality among California Seventh-day Adventists. Proceedings of the 19th National Meeting of the Public Health Conference on Records and Statistics, DHHS Publication No. (PHS) 81-1214, 1981.

65. Waaler H, Hjort PF: Hoyere levealder hos norske adventister 1960-1977: Et budskap om livsstil og helse? Tidsskr Nor Laegeforen 101:623-627, 1981. (Translated to English: Low mortality among Norwegian Seventh-day Adven-tists 1960-1977: A message on lifestyle and health?). ct

66. Nestel PJ, Billington T, Smith B. Low Density and High Density Lipoprotein Kinetics and Sterol Balance in Vegetarians. Metabolism 1981; 30:941-5.

67. Shultz TD: Comparative nutrient intake and biochemical interrelationships among healthy vegetarian and non-vegetarian Seventh-day Adventists, nonvegetarians, and hormone-dependent cancer subjects. Diss Abstr Int 1981; 41:4068-B.

68. Fraser GE, Jacobs DR Jr, Anderson JT, Foster N, Palta M, Blackburn H: The effect of various vegetable supplements on serum cholesterol. Am J Clin Nutr 1981; 34:1272-1277.

69. Sanchez A, Kissinger DG, Phillips RL: A hypothesis on the etiological role of diet on age of menarche. Med Hypothesis 1981; 7:1339-1345.

70. Armstrong BK, Brown JB, Clarke HT, Crooke DK, Hahnel R, Masarei JR, Ratajczak T: Diet and reproductive hormones: A study of vegetarian and nonvegetarian postmenopausal women. JNCI 1981; 67:761-767.

71. Shultz TD, Leklem JE: Urinary 4-pyridoxic acid, urinary vitamin B6 and plasma pyridoxal phosphate as measures of vitamin B6 status and dietary intake in adults. In: Methods in Vitamin B6 Nutrition: Analysis and Status Assessment (Leklem JE, Reynolds RD, eds). New York, 1981, Plenum Press. pp 297-320.

72. Editorial: Health and longevity among Seventh-day Adventists. Sth African Med J 1981; 59:925.

73. Anderson BM, Gibson RS, Sabry JH: The iron and zinc status of long-term vegetarian women. Am J Clin Nutr 1981; 34:1042-1048.

74. Gray GE, Williams P, Gerkins V, Brown JB, Armstrong B, Phillips RL, Casagrande JT, Pike MC, Henderson BE: Diet and hormone levels in Seventh-day Adventist girls. Prev Med 1982; 11:103-107.

75. Snowdon DA, Phillips RL, Kuzma JW: Age at baptism into the Seventh-day Adventist Church and risk of death due to ischemic heart disease -A preliminary report. In: Environmental Effects on Maturation (Banbury Report No.11; Hunt VR, Smith MK, Worth D, eds). New York, 1982, Cold Spring Harbor Laboratory. pp 465-472.

76. Turjman N, Guidry C, Jaeger B, Mendeloff AI, Calkins B, Phillips RL, Nair PP: Fecal bile-acids and neutral sterols in Seventh-day Adventists and the general population in California. In: Colon and Nutrition (Falk Symposium 32; Kasper H, Goebell H, eds). Lancaster, England, 1982, MTP Press, Ltd. pp 291-297.

77. Rouse IL, Armstrong BK, Beilin LJ: Vegetarian diet, lifestyle and blood pressure in two religious populations. Clin Exp Pharmacol Physiol 1982;9:327-30.

78. Ferguson LR, Alley PG: Faecal mutagens from population groups within New Zealand at different risk of colo rectal cancer. In: Mutagens in Our Environment (Sorsa M, Vainio H, eds). New York, 1982, Alan R. Liss, Inc. pp 423-429.

79. Nnakwe N, Kies C, Fox HM: Calcium and phosphorus utilization by omnivores and vegetarians. Proceedings of Nebraska Academy of Sciences and Affiliated Societies 1982; 92:29.

80. Miller AB. Risk factors from geographic epidemiology for gastrointestinal cancer. Cancer 1982;50(11 Suppl):2533-40.

81. Fraser GE, Phillips RL, Harris R: Physical fitness and blood pressure in school children. Circulation 1983; 67:405-412.

82. Shultz TD, Leklem JE: Selenium status of vegetarians, nonvegetarians, and hormone-dependent cancer subjects. Am J Clin Nutr 1983; 37:114-118.

83. McEndree LS, Kies CV, Fox HM: Iron intake and iron nutritional status of lacto-ovo-vegetarian and omnivore students eating in a lacto-ovo-vegetarian food service. Nutr Rep Int 1983; 27:199-206.

84. Marsh AG, Sanchez TV, Chaffee FL, Mayor GH, Mickelsen O: Bone mineral mass in adult lacto-ovo-vegetarian and omnivorous males. Am J Clin Nutr 1983; 37:453-456.

85. Phillips RL, Snowdon DA: The association of meat and coffee with cancers of the large bowel, breast, and prostate among Seventh-day Adventists--Preliminary results. Cancer Research 1983; 43(Suppl):2403S-2408S.

86. Jensen OM: Cancer risk among Danish male Seventh-day Adventists and other temperance society members. JNCI 1983; 70:1011-1014.

87. Rouse IL, Armstrong BK, Beilin LJ: The relationship of blood pressure to diet and lifestyle in two religious groups. J Hypertens 1983; 1:65-71.

88. Phillips RL, Snowdon DA, Brin BN: Cancer in vegetarians. In: Environmental Aspects of Cancer--The Role of Macro and Micro Components of Foods (Wynder EL, Leveille GA, Weisburger JH, Livingston EG, eds). Westport, Connecticut, 1983, Food and Nutrition Press. pp 53-72.

89. Shultz RD, Leklem JE: Nutrient intake and hormonal status of premenopausal vegetarian Seventh-day Adventists and premenopausal non-vegetarians. Nutrition and Cancer 1983; 4:247-259.

90. Snowdon DA: Epidemiology of aging: Seventh-day Adventists--A bellwether for future progress. In: Intervention in the Aging Process (Regelson W, Sinex FM, eds). New York 1983, Alan R. Liss. pp 141-149.

91. Shultz TD, Leklem JE: Dietary status of Seventh-day Adventists and nonvegetarians. J Am Diet Assoc 1983; 83:27-33.

92. Berkel J, deWaard F: Mortality pattern and life expectancy of Seventh-day Adventists in the Netherlands. Int J Epidemiol 1983; 12:455-459.

93. Semmens JB, Rouse IL, Beilin LJ, Masarei JRL: Relationship of plasma HDL-cholesterol to testosterone, estradiol, and sex-hormone-binding globulin levels in men and women. Metabolism 1983; 32:428-432.

94. Semmens JB, Rouse IL, Beilin LJ, Masarei JRL: Relationships between age, body weight, physical fitness, and sex-hormone-binding globulin capacity. Clin Chim Acta 1983; 133:295-300.

95. Jedrychowski W, Tobiasz-Adamczyk B, Olma A, Gradzikiewics P: Porownani parametrow trwania zycia w grupie czlonkow Kosciola Adwen-tystow Dnia Siodmego i w populacji ogolnej.(A comparison of life duration parameters in a group of Adventist Church followers and the general population). Polski Tygodnik Lekarski 1983; 32:14-17. 96. Abu-Assal M, Craig WJ. The Zinc Status of Pregnant Vegetarian Women. Nutr Rep Int 29 (2): 485-494, 1984.

96. Davidson L, Vandongen R, Rouse IL, Beilin LJ, Tunney A: Sex-related differences in resting and stimulated plasma noradrenaline and adrenaline. Clin Science 1983; 67:347-352.

97. Bing H, Frentzel-Beyme R. Sch6tzt die Lebensweise von Vegetariern vor einigen Erkrankungen? (Are Vegetarians protected from some Diseases by their Diet?). Akt ErnEhr 1983; 8:187-191.

98. Rouse IL, Beilin LJ, Armstrong BK, Vando-gen R: Vegetarian diet, blood pressure and cardiovascular risk. Aust NZ J Med 1984; 14:439-43.

99. Masarei JRL, Rouse IL, Lynch WJ, Robertson K, Vandongen R, Beilin LJ: Vegetarian diets, lipids and cardiovascular risk. Aust NZ J Med 1983; 14:400-404.

100. Shultz TD, Leklem JE: Vitamin B6 status of Seventh-day Adventist vegetarians, nonvegetarians, and hormone dependent cancer subjects. (Abstract) Presented at Federation of the American Society for Experimental Biology Conference, 1984. 102. Cooper R, Allen A, Goldberg R, Trevisan M, Van Horn L, Liu K, Steinhaver M, Rubenstein A, Stamler J: Seventh-day Adventist adolescents--lifestyle patterns and cardiovascular risk factors. West J Med 1984; 140:471-477.

101. Zollinger TW, Phillips RL, Kuzma JW: Breast cancer survival rates among Seventh-day Adventists and non-Seventh-day Adventists. Am J Epidemiol 1984; 119:503-509.

102. Kahn HA, Phillips RL, Snowdon DA, Choi W: Association between reported diet and all-cause mortality. Twenty-one-year follow-up on 27,530 adult Seventh-day Adventists. Am J Epidemiol 1984; 119:775-787.

103. Snowdon DA, Phillips RL: Coffee consumption and risk of fatal cancers. Am J Public Health 1984; 74:820-823.

104. Snowdon DA, Phillips RL, Choi W. Diet, obesity and risk of fatal prostate cancer. Am J Epidemiol 1984; 120:244-250.

105. Calkins BM, Whittaker DJ, Rider AA, Turjman N. Diet, nutrition intake, and metabolism in populations at high and low risk for colon cancer. Population: demographic and anthropometric characteristics. Am J Clin Nutr 1984; 40(Suppl):887-895.

106. Calkins BM, Whittaker DJ, Nair PP, Rider AA, Turjman N. Diet, nutrition intake, and metabolism in populations at high and low risk for colon cancer. Am J Clin Nutr 1984;40(Suppl):896-905.

107. Rider AA, Calkins BM, Arthur RS, Nair PP: Diet, nutrition intake, and metabolism in populations at high and low risk for colon cancer. Concordance of nutrient information obtained by different methods. Am J Clin Nutr 1984; 40(Suppl):906-913.

108. Rider AA, Arthur RS, Calkins BM: Diet, nutrition intake, and metabolism in populations at high and low risk for colon cancer. Laboratory analysis of 3-day composite of food samples. Am J Clin Nutr 1984; 40(Suppl):914-916.

109. Rider AA, Arthur RS, Calkins BM, Nair PP: Diet, nutrition intake, and metabolism in populations at high and low risk for colon cancer. Selected biochemical parameters in blood and urine. Am J Clin Nutr 1984; 40(Suppl):917-920.

110. Kritchevsky D, Tepper SA, Goodman G: Diet, nutrition intake, and metabolism in populations at high and low risk for colon cancer. Relationship of diet to serum lipids. Am J Clin Nutr 1984; 40(Suppl):921-926.

111. Nair PP, Turjman N, Kessie G, Calkins B, Goodman GT, Davidovitz H, Nimmagadda G: Diet, nutrition intake, and metabolism in populations at high and low risk for colon cancer. Dietary cholesterol, B-sitosterol, and stigmasterol. Am J Clin Nutr 1984; 40(Suppl):927-930.

112. Nair PP, Turjman N, Goodman GI, Guidry C, Calkins BM: Diet, nutrition intake, and metabolism in populations at high and low risk for colon cancer. Metabolism of neutral sterols. Am J Clin Nutr 1984; 40(Suppl):931-936.

113. Turjman N, Goodman GT, Jaeger B, Nair PP: Diet, nutrition intake, and metabolism in populations at high and low risk for colon cancer. Metabolism of bile acids. Am J Clin Nutr 1984; 40(Suppl):937-941.

114. Stich HF, Hornby AP, Dunn BP. The effect of dietary factors on Nitrosorpoline levels in human urine. Int J Cancer 1984; 33:625-8.

115. Kurup PA, Jayakumari N, Indira M, Kurup GM, Vargheese T, Mathew A, Goodman GT, Calkins BM, Kessie G, Turjman N, Nair PP: Diet, nutrition intake, and metabolism in populations at high and low risk for colon cancer. Composition, intake and excretion of fiber constituents. Am J Clin Nutr 1984; 40(Suppl): 942-6.

116. Tepper SA, Goodman GT, Kritchevsky D: Diet, nutrition intake, and metabolism in populations at high and low risk for colon cancer. Binding of bile salts to dietary residues. Am J Clin Nutr 1984; 40(Suppl):947-8.

117. Goodman GT, Davidovitz H, Tepper SA, Kritchevsky D: Diet, nutrition intake, and metabolism in populations at high and low risk for colon cancer. Comparison of serum hexoseaminidase levels. Am J Clin Nutr 1984; 40(Suppl):949-951.

118. Snowdon DA, Phillips RL, Fraser GE: Meat consumption and fatal ischemic heart disease. Prev Med 1984; 13:490-500.

119. Howden GF: The cariostatic effect of betel nut chewing. Papua New Guinea Med J 1984; 27:123-131.

120. Nnakwe N, Kies C, McEndree L: Calcium and phosphorus nutritional status of lacto-ovo-vegetarian and omnivore students consuming meals in a lacto-ovo-vegetarian food service. Nut Rep Intl 1984;29:365-9.

121. Snowdon DA, Sumbureru D, Kuzma JW: Bereavement and risk of death from major causes among Seventh-day Adventists. (Abstract) Am J Epidemiol 1984; 120:480.

122. Hodgkin JE, Abbey DE, Euler G, Magie AR. COPD prevalence in nonsmokers in high and low photo-chemical air pollution areas. Chest 1984;86:830-8.

123. Modeste NN, Abbey DE, Hopp JW: Hypertension in a Caribbean population. Intl Quarterly of Commun Health Education 1984-85; 5:203-211.

124. Spuehler J, Howie B, Shultz TD: Dietary nutrients and plasma and urinary hormone levels in premenopausal Seventh-day Adventist (SDA) vegetarians. (Abstract) Federation Proc. 1985;44:768.

125. Jedrychowski W, Tobiasz-Adamczyk B, Olma A, Gradzikiewicz P: Survival rates among Seventh-day Adventists compared with the general population in Poland. Scand J Soc Med 1985; 23:49-52.

126. Halvorsen BA, Svendsen B: Lavere dodelighet av kreft og hjerte- og karsykdommer hos adventister. Tidsskr Nor Laegeforen 1985; 24:1620-1625.

127. Phillips RL, Snowdon DA: Dietary relationships with fatal colo-rectal cancer among Seventh-day Adventists. J Natl Ca Instit 1985; 74:307-317.

128. Snowdon DA, Phillips RL: Does a vegetarian diet reduce the occurrence of diabetes? Am J Public Health 1985; 75:507-512.

129. Lipkin M, Uehara K, Winawer S, Sanchez A, Bauer C, Phillips R, Lynch HT, Blattner WA, Fraumeni JF: Seventh-day Adventist vegetarians have a quiescent proliferative activity in colonic mucosa. Cancer Letter 1985; 26:139-144.

130. Howie BJ, Shultz TD: Dietary and hormonal interrelationships among vegetarian Seventh-day Adventist and nonvegetarian men. Am J Clin Nutr 1985; 42:127-134.

131. Mack TM, Berkel J, Bernstein L, Mack W: Religion and Cancer in Los Angeles County. Natl Ca Institute Monograph 1985; 69:235-245.

132. Repace JL, Lowrey AH: A quantitative estimate of non-smokers' lung cancer risk from passive smoking. Environmental International 1985;11:3-22.

133. Snowdon DA: Diet and ovarian cancer. Letter to the Editor. JAMA 1985; 254:356-357.

134. Register UD: The Seventh-day Adventist diet and lifestyle and the risk of major degene-rative disease. In: Frontiers in Longevity Research--Applications of Nutritional and Other Discoveries in the Prevention of the Age-Related Disorders (Morin RJ, ed). Springfield, Illinois, 1985, Charles C. Thomas. pp 74-82.

135. Shultz TD, Leklem JE. Supplementation and Vitamin B-6 Metabolism. In: Current Topics in Nutrition and Disease. 1985; Vol. 13. Alan R Liss, New York.

136. FEnnebE V: The Troms÷ heart study: Coronary risk factors in Seventh-day Adventists. Am J Epidemiol 1985; 122:789-793.

137. FitzSimmons SC: Familial and environ-mental risk factors for elevated blood pressure in youth. Doctoral Dissertation in Epidemiology. University of California, Berkeley, 1985.

138. Ferguson LR, Alley PG, Gribben BM: DNA-damaging activity in ethanol-soluble fractions of feces from New Zealand groups at varying risks of colorectal cancer. Nutr Cancer 1985; 7:93-103.

139. Hirayama T. Mortality in Japanese with lifestyles similar to Seventh-day Adventists: a strategy for risk reduction by lifestyle modification. Natl Cancer Inst Monogr 1985;69:143-53.

140. Melby CL, Hyner GC, Zoog B. Blood pres-sure in vegetarians and non-vegetarians: a cross-sectional analysis. Nutr Res 1985;5:1077-82.

141. Linkosalo E, Ohtonen S, Markkanen H. Caries, periodontal status & some salivary factors in lactovegetarians. Scand J Dent Res 1985;93:304-8.

142. Stich HF, Hornby AP, Dunn BP: Beta-carotene levels in exfoliated mucosa cells of population groups at low and elevated risk of oral cancer. Int J Cancer 1986; 37:389-393.

143. Wulf HC, Iversen AS, Husum B, Niebuhr E: Very low sister-chromatid exchange rate in Sev-enth-day Adventists. Mutat Res 1986; 162:131-135.

144. Kuratsune M, Ikeda M, Hayashi T: Epidemiologic studies on possible health effects of intake of pyrolysates of foods, with reference to mortality among Japanese Seventh-day Adventists. Environ Health Perspectives 1986; 67:143-146.

145. Phillips RL, Snowdon DA: Mortality among Seventh-day Adventists in relation to dietary habits and lifestyle. In: Plant Proteins: Application, Biologic Effect, and Chemistry (Ory RL, ed). Washington DC, 1986, American Chemical Society. pp 162-174.

146. Calkins BM: The consumption of fiber in vegetarians and non-vegetarians. In: Handbook of Dietary Fiber and Nutrition (Spiller G, ed). Boca Raton, Florida, 1986, CRC Press, Inc. pp 407-414.

147. Fisher M, Levine PH, Weiner B, Ockene IS, Johnson B, Johnson MH, Natale AM, Vaudreuil CH, Hoogasian J: The effect of vegetarian diets on plasma lipid and platelet levels.Arch Int Med 1986;146:1193-7.

148. Mills PK: Dietary relationships to fatal breast cancer among Seventh-day Adventists. Ph.D. Dissertation, University of Texas, School of Public Health, 1986. (Available from University Microfilms International, Ann Arbor, Michigan.)

149. Chan JY. A viewpoint of a Seventh-day Adventist. Aust Fam Physician 1986;15(9):1154.

150. Fraser GE, Dysinger PW, Best C, Chan R: IHD risk factors in middle-aged Seventh-day Adventist men and their neighbors. Am J Epidemiol 1987;126:638-46.

151. Schultz TD, Leklem JE. Vitamin B6 status and bioavailability in vegetarian women. Am J Clin Nutr 1987;46:647-51.

152. Beilin LJ, Margetts BM. Vegetarian Diet and Blood Pressure. Biblthca Cardiol 1987;41:85-105.

153. Beilin LJ, Armstrong BK, Margetts BM, Rouse IL, Vandongen R. Vegetarian diet and blood pressure. Nephron 1987;47(Suppl 1):37-41.

154. Schultz TD, Wilcox RB, Spuehler JM, Howie BJ. Dietary and hormonal inter-relationships in premonopausal women: evidence for a relationship between dietary nutrients and plasma prolactin levels. Am J Clin Nutr 1987;46:905-11.

155. Ringstad J, FEnnebE V: The Troms÷ Heart Study: Serum selenium in a low risk population for cardiovascular disease and cancer and matched controls. Ann Clin Res 1987; 19:351-4

156. Scholfield DJ, Behall KM, Bhathena SJ, Kelsay J, Reiser S, Revett KR. A study on Asian Indian and American vegetarians: indications of a racial predisposition to glucose intolerance. Am J Clin Nutr 1987; 46:955-61.

157. Morgan JW: Case-control study of vitamin A intake and colorectal cancer in Seventh-day Adventists. Dissertation thesis, Loma Linda University. (submitted to University Microfilms)

158. King C: Factors associated with clinical gall bladder disease among Seventh-day Adventist women. Dissertation thesis, Loma Linda University, 1987.

159. Kissinger DG, Sanchez A: The association of dietary factors with the age of menarche. Nutr Res 1987; 7:471-479.

160. Sellers EEB: A prospective longitudinal study of psychosocial variables associated with the incidence of cancer among Seventh-day Adventists. Ph.D. Dissertation, University of Michigan, 1987. (Available from University Microfilms International, Ann Arbor, Michigan.)

161. Euler GL, Abbey DE, Magie AR, Hodgkin JE: Chronic obstructive pulmonary disease symptom effects of long-term cumulative exposure to ambient levels of total suspended particulates and sulfur dioxide in California Seventh-day Adventist residents. Arch Environ Health, July/August 1987: 42,4:213-222.

162. Hosken B. Adventists and Longevity. RECORD, January 16, 1988.

163. Linkosalo E. Lactovegetarian diet and dental Health. Dissertation 1988. Univ. of Kuopio, Finland.

164. Mills PK, Annegers JF, Phillips RL: Animal product consumption and subsequent fatal breast cancer risk among Seventh-day Adventists. Am J Epidemiol 1988; 127,3:440-453.

165. Fraser GE: Determinants of ischemic heart disease in Seventh-day Adventists: A review. Am J Clin Nutr 1988; 48:833-836.

166. Linkosalo E, Halonen P, Markkanen H. Factors related to dental health and some salivary factors in Finnish Seventh-day Adventists. Proc Finn Dent Soc 1988; 84:279-89.

167. Mills PK, Beeson WL, Abbey DE, Fraser GE, Phillips RL: Dietary habits and past medical history as related to fatal pancreas cancer risk among Adventists. Cancer 1988; 61:2578-85.

168. Linkosalo E, SyrjEnen S, Alakuijala P. Salivary composition and dental erosions in lacto-ovo-vegetarians. Proc Finn Dent Soc 1988;84:253-60.

169. Laidlaw SA, Shultz TD, Cecchino JT, Kopple JD. Plasma and urine taurine levels in vegans. Am J Clin Nutr 1988; 47:660-3.

170. Euler GL, Abbey DE, Hodgkin JE, Magie AR: Chronic obstructive pulmonary disease symptom effects of long-term cumulative exposure to ambient levels of total oxidants and nitrogen dioxide in California Seventh-day Adventist residents. Arch Environ Health, July/August 1988; 43,4:279-85.

171. Linkosalo E, Markkanen S, Alakuijala P. Effects of some commercial health beverages, effervescent vitamin C preparations and berries on human dental enamel. Proc Finn Dent Soc 1988;84:31-38.

172. Abbey DE, Euler GL, Moore JK, Petersen F, Hodgkin JE, Magie AR: Applications of a method for setting air quality standards based on epidemiological data. JAPCA 1989; 39:437-45.

173. Linkosalo E. Dietary habits and dental health in Finnish Seventh-day Adventists. Proc Finn Dent Soc 1988; 84:109-15.

174. Snowdon DA. Animal product consumption and mortality because of all causes combined, coronary heart disease, stroke, diabetes, and cancer in Seventh-day Adventists. Am J Clin Nutr 1988; 48:739-48.

175. Schultz TD, Rose DP. Effect of high-fat intake on lactogenic hormone bioactivity in premenopausal women. Am J Clin Nutr 1988; 48:791-4.

176. Beilin LJ, Rouse IL, Armstrong BK, Margetts BM, Vandongen R. Vegetarian diet and blood pressure levels: incidental or causal association? Am J Clin Nutr 1988; 48:806-10.

177. FEnnebE V. The Troms÷ Heart Study: diet, religion, and risk factors for coronary heart disease. Am J Clin Nutr 1988; 48:826-9.

178. Marsh AG, Sanchez TV, Michelsen O, Chaf-fee FL, Fagal SM. Vegetarian lifestyle and bone mineral density. Am J Clin Nutr 1988; 48:837-41.

179. Tylavsky FA, Anderson JJB. Dietary factors in bone health of elderly lacto-ovo-vegetarian and omnivorous women. Am J Clin Nutr 1988;48:842-9.

180. Hunt IF, Murphy NJ, Henderson C. Food and nutrient intake of Seventh-day Adventist women. 1988; Am J Clin Nutr 48:850-1.

181. Kelsay JL, Frazier CW, Prather ES, Canary JJ, Clark WM, Powell AS. Impact of variation in carbohydrate intake on mineral utilization by vegetarians. Am J Clin Nutr 1988; 48:875-9.

182. Ringstad J, FEnnebE V. The Troms÷ Heart Study: Selenium in a low-risk population for cardio-vascular disease and cancer.(Abstract) Am J Clin Nutr 1988; 48:925.

183. Thomas EC. Consumption of sodium, iron, and zinc by vegan and lacto-ovo-vegetarian Seventh-day Adventist college students. (Abstract) Am J Clin Nutr 1988; 48:925.

184. Snowdon DA, Kane RL, Beeson W, Burke GL, Sprafka JM, Potter J, Iso H, Jacobs DR, Phillips RL. Is Early Natural Menopause a Biologic Marker of Health and Aging? Am J Public Health 1989; 79:709-14.

185. Kuzma JW, Lindsted KD: Determinants of long-term (24-year) diet recall ability using a 21-item food frequency questionnaire. Nutr Cancer 1989; 12:151-60.

186. Lindsted KD, Kuzma JW: Long-term (24-Year) Recall Reliability in Cancer Cases and Controls Using a 21-Item Food Frequency Questionnaire. Nutr Cancer 1989; 12:135-49.

187. Fraser GE, Babaali H. Determinants of High Density Lipoprotein Cholesterol in Middle-Aged Seventh-day Adventist Men and Their Neighbors. Am J Epidemiol 1989; 130:958-65.

188. Beeson WL, Mills PK, Phillips RL, Andress M, Fraser GE. Chronic Disease Among Seventh-day Adventists, A Low-Risk Group.Cancer 1989;64:570-81.

189. Mills PK, Beeson WL, Phillips RL, Fraser GE. Dietary Habits and Breast Cancer Incidence Among Seventh-day Adventists. Cancer 1989; 64:582-90.

190. Mills PK, Beeson WL, Phillips RL, Fraser GE. Prospective Study of Exogenous Hormone Use and Breast Cancer in Seventh-day Adventists. Cancer 1989; 64:591-7.

191. Mills PK, Beeson WL, Phillips RL, Fraser GE. Cohort Study of Diet, Lifestyle, and Prostate Cancer in Adventist Men. Cancer 1989; 64:598-604.

192. Sabat1-Casellas J. Anthropometric Parameters in Public School Students and Seventh-day Adventist Vegetarian and Meat-eating Students. DrPH Dissertation, Loma Linda University, 1989. (Available from University Microfilms Inter-national, Ann Arbor, Michigan.)

193. Mills PK, Preston-Martin S, Annegers JF, Beeson WL, Phillips RL, Fraser GE. Risk Factors for Tumors of the Brain and Cranial Meninges in Seventh-day Adventists. Neuroepidemiology 1989; 8:266-75.

194. Hunt IF, Murphy NJ, Henderson C, Clark VA, Jacobs RM, Johnston PK, Coulson AH. Bone mineral content in postmenopausal women: comparison of omnivores and vegetarians. Am J Clin Nutr 1989; 50:517-23. t

195. Lombard KA and Mock DM. Biotin nutri-tional status of vegans, lacto-ovo vegetarians, and non-vegetarians. Am J Clin Nutr 1989; 50:486-90.

196. Nieman DC, Sherman KM, Arabatzis K, Underwood BC, Barbosa JC, Johnson M, Shultz TD, Lee J. Hematological, Anthropometric, and Metabolic Comparisons Between Vegetarian and Nonvegetarian Elderly Women. Int J Sports Med 1989; 10:243-51.

197. Nieman DC, Underwood BC, Sherman KM, Arabatzis K, Barbosa JC, Shultz TD. Dietary status of Seventh-day Adventist vegetarian and non-vegetarian elderly women. J Am Diet Assoc 1989; 89:1763-1769.

198. Marsh AG, Christensen DK, Sanchez TV, Mickelsen O, Chaffee FL. Nutrient similarities and differences of older lacto-ovo-vegetarian and omnivorous women. Nutr Rep Int 1989; 39:19-24.

199. Melby CL, Goldflies DG, Hyner GC, Lyle RM. Relation between vegetarian/nonvegetarian diets and blood pressure in back and white adults. Am J Public Health 1989; 79:1283-8.

200. Beeson WL, Fraser GE, Mills PK. Valida-tion of record linkage to 2 California population-based tumor registries in a cohort study. Proceedings of the 1989 public health conference on records and statistics. DHHS publication No.(PHS)90-1214,1990, pp.196-201.

201. Ross JK, Pusateri DJ, Shultz TD. Dietary and hormonal evaluation of men at different risks for prostate cancer: fiber intake, excretion, and composition, with in vitro evidence for an association between steroid hormones and specific fiber components. Am J Clin Nutr 1990; 51:365-70.

202. Pusateri DJ, Roth WT, Ross JK, Shultz TD. Dietary and hormonal evaluation of men at different risks for prostate cancer: plasma and fecal hormone-nutrient interrelationships. Am J Clin Nutr 1990;51: 371-7.

203. Snowdon DA. Early Natural Menopause and the Duration of Postmenopausal Life. J Am Geriatr Soc 1990; 38:402-8.

204. Fraser GE, Phillips RL, Beeson WL. Hypertension, anti-hypertensive medication and risk of renal carcinoma in California Seventh-day Advent-ists. Int J Epidemiol 1990; 19(4):832-8.

205. Hopkins RJ, Russell RG, O'Donnoghue M, Wasser-man S, Lefkowitz A, Morris JG. Seroprevalence of Helicobacter pylori in SDA and other groups in Maryland. Arch Int Med 1990; 150: 2347-8.

206. Mills PK, Newell GR, Beeson WL, Fraser GE, Phillips RL. History of Cigarette Smoking and Risk of Leukemia and Myeloma: Results from the Adventist Health Study. J Natl Cancer Inst 1990; 82:1832-6.

207. Sumbureru D. The influence of lifestyle on longevity among black Seventh-day Adventists in California: An epidemiologic approach. DrPH Dissertation, Loma Linda Un iversity, 1988. (Available from University Microfilms International, Ann Arbor, Michigan.)

208. Sabat1 J, Lindsted KD, Harris RD, Johnston PK. Anthropometric parameters of school-children with dif-ferent life-styles. Am J Dis Children 1990; 144:1159-63.

209. Barbosa JC, Shultz TD, Filley SJ, Nieman DC. The rela-tionship among adiposity, diet, and hormone concentra-tions in vegetarian and nonvegetarian post-meno-pausal women. Am J Clin Nutr 1990;51:798-803.

210. Lindsted K, Kuzma JW. Husband-wife concordance and changes in dietary practices by surviving spouses of can-cer cases. Nutr Cancer 1990;13:175-87.

211. Murphy FG, Blumenthal DS, Dickson-Smith J, Peay RP. The mortality profile of black Seventh-day Adventists residing in metropolitan Atlanta: a pilot study. Am J Public Health 1990; 80:984-5.

212. Mills PK, Beeson WL, Phillips RL, Fraser GE. Bladder cancer in a low risk population: Results from the Adventist Health Study. Am J Epidemiol 1991; 133:230-9.

213. Resnicow K, Barone J, Engle A, Miller S, Haley N, Fleming D, Wynder , E. Diet and serum lipids in vegan vegetarians: A model for risk reduction. J Am Diet Assoc 1991; 91:447-53.

214. Lindsted KD, Tonstad S, Kuzma JW. Self-report of physi-cal activity and patterns of mortality in Seventh-day Adventist men. J Clin Epidemiol 1991; 44:355-64.

215. Lindsted K, Tonstad S. Body mass index and patterns of mortality among Seventh-day Adventist men. Int J Obesity 1991:15:397-406.

216. Fraser GE, Beeson WL, Phillips RL. Diet and lung cancer in California Seventh-day Adventists. Am J Epidemiol 1991; 133:683-93.

217. Ullman D, Phillips RL, Beeson WL, Dewey HG, Brin BN, Kuzma JW, Mathews CP, Hirst AE. Cause-specific mor-tality among physicians with differing life-styles. JAMA 1991; 265:2352-9.

218. Sabat1 J, Lindsted KD, Harris RD, Sanchez A. Attained height of lacto-ovo vegetarian children and adolescents. Eur J Clin Nutr 1991; 45:51-8.

219. FEnnebE V, Helseth A. Cancer Incidence in Norwegian Seventh-day Adventists 1961 to 1986. Cancer 1991; 68:666-71.

220. Abbey DE, Mills PK, Petersen FF, Beeson WL. Long-term Ambient Concentrations of Total Suspended Particulates and Oxidants as Related to Incidence of Chronic Disease in California Seventh-day Adventists. Environ Health Perspectives 1991; 94:43-50.

221. Mills PK, Abbey D, Beeson WL, Petersen F. Ambient Air Pollution and Cancer in California Seventh-day Adventists. Arch Environ Health 1991; 46:271-280.

222. Melby CL, Goldflies DG, Hymer GC. Blood Pressure and Anthropometric differences in regularly exercising and nonexercising black adults. Clin & Exper Hyper-Theory & Practice 1991; 6:1233-48.

223. Editorial. Comparative mortality of two college groups, 1945-1983. MMWR 1991; 40:579-82.

224. Kurata JH, Nogawa AN, Abbey DE, Petersen F. A Prospective Study of Risk for Peptic Ulcer Disease in Seventh-Day Adventists. Gastro-enterology 1992; 102:902-9.

225. Persky VW, Chatterton RT, Van Horn LV, Grant MD, Langenberg P, Marvin J. Hormone levels in vegetarian and nonvegetarian teenage girls: Potential implications for breast cancer risk. Cancer Research 1992;52:578-83.

226. Fraser GE, Sabat1 J, Beeson WL, Strahan TM. A Possible Protective Effect of Nut Consumption on Risk of Coronary Heart Disease. The Adventist Health Study. Arch Int Med 1992; 152:1416-24.

227. Fraser GE, Strahan, TM, Sabat1 J, Beeson WL, Kissinger D. Effects of Traditional Coronary Risk Factors on Rates of Incident Coronary Events in a Low Risk Population: The Adventist Health Study. Circulation 1992; 86:406-13.

228. Mills PK, Beeson WL, Fraser GE, Phillips RL. Allergy and cancer: Organ site-specific results from the Adventist Health Study. Am J Epidemiol 1992; 136:287-95.

229. FEnnebE V. Mortality in Norwegian Seventh-day Adventists 1962-1986. J Clin Epidemiol 45:157-167, 1992.

230. FEnnebE V. Coronary risk factors in Norwe-gian Seventh-day Adventists: A study of 247 Seventh-day Adventists and matched controls. Am J Epidemiol 1992; 135:504-8.

231. Sabat1 J, Llorca C, Sanchez A. Lower height of lacto-ovovegetarian girls at preadolescence: An indicator of physical maturation delay? J Am Diet Assoc 1992; 92:1263-4.

232. Lindsted KD, Kuzma JW, Anderson JL. Coffee consump-tion and cause-specific mortality. J Clin Epidemiol 1992;45:733-42.

233. Giem P, Beeson WL, Fraser GE. The Incidence of Dementia and Intake of Animal Products: Preliminary Findings from the Adventist Health Study. Neuroepidemiology 1993; 12:28-36.

234. Abbey DE, Petersen F, Mills PK, Beeson WL. Long-term ambient concentrations of total suspended particulates, ozone, and sulfur dioxide and respiratory symptoms in a nonsmoking population. Arch Environ Health 1993; 48:33-46.

235. Melby CL, Goldflies DG, Toohey ML. Blood Pressure Differences in Older Black and White Long-Term Vegetarians and Nonvegetarians. J Am Coll Nutrit 1993; 12:262-9.

236. Sabat1 J. Does nut consumption protect against ischaemic heart disease? Eur J Clin Nutrit 1993; 47:S71-S75.

237. Sabat1 J, Fraser GE. The probable role of nuts in preventing coronary heart disease. Primary Cardiology 1993;19:65-72.

238. Richter A, Yang K, Richter F, Lynch HT, Lipkin M. Morphological and morphometric measurements in colorectal mucosa of subjects at increased risk for colonic neoplasia. Cancer Letters 1993; 74:65-8.

239. Sorkin JD, Muller D, Andres R. Body mass index and mortality in Seventh-day Adventist men. A critique and re-analysis. Int J Obesity 1994; 18:752-4.

240. Reed JA, Anderson JJB, Tylavsky FA, Gallagher PH, Jr. Comparative changes in radial-bone density of elderly female lactoovovegetarians and omnivores. Am J Clin Nutr 1994; 59:1197S-202S.

241. Melby CL, Toohey ML, Cebrick J. Blood pressure and blood lipids among vegetarian, semivegetarian, and nonvegetarian African Americans. Am J Clin Nutr 1994;59:103-9.

242. Fraser GE. Diet and coronary heart disease: beyond dietary fats and low-density-lipoprotein cholesterol. Am J Clin Nutr 1994;59:1117S-23S.

243. Sabat1 J, Fraser GE. Nuts: a new protective food against coronary heart disease. Current Opinion in Lipidology 1994;5:11-16.

244. Mills PK, Beeson WL, Phillips RL, Fraser GE. Cancer incidence among California Seventh-day Adventists, 1976-1982. Am J Clin Nutr 1994;59:1136S-42S.

245. Knutsen SF. Lifestyle and the use of health services. Am J Clin Nutr 1994;59:1171S-75S.

246. FEnnebE V. The healthy Seventh-day Adventist lifestyle: what is the Norwegian experience? Am J Clin Nutr 1994;59:1124S-9S.

247. Kuczmarski RJ, Anderson JJ, Koch GG. Correlates of blood pressure in Seventh-day Adventist (SDA) and non-SDA adolescents. J Am Coll Nutr 1994;13:165-73.

248. Beilin LJ. Vegetarian and other complex diets, fats, fiber, and hypertension. Am J Clin Nutr 1994;59:1130S-5S.

249. Abbey DE, Hwang BL, Burchette RJ, VanCuren T, Mills PK. Estimated Long-term Ambient Concentrations of PM10 and Development of Respiratory Symptoms in a Nonsmoking Population. Arch Environ Hlth 1995; 50(2):139-52.

250. Abbey DE, Lebowitz MD, Mills PK, Petersen FF, Beeson WL, Burchette , RJ. Long-term ambient concentrations of particulates and oxidants and development of chronic disease in a cohort of non-smoking California residents. Inhalat Toxicol 1995;7:19-34.

251. Morgan JW and Singh PN. Diet, Body Mass Index, and Colonic Epithelial Cell Proliferation in a Healthy Population. Nutr Cancer 1995;23:247-257.

252. Fraser GE, Lindsted KD, Beeson WL. Effect of Risk Factor Values on Lifetime Risk of and Age at First Coronary Event. Am J Epidemiol 1995; 142:746-58.

253. Persky V, Van Horn L. Epidemiology of soy and cancer: Perspectives and directions. J Nutr 1995; 125:709S-12S.

254. Toohey L, Harris MA, Allen KGD, Melby CL. Plasma ascorbic acid concentrations are related to cardiovascular risk factors in African-Americans. J Nutr 1996; 126:121-8.

255. McAnulty J, Scragg R. Body mass index and cardiovascular risk factors in Pacific Island Polynesian and Europeans in New Zealand. Ethn Health 1996; 3:187-95.

256. Sabat1 J, Bell HET, Fraser GE. Nut consumption and coronary heart disease risk. In Lipids in Human Nutrition. CRC Press, New York, 1996 (Gene A. Spiller, Ed).

257. Hunter DJ, Spiegelman D, Adami HO, Beeson L, Van Den Brandt PA, Folsom AR, Fraser GE, Goldbohm A, Graham S, Howe GR, Kushi LH, Marshall JR, McDermott A, Miller AB, Speizer FE, Wolk A, Yaun SS, Willet W. Cohort studies of fat intake and the risk of breast cancer - A pooled analysis. NEJM 1996;334:356-61.

258. Lindsted KD, Fraser GE, Steinkohl M, Beeson WL. Healthy Volunteer Effect in a Cohort Study: Temporal Resolution in the Adventist Health Study. J Clin Epidemiol 1996; 49:783-90.

259. Collaborative Group on Hormonal Factors in Breast Cancer. Breast cancer and hormonal contraceptives: collaborative reanalysis of individual data on 53,297 women with breast cancer and 100,239 women without breast cancer from 54 epidemio-logical studies. Lancet 1996;347:1713-28.

260. Singh PN, Tonstad S, Abbey DE, Fraser GE. Validity of selected physical activity questions in white Seventh-day Adventists and non-Adventists. Med & Science in Sports & Exercise 1996;28:1026-36.

261. Fraser GE, Singh PN, Bennett H. Variables associated with cognitive function in elderly California Seventh-day Adventists. Am J Epidemiol 1996; 143:1181-90.

262. Collaborative Group on Hormonal Factors in Breast Cancer. Breast cancer and hormonal contracept-ives: Further Results. Contraception 1996;54:1S-106S.

263. Pribi_ P. Association between nutrient intake and risk of coronary heart disease in California Seventh-day Adventists. DrPH Dissertation, Loma Linda University, 1996. (Available from University Microfilms International, Ann Arbor, Michigan).

264. Fraser GE, Sumbureru D, Pribis P, Neil RL, Frankson MAC. Association among health habits, risk factors, and all-cause mortality in a black California population. Epidemiology 1997;8:168-74.

265. Lindsted KD, Singh PN. Body Mass and 26-Year Risk of Mortality among Women who never Smoked: Findings from the Adventist Mortality Study. Am J Epidemiol 1997;146:1-11.

266. Fraser GE, Shavlik D. Risk factors, lifetime risk, and age at onset of breast cancer. Ann Epidemiol 1997;7:375-82.

267. Fraser GE, Haller-Wade TM, Morrow S. Social support in Seventh-day Adventists and their neighbors. J Religion & Health 1997;36:231-9.

268. Fraser GE, Shavlik DJ. Risk factors for all-cause and coronary heart disease mortality in the oldest-old. Arch Intern Med 1997;157:2249-2258.

269. Collaborative Group on Hormonal Factors in Breast Cancer. Breast cancer and hormone replacement therapy: collaborative reanalysis of data from 51 epi-demiological studies of 52,705 women with breast cancer and 108,411 women without breast cancer. Lancet 1997;350:1047-59.

270. Hopkins GL. An AIDS risk appraisal of students attending Seventh-day Adventist high schools in the United States and Canada. DrPH Dissertation, Loma Linda University, 1997. (Available from University Microfilms International, Ann Arbor, Michigan).

271. Murphy FG, Gwebu E, Braithwaite RL, Green-Goodman D, Brown L. Health values and practices among Seventh-day Adventist. Am J Health Behav 1997; 21(1):43-50.

272. Key TJ, Fraser GE, Thorogood M, Appleby PN, Beral V, Reeves G, Burr ML, Chang-Claude J, Frentzel-Beyme R, Kuzma JW, Mann J, McPherson K. Mortalilty in vegetarians and non-vegetarians: a collaborative analysis of 8,300 deaths among 76,000 men and women in five prospective studies. Public Health Nutr 1998;1:33-41.

273. Singh PN, Lindsted KD. Body Mass and 26-Year Risk of Mortality from Specific Diseases among Women who Never Smoked. Epidemiology 1998;9:246-54.

274. Singh PN, Fraser GE. Dietary risk factors for colon cancer in a low-risk population. Am J Epidemiol 1998;148:761-74.

275. Famodu AA, Osilesi O, Makinde YO, Osonuga OA. Blood pressure and blood lipid levels among vegetarian, semi-vegetarian, and non-vegetarian native Africans. Clin Biochem 1998; 31:545-9.

276. Lindsted KD, Singh PN. Body mass and 26y risk of mortality among men who never smoked: a re-analysis among men from the Adventist Mortality Study. Int J Obes Relat Metab Disord 1998; 22:544-8.

277. Harman SK, Parnell WR. The nutritional health of New Zealand vegetarian and non-vegetarian Seventh-day Adventists: selected vitamin, mineral and lipid levels. NZ Med J 1998; 111:91-4.

278. Hopkins GL, Hopp JW, Marshak HP, Neish C, Rhoads G. AIDS risk among students attending Seventh-day Adventist school, in North America. J Sch Health 1998; 68:141-5.

279. Fraser GE, Lindsted KD, Knutsen SF, Beeson WL, Bennett H, Shavlik DJ. The validity of dietary recall over twenty years in California Seventh-day Adventists. Am J Epidemiol 1998;148:810-18.

280. Jacobsen BK, Knutsen SF, Fraser GE. Does high soy milk intake reduce prostate cancer incidence? The Adventist Health Study. Cancer Causes & Control 1998;9:553-7.

281. Hopkins GL, Hopp JW, Marshak HH, Neish C, Rhoads G. An AIDS-risk assessment of Students attending Christian high schools in the United States of America: A practical application of the theory of planned behavior. J Res Christian Educ 1998;7:91-120.

282. Beeson WL, Abbey DE, Knutsen SF. Long-term concentrations of ambient air pollutants and incident lung cancer in California adults: Results from the AHSMOG study. Environ Health Perspect 1998; 106:813-23.

283. Toohey ML, Harris MA, Williams DW, Foster G, Schmidt DW, Melby CL. Cardiovascular disease risk factors are lower in African-American vegans compared to lacto-ovo-vegetarians. J Am Coll Nutr 1998;17:425-34.

284. Fraser GE, Shavlik DJ. The estimation of lifetime risk and average age at onset of a disease using a multivariate exponential hazard rate model. Statistics in Medicine 1999;18:397-410.

285. Jacobsen BK, Knutsen SF, Fraser GE. Age at natural menopause and total mortality and mortality from Ischemic Heart Disease: The Adventist Health Study. J Clin Epidemiol 1999;52:303-7.

286. Fraser GE. Nut consumption, lipids, and risk of a coronary event. Clin Cardiol 1999;22 (Suppl III)III-11-III-15.

287. Sabat1 J. Nut consumption, vegetarian diets, ischemic heart disease risk, and all-cause mortality: evidence from epidemiologic studies. Am J Clin Nutr 1999; 70(suppl):500S-3S.

288. Key TJ, Fraser GE, Thorogood M, Appleby PN, Beral V, Reeves G, Burr ML, Chang-Claude J, Frentzel-Beyme R, Kuzma JW, Mann J, McPherson K. Mortality in vegetarians and nonvegetarians: detailed findings from a collaborative analysis of 5 prospective studies. Am J Clin Nutr 1999;70(suppl):516S-24S.

289. Fraser GE. Associations between diet and cancer, ischemic heart disease, and all-cause mortality in non-Hispanic white California Seventh-day Adventists. Am J Clin Nutr 1999;70(suppl):532S-8S.

290. Hokin BC. Butler T. Cyanocobalamin (vitamin B-12) status in Seventh-day Adventist ministers in Australia. Am J Clin Nutr 1999;70(suppl):576S-8S.

291. Singh PN, Lindsted KD, Fraser GE. Body weight and mortality among adults who never smoked. Am J Epidemiol 1999;150:1152-64.

292. Fraser GE. Diet as Primordial Prevention in Seventh-day Adventists. Preventive Medicine 1999;29 (Suppl.):S18-S23.

293. Key TJ, Davey GK, Appleby PN. Health benefits of a vegetarian diet. Proceedings of the Nutrition Soc. 1999; 58:271-5.

294. Park JS, Oh SJ, Kim KS, Ahn SH, Kim YK. Effect of diet and apolipoprotein E (Apo E) polymorphism on the variation of serum lipid profile in Korean males. (written in Korean). Korean Circulation Journal 1999; 29:266-75.

295. Famodu AA, Osilesi O, Makinde YO, Osonuga OA, Fakoya TA, Ogunyemi EO, Egbenehkhuere IE. The influence of a vegetarian diet on haemostatic risk factors for cardiovascular disease in Africans. Thromb Res 1999; 95:31-6.

296. van den Brandt PA, Spiegelman D, Yaun S-S, Adami H-O, Beeson L, Folsom AR, Fraser G, Goldbohm RA, Graham S, Kushi L, Marshall JR, Miller AB, Rohan T, Smith-Warner SA, Speizer FE, Willett WC, Wolk A, Hunter DJ. A pooled analysis of prospective cohort studies on height, weight and breast cancer risk. Am J Epidemiol 2000; 152:514-27.

297. Myint T, Fraser GE, Lindsted KD, Knutsen SF, Hubbard RW, Bennett HW. Urinary 1-methyl histidine is a marker of meat consumption in black and white California Seventh-day Adventists. Am J Epidemiol 2000;152:752-5.

298. Singh PN, Fraser GE, Knutsen SF, Lindsted KD, Bennett HW. Validity of a physical activity questionnaire among African-American Seventh-day Adventists. Med & Science in Sports & Exercise 2001;33:468-75.

299. Smith-Warner SA, Spiegelman D, Adami HO, Beeson WL, van den Brandt PA, Folsom AR, Fraser GE, Freudenheim JL, Goldbohm RA, Graham S, Kushi LJH, Miller AB, Rohan TE, TE, Speizer FE, Toniolo P, Willett WC, Wolk A, Zeleniuch-Jacquotte A, Hunter DJ. Types of Dietary Fat and Breast Cancer: A Pooled Analysis of Cohort Studies. Int J Cancer 2001;92:767-74.

300. Smith-Warner SA, Spiegelman D, Yaun SS, Adami HO, Beeson WL, van den Brandt PA, Folsom AR, Fraser GE, Freudenheim JL, Goldbohm RA, Graham S, Miller AB, Potter JD, Rohan TE, Speizer FE, Toniolo P, Willett WC, Wolk A, Zeleniuch-Jacquotte A, Hunter DJ. Intake of Fruits and Vegetables and Breast Cancer: A Pooled Analysis of Cohort Studies. JAMA 2001;285:769-76.

301. Fraser GE, Shavlik DJ. Yen years of life. Is it a matter of choice? Arch Int Med 2001;161:1645-52.

302. Knutsen SF, Fraser GE, Lindsted KD, Beeson WL, Shavlik DJ. Validation of assessment of nutrient intake. Comparing biological measurements of Vitamin C, Folate, Alpha-tocopherol and Carotene with 24-hour dietary recall information in non-Hispanic blacks and whites. Annals Epidemiol 2001 (in press).

24

Health Fairs and Exhibits

Louis Sullivan, M. D. President of Morehouse School of Medicine in Atlanta, Georgia, says "If we empower people to control their health risks, we can prevent up to 70 percent of all premature deaths in our country." The public is getting this message and your church will find many people interested in attending a health fair where they can be tested to evaluate their risk of disease and receive information to reduce that risk. Health fairs are proven to attract attention and often receive free media coverage. Health fairs can make a big impact on your community that will give your church an opportunity to build and enhance relations with its neighbors while most effectively advertising its calendar of health education seminars. The friendships formed through these contacts will include many who will be interested in pursuing spiritual wellness as well as physical wellness.

Step 1: Establish Your Goals and Objectives

Most churches will include the following goals and objectives, but some may wish to add more. You may bring this suggested list to the church board, but it is important that they discuss, understand, and establish the final list so they will be more enthusiastic and willing to dedicate finances. Written goals are also the basis of demonstrating success. Some potential goals and objectives are:

1. Build awareness of the church in the community.
2. Demonstrate the unselfish interest of the Seventh-day Adventist Church in the health and well-being of people in the community.
3. Teach the most important health practices that reduce risk of disease.
4. Evaluate the health status of the participants
5. Encourage modification of behaviors to improve the quality and quantity of life of church members and the public.

6. Network with other service organizations so that the church can do a better job of referring people to other agencies for additional services and these organizations will feel comfortable referring their contacts to health promotion seminars conducted by the church.
7. Advertise a calendar of follow-up health promotion seminars such as:
   Cooking Schools
   Smoking Cessation:
   Breathe Free: The Plan to Stop Smoking (The Health Connection Catalog nos. 15230 and 35400)
   Stress Management:
   Stress: *Beyond Coping* (Catalog nos. 35250 and 35280)
8. Increase church membership.

It is important that church members understand clearly that overt attempts to evangelize members of the public who attend a health fair in North America will most likely only prevent future community participation. However, health fairs increase attendance at follow-up seminars where close personal relationships between members and nonmembers have time to develop and bear fruit. These friendships and a careful planning of the sequence in which seminars are offered will help participants understand that spiritual health impacts physical well being. This investment of time and unselfish service will result in opportunities for Bible study and baptisms.

Cooking schools and stop smoking programs allow friendships to be formed but little opportunity for spiritual matters to come up naturally. Graduates of these programs should be encouraged to attend *Stress Beyond Coping* classes. Stress management easily adds more spiritual content since so many stressors relate to inter-personal relationships. Many previously secular people who complete this class will be ready to attend *In Pursuit of Excellence,* a bridge between health promotion seminars and standard evangelism that helps secularly minded people develop faith in the Bible while teaching healthy lifestyle principles. (*In Pursuit of Excellence,* Catalog no.30250)

Step 2: Get Church Board Approval and Support

About three months in advance, set up an ad hoc steering committee composed of the church Health Ministries leader, other members of the Health Ministries committee, Community Services director, Personal Ministries director, Outreach director, Pastor, Communications director, and other members at large. Meet as needed.

As soon as plans are finalized, have a suggested date/place/budget OK'd by the Church Board at its next meeting. If it's your first health fair, include some one-time purchases of items such as sheets for tablecloths and the large banner for out front.

Step 3: Choose a Theme:

CELEBRATIONS® is the acronym adopted by the General Conference and North American Division Health Ministries Departments to present the principles of the Adventist lifestyle to members of the church and the public. Any Seventh-day Adventist church or institution can use this acronym without specific permission in connection with their health events.

"Fill your life with CELEBRATIONS"® makes an ideal theme for a health fair because it provides a framework for all potential exhibits and activities as demonstrated in Step 4 . This acronym and theme proclaim to our communities that we understand and assist people with the physical, mental, social, and spiritual aspects of health. It has a positive ring and correctly represents the practice of health principles as a fun and enjoyable lifestyle.

You can emphasize this theme by greeting participants with a banner behind the registration desk.

Fill Your Life With CELEBRATIONS® Banner (Catalog no. 41640)

Step 4: Plan Stations and Services:

Each station needs to relate to the theme, but this does not mean that you must have a station offering services for each letter of the acronym. We are giving suggestions for twelve stations with a menu of ideas for each, but you can have fewer stations and services and still introduce your participants to all twelve basic health principles by providing them with the Fill Your Life With CELEBRATIONS® pamphlet at registration:

Fill Your Life With CELEBRATIONS® Pamphlet (Catalog no. 41690)

This pamphlet can serve additional purposes. You might suggest participants obtain a signature by each symbol of the stations they visit in order to receive a free gift or a ticket for a grand prize drawing. This will encourage participants to visit all of the booths and help them get acquainted with and learn the name of the person signing.

By networking with nonprofit groups (such as those listed at Station Twelve) you may find supplemental free handouts are available. We do not suggest any specific free material because these items can quickly disappear and quantities often are limited. Everything we list is available for purchase from The Health Connection as are all the products referred to where the title is in italics followed by a catalog number. Information on how to order these items is provided at the end of this chapter. Only items already available are listed, but more are in production. The General Conference Health Ministries Department will offer a revised version of this article on its web site when new products and ideas make that appropriate.

Backdrops are suggested for each station for several reasons:

- To identify and define the space for each service
- To provide additional information on the topic

The outline of suggested stations and services that follows lists only the title for each station. You can produce a sign with this title inexpensively. If your budget allows you to produce a larger banner with added information, you can obtain suggestions from the General Conference Health Ministries web site: www.health20-20.org. The suggestions available on the web site will continue to grow after this manual is published and eventually may be collected on a CD in a form that will make it easier for you to produce large informative banners for each station.

Children's activities are important at each station because:

- Participants often bring their children and may not want to leave them with an unknown baby sitter even if such a service is provided away from the stations.
- Parents may be unable to participate in the services provided for them unless activities are provided to entertain their children.
- Providing fun learning activities for children shows the church's interest in, and ability to help and teach, children. Later, when you send out advertising for Vacation Bible School, having provided activities for children can help build attendance at VBS and develop a growing relationship with the family.
- Children remind their parents of important health practices they learn.
- Adults often learn and remember more from what they overhear of the children's activities than the adult material.
- Adults, teens, and children will enjoy most of these activities.

Your church or institution must decide what stations and services your available staff and resources can provide, but after reading through the exciting possibilities below you will have a good idea of how to relate whatever you select to the CELEBRATIONS® theme. Where multiple activities, displays, and handouts are suggested, consider the list a menu of effective possibilities from which you can choose. It is not necessary to use all the ideas listed. As much as possible we have tried to include ideas that save your budget along with items that can be purchased to save your time.

In some cases we have mixed several topics that relate to the word identifying the station because of available products and to demonstrate how you can teach more than one specific application of each principle represented by the acronym in a single area. Depending on available staff, space, resources and community interest you may decide to have some stations much larger than others. We used nutrition to demonstrate how you could have three spaces side-by-side that deal with different subtopics when good materials, staff, and community interest makes it plausible.

Station One: Choices

Objective: To present the benefits and consequences of lifestyle choices

Backdrop: Create a sign highlighting the "C" in the word Choices

Display: Staff may wear Magic Thinking Caps that say "Making healthy choices means we use these (pointing to top of cap) to think through the facts and consequences of our behavior!" at which time they flip up the brim of their caps to expose the words: "Think, Think, Think" then say "Our free comparison of your health age to your chronological age will help you do just that!"
Magic Thinking Cap (Catalog no,34670)

Assessment Tool: A quick, fun comparison of health age and chronological age based on Research. *Your Health Age Computer Health Assessment Software (Catalog no. 35140)*

Activities: These games serve as attention-grabbing displays and activities demonstrating the importance of choices. They can be played by teams or individuals:
Wheel of Choices Game (Catalog no,38440). Choices include such items as STD's, date rape, teen pregnancy.
Smoker's Roulette Game (Catalog no. 22050). The lifestyle choice that kills the most people You could adapt the Wheel of Choices Game by pasting on different pictures and creating new cards to broaden its scope to the health principles in *CELEBRATIONS®.*

Children's Activities: Sing-along with tape of the song Positive Choices which promotes an understanding of self worth and good decision making skills. Use with or without puppets:
Positive Choices: No Smokin' Joe Soundtrack (Catalog no,38025)

Dental Hygiene Demonstration
Flossy the Tooth Puppet Catalog no, 47040).

Handout: Report from Health Age Appraisal

Station Two: Exercise

Objective: To present the benefits and guidelines of exercise for physical fitness

Backdrop: Create a sign highlighting the letter E" in the word Exercise

Assessment Tool: *Your Fitness Score Computer Health Assessment Software (Catalog no.35160).*

Activity: Measure any of the following: pulse, heart rate, strength, flexibility, posture.

Children's Activity: Play catch with soft colorful balls

Handout: Assessment Report

Station Three: Liquids

Objectives:
1. To demonstrate the importance of healthful beverages, especially water.
2. To demonstrate simple hydrotherapy.
3. To demonstrate the importance of hand washing and cleanliness
4. To demonstrate principles of osteoporosis prevention
5. To demonstrate non-alcoholic party drinks.

Backdrop: Create a sign highlighting the letter "L" in the word Liquids.

Table Display: (Objective 1) Pour all the different colors of vegetable and fruit juices, milk, and soy drinks into glasses arranged artistically in front of containers.

Activity: (Objective 2) Demonstrate simple hydrotherapy for sore throat or headache

Activity for all ages: Objective 3) Hand washing demonstration requiring basin and water and the following: *Germ Detective Powder (Cat. no. 38350) and UV Lamp (Cat. No. 38370) Objective 4: 28895 Mr. Thrifty Skeleton*

Handout: (Objective 5): *Non-alcoholic Mocktails Pamphlet (Cat. no. 23210).* Free bottled water, fruit juice, herb tea, etc. Look for retailers who will supply the drinks in exchange for subtle advertising by a sign stating who provided the healthful beverages.

Station Four: Environment

Objective: To demonstrate the importance of preserving and applying the health components of the environment such as sun, soil, water, food, and air. Emphasize sun and soil at this station since water, food, and air are covered at other stations.

Backdrop: Create a sign highlighting the letter "E" in the word Environment.

Assessment Tool: Skin cancer screening by dermatologist.

Activity: *Sun Sense (Cat. no. 34340)* is a 10-minute video you can have playing in a section of the booth with chairs if space permits or in a separate room for those who would like more detailed information on the benefits of sun, as well as potential damage to unprotected skin and eyes and how to prevent it. This short video is designed to appeal to and instruct both children and adults.

Children's Activity: Table with crayons and paper and adult suggesting everyone draw a picture of the sun, kids putting on sunscreen before they go outdoors, etc. Tape some completed art projects along front edge of table for inspiration and atmosphere.

Handouts: *Food, The Planet and You Pamphlet (Cat. no. 28580).* Free handout on sun safety tips may be provided courtesy of the dermatologist if requested.

Station Five: Belief

Objective: To present the connection between body and mind, faith and health. To assess stressors and coping strategies.

Backdrop: Create a sign highlighting the letter "B" in the word Belief
Subtitle: Some Beliefs Can Help Relieve Stress

Poster: *101 Stress Relievers Poster (Cat no. 37450)*

Assessment Tool: *Your Stress Profile Computer Health Assessment Software 35150*

Children's Activity: Bee Puppet can help kids and adults) understand and accept the importance of this word belief that starts with "B" saying something like:
"B stands for me, the Bee, and also for Belief. What are some things it's good for kids to believe in? Acknowledge whatever they come up with and suggest noncontroversial things like: "Don't you bee-lieve:
• that firemen and policemen are heroes
• that your parents love you

• that what your parents and teachers tell you is important
• that you are a valuable person able to make valuable contributions
• that forgiving is better than revenge
• that good is stronger than evil

Oh all these bee-liefs make this bee so much happier. Don't they make you happier too?"
Honey Bee Puppet (Cat. no.44260)

Handout: Stress Assessment Report Promotion Flier for upcoming Stress Beyond Coping Seminar and or seminars on video tape listed below.

Videotaped seminars even the smallest church can offer (to be followed by a discussion): Skip MacCarty, D. Min.,author of *Stress Beyond Coping*, presents:
> *Handling Stress: Beyond Just Coping Videos Series (Cat. no. 44890)*

Lourdes Morales Gudmundsson, PhD, presents:
> *I Forgive You, But! Video (Cat. no. 44900 in English, 44905 in Spanish)*

Chaplain Larry Yeagley presents:
> *Grief Recovery Series of Three Videos (Cat. no. 44920)*

Linda Ferry, M.D. and Sana Johnson Quijada, M. D. present:
> *Coping with Anxiety and Depression (Cat. no. 44910)*

Station Six: Rest

Objective: To demonstrate inhibitors and enhancers of sleep, rest, and relaxation.

Backdrop: Create a sign highlighting the letter "R" in the word Rest

Assessment Tool: *How Healthy Is Your Lifestyle? Assessment Forms (Cat. no. 44595)* covers most important predictors of health and longevity including sleep. Participants complete this form with a pen.

Demonstration: Techniques for giving a relaxing massage

Activity for all: Vibrating recliner chairs with faith-building reading material on tables. Massage of neck, head, hands, or feet. Foot massage machines. (Manufacturers or

retailers may loan massage chairs and
machines.)

Handout: Flier promoting upcoming one-session
seminar on sleep secrets where you can
show the following video:
> *The Sleep Advantage Video (Cat. no. 33600)*
> with additional tips from the book:
> *Sleep Secrets for Shift Works & People
> With Off-Beat Schedules (Cat. no. 33490)*

Station Seven: Air

Objective: To present the health benefits of fresh
air and a healthy respiratory system.

Backdrop: Create a sign highlighting the first letter "A" in the word Air

Assessment Tool: Spirometer testing of volume of
inhaled and exhaled air.

Activity: Step or squat test with respiratory rate
measurement before and after exercise.

Children's Activity: Have participants blow up a
balloon, tie it with a ribbon and give it to
them. Don't just give away deflated balloons
as that would not be an activity and participants would not benefit from the messages
on the balloons.
> Balloons with anti-tobacco slogan (Cat. no.
> 11200); Big Mouth & Ciggy Puppet Program
> Kit (Cat. no. 45710)

Handouts: Brochures to promote your next
Breathe Free Plan to Stop Smoking:
> *Quit Smoking? Yes You Can With Breathe
> Free (Cat. no. 23600)*
> Brochure to help smokers stop smoking:
> *How to Stop Smoking and Breathe Free
> (Cat. no.13840)*

Station Eight: Temperance

Objective: To increase awareness of the detrimental effects of alcohol and other drugs.

Backdrop: Create a sign highlighting the "T" in
the word Temperance

Display: Death of a Liver Model (*Cat. no. 23985*)
> Substance Abuse ID Kits (*Cat. nos. 46340 or
> 10150*)
> Consequences of Drug Use Display (*Cat. no.
> 10170*)

Activity: Demonstrate how alcohol distorts
vision:
> *DWEyes Glasses (Cat.no.38020)*

Children's Activity: Let children take turns wearing The Body Uniform while explaining
how tobacco hurts the lungs and alcohol can
hurt the liver, stomach and brain and why
both are particularly hard on children.
> (*Cat. no. 26330*) *The Body Uniform*
> Show children how medicine can look like
> candy so it's important never to eat what
> looks like candy when they find it or what
> they think is candy or medicine unless their
> parents or a nurse or doctor gives it to them.
> *Pills and Candy Display (Cat. no. 11550)*
> Present short puppet program on the dan-
> gers of alcohol:
> *Groovin' On–No! Mr. Al K. Hall (Cat. no.
> 35490)*

Handouts: There are many inexpensive pamphlets on alcohol and drugs available from
The Health Connection.

Station Nine: Integrity

Objective: To portray the importance of integrity
in maintaining health.

Backdrop: Create a sign highlighting the "I" in
the word Integrity. Here you really need a
poster or banner explaining research on the
importance of integrity and character education.

Activity for all: Have the following video playing
continuously. It consists of several very
short segments that are self-contained so it is
effective with both children and adults
whether watched only a few minutes or in
entirety. This video frequently repeats two
important slogans "Integrity Matters" and
"The Golden Rule Rules ". Produced for
public schools, this video will not offend
as it teaches the importance of treating
everyone with respect.
> *Integrity Matters: Respect (Cat. no.
> 430500)*

Station Ten: Optimism

Objective: To demonstrate the physical and mental health benefits of laughter, optimism, and positive thinking.

Backdrop: Create a sign highlighting the letter "O" in the word Optimism. It is important to have a banner explaining research that supports the importance of this principle.

Assessment Tool: Physical Vision: Screening for glaucoma and other vision related problems

Activity: Mental Vision Test: Hold up half-glass of water and say: "Describe what you see." (The optimist sees a glass half full, the pessimist sees a glass half empty.)

Kid's Activity: Costumed clown painting smiling clown mouths on children or clown puppet telling the value of optimism and laughter.
  Clown Puppet (Cat. no 44430)

Handout: Put Smiling Face Sticker on back of hands saying something like "Just a little reminder that when you smile, the world smiles back at you and your health is better!"

Station Eleven: Nutrition

Nutrition Space One–Cancer Prevention:

Objective: To teach principles of nutrition and demonstrate the cancer-preventive phytonutrients found in plant foods.

Backdrop: Create a sign highlighting the "N" in the word Nutrition with a subtitle of "Cancer Prevention".

Assessment Tool: *Healthy Foods Index (Cat. no. 44840)*

Activity: Analyze Twenty-four Hour Food Recall for Nutrition Adequacy.
  Food Demonstrations (See Chap. 9)

Kid's Activity: *Five-A-Day Puppet Program Kit (Cat. no. 46180)*

Decoration: *Set of Five Fruit and Vegetable Mylar Balloons (Cat. no. 33844)* (See The Health Connection Catalog for larger selection.)

Displays: *Three Dimensional Plexiglas Pyramid* with Healthy Food Models *(Cat. no.37001)*

Handout: *Vegetarian Food Pyramid Handout (Cat. no. 24080)*

Nutrition Space Two–Weight Management:

Objective: To teach principles of nutrition and demonstrate effective weight management principles.

Backdrop: Create a sign highlighting the "N" in Nutrition with a subtitle of "Weight Management."

Assessment Tool: Scales to measure body weight and height.
  Skin-fold calipers Omron Body Fat Analyzer to measure body fat.
  Body mass index calculations from chart: *Determining Body Mass Index (Cat. no. 41200)*

Activity: Analyze Twenty-four Hour Food Recall for Nutrition Adequacy Food Demonstrations (See Chap. 9)

Displays: Amounts of Hidden Fat Display (Cat. no. 10590)
  Amounts of Hidden Sugar Display (Cat. no.10600)
  Globs of Fat Display (Cat. no. 38410)

Handout: How to use waist and hip measurements to calculate whether you are a "Pear" or "Apple" type and list of the possible health implications.

Nutrition Space Three–Coronary and Stroke Risk Reduction

Objective: To teach principles of nutrition that reduce the risk of coronary heart disease and cerebral-vascular disease.

Backdrop: Create a sign highlighting the "N" in Nutrition with a subtitle "Coronary and Stroke Risk Reduction"

Assessment Tool: *Your Coronary Risk Computer Health Assessment Software (Cat. no.35130)*

Activity: Draw blood for lab analysis of cholesterol levels, blood glucose level, and anemia. **(Medical supervision needed.)**

Displays: *Amounts of Hidden Salt Display (Cat. no. 28920)*
  Cholesterol Control Model (Cat. no. 38210)
  Death of an Artery Model (Cat. no. 22080)

Handout: Screening Reports

Station Twelve: Social Support and Service
Objective: To show the importance of social support and service in maintaining health and suggest ways to reach out to other people.
Backdrop: Create a sign highlighting the "S" in Social Support and Service
Activity: Invite representatives of community agencies needing volunteers to present the opportunities for service and recruit applicants. Examples:

Hospitals
Schools
Hospice
International Commission for the
   Prevention of Addictions
Welfare Centers
Red Cross, American Cancer Assoc.,
American Lung Assoc., etc.
Big Brothers and Sisters
Service Clubs such as Lions,
Kiwanis, and Rotary

Step 5: Develop a Time Line

In many cases, the following sample time line allows more than adequate time, but remember you are working with unpaid volunteers and you need to allow time for contingency plans if necessary. Doing these things as far in advance as possible makes it possible to do more advertising. Remember you and the other volunteer staff are investing the same time and energy in providing the health fair events whatever the size of the crowd, but everyone will be happier if more people come out. Adequate advertising on a slim budget requires more advance planning to free up volunteer hours for final reminder advertising during the last month. Advanced planning and practice with your staff allows them to be rested and confident the day of the Health Fair so they can concentrate on providing the best service with a smile and their focus on the attendees. You will of course add detail and adjust the following sample as needed.

Six Months in Advance:
• Set goals
• Develop a budget
• Submit proposal to Church Board

• Form steering committee
• Determine content
• Consider legal issues
• Set date and time
• Select and reserve location (consider adequate parking)
• Plan layout and flow
• Contact other community agencies you wish to participate
• Get commitments from volunteer professional staff
• Plan advertising campaign

Four Months in Advance:
• Create evaluation/feedback form
• Decide on staff identification and appropriate attire
• Order supplies and materials
• Get printing, backdrops, and signs done
• Solicit donated items
• Check on advertising

Two Months in Advance:
• Assemble, organize, and pack supplies for each station.
• Hold training for all staff and volunteers
• Acquaint everyone with their exact location
• Practice with any new, unfamiliar supplies
• Supply all staff with written responsibilities, instructions, and list of supplies they will bring
• Check on advertising

One Month in Advance
• Concentrate on more advertising

One Week in Advance
• Review and confirm everything

One Day in Advance
• If possible, set up and decorate stations

Health Fair Day
- Set up stations as early as possible so they are completed at least two hours before the health fair begins.
- Welcome all staff with a smile and be ready to help solve any unforeseen or unavoidable problems.
- Pass out evaluation forms to everyone–staff and participants
- Explain who will provide breaks and refreshments for staff.
- Open the door and welcome the participants with a smile!
  Follow-up
- Write thank you letters to everyone who contributed time or resources.
- Read evaluation forms and record improvements needed for next time
- Prepare a report for the church board and conference.

Exhibits

For a simpler contact with the community, plan a health exhibit booth at county fairs and shopping centers. See *How to Plan a Health Exhibit (Catalog no. 21540)*. There are many tips in this brochure that apply to health fairs as well. Especially helpful are the two pages with "Hints for Staff" and the budget form.

Resources

All items in italics throughout this chapter are available from The Health Connection. The Health Connection is the General Conference and North American Division Health Ministries Resource Center. Materials prepared by the department to empower church community outreach are available along with products produced by many Seventh-day Adventist entrepreneurs and non-Seventh-day Adventist companies. All products on the topic of nutrition are screened by members of the G. C. Nutrition Council to be sure they are scientifically sound and represent a balanced position. Request both the **School Catalog** and the **Adventist Wellness Catalog**. You need both catalogs in order to find the descriptions for items suggested in this article.

You can place orders <u>Monday-Thursday 8:30 a.m. - 5:00 p.m</u>. Use a credit card and order by phone: Toll-Free Phone 1-800-548-8700 (from USA and Canada) <u>24-Hours-a-Day, 7 Days-a-Week</u>. Fax a purchase order or credit card number with order toll free: 1-888-294-8405

Internet: www.healthconnection.org (School Catalog Only)

E-mail: sales@healthconnection.org

Publicity and Other Features

In co-operation with God's leading, much of the success in getting a good turnout hinges on *"saturation publicity."* Suggestions: use

(1) Posters in both English and other applicable languages distributed throughout the area.
(2) Flyers for church members and others to distribute.
(3) Articles placed in newspapers, including pictures of people holding a large theme banner showing dates. Also, pictures of some of the demonstrators in action.
(5) Public service announcements placed on all local radio stations
(6) Representatives appearing on local TV stations, talking about the fair and health in general.
(7) Consider at least one paid display ad in a local newspaper
(8) Place a large weather-resistant banner in front of the building several days before.

Other Suggestions

If a local hospital healthmobile is available, place it in the parking lot from 9:00 to 4:00, drawing blood for: lipid profiles (total cholesterol, HDL, LDL, LVDL, and triglycerides) and also blood glucose tests for nominal prices, through special arrangement with the local hospital lab. If doing this, advise those coming to only ingest water during the preceding 8 hours for the lipid profiles. Results of the tests were given to them 5 days later at a meeting at the church, with a physician explaining the results and advising about high cholesterol and blood sugar. If they couldn't be present, the results were mailed to them. Note: When "invasive" (blood drawing) tests are done, it must be under the auspices of a physician's office/hospital. This gives an umbrella of protection.

When people arrive, make sure they receive a directory of the location of the booths and what is being offered at each. If possible seminars should be scheduled during the day. Make sure the hours are included in the directory. Also put in lines on which to record the results of screenings. It's nice to give each one coming a pocket folder (donated/purchased from a local office supply store) in which to store handouts.

Dalton, Georgia Health Fair: *Vivian Raitz*

*T*his fair was a large one. Smaller ones than this can be quite effective. We spent about $2,000 on this fair, that included some one-time purchases of items such as sheets for tablecloths and the large banner for out front. The church provided some of the funds and private donors gave the rest. We did not pay for assistance at this fair. It was all voluntary.

Our fair followed a conference-sponsored regional rally in our church on Sabbath, featuring special health speakers in the morning, a potluck, afternoon stretching exercises and workshops. The health fair was held on Sunday in our school gymnasium, attached to the church sanctuary. It began with a 3K/8K fun run/walk, registration 8:00, fun run beginning promptly at 8:30.

Inexpensive T-shirts with logos were available to purchase at a nominal price, if desired. Participants didn't have to go the full distance, just whatever they felt comfortable doing. It was mainly for fun and fellowship. The pastor was in charge. The local Kroger store provided free power bars, water, and apples for the runners/walkers upon their return. We were careful to mention our co-sponsor, the Kroger store, in all of the releases.

The local hospital healthmobile was stationed in the parking lot from 9:00 to 4:00, drawing blood for lipid profiles and blood glucose tests for nominal prices, through a special arrangement with the local hospital lab. People were advised to only ingest water during the preceding 8 hours for the lipid profiles. Results of the tests were given to them 5 days later at a meeting in the church, with a physician explaining the results and advising about high cholesterol and blood sugar. If they couldn't be present, the results were mailed to them. (Note: When "invasive" (blood drawing) tests are done, it must be under the auspices of a physician's office/hospital. This gives an umbrella of protection.)

As people arrived, they were given a 3-page directory of what the booths were offering, where they were, and the hours of various seminars in both English and Spanish. There were spaces for recording the results of screenings. They were also given a pocket folder in which to store handouts. The booths were numbered and corresponding numbers were printed in the directories.

Our 19 booths functioned from 10:00 a.m. to 4:00 p.m. with a Spanish translator at each one. Several local organizations were involved in the fair. The "booths" were basically either 4' x 8' tables or 2' x 8' tables, with no dividers. All screening/counseling was free, except for the lipid profile and blood glucose tests.

Several seminars were scheduled during the day in adjoining rooms, as were Health-related puppet shows and vision/glaucoma screening by Professional Eye Associates. A drawing took place in their room for a free complete eye exam gift certificate.

This health fair combined volunteers from three churches, ours (Dalton, GA); Wildwood Lifestyle Center in Wildwood, Georgia, and the local Spanish church.

—Vivian Raitz, Lay assistant to the Health Director of the Georgia-Cumberland Conference

The booths can be numbered, and corresponding numbers placed in the directories.

All screening/counseling should be free, except for the lipid profile and blood glucose tests.

Other booths can be added to those listed above, such as:

A Book Sales Table—selling cookbooks, providing health handouts, and community health interest survey creating interest in upcoming seminars. (See chapter 5 for sample surveys)

American Cancer Society and other health societies—Handouts

Dental—Dentists doing simple check-ups. It's important to indicate that it's for children also.

Family Practice—Have a physician there to answer questions.

Food—You might get the youth of the church to sell healthy food at reasonable prices.

Health Food Sales—Selling meat analogs and other health-food supplies.

Ophthalmologists—doing simple eye exams.

Face painting and games booth for children.

Suggestions for Seminars

One-hour Natural Remedies seminar.

Health-related puppet shows. The skits for these were obtained from The Health Connection. They are both educational, entertaining, and create much laughter.

One-hour Vegetarian/Nutrition seminar.

Smoking Cessation seminars.

Others listed in the "stations" above.

Reporters from the local newspapers should be invited to take pictures for feature articles.

Provide baby sitting for the helpers and attending parents.

It is essential to have smiling, outgoing "people persons" at the fronts of the booths, inviting those passing to stop by.

Wildwood Health Expo Panels

A Health Expo is a proven way to arrest people' attention. Wildwood has produced a set of 16 professionally credible color panels, two for each of the natural remedies. Each panel is made with beautiful high-resolution photo art and text.

The panels come in two sizes, the regular size of 51 inches by 8 feet and mini-panels are 3 feet by 4 feet. They can be mounted on wood or plastic pipe frames and arranged in such a way as to make booth-like areas where appropriate health screening activities are conducted.

For more information contact: Charles Cleveland (706) 820-9617; e-mail: cleveland@gccsda.com

25

How to Start a Van Ministry

What is Van Ministry?

Van Ministry is a medical screening service that utilizes mobile shuttles or stationary trailer units that are driven to various high traffic locations in metropolitan and rural areas where health screening is conducted, such as: health fairs, community centers, or residential neighborhoods. This flexible screening service has the capacity to offer unlimited types of services to the general public free of charge. This service is offered as part of the humanitarian outreach of the Seventh-day Adventist Church.

The Seventh-day Adventist church has organized van ministries in 21 metropolitan areas around the world offering a wide range of services needed at the various sites. The types of services offered can include: blood pressure screening, health age appraisal, lifestyle factor evaluation, cholesterol screening, glucose level screening, pulmonary function testing and bone density scanning, and others. Services are offered free of charge. The Michigan Conference Van Ministry alone screens 7,000 clients per year, which feeds a year-round seminar cycle that leads back to the local churches.

Why a Van Ministry?

Van ministry presents the opportunity for local churches to reach out to people and share the Gospel in tangible ways by meeting felt needs. For example, there are many people (working and non-working) who do not have the ability to pay for health care, this affords us the opportunity to provide health screening as a free public service of the Church. With the rising cost of medical care this need has become extremely profound; cuts in welfare entitlements and food stamps combined with a slowing economy has necessitated people finding alternative methods for their health care needs. All free services that are provided have no strings attached. These free services are offered to anyone regardless of race, religion, or background. When individuals are screened and realize that this service is totally free many barriers are overcome. Van Ministry has the unique ability to screen thousands of clients in any given area in a short period of time thus imitating the methods of Jesus.

Clients are given information and literature that addresses lifestyle and health issues they face. After the screening is completed clients are given invitations to follow-up health and lifestyle seminars. Professional specialists are recruited from the area churches to provide these seminars.

The goal of this chapter is not only to share the theory of van ministry but also to provide you with some of the forms and resource materials necessary for your church or conference to start and follow-up a van ministry.

1. How to Start a Van Ministry

To start a van ministry it is necessary to look at some of the basic forms that are needed to put the undergirding structure together. Guidelines are an aid in making sure that operations are proficient as well as professional while working with the people in your community.

Guidelines for Working With a Van Ministry. There are 12 points that must be considered if you decide to start this kind of ministry. All services and procedures must be conducted in a professional way. Using established medical procedures, plainly state what you will do and how you will do it. Following these guidelines will help you in establishing your van ministry and avoid any possible liability issues.

1. The local church will provide all health professionals and volunteers to staff the van during the time that the church will be using the van (usually 3-5 people)
2. The staff that the church provides will be available for a general training Session for those who will be working as volunteers on the van.

3. The local church provides qualified trained health professionals for invasive procedures such as cholesterol screening and the drawing of blood.
4. The local church provides the follow-up of the interests that are generated and provides the necessary materials for that follow-up.
5. The local church calls and makes the necessary scheduling of dates, times and locations.
6. Those who are on a yearly schedule will return the tank full of gasoline or there will be an additional charge.

7. Record all mileage in the record book in the van.
8. Van must be returned clean or a cleaning fee will be charged (vacuumed, tables cleaned, trash dumped, windows clean, and equipment stored properly).
9. Van Ministry Follow-up form completed by coordinator and put on the dashboard.
10. Van registration forms completed (date, location etc.) originals put on dashboard. (Copies are forwarded by the Van Ministry area quadrant leader.

Van Ministry Local Church Coordinator Job Description

Purpose: Coordinates the activities of the local church as it relates to Van Ministry.
Duties:
1. Establish screening sites, times, and scheduling for the local church.
2. Drive or arrange for a driver to drive the van from home base to the screening site then back to home base again.
3. Complete and/or pass out all paper work at the proper times: van usage, Driver questionnaire, site insurance, general description form and other forms.
4. Work with the pastor, personal ministries leader/assistant to establish, train, encourage, and motivate regular volunteers for Van Ministry.
5. Work with the pastor, personal ministries leader/assistant to promote, inform and update congregation and church board concerning Van Ministries.
6. Forward all van interests (copies from your zip code area) to the pastor, personal ministries leader/assistant and/or the interest coordinator.
7. Inform Van Ministries director of the progress of the follow-up being done with Van Ministry interests using the Follow-up form.
8. Member of the Van Board (board meets once a quarter).
9. Coordinate fair screenings.
10. Disaster Response Coordination Liaison to:
    A. Communicate to local church members concerning Disaster Response.
    B. Coordinate local church volunteers for Disaster Response.
    C. Communication of training opportunities for those who are volunteering.
Term: Two years
Accountability: Pastor, Personal ministries council and/or church board
Qualifications: Member in good standing who loves to work with all types of people.
    A responsible and reliable person, who motivates and organizes people.
    Has a good driving record and the desire to see the lost come to faith.
Commitment: Four to six hours per month including screening (after initial setup).
Support: Quarterly Van Board meeting, Van Ministries director, Pastor
Resources: Guidelines for Health Screening Ministry, Ministry of Healing, Ministries of Compassion and Welfare Ministry

11. Report any damage to van or defective equipment on the follow-up report form.
12. No eating or drinking by anyone on the van.

Job Descriptions are a vital part of the operation of any successful ministry. Job descriptions help those who want to work with a local van ministry. If you're conducting the van ministry through your local church or conference, this job description describes the duties of the Local Church Coordinator. The Local Church Coordinator is really the hub person through which all of the other activities in van ministries revolve.

Coordinator Survey. Should be filled out yearly by all local church coordinators to aid the local church in keeping them motivated.

Van Ministry Coordinator Survey

1. Do you feel that you are being supported in your function as coordinator?
2. Do you feel that you have had sufficient training to function as coordinator?
3. What is the biggest challenge to your van ministry work with your church?
4. Do you have a sufficient amount of volunteers for your local screenings?
5. How would you like to see Van Ministry improved to serve the lost better?
6. How has the follow-up phase of a van ministry been in your local church?
7. Would your local church benefit from more training and organization?
8. Would your local church benefit from additional motivational sermons?
9. Do you have any other input you would like to share?
10. Do you feel Van Ministry is worth the money expended?

Goal. All ministries must have a goal which they are designed to reach; this goal is to enlarge the kingdom of God. The way in which it will be done is by means of the The Evangelistic Cycle (page 321.) The Cycle Method of Evangelism is a means by which you can help people come to wholeness. To achieve wholeness there is a systematic process that's outlined in scripture by which we help people to move from one step to another. This six-step process will aid your church in evaluating whether you are on track in the cycle. This process has proven effective whether dealing with physical, social, mental, or spiritual needs. It's all the same process.

To recruit volunteers a Van Ministry Volunteer Survey will need to be given out either in your local church or in the civic organization that you plan to recruit from. This volunteer survey is given to individuals within your organization or the church to give members the opportunity to volunteer during the screening process.

How to determine that a ministry is needed in an area? Use an assessment tool such as a Community Health Interest Survey (see chapter 5). As part of that survey residents are asked; what is the greatest need of this community? By asking residents you are gathering empirical unbiased evidence that there's actually a need in the community. Another way to establish community need is to begin to contact various service type agencies or social agencies in your community and find out what are the most pressing needs of the community. It is always wise to work in cooperation with your service agencies such as the Salvation Army, Purple Heart, American Red Cross, Social Services, and employment type agencies that are offered through either Civic or the Federal Government. These agencies have been working a long time in the community and can aid you in knowing what the community needs. Cooperating with these service agencies helps your church not to duplicate services and to form a working relationship. These agencies can refer people to you and you can also refer clients that you cannot serve to them.

Another vital area that needs to be considered is demographics. Before starting a van ministry it is necessary to collect demographic information that will help you access the needs of the people in your community. Demographic material is available at any library. It is necessary to have the zip codes of the cities or the county that you are planning to screen. Usually a printout of the demographics of that area may be obtained for a small fee. The library receptionist will help

by aiding you to get on line or obtain printed copies or books of demographics for the cities in your area. In that information, you will find various needs and buying patterns, living patterns as well as family groups and social economic levels of those residing in that community. This will give you the complete overview of the various patterns of your target community.

Another method of continual assessment is to keep track of the people that you screen and

Van Ministry Volunteer Survey

I am willing to work with the Van Ministry Project, either as a Van Worker or to Follow-up Interests. I will be trained and prepared to perform the tasks for the health outreach and /or follow-up work. I am available on the following days and times. This means a two to three hour commitment on the days that I choose. When conducting a Bible Study, I am willing to be available for a period of at least 6 weeks.

Monday: Time I am available: _____ to _____

Tuesday: Time I am available: _____ to _____

Wednesday: Time I am available: _____ to _____

Thursday: Time I am available: _____ to _____

Friday: Time I am available: _____ to _____

Sabbath: Time I am available: _____ to _____

Sunday: Time I am available: _____ to _____

Name: _____

Day Time Phone Number: _____

Night Time Phone Number: _____

E-mail Address: _____

Church You Attend: _____

Have you given Bible Studies before   Yes _____   No _____

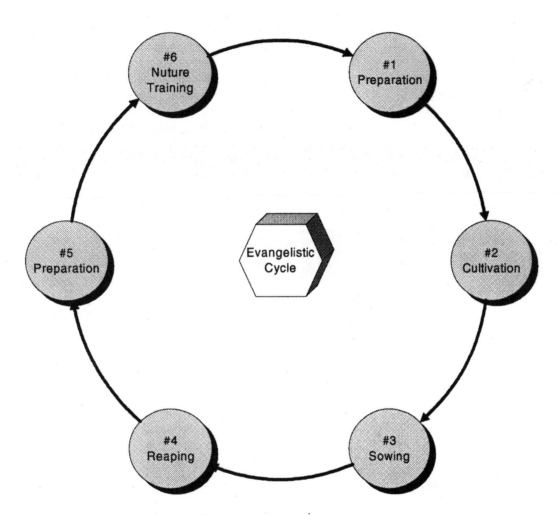

#1 Spiritual Preparation of the Congregation. *

#2 Cultivation of Interests (Bible Studies etc.). *

#3 Sowing (Pathway and Entry events). *

#4 Reaping (The Evangelistic series). *

#5 Preparation of Interests (Followup). *

#6 Nurture and training of members. *

* Represents a two month period

the type of requests that they make. They'll say, "I wish that we had some type of service that could help us with our food budget each month." Or they may say, "There's a lot of gang activity in this area and I wish someone would address that." These types of indicators will help you to know that there's a genuine need in the community and enable you to evaluate whether you have the resources, staff and volunteers to conduct that type of ministry.

What to do. One of the major expenses of van ministry is the mobile medical units that are used to conduct health screening. The shuttles if bought new and renovated for screening cost from $45,000 - $70,000. Shuttle costs may be substantially reduced by buying used shuttles from airports and other companies that operate shuttle services. Renovation may be substantially reduced by the use of volunteer laborers. Some shuttle companies will even donate a portion or all of the cost of a shuttle for a tax deduction. Major auto and bus companies have been known to donate their shuttles to worthy causes.

Another expense of van ministry is that of the necessary legal license and liability insurance.

What is actually done on the screening shuttle? The screening process can be divided into three stations. The first station step that is completed is reception. Reception is the intake

---

Van Ministries Follow-up Report Form

For the _____S.D.A Church

Total number of interests turned over in the month of _____ Total _____ .

Of the total number of interests turned over what were the various requests

Power to Cope _____ .

Powerful Promises _____ .

Discover Lessons _____ .

Seminar Interests _____ .

The number of Bible study interests turned over to

The Pastor _____ .

Bible school _____ .

Interest Coordinator _____ .

Of the numbers above how many have received a

Personal visit_____ .

Personal letter____ _____ .

Mail in lesson_____ .

Seminar invitation _____ .

Requested literature _____ .

Have ALL names been entered into the computer or recorded by the interest coordinator?

Yes _____ . No _____ .

Has ALL the follow-up literature been ordered?   Yes _____ . No _____ .

---

process that is utilized to get people on the van and to make sure that they fill out the registration form; this is done in order to obtain the information necessary to evaluate their condition. When conducting reception, there are three goals that you want to keep in mind. First, you want to make sure that your registration form is filled out completely and that whoever conducts reception looks over the form before it is passed on to the next station.

Secondly, you want to answer any questions that they may have. If they ask medical questions, please feel free to let them know that medical enquires will be answered by the health professional as they progress through the process of the screening event.

Thirdly, you want to make sure that you give them help where it is needed. Sometimes client's leave their glasses at home or maybe they're a non-reader or someone who can't understand the form. You may need to offer help in filling out the form. There are times when you may get people who don't want to fill out a form. You would want to inform clients that this screening service is part of a hypertension research project and we are gathering statistics, and writing research grants on the data that it is collected from the screening event. Once the client is done with the form and it's filled out completely, then you can move on to the next step in the process. (A sample form used by the Michigan Conference is provided below.)

The next step in the process is entitled The Lifestyle Factor Evaluation. At this station various lifestyle factors that contribute to disease are examined. These lifestyle factors are indicators to aid clients in understanding not only the condition they currently may be facing, but also gives them an indication of unhealthy lifestyle habits that will contribute to disease. Like reception, there are also three goals in this evaluation process. First, those lifestyle factors that contribute to disease will be examined. It is important that you make sure the clients understand what is being done and that these habits may contribute to disease. The lifestyle factors are found on the registration form (see suggested form below).

Secondly, a canvass on the stress question should be given. If a client responds that they are under stress by checking the appropriate box, you would say, "I see that you are under stress much of the time". If they answer in the affirmative, tell them we would like to offer them our free Biblical guides entitled "Power to Cope". If the client accepts Guide #1, they would be informed that they will receive Guides 2, 3, and 4 at a later time. It is very important that clients are informed of exactly what they are receiving and that these guides are absolutely free.

Thirdly, the needed literature will be distributed. For example, on the registration form there's a line that records the amount of tobacco smoked. If they record that they smoke tobacco, they will be given a free pamphlet on How You Can Stop Smoking. If they drink alcohol, they are given a free pamphlet that's entitled "How to Stop Drinking." Each lifestyle factor has its corresponding piece of literature. All literature sources used on the mobile shuttles may be obtained from Michigan Conference van ministries.

How are clients informed of local church ministries? The organization or the local churches that are operating in your district should provide information that gives an insight to the type of programs that your organization or your local church offers. Publish this in a directory that can be handed out. By doing so, you make people in the community aware of what types of groups you have to offer, be it Alcoholics Anonymous, Narcotics Anonymous, continuing support groups, or various programs your churches put on to aid spiritual development.

2. How to Follow-up Interests From Your Van Ministry

When people come on the van, they fill out the registration form. This registration form has a battery of information that is asked of the people that come on the van. The reason this information is asked is three-fold. First, it gives a better idea of what the life circumstances are of those that are screened. Secondly, it helps to access specific needs. Thirdly, it gives clients a list of seminars that they can attend that are a follow-up to the screening that has been offered in their community. The registration form reveals their needs; this is what is needed to conduct a meaningful follow-up.

The Follow-up Form (page 322) gives the instructions and the type of materials that are necessary in order to address the needs of the people who are visited. Clients are visited for two reasons, first in order to give the follow-up materials, and secondly to actually meet the individual and address their specific concerns in a personal way. This can be done through the mail, but we prefer that it be done with a visit. A visit gives the opportunity to address those specific needs without the delay of the mail. It is recommended that there be a (two by two) partnership in the visitation of any individual that has requested information. In that way, you will have a partner that can support you by praying as you cover the request that has been made by the individual that came on the van.

In the canvass at the door we always like to address who we are quickly. We also want to address why we're there, and what we're going to do while we're there. It takes relatively few seconds to inform people of why you are there. Make sure to inform people that you have a copy of the screening form so that when they see you at the door, they know that you are there because they requested the material.

A canvass may go something like this, "Hi, I'm _____," (and you introduce your partner). Then you say, "We're from _____, and we have come to deliver your free materials and we would like to know if there is a convenient time that we can drop by next week to give you other materials?" In that way you offer them the opportunity to schedule a time that's convenient for them for you to come back to drop off the requested material. During this follow-up process, you will want to regard the wishes of the people whom you are following up. For example, if they tend to be hesitant or reluctant, you quickly cover the material, give them their Guides and leave until the next scheduled visit. If they welcome you in, that's fine, but do not push your presence.

If they are not interested in more materials, simply let them know what's available, and abide by their choice.

The Van Ministry Follow-up Report Form is necessary for the organization of the local church that is doing the follow-up for two reasons. First, it helps the Conference Coordinator to gauge the progress of the local church; secondly, it aids the local church board or local organizational board to have a monthly report of what's been done.

A record of the total number of interests that were screened is turned over to the various church department heads each month. The total number of requests is listed for those who requested Power to Cope, Powerful Promises, Discover Lessons, and those who are seminar interests. All totals are recorded in the appropriate spaces and the coordinator keeps the original forms and copies are distributed to all concerned in order to give an accurate report of van ministry activities. When spiritual resources are requested (either Bible studies or biblical guides,) copies are turned over to, the Pastor, Bible school, personal ministry's leader, or the interest coordinator.

The software necessary for the Biblical follow-up is called Soul Save 2001 and it is available for a fee from the Michigan Conference Van Ministry (P.O. Box 2244, Belleville, MI 48112. Or call (734) 483-8301. Another section on the follow-up form covers how many people received a personal visit, personal letter, seminar invitation, and how many requested literature. These numbers are necessary in order for the various departments to stock material as well as supply those who will be going out on visitation.

There is a place on the form to report whether all of the interests have been entered into the computer. Soul Save or other database entries help to develop a mailing list so that information can be mailed out to those who are screened. This form gives a birds eye view of what's been happening from month to month. It also aids in supplying more efficient follow-up of people who request materials.

3. How to Start Supporting Ministries

As those who conduct van ministry soon realize, there are many needs. As these needs manifest themselves, the Spirit of God will burden believers to develop various ministries to address those types of needs. Demographics help you to some extent, but it's only a matter of experience that helps you to determine what the real needs of those whom you screen are.

You will first want to screen over a relatively long period of time, at least six months to a year. This will help determine what type of ministry you want to start as a felt need ministry in your community. Once you determine the felt needs, you'll want to take the steps that are necessary to establish those specific types of outreach ministries. For example, the first ministry that tends to be successful in most communities is a food bank. When you establish a food bank, you'll want to look at what type of resources you have available. You'll want to make sure that you establish a ministry that is permanent in order to establish a clientele and help people to know their needs will be addressed on a continual basis.

How do you do this? In the Scriptures, the admonition is given to us, to count the cost before you build. You'll want to have a planning session to gather the necessary facts in order to make an informed decision on whether you want to start a particular type of ministry. Next, you'll want to do an assessment of the needs in the community. Thirdly, cooperating with community service agencies helps you not duplicate services and to form working relationships with community agencies that can refer people to you. You can also refer people to them.

How do you take that step once you've established that there is a genuine need? The first thing is to develop a step-by-step plan to establish that needed type of ministry. If you are establishing a ministry in a church context, you'll want to put a proposal together. It doesn't have to be anything elaborate, just an instrument which you can pass onto your board members or whatever committee you're involved with to share your vision and the process which you will follow in order to establish this ministry.

You do not want to do things alone. You'll want to gather support people as you build the vision and follow through with the process that's been voted on by your organization. It is highly recommended that you establish a time line for starting your ministry.

If you are establishing a food bank , contact the local agency that's responsible for the distribution of food bank items. This distribution process is generally done by a central agency. In the Metro/Detroit area, the most frequently used agency is the Gleaners Food System. You'll want to approach the agency and request an application. A fee for the application process is typical, then the food bank system you are using will evaluate your organization. Once the evaluation is done, they will give you approval or suggest changes needed to come into compliance.

There are three major issues that need to be considered. First, does your church have space sufficient to store food for emergency situations? It doesn't have to be a large space, but it does have to be adequate. Secondly, you'll need to have a 501C3 status with the Internal Revenue Service (IRS). Any organization without this status cannot be a food bank distributor. Thirdly, you'll want to make sure you have a freezer and shelving units in order to store the food properly.

You will also need a food bank coordinator. Some organizations conduct food bank once a month, some once a week. The times do vary, but you want to make sure that you have the resources and the time allotted with your volunteers to fulfill your commitment to the community. It's tragic to have an organization or a church start a food bank and then in midstream drop out because of improper planning. With food banks you want to make sure that yours is located in an area where the need is established. You will have people who have transportation needs, people who cannot get transportation, and some who use local bus service. You will also want to publicize your food bank; publication can be done very simply. Some food banks operate solely by word of mouth, as low-income people, the working poor, or people who have medical conditions find out about your food bank they will come.

We recommend that you set the food bank up in what's called a supermarket style. You have a line of tables where all the items are set out and limit signs are posted. People are allowed to pick and choose what they want. This preserves the dignity and the right to choose of individuals. We recommend that you don't shove some things in a bag and give it to people. You want to make sure that people have the dignity to choose what they would like and the amount that they would like within the limits posted.

Food banks are not only for low income or the poor. Some people who work do not have enough money to meet their needs. There also are people who have medical conditions, injuries, or short-term situations that they face. People must always be treated with respect and dignity because they belong to God.

It's also necessary to recruit your project volunteers. You use the same process that is outlined in part one. Pass out a volunteer form during your church hour or anytime when your civic organization meets. This form will help you evaluate the amount of volunteers and support staff that are available. It's recommended that you have at least six to eight volunteers each time you conduct your food bank. As your food bank grows you will need to add more volunteers, because you want to make sure that people are cared for.

It generally takes time, three, four, sometimes even six months in order to establish a steady clientele. Don't turn anyone away or give them the third degree, or ask inappropriate questions. If people are coming, there is a need. We do set limits on people. If people become selfish and greedy, then we curb those types of abuses. In terms of a screening process, we simply have them fill out a registration form, get their name and address and let them choose what they would like.

We also give people the opportunity to give a donation as part of the food bank. This donation helps establish the dignity of individuals. People feel much better about themselves when they contribute at least a little bit towards the food products they receive. If there are clients who cannot afford to give a donation, the food is offered to them free or by agency referral.

As part of your food bank or other support ministry, you'll want to offer follow-up services. For example, one food bank started in the southwest Detroit area, offered a financial management seminar. It was either conducted before or after the food bank time, and covered budgeting issues, how to manage money, and how to stretch your dollar. Any of these tips help people to eventually get off of the assistance that's offered through food banks and other agencies.

The goal of all ministries is to empower people , to help them help themselves. When we do this we go that much further in helping people to feel dignity and to eventually become God dependent.

Another type of community outreach that can naturally result from mobile medical screening, are Co-ops. Co-ops are different from food banks in the sense that Co-ops are purchasing co-operatives where the people get together and buy large amounts of food at bulk prices. Co-ops tend to attract lower and higher income community residents. When food is purchased at bulk prices, it substantially lowers the cost of the items. These bulk items can relieve the financial stress that people may feel as a result of an illness, being poor even though working, or not having employment at all. Co-ops are conducted in the same way that food banks are with the exception that the orders are made before the people come to you. A time is set when people get together to order or they can actually phone the orders in to the Co-op Coordinator. On the day of pick-up, clients come with their money, expecting to receive the goods that are shipped. There are agencies, such as Country Life Food Distribution, and others who, if you have a large order at one time, will offer free shipping or large discounts for the people who manage the Co-op.

With a food Co-op, you do not have to have a 501C3 status, or a storage place, because people come on the day the co-op is conducted and pick up their goods as they pay for them. As with the food bank, you'll want to offer follow-up services for the people who come to a food co-op. You can offer financial management, home budgeting; you can also offer the opportunity to engage in special groups. Some of these groups include Grief Recovery, Vegetarian Cooking Schools, Stress Reduction Seminars, and also Discover Bible School. These types of seminars are offered in addition to the services that you already offer and are conducted either in conjunction with your food banks or co-ops or at another time.

Some fantastic stories come out of these activities that can be used to foster interest in continuing activity. One story comes to mind of a man who came to a screening van in Taylor, Michigan. He mentioned that he was going to commit suicide on Thanksgiving Day. The person who was taking the interview recorded his statement on the form. This man immediately became a priority, and was put in contact with a psychologist who works with mental health services. He began counseling. A follow-up team paid him a visit. T he first visit, he was not there. The second visit the team left the first Bible study video designed to encourages people. For several visits afterward, this man didn't answer the door but the team left the videos anyway. About the fourth or fifth video, the man's wife came to the door and said, "Are you the people who are leaving the videos on our doorstep?" The person who was following up said, "Yes, I am." The dear lady shared just how encouraging the videos had been to her and the family and she even requested additional videos to give to other family members that lived outside of the household. That man now knows that Seventh-day Adventists love him and want to help him. The entire family is enjoying the videos and finding out more about how God can help them to work through the struggles of living life in today's challenging social climate.

This is the type of experiences that your church will have as you minister unselfishly to the needs of the community. You might write these stories for publication in your church newsletter or start your own newsletter, including stories that will inform people about what you're doing in your van ministry and follow-up. You will begin to develop a list of people to whom to mail your newsletter; this will encourage them as well as aid your ministry financially. Most rewarding of all is the good will and loyal clientele you build in your community and the souls that come into the church as a result.

26

Alternate Methods and Quarkery

"Alternative medicine" has become the politically correct term for questionable practices formerly labeled quack and fraudulent. In recent years, most media reports have contained no critical evaluation and have featured the views of proponents and their satisfied clients.

To avoid confusion, "alternative" methods should be classified as genuine, experimental, or questionable. Genuine alternatives are comparable methods that have met science-based criteria for safety and effectiveness. Experimental alternatives are unproven but have a plausible rationale and are undergoing responsible investigation. The most noteworthy is use of a 10%-fat diet for treating coronary heart disease. Questionable alternatives are groundless and lack a scientifically plausible rationale. The archetype is homeopathy, which claims that "remedies" so dilute that they contain no active ingredient can exert powerful therapeutic effects. Blurring these distinctions enables promoters of quackery to argue that because some practices labeled "alternative" have merit, the rest deserve equal consideration and respect. Enough is known, however, to conclude that most questionable "alternatives" are worthless.

The "alternative movement" is part of a general societal trend toward rejection of science as a method of determining truths. In line with this philosophy, "alternative" proponents assert that scientific medicine (which they mislabel as allopathic, conventional, or traditional medicine) is but one of a vast array of health-care options.

Under the rules of science, people who make the claims bear the burden of proof. It is their responsibility to conduct suitable studies and report them in sufficient detail to permit evaluation and confirmation by others. But instead of conducting scientific studies, they use anecdotes and testimonials to promote their practices and political maneuvering to keep regulatory agencies at bay.

When someone feels better after having used a product or procedure, it is natural to credit whatever was done. This is unwise, however, because most ailments resolve by themselves and those that persist can have variable symptoms. Even serious conditions can vary enough from day to day to enable useless methods to gain large followings. Without controlled clinical trials, any treatment that is used could receive credit for the body's natural recuperative ability. In addition, taking action often produces temporary relief caused by a placebo effect. This effect is a beneficial change in a person's condition that occurs in response to a treatment but is not due to the pharmacologic or physical aspects of the treatment. Belief in the treatment is not essential, but the placebo effect may be enhanced by such factors as faith, sympathetic attention, sensational claims, testimonials, and the use of scientific-looking charts, devices, and terminology. Another drawback of individual success stories is that they don't indicate how many failures might occur for each success. People who are not aware of these facts tend to give undeserved credit to "alternative" methods.

Many "alternative" approaches are rooted in vitalism, the concept that bodily functions are due to a vital principle or "life force" distinct from the physical forces explainable by the laws of physics and chemistry and detectable by scientific instrumentation. Practitioners whose methods are based on vitalistic philosophy maintain that diseases should be treated by "stimulating the body's ability to heal itself" rather than by "treating symptoms." Homeopaths, for example, claim that illness is due to a disturbance of the body's "vital force," which they can correct with special remedies, while many acupuncturists claim that disease is due to imbalance in the flow of "life energy" (chi or Qi), which they can balance by twirling needles in the skin. Many chiropractors claim to assist the body's "Innate

Intelligence" by adjusting the patient's spine. Naturopaths speak of "Vis Medicatrix Naturae." Ayurvedic physicians refer to "prana." And so on. The "energies" postulated by vitalists cannot be measured by scientific methods. Although vitalists often pretend to be scientific, they regard personal experience, subjective judgment, and emotional satisfaction as preferable to objectivity and hard evidence.

"Alternative" practitioners often claim that their approaches promote general health and are cost-effective against chronic health problems. However, there is no published evidence that they are more likely than mainstream physicians to persuade their patients to adopt a healthy lifestyle. Nor have any vitalistic approaches been proven effective or cost-effective against any disease.

"Complementary medicine" and "integrated medicine" are described by their proponents as a synthesis of standard and alternative methods that uses the best of both. Typically, they credit alternatives for any improvement experienced by the patient and blame standard treatments for any negative effects. No published data indicate the extent to which "complementary" practitioners actually use proven therapies or the extent to which they burden patients with medically useless methods. However, there is good reason to believe that most of them provide substandard care and undermine their patients' confidence in standard care.

Many news reports have exaggerated the significance of the National Institutes of Health (NIH)'s National Center for Complementary and of Alternative Medicine (NCCAM). Creation of this center—which was originally called the Office of Unconventional Medicine—was spearheaded by promoters of quack cancer therapies who wanted more attention paid to their methods. Many of it advisory panel members have been promoters of "alternative" methods, and none of its publications have criticized any method. Although it has funded some significant research projects during the past three years, none of its earlier grants yielded useful findings.

Commonly Used Methods

Each of the following approaches has at least one of the following characteristics: (a) its rationale or underlying theory has no scientific basis, (b) it has not been demonstrated safe and/or effective by well-designed studies, (c) it is deceptively promoted, or (d) its practitioners are not qualified to make appropriate diagnoses.

Aromatherapy involves the use of aromatic oils from plants to affect mood or promote health. The oils are administered in small quantities through inhalation, massage, or other applications to the skin. Aromatherapy products include diffusers, lamps, pottery, candles, pendants, earrings, shampoos, skin creams, lotions, bath salts, and shower gels. The aromatic oils are alleged to contain hormones, antibiotics, and antiseptics, and to represent the "life force," "spirit," or "soul" of the plant. Some proponents claim that aromatherapy is a complete medical system that can "revitalize cells," strengthen defense mechanisms, and cure the cause of disease. Although pleasant odors may enhance a person's effort to relax, there is no scientific evidence that they can influence the course of any disease.

"Chinese medicine," often called **"Oriental medicine"** or **"traditional Chinese medicine (TCM),"** encompasses a vast array of folk medical practices based on mysticism. It holds that the body's vital energy (chi or qi) circulates through hypothetical channels, called meridians, that have branches connected to bodily organs and functions. Illness is attributed to imbalance or interruption of chi. Ancient practices such as acupuncture and Qigong are claimed to restore balance by removing the interruptions.

Traditional **acupuncture**, as now practiced, involves the insertion of stainless steel needles into various body areas. A low-frequency current may be applied to the needles to produce greater stimulation. The treatment is applied to "acupuncture points," which are said to be located throughout the body. Originally there were 365 such points, corresponding to the days of the year, but the number identified by proponents during the past 2,000 years has increased gradually to over 2,000. Some practitioners place needles at or near the site of disease, while others select points on the basis of symptoms. In traditional acupuncture a combination of points is usually used. However, the existence of "meridians," "acupuncture points," or chi has never been scientifically validated.

The diagnostic process used by TCM practitioners may include questioning (medical history, life-style), observations (skin, tongue, color), listening (breath sounds), and pulse-taking. Medical science recognizes only one pulse, corresponding to the heartbeat, which can be felt in the wrist, neck, feet, and various other places throughout the body. TCM practitioners check six alleged pulses at each wrist and identify more than twenty-five alleged pulse qualities such as "sinking," "slippery," "soggy," "tight," and "wiry." TCM's "pulses" supposedly reflect the type of imbalance, the condition of each organ system, and the status of the patient's "chi."

The herbs prescribed by Chinese medicine practitioners in the United States are not regulated for safety, potency, or effectiveness. There is also the risk that acupuncturists whose approach to diagnosis is not based on scientific concepts will fail to diagnose dangerous conditions.

Some acupuncturists reject Chinese medicine's trappings and postulate that pain relief occurs through mechanisms such as the production of endorphins (chemicals similar to narcotics). Although acupuncture may relieve pain, such relief tends to be short-lived. The evidence supporting claims that acupuncture is effective consists mostly of practitioners' observations and poorly designed studies. Acupuncture has not been proven to influence the course of any organic disease.

In 1997, a Consensus Development Conference sponsored by the National Institutes of Health and several other agencies concluded that "there is sufficient evidence . . . of acupuncture's value to expand its use into conventional medicine and to encourage further studies of its physiology and clinical value." This conclusion reflected the bias of the panelists who were selected by a planning committee dominated by acupuncture proponents

Ayurvedic medicine is a set of practices promoted by proponents of transcendental meditation (TM). Ayurveda (meaning "life knowledge") is a traditional Indian approach that includes meditation, "purification" procedures, rejuvenation therapies, herbal and mineral preparations, exercises and dietary advice based on "body type." Its origin is traceable to four Sanskrit books called the *Vedas*—the oldest and most important scriptures of India, shaped sometime before 200 BC. These books attributed most disease and bad luck to demons, devils, and the influence of stars and planets. Ayurveda's basic theory states that the body's functions are regulated by three "irreducible physiological principles" called *doshas*, whose Sanskrit names are *vata, pitta,* and *kapha.* Like the "sun signs" of astrology, these terms are used to designate body types as well as the traits that typify them. Like astrologic writings, ayurvedic writings contain long lists of supposed physical and mental characteristics of each constitutional type. Through various combinations of *vata, pitta,* and *kapha,* ten body types are possible. However, one's *doshas* (and therefore one's body type) can vary from hour to hour and season to season.

Ayurvedic proponents claim that the symptoms of disease are always related to "imbalance" of the doshas, which can be determined by feeling the patient's wrist pulse or completing a questionnaire. Some proponents claim that the pulse can be used to detect diabetes, cancer, musculoskeletal disease, asthma, and "imbalances at early stages when there may be no other clinical signs and when mild forms of intervention may suffice." "Balance" is supposedly achieved through a multitude of procedures and products, many of which are said to be specific for specific body types.

TM is a technique in which the meditator sits comfortably with eyes closed and mentally repeats a Sanskrit word or sound (mantra) for 15 to 20 minutes, twice a day. It is alleged to help people think more clearly, improve their memory, recover immediately from stressful situations, reverse their aging process, and enjoy life more fully. Proponents also claim that "stress is the basis of all illness" and that TM is "the single most effective thing you can do to improve all aspects of health and to increase inner happiness and learning ability." These claims are unsubstantiated and probably are untestable.

Deepak Chopra, M.D., a leading ayurveda proponent, claims that "If you have happy thoughts, then you make happy molecules. On the other hand, if you have sad thoughts, and angry thoughts, and hostile thoughts, then you make those molecules which may depress the immune system and make you more susceptible to disease." Chopra promises "perfect health" to those who can harness their consciousness as a healing force. Meditation may temporarily relieve stress—as would many types of relaxation techniques—but the rest of these claims have no scientific basis.

Chelation therapy is a series of intravenous administrations of a synthetic amino acid (EDTA) plus various other substances. Proponents claim that chelation can reverse atherosclerosis, is an effective alternative to bypass surgery, and works against many other diseases. However, recent well-designed studies have demonstrated that chelation therapy is not effective against either coronary artery disease or intermittent claudication (a condition in which circulation to the legs is impaired). It is safe to assume that improvements reported by heart-disease patients undergoing chelation therapy are due to improvements in lifestyle (smoking cessation, dietary change, appropriate exercise, and weight control), the same measures recommended by scientific practitioners. Chelation therapy is the most dangerous form of "alternative" therapy because proponents advertise that people advised to have bypass surgery should see them instead. The Federal Trade Commission has obtained a cease-and-desist order barring the leading chelation organization from advertising that chelation is effective against cardiovascular disease, but many practitioners still do so.

Chiropractic encompasses many practices, most of which are related to the false premise that spinal problems are the cause, or underlying cause, of most ailments. Whereas nearly all chiropractors manipulate the spine as their primary method of treatment, their rationale and techniques vary considerably.

D.D. Palmer, chiropractic's founder, postulated that the body's "vital force," which he termed "Innate," expressed itself through the nervous system. Chiropractors who cling strictly to this notion allege that misalignments ("subluxations") of the vertebra cause most illnesses by interfering with the flow of "nerve energy" to body organs. Most chiropractors acknowledge the importance of other factors in disease but tend to regard mechanical disturbances of the nervous system as an underlying cause. In addition, many chiropractors engage in unscientific diagnostic procedures (primarily hair analysis and applied kinesiology), prescribe inappropriate food supplements, and utilize homeopathic remedies. A small percentage of chiropractors denounce Palmer's theories, spurn unscientific practices, and confine their practice to musculoskeletal problems.

Although chiropractic schools are accredited, they do not provide the depth of diagnostic and therapeutic training that physicians receive. Whereas most medical school faculties are large and contain experts in every aspect of medical practice, chiropractic schools have few or no physicians on their faculty. While the patients studied by medical students encompass the full range of disease, the vast majority seen by chiropractic students seek help for musculoskeletal problems. Although some of their courses are based on standard medical textbooks, chiropractic students lack the experiences needed to make the information meaningful. Chiropractic instruction in such subjects as pediatrics, obstetrics, and gynecology is usually limited to the classroom, with little or no actual patient contact and no experience with hospitalized patients. Moreover, since much of chiropractic is based on a false premise, neither length of study nor accreditation of its schools can ensure that those who graduate will practice competently.

Chiropractic has received considerable favorable publicity since studies by the RAND Corporation and the U.S. Agency for Health Care Policy and Research (AHCPR) concluded that spinal manipulation may be appropriate for certain cases of low-back pain. However, most of the research upon which this conclusion was based was done by medical doctors and physical therapists and does not reflect what takes place in most chiropractic offices.

Many chiropractors urge everyone to have their spine checked weekly or monthly for "preventative maintenance." There is no scientific evidence supporting this practice. Some chiropractors take full-spine x-rays of all or most of their patients. This procedure has little or no diagnostic value and involves a large amount of radiation.

Consumers who wish to have chiropractic care should choose a chiropractor whose practice is limited to treating musculoskeletal problems and whose work is respected by local medical doctors. If spinal manipulation can help, it generally does so within two weeks. It is wise to avoid chiropractors who prescribe dietary supplements, homeopathic remedies, or herbal products for the treatment of disease or who sell any of these products in their offices. For dietary advice, the best sources are registered dietitians. For additional information, see http://www.chirobase.org.

Clinical ecology, which proponents also misrepresent as "environmental medicine," is not a recognized medical specialty. It is based on the notion that multiple common symptoms are triggered by hypersensitivity to common foods and chemicals. Proponents typically suggest that the immune system is like a barrel that continually fills with chemicals until it overflows, signaling the presence of disease. However, some also say that "immune system dysregulation" can be triggered by a single serious episode of infection, stress, or chemical exposure. Potential stressors include practically everything that modern humans encounter, such as urban air, diesel exhaust, tobacco smoke, fresh paint or tar, organ-

ic solvents and pesticides, certain plastics, newsprint, perfumes and colognes, medications, gas used for cooking and heating, building materials, permanent press and synthetic fabrics, household cleaners, rubbing alcohol, felt-tip pens, cedar closets, tap water, and even electromagnetic forces.

Clinical ecologists typically base their diagnoses on "provocation-neutralization" testing. In this test, the patient reports symptoms that develop within ten minutes after various concentrations of suspected substances are administered under the tongue or injected into the skin. If any symptoms occur, the test is considered positive and lower concentrations are given until a dose is found that "neutralizes" the symptoms. Researchers at the University of California have demonstrated that these procedures are not valid.

Treatment requires avoidance of suspected substances and involves lifestyle changes that can range from minor to extensive. Generally, patients are instructed to modify their diet and to avoid such substances as scented shampoos; after-shave products; deodorants; cigarette smoke; automobile exhaust fumes; and clothing, furniture, and carpets that contain synthetic fibers. Extreme restrictions can involve staying at home for months or avoiding physical contact with family members. In many cases the patient's life becomes centered around the illness.

Craniosacral therapy, also called **craniopathy** and **cranial osteopathy**, is based on the notion that bones of the skull are moveable and can be manipulated. Some practitioners claim to attune themselves to the patient's "rhythm" while holding the patient's skull in their hands. Some claim to improve the flow of "life energy," thereby curing or preventing a wide variety of health problems. Some claim to remove blockages to the flow of cerebrospinal fluid. Some claim to realign the skull bones. Actually, the bones of the skull fuse early in life and cannot be moved independently.

Electrodiagnosis involves the use of various devices purported to diagnose and treat "energy imbalances" alleged to signify disease. The procedure, also called Electroacupuncture according to Voll (EAV), was initiated during the 1970s by a German physician who developed the first model of the device. Subsequent models include the *Vega, Dermatron, Accupath 1000,* and *Interro.* Proponents claim these devices measure disturbances in the body's flow of "electro-magnetic energy" along "acupuncture meridians." Actually, they are little more than fancy galvanometers that measure electrical resistance of the patient's skin when touched by a probe. One wire from the device goes to a brass cylinder covered by moist gauze, which the patient holds in one hand. A second wire is connected to a probe, which the operator touches to "acupuncture points" on the patient's other hand or foot. This completes a low-voltage circuit and the device registers the flow of current. The information is then relayed to a gauge that provides a numerical readout. The size of the number actually depends on how hard the probe is pressed against the patient's skin. The "treatment" selected depends on the scope of the practitioner's practice and may include acupuncture, dietary change, vitamin supplements and/or homeopathic remedies. Some EAV devices have been seized by state and federal regulators, but hundreds remain in use.

Herbalism is practiced mainly by naturopaths, chiropractors, acupuncturists, iridologists, and unlicensed "herbalists," many of whom prescribe herbs for virtually every health problem. While some attempt to base their prescriptions on research findings, others are guided by such perceptions as "astrological influences" and the "Doctrine of Signatures" (the ancient belief that the form and shape of a drug source determine its therapeutic value). Many herbs contain hundreds or even thousands of chemicals that have not been completely catalogued. While some of these may turn out to be useful as therapeutic agents, others could well prove toxic. Most herbal products sold in the United States are not standardized, which means that determining the exact amounts of their ingredients can be difficult or impossible. With safe and effective medicines available, treatment with herbal products makes little sense. Moreover, many herbal practitioners are not physicians and lack adequate training in the diagnosis and treatment of disease.

Homeopathy is based on a 200-year-old notion that if large amounts of a substance can produce symptoms in a healthy individual, tiny amounts can cure diseases having those symptoms. This idea is scientifically unsupportable.

Homeopathic products are made from minerals, plant substances, and several other sources. If the original substance is soluble, one part is diluted with either nine or ninety-nine parts of distilled water and/or alcohol and shaken vigorously; if insoluble, it is finely ground and pulverized in similar proportions with powdered lactose (milk sugar). One part of the diluted medicine is diluted, and the process is repeated until the desired concentration is reached. Dilutions of 1 to 10 are designated by the Roman numeral X (1X = 1/10, 3X = 1/1,000, 6X = 1/1,000,000). Similarly, dilutions of 1 to 100 are designated by the Roman numeral C (1C = 1/100, 3C = 1/1,000,000, and so on). Most remedies today range from 6X to 30X, but many products of 30C or more are marketed.

A 30X dilution means that the original substance has been diluted 10^{30} times. Assuming that a cubic centimeter of water contains fifteen drops, 10^{30} is greater than the number of drops of water that would fill a container more than fifty times the size of the Earth. Since the least amount of a substance in a solution is one molecule, a 30C solution would have to have at least one molecule of the original substance dissolved in a minimum of 10^{60} molecules of water. This would require a container more than 30 billion times the size of the Earth.

Actually, the laws of chemistry state that there is a limit to the dilution that can be made without losing the original substance altogether. This limit, called Avogadro's number (6.023×10^{23}), corresponds to homeopathic potencies of 12C or 24X (1 part in 10^{24}). Proponents acknowledge that there is virtually no chance that even one original molecule would remain after extreme dilutions. But they claim that the vigorous shaking or pulverizing with each step of dilution leaves behind a "spirit-like" essence that cures by reviving the body's "vital force." This notion is unsubstantiated and clashes with the laws of physics. Moreover, if it were true, any molecule in the diluting substance might imprint an "essence" that could exert powerful (and unpredictable) medicinal effects. Although the FDA permits the sale of homeopathic remedies, it does not recognize them as effective.

Iridology is based on the notion that each area of the body is represented by a corresponding area in the iris of the eye (the colored area surrounding the pupil). Iridologists claim that states of health and disease can be diagnosed according to the color, texture, and location of various pigment flecks in the eye. Iridology practitioners purport to diagnose "imbalances" and treat them with vitamins, minerals, herbs, and similar products. They may also claim that the eye markings can reveal a complete history of past illnesses as well as previous treatment. The late Bernard Jensen, D.C., the leading American iridologist, stated that "Nature has provided us with a miniature television screen showing the most remote portions of the body by way of nerve reflex responses." He also claimed that iridology analyses are more reliable and "offer much more information about the state of the body than do the examinations of Western medicine." However, in two large studies, Jensen and seven other prominent iridologists could not distinguish between patients who had kidney or gallbladder disease and those who were healthy.

Macrobiotics is a quasireligious approach centered around a semivegetarian diet claimed to improve health and prolong life. Proponents suggest that the diet is effective in preventing and treating cancer, AIDS, and other serious diseases. There is no scientific evidence to support these claims. Macrobiotic proponents base their recommendations for foods on the amount of "yin" or "yang" (alleged "energy modes") rather than nutrient content. Macrobiotic practitioners may base their recommendations on pulse diagnosis and other unscientific procedures related to Chinese medicine. These include "ancestral diagnosis," "astrological diagnosis," "aura and vibrational diagnosis," "environmental diagnosis" (including consideration of celestial influences" and tidal motions), and "spiritual diagnosis" (an evaluation of "atmospheric vibrational conditions" to identify spiritual influences, including memories and "visions of the future").

Today's leading proponent is Michio Kushi, founder and president of the Kushi Institute in Becket, Massachusetts. According to Institute publications, the macrobiotic way of life should include chewing food at least 50 times per mouthful (or until it becomes liquid), not wearing synthetic or woolen clothing next to the skin, avoiding long hot baths or showers, having large green plants in your house to enrich the oxygen content of the air, and singing a happy song every day. Kushi claims that cancer is largely due to improper diet, thinking, and way of life, and can be influenced by changing these factors. He recommends "yin foods" for cancers due to excess yang, and "yang foods" for tumors that are predominantly yin. His books contain case histories of people whose cancers have supposedly disappeared after they adopted macrobiotic eating. However, the only reports of efficacy are testimonials by patients, many of whom received conventional cancer therapy. The diet itself can cause cancer patients to undergo serious weight loss.

Some versions of macrobiotic diets contain adequate amounts of nutrients, but others do not. Studies of children living in several macrobiotic communities have found that they tended to be smaller, shorter, and to weigh less than children fed normal diets. Deficiencies of vitamin B12, iron, and vitamin D have also been reported.

Naturopathy is based on the belief that the cause of disease is violation of nature's laws. Naturopaths claim to remove the underlying causes of disease and to stimulate the body's natural healing processes. They state that diseases are the body's effort to defend itself and that cures result from increasing the patient's "vital force" by ridding the body of waste products and "toxins." Like some chiropractors, many naturopaths believe that virtually all ailments fall within the scope of their practice. Naturopathic treatments can include "natural food" diets, vitamins, herbs, tissue minerals, cell salts, manipulation, massage, exercise, diathermy, colonic enemas, acupuncture, and homeopathy. Although naturopaths claim that they stress prevention of disease, they tend to oppose immunization procedures.

Natural hygiene is an offshoot of naturopathy that emphasizes fasting; a raw-food diet of vegetables, fruits, and nuts; and food-combining, a dietary practice based on the incorrect notion that certain food combinations can cause or correct ill health. Natural hygienists oppose immunization, fluoridation, and food irradiation and eschew most forms of medical treatment.

Orthomolecular therapy is defined by its proponents as "the treatment of disease by varying the concentrations of substances normally present in the human body." It dates back to the early 1950s when a few psychiatrists began adding massive doses of nutrients to their treatment of severe mental problems. The original substance was vitamin B3 (nicotinic acid or nicotinamide), and the therapy was termed "megavitamin therapy." Later the treatment regimen was expanded to include other vitamins, minerals, hormones, and diets, any of which may be combined with conventional drug therapy and electroshock treatments. A few hundred physicians now use this approach to treat a wide variety of conditions, both mental and physical.

The human body has limited capacity to use vitamins in its metabolic activities. When vitamins are consumed in excess of the body's physiological needs, they function as drugs rather than vitamins. A few situations exist in which high doses of vitamins are known to be beneficial, but they must still be used with caution because of potential toxicity. For example, large doses of niacin can be very useful as part of a comprehensive, medically supervised program for control-

ling abnormal blood cholesterol levels. "Orthomolecular" practitioners go far beyond this, however, by prescribing large amounts of supplements to all or most of the patients they treat.

Reflexology, also called **zone therapy**, is based on beliefs that each body part is represented on the hands and feet and that pressing on the hands and feet can have therapeutic effects in other parts of the body. Proponents claim that the body is divided into ten zones that begin or end in the hands and/or feet, and that each organ or body part is "represented" on the hands feet. Proponents also claim that abnormalities can be diagnosed by feeling the feet and that pressing each area can stimulate the flow of energy, blood, nutrients, and nerve impulses to the corresponding body zone. The pathways postulated by reflexologists have not been anatomically demonstrated.

Most reflexologists claim that their foot massages can relieve stress, which presumably is correct but does not require the services of a "certified reflexologist" for $35 to $100 per session. Many practitioners claim foot reflexology can cleanse the body of toxins, increase circulation, assist in weight loss, and improve the health of organs throughout the body. Some claim that reflexology is effective against a large number of serious diseases. There is no scientific support for these assertions.

Therapeutic Touch is a method in which the hands are used to "direct human energies to help or heal someone who is ill." Proponents claim that healers can detect and correct "energy imbalances" by stroking the body or placing their hands above the afflicted part. Healing supposedly can result from a transfer of "excess energy" from healer to patient. Neither the forces involved nor the alleged therapeutic benefits have been demonstrated by scientific testing. It is safe to assume that any reactions to the procedure are psychological responses to the "laying on of hands."

As taught by its leading proponent, TT involves four steps: (1) "centering," a meditative process said to align the healer with the patent's energy level, (2) "assessment," said to be performed by using one's hands to detect forces emanating from the patient, (3) "unruffling the field," said to involve sweeping "stagnant energy" downward to prepare for energy transfer, and (4) transfer of "energy" from practitioner to patient. "Non-contact therapeutic touch" is done the same way, except that the "healer's" hands are held a few inches away from the body.

There is no scientific evidence that the "energy transfer" postulated by proponents actually occurs. In 1996, Linda Rosa, R.N., published a critique of all of the studies related to TT she could locate in nursing journals and elsewhere. She concluded: "The more rigorous the research design, the more detailed the statistical analysis, the less evidence that there is any observed—or observable—phenomenon."

A few years ago, Rosa's daughter Emily tested whether 21 experienced TT practitioners could detect whether one of her hands was near theirs. Each subject was tested ten or twenty times. During the tests, the practitioners rested their forearms and hands, palms up, on a flat surface, approximately 10 to 12 inches apart. Emily then hovered her hand, palm down, a few inches above one of the subject's palms. A cardboard screen was used to prevent the subjects from seeing which hand was selected. The practitioners correctly located Emily's hand only 122 (44%) out of 280 trials, which is no better than would be expected by guessing. The test results were published in JAMA on April 1, 1998. The study showed that the TT practitioners were unable to detect Emily's "human energy field." Their failure to substantiate TT's most fundamental claim is unrefuted evidence that the claims of TT are groundless and that further professional use is unjustified.

Fad Diagnoses

Some "alternative" practitioners misdiagnose large numbers of their patients with one or more conditions considered rare or even nonexistent by scientific practitioners. Some of these diagnoses are based on the patient's history (typically including fatigue and other common emotionally related symptoms), while others are based on inappropriate or misinterpreted laboratory tests.

Many of these practitioners describe themselves as practicing "holistic," "complementary," or "nutritional" medicine and prescribe "nutritional" products to virtually every patient they see. Their "fad diagnoses" include: hypoglycemia (a real but uncommon condition in which blood sugar is low); hypothyroidism (a real but uncommon condition in which the thyroid gland is underactive); "Candidiasis hypersensitivity" (a nonexistent condition sometimes referred to as "yeast allergy"); " and "environmental illness" (a nonexistent condition also called "multiple chemical sensitivity"); and "mercury amalgam toxicity." Chronic fatigue syndrome, Lyme disease, and "parasites" although not rare, are also overdiagnosed by such practitioners. They may also claim that large numbers of Americans have multiple symptoms caused by undiagnosed food allergies.

"Mercury-amalgam toxicity" is diagnosed by a few hundred dentists who falsely claim that the mercury in silver-mercury fillings is toxic and causes a wide range of illnesses. These dentists recommend replacing these fillings with other materials, which can cost thousands of dollars. The American Dental Association considers this practice unethical.

Questionable Cancer Treatments

The American Cancer Society (ACS) has defined questionable methods as lifestyle practices, clinical tests, or therapeutic modalities promoted for general use for the prevention, diagnosis, or treatment of cancer and which are, on the basis of careful review by scientists and/or clinicians, deemed to have no real evidence of value. Promoters claim that their methods are natural and nontoxic and that standard therapies are highly dangerous. They typically explain their approaches in commonsense terms that appear to offer patients an active role: (a) cancer is a symptom, not a disease; (b) symptoms are caused by diet, stress, or environment; (c) proper fitness, nutrition, and mental attitude allow biologic and mental defense against cancer; and (d) conventional therapy weakens the body's reserves, treats the symptoms rather than the disease. None of these assertions is accurate.

Cancer cures attributed to questionable methods usually fall into one or more of five categories: (1) the patient never had cancer; (2) a cancer was cured or put into remission by proven therapy, but questionable therapy was also used and erroneously credited for the beneficial result; (3) the cancer is progressing but is erroneously represented as slowed or cured; (4) the patient has died as a result of the cancer (or is lost to follow-up) but is represented as cured; or (5) the patient had a spontaneous remission (very rare) or slow-growing cancer that is publicized as a cure. The most publicized methods include the following.

Antineoplastons. Stanislaw R. Burzynski, M.D., Ph.D., has given the name "antineoplastons" to substances he claims can "normalize" cancer cells that are constantly being produced within the body. He has published many papers stating that antineoplastons extracted from urine or synthesized in his laboratory have proven effective against cancer in laboratory experiments. He also claims to have helped many people with cancer get well. Saul Green, Ph.D., a biochemist who worked for many years at Memorial Sloan-Kettering Hospital doing research into the mechanisms and treatment of cancer, has analyzed Burzynski's publications and found no evidence that any of the substances Burzynski calls "antineoplastons" have been proven to "normalize" tumor cells.

CanCell, originally called Entelev, is a liquid claimed to "lower the voltage of the cell structure by about 20%," causing cancer cells to "digest" and be replaced with normal cells. CanCell has also been promoted for the treatment of AIDS, amyotrophic lateral sclerosis, multiple sclerosis, Alzheimer's disease, "extreme cases of emphysema and diabetes," and several other diseases. In 1989, the FDA reported that CanCell contained inositol, nitric acid, sodium sulfite, potassium hydroxide, sulfuric acid, and catechol. Subsequently, its promoters claimed to be modifying the formulation to make it more effective. They have also claimed that CanCell can't be analyzed because it varies with atmospheric vibrations and keeps changing its energy. Laboratory tests conducted by the National Cancer Institute Laboratory between 1978 and 1991 found no evidence that CanCell was effective against cancer. The FDA has obtained an injunction forbidding its distribution to patients.

Hulda Clark, Ph.D., N.D., claims that (a) all cancers and many other diseases are caused by "parasites, toxins, and pollutants"; (b) cancers can be detected with a blood test for ortho-phospho-tyrosine and a device that identifies diseased organs and toxic substances; (c) cancers can be cured by killing the parasites and ridding the body of environmental chemicals; (d) black walnut hulls, wormwood, and common cloves can rid the body of over 100 types of parasites; and (e) the amino acids ornithine and arginine improve this recipe. Her book *The Cure for All Cancers,* contains 103 case histories of her supposed cancer cures. However, judging from her descriptions (a) most did not have cancer, and (b) of those that did, most had received standard medical treatment or their tumors were in early stages.

Devices of many types are used with unfounded claims that they are effective against cancer. These include devices that pass low-voltage electrical current through tumors or the body, "electroacupuncture" devices purported to measure the electrical resistance of "acupuncture points," electrical devices claimed to "charge" blood samples taken from patients and later reinjected, negative ion generators claimed to have an effect against tumors, radionics devices claimed to diagnose and cure cancer by analyzing and emitting radio waves at the correct frequencies, magnets claimed capable of curing cancers by "improving circulation" or by intracellular effects, and projectors of colored light claimed to exert healing effects

Essiac is an herbal remedy that was prescribed and promoted for about fifty years by Rene M. Caisse, a Canadian nurse who died in 1978. Shortly before her death, she turned over the formula and manufacturing rights to the Resperin Corporation, a Canadian company that has provided it to patients under a special agreement with Canadian health officials. Several reports state that the formula contains burdock, Indian rhubarb, sorrel, and slippery elm, but there may be additional ingredients. Essiac tea claimed to be Caisse's original formulation is also marketed in the United States. Several animal tests using samples of Essiac have shown no anti-tumor activity. Nor did a review of data on 86 patients performed by the Canadian federal health department during the early 1980s.

Fresh cell therapy, also called live cell therapy or cellular therapy, involves injections of fresh embryonic animal cells taken from the organ or tissue that corresponds to the unhealthy organ or tissue in the patient. Proponents claim that the recipient's body automatically transports the injected cells to the target organ where they repair and rejuvenate the ailing cells. The American Cancer Society states that fresh cell therapy has no proven benefit and has caused serious side effects (infections and immunologic reactions to the injected protein) and death. In 1984, The FDA issued an Import Alert asking the U.S. Customs and Postal Services to block the importation of all "cell therapy" powders and extracts intended for injection.

Gerson method. Proponents of the Gerson diet claim that cancer can be cured only if toxins are eliminated from the body. They recommend "detoxification" with frequent coffee enemas and a low-sodium diet that includes more than a gallon a day of juices made from fruits, vegetables, and raw calf's liver. Gerson protocols have also included liver extract injections, ozone enemas, "live cell therapy," thyroid tablets, royal jelly capsules, linseed oil, castor oil enemas, clay packs, laetrile, and vaccines made from influenza virus and killed *Staphylococcus aureus* bacteria.

The Gerson method was developed by Max Gerson, a German-born physician who emigrated to the United States in 1936 and practiced in New York City until his death in 1959. Still available at a clinic near Tijuana, Mexico, Gerson therapy is actively promoted by his daughter, Charlotte Gerson, through lectures, talk show appearances, and publications of the Gerson Institute in Bonita, California.

An NCI analysis of Dr. Gerson's book *A Cancer Therapy: Results of Fifty Cases* concluded in 1959 that most of the cases failed to meet the criteria (such as histologic verification of cancer) for proper evaluation of a cancer case. A more recent review of the Gerson treatment rationale concluded: (a) the "poisons" Gerson claimed to be present in processed foods have never been identified, (b) frequent coffee enemas have never been shown to mobilize and remove poisons from the liver and intestines of cancer patients, (c) there is no evidence that any such poisons are related to the onset of cancer, (d) there is no evidence that a "healing" inflammatory reaction exists that can seek out and kill cancer cells.

Charlotte Gerson claims that treatment at the clinic has produced high cure rates for certain cancers. In 1986, however, a Gerson publicist admitted that patients had not been monitored after they left the facility. A naturopath who visited the clinic in 1983 was able to track 21 patients over a five-year period (or until death) through annual letters or phone calls. At the five-year mark, only one was still alive (but not cancer-free); the rest had succumbed to their cancer.

Gonzalez metabolic therapy. Nicholas Gonzales, M.D., of New York City, offers an elaborate program with "10 basic diets with 90 variations" and typically prescribes coffee enemas and up to 150 pills a day in 10 to 12 divided doses. In 1994, after investigating six of Gonzalez's cases, New York State licensing authorities had concluded: (a) his "alternative protocol" did not entitle him to an alternative standard of care; (b) he had failed to correctly interpret signs and symptoms of disease progression, (c) he had treated the patients incompetently, and (d) his record-keeping was inadequate. He was placed on probation for three years with a stipulation that he undergo retraining and his work be supervised by the Office of Professional Conduct. A recent ABC-TV "20/20" program revealed that Gonzalez was using a "psychic" hair test to gauge his patients' progress.

Hydrazine sulfate. In the mid-1970s hydrazine sulfate was proposed for treating the progressive weight loss and body deterioration characteristic of advanced cancer. Based on animal data and preliminary human studies, it has also been claimed to cause tumor regression and subjective improvement in patients. However, three recent trials sponsored by the National Cancer Institute found that hydrazine sulfate was no better than a placebo. The trials involved a total of 636 patients with three types of cancer. In one study nerve damage occurred more often and the quality of life was significantly worse in the hydrazine sulfate group.

"Hyperoxygenation" therapy, also called "bio-oxidative therapy" and "oxidative therapy," is based on the erroneous concept that cancer is caused by oxygen deficiency and can be cured by exposing cancer cells to more oxygen than they can tolerate. The most touted agents are hydrogen peroxide, germanium sesquioxide, and ozone. Although these compounds have been the subject of legitimate research, there is little or no evidence that they are effective for the treatment of any serious disease, and each has demonstrated potential for harm. Germanium products have caused irreversible kidney damage and death. The FDA has banned their importation and seized products from several U.S. manufacturers.

Immuno-augmentative therapy (IAT) was developed by Lawrence Burton, Ph.D., a zoologist who claimed to treat cancer patients by manipulating an immune defense system that he postulated. He claimed to accomplish this by injecting protein extracts isolated with processes he had patented. However, experts believe that the substances Burton claimed to use cannot be

produced by these procedures and have not been demonstrated to exist in the human body. NCI scientists who analyzed treatment materials given to several patients concluded that the materials were dilute solutions of ordinary blood proteins, primarily albumin. None contained Burton's postulated components. Burton did not publish detailed clinical reports, divulge to the scientific community the details of his methods, publish meaningful statistics, conduct a controlled trial, or provide independent investigators with specimens of his treatment materials for analysis. During the mid-1980s, several of his patients developed serious infections following IAT. Burton died in 1993, but the clinic is still operating.

Laetrile, which achieved great notoriety during the 1970s and early 1980s, is the trade name for a synthetic relative of amygdalin, a chemical in the kernels of apricot pits, apple seeds, bitter almonds, and several other fruits and nuts. Many laetrile promoters have called it "vitamin B17" and falsely claimed that cancer is a vitamin deficiency disease that laetrile can cure. Claims for laetrile's efficacy have varied considerably. First it was claimed to prevent and cure cancer. Then it was claimed not to cure, but to "control" cancer while giving patients an increased feeling of well being. More recently, laetrile has been claimed to be effective, not by itself, but as one component of "metabolic therapy" (described below).

Although laetrile has been promoted as safe and effective, clinical evidence indicates that it is neither. When broken down by enzymes in the body, it forms glucose, benzaldehyde, and a cyanide compound. Some cancer patients treated with laetrile have suffered nausea, vomiting, headache and dizziness, and a few have died from cyanide poisoning. Laetrile has been tested in at least twenty animal tumor models and found to have no benefit either alone or together with other substances. Several case reviews have found no benefit for the treatment of cancer in humans.

In response to political pressure, a clinical trial was begun in 1982 by the Mayo Clinic and three other U.S. cancer centers under NCI sponsorship. Laetrile and "metabolic therapy" were administered as recommended by their promoters. The patients had advanced cancer for which no proven treatment was known. Of 178 patients, not one was cured or stabilized, and none had any lessening of any cancer-related symptoms. The median survival rate was about five months from the start of therapy. In those still alive after seven months, tumor size had increased. Several patients experienced symptoms of cyanide toxicity or had blood levels of cyanide approaching the lethal range. Few sources of laetrile are now available within the United States, but several Mexican clinics still utilize it.

Livingston-Wheeler regimen. Virginia C. Livingston, M.D., who died in 1990, postulated that cancer is caused by a bacterium she called Progenitor cryptocides, which invades the body when "immunity is stressed or weakened." She claimed to counter this by strengthening the body's immune system with vaccines (including one made from the patient's urine); "detoxification" with enemas; digestive enzymes; a vegetarian diet that avoided chicken, eggs, and sugar; vitamin and mineral supplements; visualization; and stress reduction. She claimed to have a very high recovery rate but published no clinical data to substantiate this. Scientists who attempted to isolate the organism she postulated found that it was a common skin bacterium. Researchers at the University of Pennsylvania Cancer Center compared 78 of its patients with similar patients treated at the Livingston-Wheeler Clinic. All had advanced cancers for which no proven treatment was known. As expected, the study found no difference in average survival time of the two groups. However, Livingston-Wheeler patients reported more appetite difficulties and pain.

Mental imagery involves the use of detailed mental images in an attempt to control a situation. For example, cancer patients may imagine that their white blood cells are little knights in white armor attacking their tumors, which they picture as black dragons. Imaging may have

some usefulness as a relaxation technique in dealing with tension or chronic pain, but there is no scientific evidence that it can influence the course of any organic disease.

O. Carl Simonton, M.D., claims that cancers can be affected by relaxation and visualization techniques. He claims that this approach can lessen fears and tension, strengthen the patient's will to live, increase optimism, and alter the course of a malignancy by strengthening the immune system. However, he has not published the results of any well-designed study testing his ideas. Simonton theorizes that the brain can stimulate endocrine glands to inspire the immune system to attack cancer cells. Toward this end, he has advised cancer patients to imagine their cancer being destroyed by their white blood cells. However, there is no scientific evidence that white cells actually attack cancer cells in this manner or that "immune suppression" is a factor in the development of common cancers.

"Metabolic therapy." Proponents of "metabolic therapy" claim to diagnose abnormalities at the cellular level and correct them by normalizing the patient's metabolism. They characterize cancer, arthritis, multiple sclerosis, and other "degenerative" diseases as the result of metabolic imbalance caused by a buildup of "toxic substances" in the body. They claim that scientific practitioners merely treat the symptoms of the disease while they treat the cause by removing "toxins" and strengthening the immune system so the body can heal itself. The "toxins" are neither defined nor objectively measurable. "Metabolic" treatment regimens vary from practitioner to practitioner and may include a "natural food" diet, coffee enemas, vitamins, minerals, glandulars, enzymes, laetrile, and various other nostrums that are not legally marketable in the United States. No scientific study has ever shown that "metabolic therapy" or any of its components is effective against cancer or any other serious disease.

Pau d'arco tea, sold through health food stores and by mail, is also called taheebo, lapacho, ipe roxo, or ipes. The tea is claimed to be an ancient Inca Indian remedy prepared from the inner bark of various species of *Tabebuia,* an evergreen tree native to the West Indies and Central and South America. Proponents claim that pau d'arco tea is effective against cancer and many other ailments. *Tabebuia* woods contains lapachol, which has been demonstrated to have antitumor activity in a few animal tumor models. However, no published study has shown a significant effect on cancer in humans. Studies during the early 1970s found that low doses of lapachol can cause nausea and vomiting and can interfere with blood clotting.

Revici Cancer Control, also called lipid therapy and "biologically guided chemotherapy," is based on the notion that cancer is caused by an imbalance between constructive ("anabolic") and destructive ("catabolic") body processes. Its main proponent, the late Emanuel Revici, M.D., prescribed lipid alcohols, zinc, iron, and caffeine, which he classified as anabolic, and fatty acids, sulfur, selenium, and magnesium, which he classified as catabolic. His formulations were based on his interpretation of the specific gravity, pH (acidity), and surface tension of single samples of the patient's urine. Scientists who have offered to evaluate Revici's methods were unable to reach an agreement with him on procedures to ensure a valid test. However, his method of urinary interpretation is obviously not valid. The specific gravity of urine reflects the concentration of dissolved substances and depends largely on the amount of fluid a person consumes. The acidity depends mainly on diet, but varies considerably throughout the day. Thus, even when these values are useful for a metabolic determination, information from a single urine sample would be meaningless. The surface tension of urine has no medically recognized diagnostic value.

Shark cartilage. Powdered shark cartilage is purported to contain a protein that inhibits the growth of new blood vessels needed for the spread of cancer. Although a modest anti-angiogenic effect has been observed in laboratory experiments, it has not been demonstrated that feeding shark cartilage to humans significantly inhibits angiogenesis in patients with cancer. Even if direct applications were effective, oral administration would not work because the protein would be digested rather than absorbed intact into the body.

Nevertheless, in the spring of 1993, "60 Minutes" aired a program promoting the claims of biochemist/entrepreneur I. William Lane, Ph.D., co-author of the book *Sharks Don't Get Cancer.* The program highlighted a Cuban study of 29 "terminal" cancer patients who received shark-cartilage preparations. Narrator Mike Wallace filmed several of the patients doing exercise and reported that most of them felt better several weeks after the treatment had begun. The fact that "feeling better" does not indicate whether a cancer treatment is effective was not mentioned. Nor was the fact that sharks do get cancer, even of their cartilage. NCI officials subsequently reviewed the Cuban data and concluded that they were "incomplete and unimpressive." A well-designed clinical trial involving 58 patients subsequently found no benefit.

Vitamin C. The claim that vitamin C is useful for treating cancer is largely attributable to Linus Pauling, Ph.D. During the mid-1970s, Pauling began claiming that high doses of vitamin C are effective in preventing and curing cancer. In 1976 and 1978, he and a Scottish physician, Ewan Cameron, reported that a group of 100 terminal cancer patients treated with 10,000 mg of vitamin C daily had survived three to four times longer than historically matched patients who did not receive vitamin C supplements. However, the vitamin C patients were Cameron's, while the other patients were managed by other physicians. Cameron's patients were started on vitamin C when he labeled them "untreatable" by other methods, and their subsequent survival was compared to the survival of the "control" patients after they were labeled untreatable by their doctors. Cameron's patients were labeled untreatable much earlier in the course of their disease—which meant that they entered the hospital before they were as sick as the other doctors' patients and would naturally be expected to live longer. Nevertheless, to test whether Pauling might be correct, the Mayo Clinic conducted three double-blind studies involving a total of 367 patients with advanced cancer. All three studies found that patients given 10 g of vitamin C daily did no better than those given a placebo.

Protecting Yourself

Faced with the prospect of chronic suffering, deformity, or death, many individuals are tempted to try anything that offers relief or hope. Many intelligent and well-educated individuals resort to worthless methods with the belief that anything is better than nothing. However, few methods labeled "alternative" are sensible choices.

Reliable Information Sources

- Quackwatch focuses on quackery-related information that is difficult or impossible to get elsewhere. It operates http://www.quackwatch.com and several Web sites.
- The National Council Against Health Fraud serves as a clearinghouse for information on health frauds, quackery, and "alternative" methods. It publishes position papers, fact sheets, an electronic newsletter, and a bimonthly print newsletter. Most of these documents can be accessed on its Web site: http://www.ncahf.org.
- The Committee for the Scientific Investigation of Claims of the Paranormal (CSICOP) investigates paranormal and fringe-science claims. It publishes a bimonthly magazine, *The Skeptical Inquirer*, and maintains subcommittees on paranormal health claims and several other topics. Its address is P.O. Box 703, Buffalo, NY 14226.

Recommended Publications

- S. Barrett and others. Consumer Health: A Guide to Intelligent Decisions, 7th Edition. St. Louis: McGraw Hill, 2002.
- S. Barrett and WT Jarvis, editors.The Health Robbers: A Close Look at Quackery in America. Amherst, NY: Prometheus Books, 1993.
- S. Barrett and V. Herbert. The Vitamin Pushers: How the "Health Food" Industry Is Selling America a Bill of Goods. Amherst, NY: Prometheus Books, 1994
- S. Homola. Inside Chiropractic: A Patient's Handbook. Amherst, NY: Prometheus Books, 1999.
- Scientific Review of Alternative Medicine, a peer-reviewed journal published quarterly by Prometheus Books, Amherst, NY.

27

Nutrition Fads, Fallacies and Quackery

Erroneous nutrition concepts lead Americans to waste billions of dollars annually and sometimes to jeopardize their health. This chapter illustrates how misinformation is used to promote vitamin and mineral supplements, "health foods," "organic" foods, "natural" foods, herbs, related products, weight-control scams, and dietary fads.

Food faddism typically involves beliefs that specific foods have special curative properties and that certain foods should be eliminated as harmful. To promote the use of supplements, the dietary supplement industry suggests that the processing of food removes its nourishment. It is true that processing can change the nutrient content of food, but the changes are not drastic. The negative effects of some food-processing operations are more than balanced by the overall positive effects, especially the continuous availability of most types of food items at reasonable cost. Eating moderate amounts of a wide variety of foods, including some uncooked fruits and vegetables, provides an adequate supply of nutrients.

Table 1 lists 25 misleading statements used to promote nutrition quackery.

Stress Supplements

Many vitamin manufacturers advertise that extra vitamins are needed to protect against "stress." While some companies list only physical stresses that supposedly increase vitamin needs, some include mental stress, overwork, and the like. Some companies market products for the "special needs" of athletes, housewives, busy executives, and smokers. Others make no health claims at all, relying only on the product's name to sell it.

"Stress-formulas" typically contain several times the RDA for vitamin C and several B-vitamins. The products manufactured by drug companies do not provide toxic amounts of these ingredients. But some marketed by health-food industry companies contain enough vitamin C to cause diarrhea, and some contain enough B6 to cause nerve damage over a long period of time. Some formulas contain questionable food substances such as spirulina, bee pollen, and ginseng to make them appear more "complete." Herbal and homeopathic "stress formulas" are also available.

Although vitamin needs may rise slightly in certain physical conditions, they seldom exceed the RDA, and they are easily met by eating a balanced diet. Anyone really in danger of deficiency as a result of illness would be very ill and probably require hospitalization.

Some vitamin manufacturers suggest that strenuous physical activity increases the need for vitamins so that people who engage in vigorous exercise or athletics should take supplements. Strenuous exercise does increase the need for calories, water, and a few nutrients. However, the nutrient needs are unlikely to exceed the RDAs. Even if above-RDA amounts were necessary, they would be supplied by the increase in food intake normally associated with exercising. The belief that extra vitamins are useful to athletes is also tied to the idea that extra vitamins provide extra energy—which is untrue. No scientific evidence shows that emotional stress increases one's need for vitamins.

"Natural" vs Synthetic Vitamins

Many promoters claim that "natural" vitamins are better than the synthetic vitamins. Such claims are unfounded. A few synthetic vitamins have slightly different structures than their natural counterparts, but these differences are of no importance inside the body. Vitamins are specific molecules; the body makes no distinction between vitamins made in the "factories" of nature and those made in the factories of chemical companies. The prices of "natural" vitamins tend to be higher than those of synthetic vitamins.

Antioxidants and Other Phytochemicals

Many "antioxidant" products are marketed with claims that, by blocking the action of free radicals, they can help prevent heart disease, cancer, and various other conditions associated with aging.

Free radicals are atoms or groups of atoms that have at least one unpaired electron, which makes them highly reactive. Free radicals promote beneficial oxidation that produces energy and kills bacterial invaders. In excess, however, they produce harmful oxidation that can damage cell membranes and cell contents. It is known that

Table 1: How Nutrition Quacks Promote Their Wares

Quackery can be defined as the promotion of unsubstantiated health methods for profit. Profit includes personal aggrandizement as well as monetary gain. Here are 25 ways to spot nutrition quacks.

- When talking about nutrients, they tell only part of the story.
- They claim that most Americans are poorly nourished.
- They recommend "nutrition insurance" for everyone.
- They say that most diseases are due to faulty diet and can be treated with "nutritional" methods.
- They allege that modern processing methods and storage remove all nutritive value from our food.
- They claim that diet is a major factor in behavior.
- They claim that fluoridation is dangerous.
- They claim that soil depletion and the use of pesticides and "chemical" fertilizers result in food that is less safe and less nourishing.
- They claim you are in danger of being "poisoned" by ordinary food additives and preservatives.
- They charge that the Recommended Dietary Allowances (RDAs) have been set too low.
- They claim that under everyday stress your need for nutrients is increased.
- They recommend "supplements" and "health foods" for everyone.
- They claim that "natural" vitamins are better than "synthetic" ones.
- They suggest that a questionnaire can be used to indicate whether you need dietary supplements.
- They say it is easy to lose weight.
- They promise quick, dramatic, miraculous results.
- They routinely sell vitamins and other "dietary supplements" as part of their practice.
- They use disclaimers couched in pseudomedical jargon.
- They use anecdotes and testimonials to support their claims.
- They claim that sugar is a deadly poison.
- They display credentials not recognized by responsible scientists or educators.
- They offer to determine your body's nutritional state with a laboratory test or a questionnaire.
- They claim they are being persecuted by orthodox medicine and that their work is being suppressed because it's controversial.
- They warn you not to trust your doctor.
- They encourage patients to lend political support to their treatment methods.

© 2000, Stephen Barrett, M.D., and Victor Herbert, M.D.

people who eat adequate amounts of fruits and vegetables high in antioxidants have a lower incidence of cardiovascular disease, certain cancers, and cataracts. Fruits and vegetables are rich in antioxidants, but it is not known which dietary factors are responsible for the beneficial effects. Each plant contains hundreds, and possibly thousands, of phytochemicals (plant chemicals) whose presence is dictated by hereditary factors. Only well-designed long-term research can determine whether any of these chemicals, taken in a pill, would be useful for preventing any disease.

The most publicized nutrients with antioxidant properties are vitamin C, vitamin E, and beta-carotene (which the body converts into vitamin A). Evidence exists that vitamin E can help prevent atherosclerosis by interfering with the oxidation of low-density lipoproteins (LDL), a factor associated with increased risk of heart disease. However, vitamin E also has an anticoagulant effect that can promote excessive bleeding. Some epidemiologic studies have found that people who took vitamin E supplements had fewer deaths from heart disease. These studies did not prove that taking vitamin E was useful because they did not rule out the effects of other lifestyle factors or consider death rates from other diseases. Moreover, other studies have had conflicting results. The only way to settle the question scientifically is to conduct long-term double-blind clinical studies comparing vitamin users to nonusers and checking death rates from all causes.

So far, with at least ten important studies completed, antioxidant supplementation has not been demonstrated to be beneficial. In fact, beta-carotene is suspected of promoting cancer, and vitamin E has been found to interfere with the potential benefit of certain cholesterol-lowering drugs. Harvard University's Charles Hennekens, M.D., who participated in two of the published studies, has pointed out that even if antioxidants could provide the benefits suggested by epidemiologic studies, smoking cessation and other lifestyle factors would have a far greater effect on the rates of lung cancer and coronary heart disease. The Medical Letter has concluded that (a)

the benefits of taking high doses of vitamin E remain to be established, (b) there is no convincing evidence that taking supplements of vitamin C prevents any disease, and (c) no one should take beta-carotene supplements.

The American Heart Association recommends that "the most prudent and scientifically supportable recommendation for the general population is to consume a balanced diet with emphasis on antioxidant-rich fruits and vegetables and whole grains."

Research is also being done to determine whether taking supplements or eating foods rich in antioxidants can protect against age-related macular degeneration (AMD), a disease in which the central portion of the retina deteriorates so that only peripheral vision remains. So far, the research results have been inconclusive.

Many types of pills described as "concentrates" of fruits and/or vegetables are being marketed. Critics of these products state that it is not possible to condense large amounts of produce into a pill without losing fiber, nutrients, and many other phytochemicals. Although some products contain significant amounts of nutrients, these nutrients are readily obtainable at lower cost from foods.

Amino Acid Products

Many supplement products containing amino acids are marketed as weight-loss and/or ergogenic aids despite lack of evidence that they are effective for either purpose. The Federation of American Societies for Experimental Biology (FASEB) has sharply criticized this situation. Following extensive review of the scientific literature, FASEB experts concluded: (a) single- or multiple-ingredient capsules, tablets, and liquid products are used primarily for pharmacologic purposes or enhancement of physiologic functions rather than for nutritional purposes; (b) little scientific literature exists on most amino acids ingested for these purposes; (c) no scientific rationale has been presented to justify ingestion of amino acid supplements by healthy individuals; and (d) safety levels for amino-acid supplement use have not been established.

Meganutrient Claims vs Facts

Claims are widespread that high dosages of vitamins and minerals can prevent or cure a great diversity of ailments. Dr. Linus Pauling, a Nobel Prize winner in chemistry and former professor of chemistry at Stanford University, was the chief theoretician for this approach, which he termed "orthomolecular" treatment (ortho is Greek for "right"). This approach supposedly provides the correct amounts of nutritionally "right" molecules normally found in the body. It began during the early 1950s as megavitamin therapy for schizophrenia and is also called "nutritional medicine."

Experiments on the possible value of vitamin C for preventing infections have been conducted by medical investigators ever since the vitamin became commercially available during the 1930s. At least 15 well-designed double-blind studies have shown that supplementation with vitamin C does not prevent colds, and that, at best, it may slightly reduce the symptoms of a cold. Slight symptom reduction may occur because of an antihistamine-like effect, but whether this has practical value is debatable.

Multivitamins vary greatly in the types and amounts of their individual ingredients. Vitamins in excess of the body's needs seldom serve a useful function and can be harmful. Excess amounts of fat-soluble vitamins (A, D, E, K) are stored in body fat, where they can build up to toxic levels over a period of time. Excess water-soluble vitamins (C and the eight B-complex vitamins) are excreted through the urine, but these can still have adverse effects.

As with fat-soluble vitamins, excess amounts of most minerals are stored in the body and can gradually build up to toxic levels. An excess of one mineral can also interfere with the functioning of others. Certain people can benefit from mineral supplements, but they should never be used without medical supervision.

There are only two situations in which vitamin use at higher-than-RDA levels is legitimate: (1) treatment of medically diagnosed deficiency states-conditions rare except among alcoholics; persons with intestinal absorption defects; and the poor, especially those who are pregnant or elderly and (2) certain problems for which large doses of vitamins are used as drugs-with full recognition of any risks involved. An example is the use of niacin to improve blood cholesterol levels.

Appropriate Use of Supplements

Most nutrition authorities agree that healthy individuals can get all the nutrients they need by eating sensibly. Most Americans believe this too, but many worry that their eating habits place them at risk for deficiency. The fear of not getting enough nutrients is promoted vigorously, not only by food faddists and health-food industry publicists, but also by major drug companies. Faddists tend to stress unscientific ideas that people cannot get sufficient nourishment from ordinary foods, while the drug companies use more subtle suggestions that various people may not be getting enough. Both groups fail to suggest how to obtain nutrients from foods or how to tell whether you are getting enough.

In general, vitamin and mineral supplements are useful for people who are unable or unwilling to consume an adequate diet. The population groups for whom supplements might be advisable include children under age two, women who might become pregnant, individuals on prolonged weight-reduction diets, certain elderly individuals, women at risk for osteoporosis, and vegetarians who eat no meat products.

Physicians commonly recommend vitamins for very young children until they are eating solid foods that contain enough vitamins. After the age of two, however, it is seldom necessary to continue supplements "just to be sure." The situations where supplements are appropriate for children include:

- Children with poor eating habits and those using weight-reduction diets can be given a multivitamin-mineral supplement containing nutrients not exceeding RDA levels.
- Children on strict vegetarian diets may need supplementation, particularly of vitamin B12.
- Pregnant teenagers are likely to need supplementary iron and folic acid.

- Children up to the age of 14 in areas with negligible amounts of fluoride in the drinking water should be given fluoride drops or tablets prescribed by a physician or dentist.

The U.S. Preventive Services Task Force recommends that women who might become pregnant take a daily multivitamin or multivitamin/mineral supplement that contains 0.4 mg of folic acid in order to reduce the risk of birth defects in their offspring. Although a well-balanced diet will provide adequate amounts of folic acid, the task force felt that, for some women, achieving adequate dietary intake might be more difficult than taking supplements.

Individuals using prolonged weight-reduction diets, particularly diets that are below 1200 calories per day or are nutritionally unbalanced, may benefit from a multivitamin-mineral supplement. People recovering from surgery or serious illnesses that have disrupted normal eating habits may also benefit from supplementation.

Elderly individuals who become sedentary or lose interest in eating may not get sufficient nutrients; they too may benefit from multivitamin-mineral supplementation. Unadvertised brands costing about 5¢ per day are available.

Because iron deficiency is not rare, a National Academy of Sciences committee has recommended that pregnant women take a 30-mg supplement daily during the second and third trimester. Although adequately nourished women do not need supplementation, it is simpler and less costly to supplement the diet than to measure blood iron levels several times during the pregnancy. The committee also suggested that although the best way to obtain nutrients is from food, pregnant women who ordinarily do not consume an adequate diet might benefit from a multivitamin-mineral supplement containing moderate dosages of iron, zinc, copper, calcium, vitamin B6, folic acid, vitamin C, and vitamin D.

Women should be sure that their intake of calcium is adequate to help prevent thinning of their bones (osteoporosis). The National Academy of Sciences advises Americans and Canadians at risk for osteoporosis to consume between 1000 and 1300 milligrams of calcium per day. This can be done with adequate intake of dairy products, but some women prefer calcium supplements. Women should discuss this matter with their physician or a registered dietitian.

Unless they choose a proper balance of foods, vegetarians who completely avoid animal products are at risk for several deficiencies, especially vitamin B12. The other nutrients at risk are riboflavin, calcium, iron, and the essential amino acids lysine and methionine. Vegetarian children not exposed to sunlight are at risk for vitamin D deficiency. Zinc deficiency can occur in vegans because the phytic acid in whole grains binds zinc, and there is little zinc in fruits and vegetables. Since B12 is present only in animal foods and a limited number of specially fortified foods, vegans should probably take B12 supplements prescribed by a physician or use B12 supplemented food.

B12 deficiency can also be a problem for older adults. As people age, many develop gastric atrophy (damage to the stomach lining) that impairs their ability to absorb B12. After a few years, when body stores are used up, the deficiency causes anemia and, if not corrected in time, will permanently damage the nervous system. Supplementing with at least 25 micrograms per day will ensure that the body absorbs enough to prevent deficiency. Some experts believe that gastric atrophy is common enough that everyone over 50 should take B12 supplements.

The best way to get vitamins and minerals is from foods in a balanced diet. If your diet is missing any nutrients, it may also lack components (such as fiber) that will not be supplied by pills. If you think your diet may be deficient, analyze it by recording what you eat for several days and comparing the number of portions of food in the various food groups with those recommended in the U.S. Department of Agriculture's Food Guide Pyramid. You can also assess the quality of your diet using the American Medical Association's Personal Nutritionist page or the U.S. Department of Agriculture's Interactive Healthy Eating Index. If a problem exists, it usually is better to correct the diet than to take supplements.

For professional advice, ask a registered dietitian (R.D.) or physician to help you. If you have a shortfall, try to correct it by adjusting your diet. If this is impossible, and you conclude that you need a supplement, purchase one whose label lists nothing above 100% of the Daily Value—and take one every other day. Since products meeting this description can be obtained for about a nickel per pill, this method would cost no more than a dollar a month.

"Organic" Foods

Promoters of "organic" and "organically grown" foods suggest that these are safer and more nutritious than conventionally grown foods. The terms attempt to describe the methods by which foods are produced. "Organically grown" may be the more appropriate term because in scientific usage, "organic" refers to compounds that contain carbon, which all food substances do. The most common concept of "organically grown" food was articulated in 1972 by Robert Rodale, editor of Organic Gardening and Farming magazine, at a government hearing:

Food grown without pesticides; grown without artificial fertilizers; grown in soil whose humus content is increased by the additions of organic matter, grown in soil whose mineral content is increased by the application of natural mineral fertilizers; has not been treated with preservatives, hormones, antibiotics, etc.

Many scientists believe this definition is inherently misleading and cite the following facts:

- "Organic" promoters imply that their products are pesticide-free, but surveys have found no significant differences in pesticide levels between organic and conventionally grown foods. Pesticides on the outside of fruits and vegetables may be removed by washing. The tiny amounts found in some foods pose no health risk. FDA data show that dietary intakes of pesticides are well within recognized safety standards.
- Plants obtain nutrients from soil in their inorganic state. Organic fertilizers must decompose before their nutrients become available for absorption. What counts is the availability of required nutrients rather than the type of fertilizer.

- Plant nutrient content is determined primarily by heredity. Mineral levels may be affected by the mineral content of the soil, but this has no significance in the overall diet. If essential nutrients are missing from the soil, the plant will not grow. If plants grow, that means the essential nutrients are present. Experiments have found no difference in the nutrient content of organically grown crops and those grown under standard agricultural conditions.
- The taste of raw food is determined by the product's genetic programming, ripeness when harvested, and freshness.

Foods labeled organic nearly always cost more than their conventional counterparts. Since they cannot be told apart by their appearance, some storekeepers have labeled conventionally grown foods "organic" to increase profits.

"Health Foods"

"Health foods" are claimed to be special foods that can benefit people's health. The terms health food, natural food, organic food, and organically grown food are often used interchangeably by both sellers and consumers. Vegetarian foods and foods labeled "dietetic" may also be referred to as health foods.

Nutrition authorities believe that the term "health food" is inherently misleading, because most foods are healthy when eaten in moderation and can be unhealthy when eaten in excess amounts. Some foods popular as "health foods" are rich in nutrients, but no food has unique health-promoting properties. All foods can contribute to health when eaten as part of a varied and balanced diet. The problem with so-called health foods is that they are promoted with false claims and usually are overpriced.

The foods eaten are not useful in the body until they are broken down into their component nutrients before being absorbed from the digestive tract; thus claims that certain foods are especially healthful should be evaluated by considering the components of these foods. Confronted with such claims, intelligent consumers should ask the following:

- What are the food's significant components and their nutritional value?
- Can special health claims made about it be scientifically justified?
- What other foods are comparable?

- How do comparable foods compare in price?

Table 2 lists commonly promoted "health foods," supplements, hormones, and other products sold in health-food stores.

Table 2: Popular Supplement and Health Food Products

The following are commonly promoted "health foods," supplements, and other products sold in health-food stores.

Aloe vera: Unsubstantiated claims are made that aloe vera products can cure or alleviate colitis, bursitis, asthma, glaucoma, hemorrhoids, boils, arthritis, intestinal problems, acne, poison ivy, anemia, tuberculosis, cancer, diabetes, depression, multiple sclerosis, stretch marks, varicose veins, and even blindness. Aloe skin creams or gels are probably harmless; and even though it will not reverse the aging process, topical aloe may exert some skin softening and moisturizing effects. However, aloe juice is a harsh laxative that can cause gastrointestinal upset.

Bee pollen: Bee pollen is flower pollen harvested from bees. Although claimed to be a "perfect food," it contains no nutrients that are not present in conventional foods and costs much more than ordinary foods containing the same nutrients. It is also touted as an aid to athletic performance, although actual tests on swimmers and runners have shown no benefit. In susceptible individuals, bee pollen can cause anaphylactic shock, a life-threatening allergic reaction in which swelling of the throat can cause suffocation.

Chlorophyll: Chlorophyll, the pigment responsible for the green color of plants, helps "trap" the energy from sunlight, enabling the plant to synthesize carbohydrates. Claims that chlorophyll is effective against many diseases and can reduce odors are not substantiated. It can kill certain bacteria but is too weak to have practical use as an antibiotic or a toothpaste additive. Chlorophyll is sometimes said to function as the "blood" of plants, but it does not.

Enzymes (oral): Many products containing enzymes are claimed to enhance body processes. Enzymes are proteins that act as catalysts in the body. Those present in food are treated in the digestive tract in the same way as any other protein: acid in the stomach and other digestive chemicals reduce them to smaller constituents that are no longer enzymes by the time they are absorbed into the body. The tiny amounts of amino acids oral enzymes provide make no significant nutritional contribution. Pancreatic enzymes have some legitimate medical uses in diseases that cause decreased secretion of pancreatic enzymes into the intestine, but these conditions are not appropriate for self-diagnosis or self-treatment.

Fish-oil capsules: Epidemiologic research has found that Arctic dwellers and others whose diet is rich in certain fatty acids have less heart disease than other Americans or Europeans. Other research has found that supplements of omega-3 fatty acids (found in fish oils) can help lower blood cholesterol levels and inhibit clotting, which means they may be useful in preventing atherosclerotic heart disease but harmful in promoting internal bleeding. However, it is not known what dosage is appropriate or whether long-term use is safe or effective. Most authorities believe it is unwise to self-medicate with fish-oil capsules; they should be used only by individuals at high risk for heart disease who are under close medical supervision. However, eating fish once or twice a week may be beneficial.

Germanium: "Organic germanium" is touted as a "miracle drug" for a wide range of health problems. Proponents claim that cancer, heart disease, mental deficiency, and many other problems are due to an "oxygen deficiency" that organic germanium can eradicate. There is no scientific evidence to support these claims. A few germanium compounds have been tested for anti-tumor activity, but no practical application has been found. Although many health-food stores sell germanium products, it is illegal to market them with therapeutic claims. The FDA has banned importation of germanium products intended for human consumption and has seized germanium products from several U.S. manufacturers. Germanium supplements have caused irreversible kidney damage and death.

Table 2: Popular Supplement and Health Food Products, con't.

Granola: Granola is the common term used to describe breakfast cereals and candy bars composed largely of oats plus other grains, dried fruits, seeds, and nuts. Touted as "natural" and rich in nutrients, granola products tend to be high in sugar (usually brown sugar and/or honey), fats (from vegetable oils, nuts, seeds, and coconut), and calories.

Guarana: An herb that contains a significant amount of caffeine, a fact that is sometimes omitted on product labels.

Lecithin: Lecithin is manufactured by the liver and occurs in many foods, including soybeans, whole grains, and egg yolks. Claims that lecithin supplements can dissolve blood cholesterol, rid the bloodstream of undesirable fats, cure arthritis, improve brain power, and aid in weight reduction are unsupported by scientific evidence.

Melatonin: Melatonin is a hormone produced from the amino acid L-tryptophan by the pineal gland, a small structure near the center of the brain. Its secretion increases when it is dark, which signals the body that it is time to sleep. In most people, blood levels peak near puberty and steadily decline with age. Melatonin products appear to improve some people's sleep and protect against "jet lag," but no clinical trials have been conducted. The effective dose is usually less than 0.1 to 0.3 mg, which is far below the 2 to 3 mg doses commonly sold in health-food stores. Claims that melatonin supplements can improve sex life, protect against many diseases, or reverse the aging process are un-substantiated. Adverse reactions have been reported, and it is not known whether melatonin is safe for long-term use.

Octacosanol: This substance, found in wheat germ oil and many other plant oils, is not essential in the human diet. Claims that it improves stamina and endurance, reduces blood cholesterol, and helps reproduction have not been substantiated.

Protein supplements: Protein powders, tablets, and liquids have been advertised as strength-promoting and especially important to athletes. These claims are incorrect. The RDA for protein is easily obtained by eating a well-balanced diet. Supplements provide no additional benefit and, in large amounts, can cause nutritional imbalances and kidney problems.

Raw milk: Raw milk is milk in its natural (non-pasteurized) state. Contaminated raw milk can be a source of harmful bacteria, such as those that cause undulant fever, dysentery, salmonellosis, and tuberculosis. "Certified" milk, obtained from cows certified as healthy, is unpasteurized milk with a bacteria count below a specified standard, but it still can contain significant numbers of disease-producing organisms. Any unpasteurized milk can be dangerous. The risks of raw milk are not related to mishandling; thus the only way to avoid them is not to consume the product.

Resveratrol: This compound, found largely in the skins of red grapes, is touted as an antioxidant and a phytoestrogen. Laboratory tests have demonstrated that it may help prevent cardiovascular disease and cancer, However, further studies in animals and humans are necessary to determine whether resveratrol supplementation makes sense.

Wheat grass juice: A juice, made from sprouted wheat berries, said to be high in chlorophyll and claimed to "cleanse" the body, neutralize toxins, slow the aging process, and prevent cancer. Its principal proponent, the late Ann Wigmore, attributed these supposed benefits to enzymes in the plant that supplement the body's enzymes when ingested. These claims are false. The enzymes in foods are not absorbed into the body but are digested like other proteins. Even if they could be absorbed intact, enzymes from plants would not enhance the metabolic processes of humans.

© 2002 Stephen Barrett, M.D.

"Natural" Foods

"Natural" foods are said to be those produced with minimal processing and without additives or artificial ingredients. The word "natural," like the word "organic," usually means that the product is higher-priced. Advocates of "natural foods" say that processing reduces nutritional value and that additives are harmful. Critics of the designation "natural" maintain that the American food supply is the safest and best the world has ever seen. They also state that "natural" cannot be meaningfully defined because there is no sharp dividing line between processed and unprocessed foods.

To promote "natural" foods, the health-food industry alleges that too many chemicals are added to our foods. The important issue, however, is not the number of chemicals, but whether they are safe and serve useful purposes. It is illogical to condemn additives with sweeping generalizations; the only proper way to evaluate them is individually. This is the responsibility of the FDA, which has paid a great deal of attention to this matter. Food additives have survived stringent evaluation procedures not applied to the great majority of natural products. To remain in use, additives must be judged not only safe but also functionally important.

To protect consumers, the FDA sets tolerance levels in foods and conducts frequent "market basket" studies wherein foods from regions throughout the United States are purchased and analyzed. The agency's annual Total Diet Study finds that dietary intakes of pesticides for all population groups are well within international and Environmental Protection Agency standards.

"Medicinal" Use of Herbal Products

Americans spend billions of dollars per year for capsules, tablets, bulk herbs, and herbal teas. Although many of these items are consumed for their flavor, most are probably used for supposed medicinal qualities. Sales by multilevel distributors and pharmacies amount to hundreds of millions more for products that are obviously intended for self-medication. Herbs are also marketed by naturopaths, acupuncturists, iridologists, chi-

ropractors, and unlicensed herbalists, many of whom prescribe them for the entire gamut of health problems. Many such practitioners are not qualified to make appropriate medical diagnoses or to determine how the products they prescribe compare to proven drugs.

Herbal advocates like to point out that about half of today's medicines were derived from plants. (Digitalis, for example, was originally derived from leaves of the foxglove plant.) This statement is true but misleading. Drug products contain specified amounts of active ingredients. Herbs in their natural state can vary greatly from batch to batch and often contain chemicals that cause side effects but provide no benefit.

Many herbal products are marketed as "dietary supplements," even though they have little or no nutritional value. No legal standards exist for their processing, harvesting, or packaging. In many cases, particularly for products with expensive raw ingredients, contents and potency are not accurately disclosed on the label. Many products marketed as herbs contain no useful ingredients, and some even lack the principal ingredient for which people buy them. Surveys conducted in the United States have found that the ingredients and doses of various products vary considerably from brand to brand and even between lots of the same product. Some tests have found that one or more ingredients listed in on the label were absent from the product. Some manufacturers are trying to develop industry-wide quality-assurance standards, but possible solutions are a long way off.

To make a rational decision about an herbal product, it would be necessary to know what it contains, whether it is safe, and whether it has been demonstrated to be as good or better than pharmaceutical products available for the same purpose. For most herbal ingredients this information is incomplete or unavailable.

"Popularity" is not a reliable sign of effectiveness. In 1999, Consumer Reports asked its readers in the United States and Canada to rate the standard and "complementary" therapies they had used most often for the two most serious or bothersome medical conditions they had encountered during the previous two years. Prescription drugs scored significantly better than herbs for each of the reported problems where both were used.

Even when a botanical product has some effectiveness, it may not be practical to use. Garlic, for example, has been demonstrated to lower cholesterol. However, prescription drugs are more potent for this purpose, and garlic has anticoagulant properties. No data are available to indicate the risk of combining garlic with other widely used products (vitamin E, ginkgo, fish oil, and aspirin) that can interfere with blood clotting.

The best source of information about herbs is the Natural Medicines Comprehensive Database, which is available online (http://www.natural-database.com) and in print for $92 per year (or $132 for both versions). The online version is updated daily, while the print version is updated several times a year. The 1999 book covered 964 herbs and dietary supplements, of which only 15% had been proven safe and only 11% had been proven effective. Another excellent resource is the Professional's Handbook of Complementary & Alternative Medicines, which provides practical advice for over 300 herbs. The widely touted Commission E Report and its derivative, the PDR for Herbal Medicine, are not as reliable or practical.

The recent entry of drug companies into the herbal marketplace may result in standardization of dosage for some products, and recent public and professional interest in herbs is likely to stimulate more research. However, with safe and effective medicines available, treatment with herbs rarely makes sense, and many of the conditions for which herbs are recommended are not suitable for self-treatment.

Table 3 provides information about 10 popular herbs.

Weight-Reduction Schemes

Many weight-reduction schemes are promoted to the public as a solution to obesity. Fad diet books typically have several things in common. They claim to offer a revolutionary new idea based on the author's personal experience. They suggest that certain nutrients, foods, or food combinations are either the key to weight reduction or villains that prevent it. And they contain inaccurate biochemical information. Many fad diets are unbalanced and lack important nutrients. During the past three decades, many best-selling diet plans have emphasized proteins, some recommending "unlimited" amounts and others using small amounts. "Food-combining" schemes also have been popular. *Fit for Life*, which sold over 3 million copies, claims that obesity caused accumulation of "toxic waste" from incomplete assimilation of foods eaten in the wrong combinations.

Many promoters of dietary schemes would have us believe that a special substance or combination of foods will automatically result in weight reduction. That's simply not true. To lose weight, you must eat less, or exercise more, or do both.

There are about 3,500 calories in a pound of body weight. To lose one pound a week, you must consume about 500 fewer calories per day than you metabolize. Most fad diets, if followed closely, will result in weight loss—as a result of caloric restriction. But they are invariably too monotonous and are sometimes too dangerous for long-term use. Moreover, dieters who fail to adopt better exercise and eating habits will regain the lost weight—and possibly more. Because "dieting" is usually unsuccessful, many experts believe that people's emphasis should be on fitness (readily attainable through exercise) and control of cardiovascular risk factors (abnormal blood cholesterol levels, high blood pressure, and elevated blood sugar levels).

The most drastic way to reduce caloric intake is to stop eating completely. After a few days, body fats and proteins are metabolized to produce energy. The fats are broken down into fatty acids that can be used as fuel. In the absence of adequate carbohydrate, the fatty acids may be incompletely metabolized, yielding ketone bodies and thus ketosis. Prolonged fasting is unsafe, because it causes the body to begin to digest proteins from its muscles, heart, and other internal organs.

Table 3: Ten Popular Herbs

Echinacea. Test-tube evidence suggests that echinacea stimulates immune processes. Taking echinacea at the first sign of a cold may reduce the infection's duration, but most studies have not found echinacea able to prevent colds. Echinacea should not be taken by people with an autoimmune disease (such as type 1 diabetes, rheumatoid arthritis, or multiple sclerosis) or a disease that causes immune suppression.

Garlic. Allicin, a component of garlic, has been shown to inhibit the production of cholesterol by the liver. Population studies have found an association between lower cholesterol levels and increased intake of garlic, onions, and related vegetables. However, most well-designed clinical trials have not found a cholesterol-lowering benefit for garlic supplements, and its anticoagulation property may undesirably enhance that of other blood-thinners.

Ginkgo biloba. Ginkgo biloba contains compounds that can increase blood flow to the brain. A 1997 clinical trial found that patients with dementia caused by small strokes or Alzheimer's disease who took 120 mg of ginkgo extract a day scored modestly higher in mental performance tests and had a slightly delayed mental decline than those who took a placebo. There is no evidence that ginkgo will cure or prevent Alzheimer's disease or will generally improve mental sharpness or memory. Ginkgo's anticoagulation property may undesirably enhance that of other blood-thinners.

Ginseng. Ginseng may help improve sleep, appetite, and work efficiency. However, it can raise blood pressure and many ginseng products contain little or none of the active ingredient.

Green tea. Epidemiologic and animal studies suggest that green tea may help prevent atherosclerosis. However, clinical trials are needed to accurately assess its usefulness.

Kava. Small studies suggest that kava may be useful for treating anxiety, stress, and restlessness. However, chronic, heavy use can cause adverse effects. Additional studies are needed.

Milk thistle. Studies suggest that milk-thistle extract may have a useful role in treating various liver diseases. However, most of the supporting research has not been well-designed.

Saw palmetto. Saw palmetto may relieve symptoms of benign enlargement of the prostate gland, such as slow urine flow, which is common in older men. A 1998 review of 18 clinical trials found that about 75% of those who used saw palmetto for 2 months reported an improvement. However, a survey of Consumer Reports readers found that about half improved, compared with about 75% of prescription drug users.

St. John's wort. St. John's wort is widely promoted as an antidepressant. Its mechanism of action is unknown, and the active ingredient, if any, has not been ascertained. A few studies have found it somewhat more effective than a standard antidepressant, but none lasted more than 6 weeks, some were poorly designed, and significant side effects and adverse drug interactions have been reported. NIH is sponsoring a long-term study that should help determine whether its use is practical. St. John's wort should not be combined with standard antidepressants or used by women who are pregnant or are breastfeeding. A Good Housekeeping Institute analysis of six widely available St. John's wort supplement capsules and four liquid extracts revealed a lack of consistency of the suspected active ingredients, hypericin and pseudohypericin. The study found a 17-fold difference between the capsules containing the smallest and the largest amounts of hypericin, based on the manufacturer's maximum recommended dosage.

Valerian. Valerian appears to exert mild sedative-hypnotic effects, but most supportive studies have been methodologically flawed. A U.S. Pharmacopeia expert panel has determined that there is not enough evidence to support its use for treating insomnia.

© 2002 Stephen Barrett, M.D.

Low-carbohydrate diets also produce ketosis. As it begins, large amounts of water will be shed, leading the dieter to think that significant weight reduction is taking place. However, most of the loss is water rather than fat; the lost water is regained quickly when eating is resumed. Appetite, often reduced during ketosis, also returns when a balanced diet is resumed.

Most low-carbohydrate diets do not attempt to limit the intake of proteins, fats, or total calories. (In other words, their fat content tends to be very high.) Promoters claim that unbalancing the diet will lead to increased metabolism of unwanted fat even if the calories are not restricted. This is not true, but calorie reduction is likely to occur because the diet's monotony tends to discourage overeating.

The most widely used low-carbohydrate diet is the one advocated by Robert C. Atkins, M.D., of New York City. His 1972 book *Dr. Atkins' Diet Revolution* sold millions of copies within the first two years. His 1992 update, *Dr. Atkins' New Diet Revolution*, has sold even more. Although he has advocated the diet for nearly 30 years, he has never bothered to publish any long-term results. Many experts have warned that the unlimited intake of saturated fats under his food plan may increase the dieter's risk of heart disease.

Mail-order diet pills are typically "guaranteed" to produce effortless, rapid and permanent weight loss. Dozens of such pills are offered each year through direct mail solicitations and newspaper advertising. Some of these, as well as others sold over the counter, contain phenylpropanolamine (PPA), a nasal decongestant that can have a temporary effect on appetite. However, there is no evidence that PPA offers any long-term benefit for weight control, many users have experienced severe anxiety reactions, and several cases have been reported of young adults who suffered a stroke after using products containing PPA. As a result, the FDA has proposed to ban it as a weight-control product ingredient.

Other mail-order pills have been falsely claimed to block absorption of starch, fat, or calories; to flush fat out of the body; or to step up the body's "fat-burning system." Some contain a fiber (e.g., chitosan) that is claimed to curb appetite by absorbing water and swelling to fill the stomach. However, the amount of fiber is too small to actually fill the stomach, and even if it could, that would not necessarily curb a person's appetite.

Spirulina, a dark-green powder or pill derived from algae, is said by its promoters to suppress appetite. However, there is no scientific evidence to support this claim.

Extracts of *Gymnema sylvestre*, a plant grown in India, are alleged to cause weight loss by preventing sugar from being absorbed into the body. Chewing the plant's leaves can prevent the taste sensation of sweetness. But there is no reliable evidence that the chemicals they contain can block sugar absorption or produce weight loss.

Supplements containing chromium picolinate are promoted with unsubstantiated claims that it promotes fat loss and increases lean muscle mass. The FTC has stopped two companies from making such claims, but others have continued to do so.

Products containing ma huang are marketed as weight-loss aids even though they have not been proven safe or effective for this purpose. Ma huang is an herb that contains ephedrine, a nasal decongestant and nervous-system stimulant. Ephedrine can raise blood pressure and therefore is hazardous to individuals with high blood pressure. Deaths have been reported among users of stimulants containing ephedrine and caffeine.

Colon "Cleansing" and "Detoxification"

The importance of "regularity" to overall health has been greatly overestimated for thousands of years. This concern is still embodied in the concept of "autointoxication" and has been promoted by unfounded warnings against "irregularity."

The theory of "autointoxication" states that stagnation of the large intestine (colon) causes toxins to form that are absorbed and poison the body. Some proponents depict the large intestine as a "sewage system" that becomes a "cesspool" if neglected. Others state that constipation causes hardened feces to accumulate for months (or even years) on the walls of the large intestine and block it from absorbing or eliminating properly. This, they say, causes food to remain undigested and wastes from the blood to be reabsorbed by the body.

Around the turn of the twentieth century, many physicians accepted the concept of autointoxication, but it was abandoned after scientific observations proved it wrong. Among other things, direct observation of the colon during surgical procedures or autopsies found no evidence that hardened feces accumulate on the intestinal walls. Careful observations have also shown that the bowel habits of healthy individuals can vary greatly. Although most people have a movement daily, some have several movements each day, while others can go several days or even longer with no adverse effects.

Despite these facts, some people claim that "death begins in the colon" and that "90 percent of all diseases are caused by improperly working bowels." The practices they recommend include fasting, periodic "cleansing" of the intestines, and colonic irrigation. Fasting is said to "purify" the body. "Cleansing" can be accomplished with a variety of herbal and fiber-containing products. Colonic irrigation involves inserting a rubber tube into the rectum and pumping large amounts of water in and out to wash out the contents of the large intestine. Some practitioners add herbs, coffee, enzymes, wheat or grass extract, or other substances to the enema solution. Some entrepreneurs claim that "detoxing" can "jump-start" a diet by shedding 5 or 10 pounds before beginning the diet.

The danger of these practices depends upon their extent of use and whether they are substituted for necessary medical care. Whereas a 1-day fast is likely to be harmless, prolonged fasting can be fatal. "Cleansing" is unlikely to be physically harmful, but the products involved can be expensive. Colonic irrigation has considerable potential for harm. The process can be very uncomfortable, since the presence of the tube can induce severe cramps and pain. If the equipment is not adequately sterilized between treatments, disease germs from one person's large intestine can be transmitted to others. Cases of heart failure (from

excessive fluid absorption into the bloodstream) and electrolyte imbalance have also been reported.

Constipation should be defined by the hardness of the stool rather than the frequency of the movements. Ordinary constipation usually can be remedied by increasing the fiber content of the diet, drinking adequate amounts of water, and engaging in regular exercise. If the bowel is basically normal, dietary fiber increases the bulk of the stool, softens it, and speeds transit time. Defecating soon after the urge is felt also can be helpful because if urges are ignored, the rectum may eventually stop signaling when defecation is needed. Stimulant laxatives (such as cascara or castor oil) can damage the nerve cells in the colon wall, decreasing the force of contractions and increasing the tendency toward constipation. Thus, people who take strong laxatives whenever they "miss a movement" may wind up unable to move their bowels without them. Frequent enemas can also lead to dependence. A doctor should be consulted if constipation persists or represents a significant change in bowel pattern.

Macrobiotic Diets

Macrobiotics is a quasireligious philosophical system founded by the late George Ohsawa. (Macrobiotic means "way of long life.") The system advocates a vegetarian diet in which foods of animal origin are used as condiments rather than as full-fledged menu items. The optimal diet is achieved by balancing "yin" and "yang" foods. Ohsawa outlined a 10-stage "Zen" macrobiotic diet in which each stage is progressively more restrictive. The diet was alleged to enable individuals to overcome all forms of illness, which Ohsawa said were due to excesses in diet.

In 1971 the AMA Council on Foods and Nutrition said that followers of the diet, particularly the highest level, stood in "great danger" of malnutrition, and that several deaths had been reported.

Current proponents espouse a diet that is less restrictive but still can be nutritionally inadequate. They recommend whole grains (50% to 60% of each meal), vegetables (25% to 30% of each meal), whole beans or soybean-based products (5% to 10% of daily food), nuts and seeds (small amounts as snacks), miso soup, herbal teas, and small amounts of white meat or seafood once or twice a week.

Today's leading proponent is Michio Kushi, a former student of Ohsawa, who founded and heads the Kushi Institute in Becket, Massachusetts. Institute publications recommend chewing food at least 50 times per mouthful (or until it becomes liquid), not wearing synthetic or woolen clothing next to the skin, avoiding long hot baths or showers (unless you have been consuming too much salt or animal food), having large green plants in your house to enrich the oxygen content of the air, and singing a happy song every day.

Kushi claims that macrobiotic eating can help prevent cancer and many other diseases. He also presents case histories of people whose cancers have supposedly disappeared after they adopted the macrobiotic diet.

Promotion of Questionable Nutrition

Food faddism is promoted through practitioners, health resorts, retail establishments, trade organizations, and media outlets. Freedom of speech and freedom of the press make it legal for anyone to make false or unproven health claims about a product as long as the claims are not made while selling the product. Most claims directed to the public about health foods and related products are not found on labels (where they would be illegal) but reach consumers through other channels of communication.

Unsubstantiated claims appear in newspapers, magazines, books, newsletters, pamphlets, lectures, and on radio and television talk shows. Many of those who make the claims have no direct connection with supplement manufacturers, while others are paid as "consultants." Retailers absorb misinformation from health-food magazines, trade publications, materials distributed by manufacturers, and seminars sponsored by trade organizations. Many health-food stores display or distribute free literature (newsletters, flyers, and article reprints) containing claims that

would be illegal on product labels. Illegal oral claims are made quite often in the privacy of health-food stores, practitioners' offices, and customers' homes (by multilevel distributors). Products are also promoted through the use of pseudodiagnostic tests that supposedly detect vitamin and mineral deficiencies, allergies, or "imbalances."

Publications

Rodale Press was founded by J.I. Rodale, who was best known for his interests in "organic farming" and "health foods." *Prevention*, its leading magazine, was launched in 1950 as a device to promote the products of its advertisers. It did this by attacking ordinary foods and recommending supplements and health foods with claims that often were ludicrous. During the 1980s, *Prevention* shifted toward the scientific mainstream and acquired a prominent editorial advisory board. Today the magazine emphasizes dietary improvement, appropriate exercise programs, and other health-promoting activities. Although much of its advice is accurate, its coverage of nutrition news has been unbalanced, it promotes dubious "alternative" methods, and it tends to encourage undue experimentation with dietary supplements. Rodale's book division and the Prevention Book Club have marketed some authoritative books, but most of their nutrition-related books contain questionable ideas.

The book most widely used as a sales tool today is *Prescription for Nutritional Healing* by urologist James Balch, M.D., and his wife Phyllis A. Balch, "C.N " The book's jacket describes Dr. Balch as a urologist who "has helped patients to assume a portion of responsibility for their own well-being" and Mrs. Balch as a "certified nutrition consultant" who works in her husband's practice and has established a health-food store. The "C.N. " designation is a dubious credential issued by the American Association of Nutritional Consultants, an organization whose only requirement for professional membership is payment of $50. The book lists nutrients that are "essential," "very important," or "helpful" for more than 250 health problems. Some lists contain more than 30 items. The authors recommend daily dosages of 3000 mg or more of vitamin C for everybody ("for maintaining good health") and higher doses (up to 30,000 mg/day "under a doctor's supervision") for dozens of problems. They also recommend daily dosages of vitamin A ranging from 50,000 to 100,000 IU for many conditions, and 75,000 IU for "maintaining healthy eyes." The vitamin C dosages are high enough to produce severe diarrhea; the vitamin A dosages are high enough to cause liver injury.

Health-Food Stores

No special knowledge or training is required to become a health-food-store salesperson. Personnel in these stores typically obtain information by reading books and magazines that promote supplement products for the treatment of virtually all health problems. Retailers also get information from manufacturers and can attend seminars at trade shows sponsored by industry groups and trade magazines.

Although storekeepers cannot legally "diagnose" or "prescribe," they commonly do both. Investigators from the American Council on Science and Health demonstrated this in 1983 by making 105 inquiries at stores in three states. When asked about symptoms characteristic of glaucoma, 17 out of 24 suggested a wide variety of products for a person not present; none recognized that urgent medical care was needed. Asked by telephone about a sudden, unexplained 15-pound weight loss in 1 month's time, nine out of 17 recommended products sold in their store; only seven suggested medical evaluation. Seven out of 10 stores carried "starch blockers" despite an FDA ban. Nine out of 10 recommended bone meal and dolomite, products considered hazardous because of possible lead contamination. Nine retailers made false claims of effectiveness for bee pollen, and 10 did so for RNA. The investigators concluded that most health-food store clerks give advice that is irrational, unsafe, and illegal.

In 1993, posing as potential customers, FDA agents visited local health-food stores throughout the United States. The investigators asked: (a)

"What do you sell to help high blood pressure?" (b) "Do you have anything to help fight infection or help my immune system?" and/or (c) "Do you have anything that works on cancer?" Of 129 inquiries, 120 resulted in recommendations for products. In 23 cases the retailer looked up the answer in *Prescription for Nutritional Healing* or advised the agent to refer to or purchase the book.

In 1998, in Oahu, Hawaii, a researcher posing as the daughter of a cancer patient asked personnel at 40 health-food stores whether they had any product that would be effective against metastatic breast cancer. After products were suggested, if store personnel provided no further information, the researcher asked: (a) How does the product work? (b) Do you recommend any particular brand (if more than one brand available)? (c) Could I write down some prices? (d) How much of the product does my mother need to take per day? (e) Can the product(s) be taken together with the medication my mother is receiving from her physician? and (f) Is there anything else you can recommend? Personnel in 36 of the stores recommended one or more of 38 inappropriate products, the most common of which were shark cartilage (recommended by 17) and essiac (recommended by eight), and maitake mushrooms (recommended by seven).

Pharmacists

Pharmacists play an important role in the vitamin marketplace. Virtually every pharmacy stocks and sells supplements that are irrationally formulated, and many stock dubious herbal and homeopathic products in addition to standard drugs. Chain drugstores are more likely to do so than individually owned stores.

Although pharmacists are generally regarded as experts, surveys suggest that most give poor advice about supplement products. In 1985, for example, reporters from Consumer Reports magazine visited 30 drugstores in Pennsylvania, Missouri, and California. The reporters complained of feeling tired or nervous and asked whether a vitamin product might help. Seventeen were sold a vitamin product and one was sold an amino acid preparation. Only nine of the 30 pharmacists suggested that a doctor be consulted.

Not long afterward, two dietitians examined the labels of vitamin products at five pharmacies, three groceries, and three health-food stores in New Haven, Connecticut. Products were considered appropriate if they contained between 50% and 200% of the U.S. RDA and no more than 100% of others for which Estimated Safe and Adequate Daily Dietary Intakes exist. Only 16 out of 105 (15%) of the multivitamin-mineral products met these criteria.

Dr. Merlin Nelson, a pharmacy educator, mailed a questionnaire asking pharmacists in Detroit to list their five most common reasons for recommending supplements. The most common responses included stress, colds, and athletic activity, none of which is an appropriate reason to recommend vitamins. Rather than just recommending a multivitamin to patients concerned about obtaining enough vitamins in their diet, pharmacists should offer sound nutritional advice or provide referrals to experts in nutrition such as registered dietitians.

Dubious Diagnostic Tests

Nutrition consultants, chiropractors, and small numbers of other licensed practitioners use a wide variety of tests as a basis for recommending supplements. The most widely used include hair analysis, "muscle-testing," live-cell analysis, and "nutrient deficiency" questionnaires.

Hair analysis is performed by obtaining a sample of hair, usually from the back of the neck, and sending it to a laboratory for analysis. The customer and the referring source usually receive a computerized printout that supposedly indicates deficiencies or excesses of minerals. Some also report supposed deficiencies of vitamins. Medical authorities agree that hair analysis is not appropriate for assessing the body's nutritional state. It has limited usefulness as a screening procedure for detecting toxic levels of lead or other heavy metals. Hair analysis cannot diagnose vitamin deficiency because normally there are no vitamins in hair except at the root (below the skin

surface). Nor can it identify mineral deficiencies because the lower limits of "normal" have not been scientifically established. Moreover, the mineral composition of hair can be affected by a person's age, natural hair color, and rate of hair growth, as well as the use of hair dyes, bleaches, and shampoos.

In 1999, researchers from the California Department of Health located nine laboratories and sent identical samples to six of them. The reported mineral levels, the alleged significance of the findings, and the recommendations made in the reports differed widely from one to another. The researchers concluded that the procedure is still unreliable and recommended that government agencies act vigorously to protect consumers.

Muscle-testing is part of a pseudoscientific system of diagnosis and treatment called applied kinesiology (AK). AK is based on the notion that every organ dysfunction is accompanied by a specific muscle weakness, which enables diseases to be diagnosed through muscle-testing procedures. Its practitioners, most of whom are chiropractors, also claim that nutritional deficiencies, allergies, and other adverse reactions to food substances can be detected by placing substances in the mouth so that the patient salivates. "Good" substances will make specific muscles stronger, whereas "bad" substances will cause specific weaknesses. "Treatment" may include special diets, food supplements, acupressure, and spinal manipulation. Applied kinesiology should be distinguished from kinesiology (biomechanics), which is the scientific study of movement. The concepts of applied kinesiology do not conform to scientific facts about the causes of disease. Controlled studies have found no difference between the results with test substances and with placebos. Differences from one test to another may be due to suggestibility, variations in the amount of force or leverage involved, and/or muscle fatigue.

Live-cell analysis is carried out by placing a drop of blood from the patient's fingertip on a microscope slide under a glass coverslip to slow down the process of drying out. The slide is then viewed with a dark-field microscope to which a television monitor has been attached. Both practitioner and patient can see the blood cells, which appear as dark bodies outlined in white. The practitioner may also make a videotape for himself and the patient. Proponents of live-cell analysis claim that it is useful for diagnosing vitamin and mineral deficiencies, enzyme deficiencies, tendencies toward allergic reactions, liver weakness, and many other health problems. Dark-field microscopy is a valid scientific tool in which special lighting is used to examine specimens of cells and tissues. Connecting a television monitor to a microscope for diagnostic purposes is also a legitimate practice. However, experts believe that live-cell analysis is useless in diagnosing most of the conditions that its practitioners claim to detect.

"Nutrient Deficiency" Questionnaires

Some nutrition consultants and retailers use computers to help them decide what to recommend. The tests usually involve completion of a dietary history and/or a questionnaire about symptoms that supposedly signify deficiency. Computer analysis of diet is a valuable tool that reputable nutritionists may find useful when appropriate computer programs are used. However, those used by the health-food industry are designed to tell everyone that they need large numbers of supplements.

Individual Promoters

Many individuals have developed and promoted food fads and other dubious nutrition practices. Each of the following persons has written several books and achieved notoriety.

Earl Mindell, a co-founder of the health-food-store chain Great Earth International, has a bachelor's degree in pharmacy from the University of North Dakota and "Ph.D.s" in nutrition from two nonaccredited schools. His books include *Earl Mindell's Vitamin Bible, Earl Mindell's Vitamin Bible for Kids, Unsafe at Any Meal, Earl Mindell's Herb Bible,* and *Earl Mindell's Soy Miracle.* The *Vitamin Bible* recommends self-treatment with supplements for more than 50 health

problems. The book also promotes substances that Mindell calls "vitamins" B10, B11, B13, B15, B17, P, T, and U. There is no scientific evidence that any of these substances are vitamins (essential to humans) or that supplements of any of them are beneficial. Now retired from active management of his stores, Mindell spends much of his time writing, lecturing, and appearing on talk shows.

Gary Null, Ph.D., whose books bill him as "one of America's leading health and fitness advocates," promotes dubious treatments for many serious diseases. He hosts radio and television talk shows, writes books, gives lectures, and has marketed supplement products. He has spoken out against fluoridation, immunization, food irradiation, mercury-amalgam fillings, and many forms of proven medical treatment. Null's Ph.D. was obtained from an accredited school whose requirements were considerably less than those of traditional universities.

Andrew Weil, M.D., is described on the covers of his best-selling books as "the guru of alternative medicine," "one of the most skilled, articulate, and important leaders in the field of health and healing," and "a pioneer in the medicine of the future." His advice is a mixture of sense and nonsense. The sensible part includes standard advice about diet and exercise. The nonsense includes such ideas as "improper breathing is a common cause of ill health" and the recommendation that following surgery, patients should get massive intravenous doses of vitamin C. He tends to prefer the use of "natural remedies" rather than conventional medicines. He has published nothing in scientific journals to objectively document his personal experiences with allegedly cured patients or to substantiate his claims that the nonstandard remedies he advocates are effective. His Web site contains an interactive "Vitamin Advisor" questionnaire that leads to recommendations for expensive and unnecessary vitamin supplements for everyone.

Protecting Yourself

Most Americans probably are harmed to some degree by nutrition fads and fallacies.

Promoters of nutrition quackery are skilled at arousing and exploiting fears and false hopes. Their most persuasive sales pitch is that everyone should take supplements to be sure of getting enough vitamins and minerals. However, it is more sensible for individuals worried about this to keep a food diary for several days and have a physician or registered dietitian determine whether any problem exists.

Supplements and "health foods" have been recommended for virtually every ailment. However, there is little or no scientific evidence to support such recommendations. Megadoses of vitamins and minerals have few legitimate uses and should never be taken without competent medical advice. Anyone who recommends supplements for everyone should be ignored.

To lose weight, people must eat less, exercise more, or do both. Although hundreds of "miracle" products and "revolutionary" diets have been marketed, no pill, potion, or dietary plan can produce weight loss without exercise or lowering of caloric intake. For most people, the most important factor in successful weight control is exercise.

Reliable Information Sources

- Quackwatch focuses on quackery-related information that is difficult or impossible to get elsewhere. It operates http://www.quackwatch.com and several Web sites.
- The National Council Against Health Fraud serves as a clearinghouse for information on health frauds, quackery, and "alternative" methods. It publishes position papers, fact sheets, an electronic newsletter, and a bimonthly print newsletter. Most of these documents can be accessed on its Web site: http://www.ncahf.org.
- The FDA Center for Food Safety and Nutrition provides abundant information about diet, nutrition, and government regulation. Its Web site is http://vm.cfsan.fda.gov/list.html

Recommended Publications

- S. Barrett and others. Consumer Health: A Guide to Intelligent Decisions, 7th Edition. St. Louis: McGraw Hill, 2002.
- S. Barrett and V. Herbert. The Vitamin Pushers: How the "Health Food" Industry Is Selling America a Bill of Goods. Amherst, NY: Prometheus Books, 1994.
- J.Z. Yetiv. Popular Nutrition Practices: A Scientific Appraisal. San Carlos, CA: Popular Nutrition Press, 1986.

28

Fitness Camps and Wellness

"They're miracle-workers," said 30-year-old James Shaw of Philadelphia, Pennsylvania. "What we learned here is priceless!"

It was the Summer of 1998. Far away from work, school, the noise and distractions of the city, and the busyness of life, nestled in the rolling mountains of Pennsylvania's hamlet of Pottstown, on the campus of Allegheny East Conference headquarters and Pine Forge Academy, miracles were happening. The "miracle-workers" were Gwendolyn Foster, M.P.H., director of Health Ministries for the Seventh-day Adventist Church in that regional conference; Geneva Jackson-McCleary, MD, a practicing physician in Maryland's Eastern Shore, and program director; Zeno Charles-Marcel, MD, medical director of the Oklahoma-based Lifestyle Center of America, and James Winston, MD, a physician in Philadelphia, the program's key lecturers on diabetes, hypertension, and heart disease; several pastoral advisors who conduct daily devotions, dieticians, nurses, two cooks, and a host of lifestyle counselors.

For two weeks every summer during the last 20 years, they had worked together to change lives, to share the secrets of the Adventist health message, and to teach people to embrace life to its fullest by adopting eight principles of healthy living. The name of their miracle antidote was Fitness For Life conditioning camp.

To some, this miracle sounded too good to be true. For the 59 campers attending the program from Colorado, Delaware, Ohio, New Jersey, New York, Michigan, Virginia, Georgia, Maryland, Washington, D.C., and mostly from Philadelphia, it was the miracle that changed their lives.

Camper Testimonies

"I'm 46, obese, insulin dependent, I have high blood pressure, I've had a hip replacement, and I need both knees replaced. If I saw [a profile of] such a person in the newspaper, I'd feel sorry for her," said Raynette Adams, affectionately known as "Ray-Ray" by her fellow campers. "This camp has given me the rest of my life. After just two weeks, I cut the insulin [dosage] in half, and my sugar levels are lower than ever before. I lost eight pounds, my pressure went from 142/88 to 126/58, I've lost two and three-quarter inches off my butt; three inches off my waist, and one inch off my hips. I can now do 25 full body push-ups and I've gained four and a half inches in my flexibility reach," she said grinning. "But I have gained more than that; I've gained an extended family. I'm leaving with the total program that Fitness for Life has given me. I'm going to eat right, exercise, and I've put time into my budget for me, time to do the things I want to do, time to spend with my father, time for my family. I've also obtained a list of churches so I can get my spiritual life in order, all thanks to Fitness for Life."

Coloradan Agatha Williams, who ran to the front of the room at the camp graduation to show how much better she felt, said: "Before I came here, it felt like my body was being beaten down with a hammer. If it didn't hit one system, it would hit another. My lungs, stomach, liver, gall

> "The whole issue behind health, behind helping people in the seminars is so they not only live a few years longer, it's so they live forever. It's so that they finally come to the conclusion that the God who is interested in their health is also interested in their whole well-being and their going to heaven to live with Him."

bladder, joints, everything was just beat out. But I said, 'I haven't done what I was sent here to do and it's not the way to go out. My sister heard about the program on Three Angels' Broadcasting Network and we decided to attend."

Williams says that before she attended camp she was on constant bed rest. By the end of the program, she had only walked once, but it was a mile.

"My favorite part of camp was meeting people and seeing people who weren't used to exercise and who may have been in poor health really get committed to the walking and have fun," said Shaw, who says he was in the habit of eating a terrible diet with lots of high animal fats, salt, and sugar. "I came to change my lifestyle and it wasn't exercise torture like you would expect; we had a good time and made it fun."

Joan Fobbs, of Maryland, who came to visit and encourage the campers, admitted that prior to attending camp, she'd had an addiction to sugar. "During the camp, I didn't lose any weight, just inches. But when I went home I walked, drank lots of water, ate moderately, and followed the principles I had learned, and I've lost 40 pounds."

Not only were there weight-loss miracles, those with diabetes and hypertension also saw tremendous results: Wesley Cherry, a skeptical scholarship winner from Philadelphia, became a believer when his sugar levels came down from the regular 170 - 190 range to a 70 - 90 range, while Arlette Hardy, 49, of Hyattsville, Maryland, celebrated the fact that her sugar level dropped from 254 to 90 in two weeks.

Edna Ryan, 75 of Ellenville, New York, was thrilled that her blood pressure dropped from 156/85 to 116/64. "If more people knew what this program could do for them, there would be a run for Pottstown," she said.

Living Well

How did these miracles happen? Immediately, upon arrival, campers began learning and adopting principles for optimum health. They arose daily for a 6 a.m. stretch and walk of one, two, or 2.6 miles, and enjoyed a hearty,

high-fiber breakfast at 7:30 a.m., followed by a short devotional thought given by a conference pastor. Each weekday morning was spent in lectures on the WELLNESS principles of health (see sidebar) and in-depth information is given on diabetes, obesity, hypertension, coronary artery and heart disease, and other chronic killers. Lunch consisted of a salad bar full of raw vegetables and homemade, low fat dressings, and a well-balanced entree of vegetables, protein, and starch. Afternoons were filled with more health educational seminars and activities: cooking classes on baking bread, making meat substitutes, or other recipes from scratch; recreational

Wellness

- Water
- Exercise
- Life-giving Air
- Limits (temperance)
- Nutrition
- Essential Rest
- Sunlight
- Spiritual Dimension

activities such as swimming, Taebo, or aerobics; demonstrations on hydrotheraphy and other health techniques; and private pastoral counseling. Because the camp is geared toward wellness and wholeness, there were also seminars on money and time management, financial planning, family relationships and roles, and activities such as writing a personal mission statement and group sharing time.

A 6:30 p.m. supper featured lite fare such as crackers or bread sticks with fruit or soup. Afterward there was another health lecture on chronic diseases or a demonstration and a devotional thought. Campers retired for the night at 9 p.m.

Daily Camp Program Schedule

- 5:30 a.m. - wake up
- 6 a.m. - Stretch and Walk
- 7:30 a.m. - Breakfast
- 8 a.m. - Worship
- 9 a.m. - Seminar on WELLNESS principles
- 11 a.m. - Lifestyle Lecture or Demonstration Activity
- 12:30 p.m. - Lunch
- 2 p.m. - Lifestyle Lecture
- 4 p.m. - Recreational Activity or Rest
- 6:30 p.m. - Supper
- 7 p.m. - Lecture on Chronic Diseases; Question-and-Answer Session
- 8:30 p.m. - Evening Worship
- 9 p.m. - Bedtime

Sample Menu

Breakfast

- Scambled Tofu
- Apple Muffin or Wheat Toast
- Oven Fried Potatoes

Lunch

- Salad Bar
- Blackbean with Brown Rice
- Collard Greens
- Cornbread

Supper

- Melon Wedges
- Bread Sticks and Almond Butter

Best Things About Camp

For Louise Wright and many others, the best part of camp was the food, even thought it was vegan (no eggs, no dairy, no vegetarian meat). "The food was tasty, much more so than I thought it would be," said the Philadelphian who claims her arthritis, allergies, and other ailments have dissipated. "I'm so sorry I didn't come three or five years ago because it was a wonderful, wonderful experience. I'm 64 and now that I'm truly doing what's right, I've seen the weight I wanted to lose for so long come off so easily. I want to say thank God and thanks to Fitness for Life. I hope to go home, follow the recipes, and eat this way for the rest of my life."

The neighbor who introduced Wright to the program also has a testimony. "Before I came to the Fitness for Life conditioning camp, I was so unhappy," said Louise Twyman. "I was on heart medication, I used to have anxiety attacks, I had lost a good friend in death, and I was gaining back weight I had lost," she said. "I was spiritually and emotionally drained but after doing the Fitness for Life program, I am a completely different person." So inspired was Twyman, she started a Fitness for Life chapter in Philadelphia that still meets weekly with nearly 30 members.

How do the families take the changes? Before I came to the camp, I was eating everything and anything," said camp veteran Valerie Thomas of Philadelphia, who says she gained weight having children. "After the program, I went home and became a vegetarian. I lost about 55 pounds. I've changed and I'm changing my family. Once you know what's in the food, how it's processed, and what God really wants you to do, you tend to make the right choices." Thomas says her husband and kids really don't mind the food, as long as it's tasty and good.

The evenings when the medical experts conducted question-and-answer sessions were most meaningful to Teresa Overton, a diabetic resident of the city of brotherly love. "I learned how good nutrition, exercise, and monitoring your health tie together. I was aware of the connection, but not how much of a connection until the doctors broke it down to a level where I could understand how it all [works] together," she says. "If you take care of one, the others fall into place."

Spiritual Component - Another Miracle

Another aspect of the program, emphasized in the devotionals and special church services involving campers, is the spiritual connection: "The spiritual aspect is what it's going to take to get the willpower to do this," said Delores Dupree, who won a scholarship to the program by being the first caller to her Pittsburgh radio station the day Foster was the guest on a show. "Because we're human and have temptations, it would be easy for us to fall back into the wrong way of eating. But if you have that spiritual core, that will help you stay on track."

For camp organizers, it runs even deeper than that. To Dr. Charles-Marcel, it's essential.

"The whole issue behind health, behind helping people in the seminars is so they not only live a few years longer, it's so they live forever. It's so that they finally come to the conclusion that the God who is interested in their health is also interested in their whole well-being and their going to heaven to live with Him," he says.

On the closing day of camp that summer, Cherry, a new believer in the successes of healthful living, shared with Foster that although he believes in God, he has never had a personal relationship with Him. He and a number of other campers asked if they could go to church with her. Sometime later, one of them, Louise Twyman joined the Adventist Church and has become quite an active member and Fitness for Life promoter. That was the other kind of miracle Foster and her team prayed for and believed would come.

Fitness for Life History

The Fitness for Life conditioning camp actually started 24 years ago, just after its founder, Foster, finished her Masters in Public Health at Loma Linda University in Southern California. The idea for camp came to her after she interviewed her adjunct professor, Nathan Pritikin, a layman in the health field (he was by trade a prominent engineer), who had risen to fame for his lifestyle centers that helped the rich and famous Hollywood types wage war against coronary diseases. "They'd come for two weeks and leave miraculously cured," Foster recalls. "So in 1977, I got an interview with him and he posed this question to me: 'Why is it that I'm more of a household name than are Seventh-day Adventists? Even with your universities and hospitals, I'm probably better known in the United States for lifestyle enhancement programs. And I got all I know from you. What is it? Why can I do all of this and you do not do this with all that you have?' I was embarrassed because I didn't have an answer," she says.

According to Foster, Pritikin told how during World War II when he fell ill, he got his hands on a set of Ellen White's books and philosophy of health. He implemented the principles, followed a vegetarian diet, brought himself back to health, and decided to open his famous lifestyle center to help the affluent, charging them thousands of dollars for the programs.

From that moment, Foster knew she would also start a center, not for the affluent, but for anyone who would listen and benefit from the lifestyle principle, and especially for her African American people who, plagued with hypertension, diabetes, obesity, and arthritis at alarming rates, really need it.

And so, for more than 20 years, she ran the annual conditioning camp, and changing lives, two weeks at a time for minimal fees and scholarships for those who can't afford it. Although she's worked with thousands who sing her praises, she did her best to use the program to reach many people for Christ–in and out of the Seventh-day Adventist Church. Interestingly enough, out of the 59 campers participating that summer, 50 were not Adventist.

Today, as Health Czar for the city of Philadelphia, Foster is adapting her program to work in community settings where people work during the day and attend the program at night. But 45 minutes away, in the serene setting of log cabins, Debra Carby, M.P.H., now Health Ministries director for Allegheny East Conference, just completed her first year directing the camp and plans to continue the legacy.

Why Conduct a Fitness Camp?

"Too often within our Church, we put most of our dollars in one aspect— reaping. But farming has many more benefits," Foster says. "You've got to till and nurture all the tender plants and this is a very effective way of reaching people. People who come to evangelistic meetings may slip in and out. Through the years, my campers didn't ask 'What must I do to be saved?' They wanted to know how to lost weight, how to access and prepare more healthy meals for their families, how to find time to eat right despite their busy schedules and the many demands on their lives. We worked to scratch where they itched, and to start where the people are," she says.

Alvin Kibble, a vice president for the North American Division, who was president of the conference where Foster founded the conditioning camp program, still supports the concept and agrees with Foster that Adventist churches and conferences across North America should sponsor similar programs.

"Fitness Camp provides an entering wedge for evangelism," Kibble says. "We can use it to advance the Gospel, rally our churches for outreach, and model a quality of life that many people are hungry for, praying for, and searching for."

DeWitt Williams, Health Ministries director for the church in North America is ready to see the program spread to other areas. He says that plans are in the works to hold training programs for those who are ready to launch a Fitness For Life program. It is his dream that every conference would hold a yearly fitness camp and has set up a special committee to explore ways to help other conferences set up their camps. "All of our conferences have camp sites and personnel. With imagination and commitment each conference could sponsor an annual fitness camp. I don't think we have any other program that allows non-Adventists to interact with us on a daily basis, from morning to evening–eating with us, praying with us, laughing with us, and learning with us. The program pays for itself and the rewards are rich," says Williams.

For more information about the Allegheny East program, call Debra Carby at 610-326-4610.

Celeste Ryan is co-chair of the development committee working to promote the Fitness for Life program across the North American Division.

Herghelia—The Romanian Live-In Health Institute

In the center of Romania, a few miles from Tirgu Mures, is a very nice facility for live-in programs. This is the only one of its kind in Romania. They operate a live-in program each month with about 30 in attendance. Along with this is a small school teaching young people the health message and how to win souls. Dr. Nic Dan, director of this facility, and his wife both received their masters degree at Loma Lindas School of Public Health. The institution has had excellent relations with the local medical school and with government officials.

Health Wellness Campmeetings

Slovakia stands out in the Euro-African Division in its health campmeetings. Bohumil Kern is the conference health director. He organizes a week of live-in programs at some nice facility usually in a resort type of setting. Since individuals attending pay for the weeks program all these programs are self-supporting. Approximately 50% of those attending this Newstart type of program are not members of the Adventist Church. Once they see the soundness of the health message they make inquiries as to what Adventists believe. Statistical data was kept comparing the long-term results of church growth from having a foreign evangelist come in vs. having health campmeetings. There is a rapid growth of membership for the usual evangelistic program but then the growth levels off. With the health campmeetings there is continuous growth without the leveling off. This is a major evangelistic tool in that conference.

Dr. Janka Noskova, pediatrician, translated frequently when General Conference (Scharffenberg, Proctor) or local Division leaders (Hawlitschek) lectured. As a vegetarian she came to the Adventist meetings initially since Adventists seemed to know more about this subject than others. She has now been baptized and has been elected leader of our Life and Health organization in Slovakia which is the name we give to our health outreach programs. She has organized health clubs in 16 cities and is beginning to get recognition by the government for these activities. Weight control is one of their major programs. Dr. Noskova and her husband received green cards through the U.S. Governments lottery program. In five years they can become U.S. citizens. However, she wishes to continue working on in Slovakia but use the U.S. as the place to get advanced education.

What Seventh-day Adventists Believe about Healthful Living

(From: Chapter 21, "Christian Behavior" in *Seventh-day Adventists Believe. . .*, Published for the General Conference Ministerial Association by the Review and Herald Publishing Association, 1989.)

"We are called to be a godly people who think, feel and act in harmony with the principles of heaven. For the Spirit to recreate in us the character of our Lord we involve ourselves only in those things which will produce Christlike purity, health, and joy in our lives. This means that our amusement and entertainment should meet the highest standards of Christian taste and beauty. While recognizing cultural differences, our dress is to be simple, modest, and neat, befitting those whose true beauty does not consist of outward adornment but in the imperishable ornament of a gentle and quiet spirit. It also means because our bodies are the temples of the Holy Spirit, we are to care for them intelligently. Along with adequate exercise and rest, we are to adopt the most healthful diet possible and abstain from the unclean foods identified in the Scriptures. Since alcoholic beverages, tobacco, and the irresponsible use of drugs and narcotics are harmful to our bodies, we are to abstain from them as well. Instead, we are to engage in whatever brings our thoughts and bodies into the discipline of Christ, who desires our wholesomeness, joy, and goodness."

(*Fundamental Beliefs* #21)

Christian Behavior

Christian behavior—the lifestyle of a follower of God—arises as a grateful response to God's magnificent salvation through Christ. Paul appeals to all Christians: "I beseech you therefore, brethren, by the mercies of God, that you present your bodies a living sacrifice, holy, acceptable to God, which is your reasonable service. And do not be conformed to this world, but be trans-

formed by the renewing of your mind, that you may prove which is that good and acceptable and perfect will of God" (Rom. 12:1, 2). So Christians willingly protect and develop their mental, physical, and spiritual faculties in order that they may honor their Creator and Redeemer.

Christ prayed, "'I do not pray that You should take them out of the world, but that You should keep them from the evil one. They are not of the world, just as I am not of the world.'" (John 17:15, 16). How can a Christian be both in the world and separate from it? How should the Christian lifestyle differ from that of the world?

Christians should adopt a different lifestyle, not for the sake of being different but because God has called them to live by principle. The lifestyle to which He has called them enables them to reach their full potential as His creation, making them efficient in His service. Being different also advances their mission: to serve the world—to be salt in it, light to it. Of what value would salt be without taste, or light that didn't differ from darkness?

Christ is our example. He lived so thoroughly in the world that people accused Him of being "'a glutton and a drunkard'" (Matt. 11:19, NIV), though He was not. He so consistently lived out God's principles that no one could prove Him guilty of sin (John 8:46, NIV).

Behavior and Salvation

In determining what is appropriate behavior, we should avoid two extremes. The first is accepting the rules and applications of principles to become as a means of salvation. Paul sums up this extreme with the words, "You who are trying to be justified by law have been alienated from Christ; you have fallen away from grace" (Gal. 5:4, NIV).

The opposite extreme is believing that since works do not save, they are therefore unimportant—that what a person does really doesn't matter. Paul spoke to this extreme too: "You, my brothers, were called to be free. But do not use your freedom to indulge the sinful nature" (Gal. 5:13, NIV). When each member follows his or her own conscience, "there is no mutual discipling of fellow Christians in keeping with Matthew 18 and Galatians 6:1, 2. The church becomes not the body of Christ, within which there is mutual love and care, but a collection of atomistic individuals, each of whom goes his or her own way without taking any responsibility for one's fellows or accepting any concern for them."[1]

While our behavior and our spirituality are closely related, we can never earn salvation by correct behavior. Rather, Christian behavior is a natural fruit of salvation and is grounded in what Christ has already accomplished for us at Calvary.

Temples of the Holy Spirit

Not only the church but the individual Christian is a temple for the indwelling of the Holy Spirit: "Do you not know that your body is the temple of the Holy Spirit who is in you, whom you have from God, and you are not your own?" (1 Cor. 6:19).

Christians, then, practice good health habits to protect the command center of their body temples, the mind, the dwelling place of the Spirit of Christ. For this reason Seventh-day Adventists—throughout the past 100 years—have stressed the importance of proper health habits.[2] And this emphasis has been paying off: Recent research reveals that Adventists are less likely than the general population to develop almost any of the major diseases.[3]

As Christians, we are concerned with both the spiritual and the physical aspects of people's lives. Jesus, our pattern, healed "every disease and sickness among the people" (Matt. 4:23, NIV).

The Bible views human beings as a unit (chapter 7). "The dichotomy between spiritual and material is foreign to the Bible."[4] So God's call to holiness involves a call to physical as well as spiritual health. Susannah Wesley, mother of

the founder of Methodism, aptly summarized this principle: "Whatever weakens your reason, impairs the tenderness of your conscience, obscures your sense of God, decreases the strength and authority of your mind over the body—that thing is wrong, however innocent it may be in itself."[5]

God's laws, which include the laws of health, are not arbitrary but are designed by our Creator to enable us to enjoy life at its best. Satan, the enemy, wants to steal our health, our joy, our peace of mind, and ultimately to destroy us (see John 10:10).

God's Blessings for Total Health

Attaining this health depends upon practicing a few rather simple but effective God-given principles. Some of these are obvious and quite agreeable to most people. Others, such as proper diet, are more difficult to accept since they involve orientations and habits so basic to our lifestyles. For this reason, we will devote more space to those principles that are either misunderstood, debated, or rejected.[6]

The Blessing of Exercise. Regular exercise is the simple formula for increased energy, a firm body , stress relief, healthier skin, more self-confidence, effective weight control, improved digestion and regularity, and reduced depression and the risk of heart disease and cancer. Exercise is not merely an option, it is essential to maintaining optimal health—both physical and mental.[7]

Useful activity tends to prosperity; inactivity and laziness tend to adversity (Prov. 6:6-13; 14:23). God prescribed activity for the first man and woman—care for their garden home in the open air (Gen. 2:5, 15; 3:19). Christ Himself set an example of physical activity. For most of His life He was engaged in manual labor as a carpenter, and during His ministry He walked the roads of Palestine.[8]

The Blessing of Sunlight. Light is essential to life (Gen. 1:3). It powers the process that produces the nutrients that nourish and energize our bodies and that releases the oxygen we must have to live. Sunshine promotes health and healing.

The Blessing of Water. The human body is 75 percent water, but this vital fluid is continuously being lost through exhaled air, perspiration, and waste products. Drinking six to eight glasses of pure water a day would aid in maintaining efficient, happy well-being. Another important function of water is its use for cleanliness and the relaxation it affords.

The Blessing of Fresh Air. An environment of impure air, in or outside of the home, causes the blood to carry less oxygen than is required for the optimal function of every cell. This tends to make a person less alert and responsive. It is therefore important to do everything possible to secure a generous supply of fresh air daily.

The Blessing of Temperate, Drug-Free, Stimulant-Free Living. Drugs have saturated our society because they offer stimulation and release from stress and pain. The Christian is surrounded with seductive invitations to use drugs. Even many innocent-appearing, popular beverages contain drugs: Coffee, tea, and colas contain caffeine,[9] and fruit-flavored wine coolers contain alcohol. Research has shown that the milder gateway drugs tend to lead progressively to stronger mind-altering drugs. The wise Christian will abstain from all that is harmful, using in moderation only that which is good.

1. *Tobacco.* In any form tobacco is a slow poison that has a harmful effect on the physical, mental, and moral powers. At first its effects are hardly noticeable. It excites and then paralyzes the nerves, weakening and clouding the brain. Those who use tobacco are slowly committing suicide,[10] transgressing the sixth commandment: "Thou shalt not kill" (Ex. 20:13, KJV).

2. *Alcoholic beverages.* Alcohol is one of the most widely used drugs on Planet Earth. It has devastated untold millions. Not only does it hurt those who use it, but it exacts its toll from society in general—through broken homes, accidental deaths, and poverty. Since God communicates with us only through our minds, it is well to remember that alcohol

adversely affects their every function. As the level of alcohol in the system rises, the drinker progresses through loss of coordination, confusion, disorientation, stupor, anesthesia, coma, and death. Drinking alcoholic beverages on a regular basis will eventually produce loss of memory, judgment, and learning ability.[11]

Scriptural stories involving the use of alcoholic beverages may give the impression that God approved their use. However, Scripture also indicates that God's people participated in such social practices as divorce, polygamy, and slavery—practices that God certainly did not condone. In interpreting such Scriptural passages, it is helpful to keep in mind that God does not necessarily endorse all that He permits.

Jesus' answer to the query as to why Moses permitted divorce points to this principle of interpretation. He said, "'Moses, because of the hardness of your hearts, permitted you to divorce your wives, but from the beginning it was not so'" (Matt. 19:8).[12] Eden is the divine model to which the gospel would restore us. As is true of these other practices, the use of alcohol was not a part of God's original plan.[13]

3. *Other drugs and narcotics.* There are many other harmful drugs and narcotics through which Satan destroys human lives.[14] True Christians beholding Christ will continually glorify God with their bodies, realizing that they are His prized possessions, bought with His precious blood.

The Blessing of Rest. Proper rest is essential for health of the body and mind. Christ extends to us the compassionate directive He gave His weary disciples; "'Come with me by yourselves to a quiet place and get some rest'" (Mark 6:31, NIV). Periods of rest provide much needed quietness for communication with God: "Be still, and know that I am God" (Ps. 46:10). God stressed our need for rest by setting aside the seventh day of the week as the day of rest (Ex. 20:10).

Rest is more than sleeping or ceasing our regular work. It involves the way we spend our leisure time. Weariness is not always caused by stress or by working too hard for too long: Our minds can be wearied by overstimulation through media, sickness, or various personal problems. Recreation is re-creation in the truest sense of the word. It strengthens, builds up, and refreshes the mind and body, thus preparing believers to go back to their vocations with new vigor. To live life at its best, Christians should pursue only those forms of recreation and entertainment that strengthen their bond with Christ and improve health.

Scripture lays down the following principle, which will help Christians select good recreation: "Do not love the world or the things in the world. If anyone loves the world, the love of the Father is not in him. For all that is in the world—the lust of the flesh, the lust of the eyes, and the pride of life—is not of the Father but is of the world" (1 John 2:15, 16).

1. Movies, television, radio, and videos. These media can be great educational agencies. They have "changed the whole atmosphere of our modern world and have brought us within easy contact with the life, thought, and activities of the entire globe."[15] The Christian will remember that television and videos make a greater impact on the life of an individual than does any other single activity.

   Unfortunately, video and television, with their almost continuous theatrical performances, bring influences into the home that are neither wholesome nor uplifting. If we are not discriminating and decisive, "they will turn our homes into theaters and minstrel shows of cheap and sordid kind."[16] The committed Christian will turn away from unwholesome, violent, sensual movies and television programs.

   Visual and audio media are not evil in themselves. The same channels that portray the depths of human wickedness convey the preaching of the gospel of salvation. And many other worthwhile programs are broadcast. But people can use even the good programs to avoid the responsibilities of life. Christians will not only desire to establish principles for determining what to watch but will also set time limits on their watching, so that social relationships and the responsibilities of life will not suffer. If we cannot discriminate or if we lack the power to control our media, it is much better to dispense with them altogether than to have them rule our lives either by polluting the mind or consuming excessive amounts of time (see Matt. 5:29, 30).

   Regarding our contemplation of Christ, an important Biblical principle states that "by beholding we are becoming transformed into His likeness with ever-increasing glory" (2 Cor. 3:18, NIV). Beholding brings change. But Christians must continually remember that this principle works on the negative side, too. Films graphically portraying the sins and crimes of humanity—murder, adultery, robbery, and other degrading acts—are contributing to the present breakdown of morality.

   Paul's advice in Philippians 4:8 lays out a principle that helps to identify the forms of recreation that have value: "Finally, brethren, whatever things that are true, whatever things are noble, whatever things are just, whatever things are pure, whatever things are lovely, whatever things are of good report, if there is any virtue and if there is anything praiseworthy—meditate on these things."

2. *Reading and music.* These same high standards apply to the Christian's reading and music. Music is a gift of God to inspire pure, noble, and elevated thoughts. Good music, then, enhances the finest qualities of character.

   Debased music, on the other hand, "destroys the rhythm of the soul and breaks down morality." So Christ's followers will shun "any melody partaking of the nature of jazz, rock, or related hybrid forms, or any language expressing foolish or trivial sentiments."[17] The Christian does not listen to music with suggestive lyrics or melodies (Rom. 13:11-14; 1 Peter 2:11).[18]

Reading offers much that is valuable too. There is a wealth of good literature that cultivates and expands the mind. Yet there is also a "flood of evil literature, often in most attractive guise but damaging to the mind and morals. The tales of wild adventure and of moral laxness, whether fact or fiction," are unfit for the believers because they create a distaste for a noble, honest, and pure lifestyle and hinder the development of a union with Christ.[19]

3. *Unacceptable activities.* Adventists also teach that gambling, card playing, theater going, and dancing are to be avoided (1 John 2:15-17). They question spending time watching violent sporting events (Phil. 4:8). Any activity that weakens our relationship with our Lord and causes us to lose sight of eternal interests helps to bind Satan's chains about our souls. Christians will rather participate in those wholesome forms of leisure activities that will truly refresh their physical, mental, and spiritual natures.

The Blessing of Nutritious Food. To the first couple, the Creator gave the ideal diet: "'I give you every seed-bearing plant on the face of the whole earth and every tree that has fruit with seed in it. They will be yours for food'" (Gen. 1:29, NIV). After the Fall, God added to their diet "'the plants of the fields'" (Gen 3:18, NIV).

Today's health problems tend to center on the degenerative type of diseases that are directly traceable to diet and lifestyle. The diet God planned, consisting of grains, fruits, nuts, and vegetables, offers the right nutritional ingredients to support optimum health.

1. *The original diet.* The Bible does not condemn the eating of clean animals. But God's original diet for man did not include flesh foods because He did not envision the taking of any animal's life and because a balanced vegetarian diet is the best for health—a fact for which science offers mounting evidence.[20] People consuming animal products that con-

tain bacteria or viruses that cause disease may have their health impaired.[21] It is estimated that every year, in the United States alone, millions suffer from poultry food poisoning because inspection fails to detect contamination by salmonella and other microorganisms.[22] Several experts feel that "bacterial contamination poses a far greater risk than chemical additives and preservatives in food" and expect the incidence of the diseases caused by these bacteria to rise.[23]

Furthermore, studies conducted in recent years indicate that increased meat consumption can cause an increase of atherosclerosis, cancer, kidney disorders, osteoporosis, and trichinosis, and can decrease the life expectancy.[24]

The diet God ordained in the Garden of Eden—the vegetarian diet—is the ideal, but sometimes we cannot have the ideal. In those circumstances, in any given situation or locale, those who wish to stay in optimum health will eat the best food that they can obtain.

2. *Clean and unclean flesh foods.* Only after the Flood did God introduce flesh as food. With all vegetation destroyed, God gave Noah and his family permission to eat flesh food, stipulating that they were not to eat the blood in the meat (Gen. 9:4).

Another stipulation Scripture implies that God gave Noah was that he and his family were to eat only what God identified as clean animals. It was because Noah and his family needed the clean animals for food as well as for sacrifices (Gen. 8:20) that God instructed Noah to take seven pairs of each kind of clean animal, in contrast to only one pair of each kind of unclean, with him into the ark (Gen. 7:2, 3). Leviticus 11 and Deuteronomy 14 provide extensive expositions on clean and unclean foods.[25]

By nature, unclean animals do not constitute the best food. Many are either scavengers or predators—from the lion and swine to the vulture and the bottom-dwelling, sucker-type fish. Because of their habits they are more apt to be carriers of disease.

Studies have revealed that "in addition to the moderate amounts of cholesterol found in both pork and shellfish, both foods contain a number of toxins and contaminants which are associated with human poisoning."[26]

By abstaining from unclean foods, God's people demonstrated their gratefulness for their redemption from the corrupt, unclean world around them (Lev. 20:24-26; Deut. 14:2). To introduce anything unclean into the body temple where God's Spirit dwells is less than God's ideal.

The New Testament did not abolish the distinction between the clean and unclean flesh foods. Some believe that because these dietary laws are mentioned in Leviticus, they are merely ceremonial or ritualistic, and so are no longer valid for Christians. Yet the distinction between clean and unclean animals dates back to Noah's day—long before Israel existed. As principles of health, these dietary laws carry with them an ongoing obligation.[27]

3. *Regularity, simplicity, and balance.* Successful dietary reforms are progressive and must be approached intelligently. Eventually we should learn to eliminate, or use only sparingly, foods with high fat and/or sugar content.

Furthermore, we should prepare the foods we eat in as simple and natural a way as possible, and for optimum benefit, should eat at regular intervals. Complex, stimulating diets are not the most healthful. Many condiments and spices irritate the digestive tract,[28] and their habitual use is associated with a number of health problems.[29]

The Blessing of Christian Dress. God provided the first clothing for Adam and Eve and knows that we have need of suitable clothing today (Matt. 6:25-33). We should base our choice of clothing on the principles of simplicity, modesty, practicality, health, and attractiveness.

1. *Simple.* As it does in all other areas of our lives, the Christian call to simplicity impinges upon how we dress. "Christian witness calls for simplicity.

"The way we dress demonstrates to the world who we are and what we are—not as a legal requirement handed down from the Victorian era, but as an expression of our love of Jesus."[30]

2. *Of high moral virtue.* Christians will not mar the beauty of their characters with styles that arouse the "lust of the flesh" (1 John 2:16). Because they want to witness to others, they will dress and act modestly, not accentuating the parts of the body that stimulate sexual desires. Modesty promotes moral health. The Christian's aim is to glorify God, not self.

3. *Practical and economical.* Because they are stewards of the money God has entrusted to them, Christians will practice economy, avoiding "gold or pearls or costly clothing" (1 Tim. 2:9). Practicing economy, however, does not necessarily mean purchasing the cheapest clothing available. Often higher quality items are more economical in the long run.

4. *Healthful.* It is not only diet that affects a person's health. Christians will avoid clothing styles that do not adequately protect the body or that constrict it or otherwise affect it in such ways as to cause the health to deteriorate .

5. *Characterized by grace and natural beauty.* Christians understand the warning against "the pride of life" (1 John 2:16). Referring to the lilies, Christ said, "even Solomon in all his glory was not arrayed like one of these" (Matt. 6:29). Thus He illustrated that Heaven's perception of beauty is characterized by grace, simplicity, purity, and natural beauty. Worldly display, as seen in transient fashions, has no value in God's eyes (1 Tim. 2:9).

Christians win unbelievers not by looking and behaving like the world but by revealing an attractive and refreshing difference. Peter said unbelieving spouses "may be won by the conduct of their wives, when they observe your chaste conduct accompanied by fear." Instead of adorning the exterior, he counseled, let believers concentrate on developing "the hidden person of the heart, with the incorruptible ornament of a gentle and quiet spirit, which is very precious in the sight of God" (1 Peter 3:1-4). Scripture teaches that:

a. *The character shows forth one's true beauty.* Both Peter and Paul set forth the basic principle for guiding Christian men and women in the area of adornment: "Your beauty should not come from outward adornment such as…the wearing of gold jewelry and fine clothes" (1 Peter 3:3, NIV). "I also want women to dress modestly with decency and propriety, not with braided hair or gold or pearls or expensive clothes, but with good deeds, appropriate for women who profess to worship God" (1 Tim. 2: 9, 10, NIV).

b. *Simplicity harmonizes with reformation and revival.* When Jacob called his family to dedicate themselves to God they gave up "all the foreign gods which were in their hands, and all their earrings which were in their ears," and Facob buried them (Gen. 35: 2, 4).[31] After Israel's apostasy with the golden calf, God commanded them, "Take off your ornaments, that I may know what to do to you." In penitence they "stripped themselves of their ornaments" (Ex. 33:5, 6). Paul clearly states that Scripture records this apostasy "as warnings for us, on whom the fulfillment of the ages has come" (1 Cor. 10:11, NIV).

c. *Good stewardship requires sacrificial living.* While much of the world is undernourished, materialism lays before Christians temptations ranging from expensive clothes, cars, and jewelry to luxurious homes. Simplicity of lifestyle and appearance sets Christians in stark contrast to the greed, materialism, and gaudiness of pagan, twentieth-century society, where values focus on material things rather than on people.

In view of these Scriptural teachings and the principles laid out above, we believe that Christians ought not to adorn themselves with jewelry. We understand this to mean that the wearing of rings, earrings, necklaces, and bracelets, and showy tie tacks, cuff links, and pins—and any other type of jewelry that has as its main function display—is unnecessary and not in harmony with the simplicity of adornment urged by Scripture.[32]

The Bible associates gaudy cosmetics with paganism and apostasy (2 Kings 9:30; Jer. 4:30). As to cosmetics, therefore, we believe that Christians should maintain a natural, healthy appearance. If we lift up the Savior in the way we speak, act, and dress, we become like magnets, drawing people to Him.[33]

Principles of Christian Standards

In all its manifestations, the Christian lifestyles is a response to salvation through Christ. The Christian desires to honor God and to live as Jesus would live. Although some view the Christian lifestyle as a list of don'ts, we should rather see it as a series of positive principles active in the framework of salvation. Jesus emphasized that He came that we might have life and have it more abundantly. What are the principles that guide us to the full life? When the Holy Spirit comes into the life of an individual, a decided change takes place that is evident to those around that person (John 3:8). The Spirit not only makes an initial change in the life; His effects are ongoing. The first and most prominent fruit of the Spirit is love (Galatians 5:22, 23). The most powerful argument for the validity of Christianity is a loving and lovable Christian.

Living with the Mind of Christ. "Let this mind be in you which was also in Christ Jesus" (Phil. 2:5). Under all circumstances, favorable or adverse, we should seek to understand and live in harmony with the will and mind of Christ (1 Cor. 2:16).

Ellen White has noted the beautiful results of a life that is lived in this kind of a relationship with Christ: "All true obedience comes from the heart. It was heart work with Christ. And if we consent, He will so identity Himself with our thoughts and aims, so blend our hearts and minds into conformity to His will, that when obeying Him we shall be but carrying out our own impulses. The will, refined and sanctified, will find its highest delight in doing His service. When we know God as it is our privilege to know Him, our life will be a life of continual obedience. Through an appreciation of the character of Christ, through communion with God, sin will become hateful to us."[34]

Living to Praise and Glorify God. God has done so much for us. One way in which we can show our gratitude is through the praise that we give Him.

The Psalms strongly emphasize this side of the spiritual life: "I have seen you in the sanctuary and beheld your power and your glory. Because your love is better than life, my lips will glorify you. I will praise you as long as I live, and in your name I will lift up my hands. My soul will be satisfied as with the richest of foods; with singing lips my mouth will praise you" (Ps. 63: 2-5, NIV).

For the Christian, such an attitude of praise will keep life's other affairs in an appropriate perspective. In looking upon our crucified Savior who redeemed us from the penalty and delivers us from the power of sin, we are motivated to do only "those things that are pleasing in His sight" (1 John 3:22; cf. Eph. 5:10, NIV). Christians "live no longer for themselves, but for Him who died for them and rose again" (2 Cor. 5:15). Every true Christian puts God first in all he does, in all he thinks, in all he speaks, and in all that he desires. He has no other gods before His Redeemer (1 Cor. 10:31).

Living to Be an Example. Paul said, "give no offense" to anyone (1 Cor. 10:32). "I myself always strive to have a conscience without offense toward God and men" (Acts 24:16). If our example leads others to sin, we become stumbling blocks to those for whom Christ died. "Whoever claims to live in him must walk as Jesus did" (1 John 2:6, NIV).

Living to Minister. A major reason Christians live as they do is to save lost men and women. Said Paul, "I try to please everybody in every way. For I am not seeking my own good but the good of many, so that they may be saved." (I Cor. 10:33, NIV; cf. Matt. 20:28).

Requirements and Guidelines

Because of the impact a person's lifestyle makes upon his spiritual experience and his witness, as a church organization we have set certain lifestyle standards as minimal requirements for becoming members. These standards include the abstention from tobacco, alcoholic beverages, mind-altering chemicals, and unclean flesh foods and the evidence of a growing Christian experience in matters of dress and the use of leisure time. These minimal standards do not comprehend all of God's ideal for the believer. They simply are essential first steps in developing a growing, radiant Christian experience. Such standards also provide the foundation essential to unity within the community of believers.

The development of Christian behavior—"God-likeness"—is progressive, involving a lifelong union with Christ. Holy living is nothing less than a daily yielding of the will to Christ's control and a daily conformity to His teachings as He reveals them to us in our Bible study and prayer. Because we mature at different rates, it is important that we refrain from judging weaker brothers and sisters (Rom. 14:1; 15:1).

Christians in union with the Savior have but one ideal: that they shall do their best to honor the heavenly Father, who has provided such a rich plan for their salvation. "Therefore, whether you eat or drink or whatever you do, do all to the glory of God" (1 Cor. 10:31).

References

1. L. A. King, "Legalism or Permissiveness: An Inescapable Dilemma?" *The Christian Century,* April 16, 1980, p. 436.

2. For the development of the Biblical basis of healthful living in the SDA Church, see Damsteegt, *Foundations of the Seventh-day Adventist Message and Mission,* pp. 221-240; Damsteegt, "Health Reforms and the Bible in Early Sabbatarian Adventism," *Adventist Heritage,* Winter 1978, pp. 13-21.

3. See Lewis R. Walton, Jo Ellen Walton, John A. Scharffenberg, *How You Can Live Six Extra Years* (Santa Barbara, CA: Woodbridge Press, 1981), p. 4; D.C. Neiman and H.J. Stanton, "The Adventist Lifestyle—A Better Way to Live," *Vibrant Life,* March/April 1988, pp. 14-18.

4. *Zondervan Pictorial Encyclopedia of the Bible* (Grand Rapids, MI: Zondervan Publishers, 1975), vol. 1, p. 884.

5. C.B. Haynes, "Church Standards—No. 5," *Review and Herald,* Oct. 30, 1941, p. 7.

6. For a fuller treatment of these simple health rules, see V.W. Foster, *New Start!* (Santa Barbara, CA: Woodbridge Press, 1988).

7. See e.g., Kenneth H. Cooper, *Aerobics Program for Total Well Being* (New York: M. Evans, 1982); *Physical Fitness Education Syllabus* (Loma Linda, CA: Department of Health Science, School of Health, Loma Linda University, 1976-1977); John Dignam, "Walking Into Shape," *Signs of the Times,* July 1987, p. 16; B.E. Baldwin, "Exercise," *Journal of Health and Healing* 11, No. 4 (1987): 20-23; Jeanne Wiesseman, *Physical Fitness,* Abundant Living Health Series, vol. 5 (Loma Linda, CA: School of Health Loma Linda University, n.d.), pp. 21, 37, 38, 45. See also Dianne-Jo Moore, "Walk Your Tensions Away," *Your Life and Health,* No. 4 (1984): 12, 13.

8. Among the various forms of exercise, walking ranks as one of the best. See J.A. Scharffenberg, "Adventist Responsibility in Exercise" (unpublished manuscript); White, *Testimonies,* vol. 3, p. 78; White, "Temperance," *Health Reformer,* April 1872, p. 122; Dignam, "Walking Into Shape," pp. 16, 17.

9. Caffeine has also been found to contribute to increased blood cholesterol, high blood pressure, increased gastric secretions, and peptic ulcers. It has been implicated in heart disease, diabetes, and cancers of the colon, bladder, and pancreas. Its heavy use during pregnancy increases the risk of birth defects and low-birth-weight infants. See Robert O'Brien and Sidney Cohen, "Caffeine," *Encyclopedia of Drug Abuse* (New York: Facts on File, 1984), pp. 50, 51; Marjorie V. Baldwin, "Caffeine on Trial," *Life and Health,* October 1973, pp. 10-13; E.D. Gorham, L.F. Garland, F.C. Garland, et al, "Coffee and Pancreatic Cancer in a Rural California County," *Western Journal of Medicine,* January 1988, pp. 48-53; B.K. Jacobson, and D.S. Thelle, "The Tromsssso Heart Study: Is Coffee Drinking an Indicator of a Lifestyle With High Risk for Ischemic Heart Disease?" *Acta Medica Scandinavica* 222, No. 3 (1987), 215-221; J.D. Curb, D.M. Reed, J.A. Kautz, and K. Yano, "Coffee, Caffeine and Serum Cholesterol in Japanese Living in Hawaii," *American Journal of Epidemiology,* April 1986, pp. 648-655. High consumers of coffee are also "less active in religion" (B.S. Victor, M. Lubetsky, and J.F. Greden, "Somatic Manifestations of Caffeinism," *Journal of Clinical Psychiatry,* May 1981, p. 186). For the caffeine content of the various beverages, see "The Latest Caffeine Scoreboard," *FDA Consumer,* March 1984, pp. 14-16; Bosley, "Caffeine: Is It So Harmless?" *Ministry,* August 1986, p. 28; Winston J. Craig and Thuy T. Nguyen, "Caffeine and Theobromine Levels in Cocoa and Carob Products," *Journal of Food Science,* January-February, 1984, pp. 302-303, 305.

10. Regarding the circulatory system, tobacco increases the risk of heart attacks, high blood pressure, and peripheral vascular disease such as Buerger's disease, which necessitates the amputation of fingers and toes. As to the respiratory system, tobacco brings an increase of deaths as a result of lung cancer, chronic bronchitis, and emphysema. It paralyzes the bronchial cilia that cleanse the lung and bronchi of impurities and is associated with cancer of the larynx, mouth esophagus, urinary bladder, kidney, and panreas.

It is also associated with an increase of duodenal ulcers and deaths from complications resulting form ulcers. See e.g., *Smoking and Health: A Report of the Surgeon General* (Washington, D.C.; U.S. Department of Health, Education, and Welfare, 1979).

11. See e.g., Galen C. Bosley, "The Effects of Small Quantities of Alcohol," *Ministry*, May 1986, pp. 24-27. Among social drinkers alcohol causes shrinkage of the frontal lobes, the center of moral discernment (L.A. Cala, B. Jones, P. Burns, et al, "Results of Computerized Tomography, Psychometric Testing and Dietary Studies in Social Drinkers, With Emphasis on Reversibility After Abstinence," *Medical Journal of Australia*, Sept. 17, 1983, pp. 264-269). Cf. Bosley, "Why a Health Message," *Adventist Review,* July 30, 1987, p. 15. Psychological testing of social drinkers showed that their mental abilities and intellectual performance were significantly impaired (D.A. Parker, E.S. Parker, J.A. Brody, and R. Schoenberg, "Alcohol Use and Cognitive Loss Among Employed Men and Women," *American Journal of Public Health*, May 1983, pp. 521-526). As alcohol intake increases, church attendance decreases (A.M. Eward, R. Wolfe, P. Moll and E. Harburg, "Psychosocial and Behavioral Factors Differentiating Past and Lifelong Abstainers," *American Journal of Public Health,* January 1986, p. 9.

12. See Chapter 15, footnote 8 for a discussion of wine at the Lord's Supper.

13. In the Old Testament, the general term for wine is yayin. This term designates the juice of the grape in all its stages from unfermented to fermented, though it is frequently used for fully aged wine that contains alcohol. The usual word from unfermented wine is *tirosh*. It is frequently translated as "new wine," which is freshly pressed grape juice. Both terms are rendered *oinos* in the Septuagintal Greek translation of the Old Testament (LXX). *Oinos* is the term generally used for wine in the New Testament and refers to both fermented and unfermented wine, depending on the context. (For the Old Testament see Robert P. Teachout, "The Use of 'Wine' in the Old Testament," (Th.D. dissertation, 1979, available through University Microfilms International, Ann Arbor, MI); Lael O. Ceasar, "The Meaning of *Yayin*" (unpublished M.A. thesis, Andrews University, Berrien Springs, MI, 1986; William Patton, Bible Wines (Oklahoma City, OK: Sane Press, n.d.), pp. 54-64.

The expression "strong drink" (*shekar* in Hebrew) signifies a sweet drink, usually fermented, and generally made from sources other than grapes. It includes products like beer (from barley, millet, or wheat), and date or palm wine. The expression does not refer to distilled liquors because distillation was unknown to the Israelites (Patton, pp. 57, 58, 62).

Fermented wine. Scripture condemns alcoholic wine because it brings violence, misery, and destruction (Prov. 4:17; 23:29, 35). It causes religious leaders to be oppressive (Isa. 56:10-12) and was associated with the perversion of judgment of Israel's leaders (Isa. 28:7) and of King Belshazzar (Dan. 5:1-30).

Unfermented wine. The Bible speaks favorably of unfermented wine or juice and recommends it as a great blessing. It is to be presented as an offering to God (Num. 18:12, 13; Neh. 10:37-39; 13:12, 13). It is one of God's blessings (Gen. 27:28, NIV "new wine"; Deut. 7:13; 11:14; Prov. 9:2, 3). It also is a healthful drink (1 Tim. 5:23).

14. See e.g., *Drug Enforcement Administration, Drugs of Abuse*, 3rd ed. (Washington, D.C.: United States Department of Justice, n.d.); Dan Sperling, "Drug Roundup," Adventist Review, Apr. 9, 1987, pp. 12, 13.

15. *SDA Church Manual*, p. 147.

16. *Ibid*.

17. *Ibid*., p. 148. For examples of the degradation in much modern music and entertainment, see Tipper Gore, *Raising PG Kids in an X-rated Society*, (Nashville, TN: Abingdon Press, 1987).

18. "Another form of amusement that has an evil influence is social dancing. 'The amusement of dancing, as conducted in the present day, is a school of depravity, a fearful curse to society.'— Messages to Young People, p. 399 (See also p. 192). (See 2 Cor. 6:15-18; 1 John 2:15-17; James 4:4; 2 Tim. 2:19-22; Eph. 5:8-11; Col. 3:5-10.)" In view of these influences to sin, Christians would do well not to "patronize the commercial amuse-

ments, joining with the worldly, careless, plea-sure-loving multitudes who are lovers of plea-sures more than lovers of God [2 Tim. 3:4]" (*SDA Church Manual*, p. 148).

19. *Ibid.*, pp. 146, 147.

20. On the adequacy of a vegetarian diet, see S. Havala, J. Dwyer, "The Position of American Dietetic Association: Vegetarian Diets—Technical Support Paper," *Journal of the American Dietetic Association*, March 1988, pp. 352-355; Terry D. Shultz, Winston J. Craig, et al "Vegetarianism and Health" in *Nutrition Update*, vol. 2, 1985, pp. 131-141; U.D. Register and L.M. Sonnenberg, "The Vegetarian Diet," *Journal of the American Dietetic Association*, March 1973, pp. 253-261.

21. See *Committee on the Scientific Basis of the Nation's Meat and Poultry Inspection Program, Meat and Poultry Inspection* (Washington, D.C.: National Academy Press, 1985), pp. 21-42; John A. Scharffenberg, *Problems With Meat* (Santa Barbara, CA: Woodbridge Press, 1979), pp. 32-35.

22. See, e.g., *Committee on the Meat and Poultry Inspection, Meat and Poultry Inspection*, pp. 68-123; Robert M. Andrews, "Meat Inspector: 'Eat at Own Risk,'" Washington Post, July 23, 1986. Cf. White, *Counsels on Diet and Foods* (Washington, D.C.: Review and Herald, 1946), pp. 384, 385.

23. Frank Young, Commissioner of the Food and Drug Administration and Sanford Miller, Director of the FDA's Center for Food Safety and Applied Nutrition, as quoted by Carole Sugarman, "Raising Fears Over Food Safety," *Washington Post*, July 23, 1986. Cf. White, Counsels on Diet and Foods (Washington, D.C.: Review and Herald, 1946), pp. 384, 385.

24. Scharffenberg, *Problems With Meat*, pp. 12-58.

25. See Shea, "Clean and Unclean Meats." (unpublished manuscript, Biblical Research Institute, General Conference of SDA).

26. Winston J. Craig, "Pork and Shellfish—How Safe Are They?" *Health and Healing* 12, No. 1 (1988): 10-12.

27. The New Testament concern for holiness is consistent with that of the Old Testament. There is a spiritual as well as a physical interest in people's well-being (Matt. 4:23; 1 Thess. 5:23; 1 Peter 1:15, 16).

Mark's statement that Jesus "declared all foods clean" (Mark 7:19, RSV) does not mean that He abolished the distinction between clean and unclean foods. The discussion between Jesus and the Pharisees and scribes had nothing to do with the kind of food, but with the manner in which the disciples ate. The issue was whether or not the ritual washing of hands before meals was necessary (Mark 7:2-5). In effect, Jesus said what defiles a person is not the food eaten with unwashed hands but the wicked things from the heart (Mark 7:20-23), because the food "'does not enter his heart but his stomach, and is eliminat-ed.

'" Thus Jesus declared that all foods eaten with unwashed hands are "clean" (Mark 7:19). The Greek word for food (*bromata*) used here is the general term for food that refers to all kinds of foods for human consumption; it does not des-ignate just flesh foods.

Peter's vision of the animals, recorded in Acts 10, did not teach that unclean animals had become fit for food; instead, it taught that Gentiles were not unclean and that he could asso-ciate with them without being contaminated. Peter himself understood the vision in this way, explaining, "'You know how unlawful it is for a Jewish man to keep company with or go to one of another nation. But God has shown me that I should not call any man common or unclean'" (Acts 10:28).

In his letters to the Romans and Corinthians (Rom. 14; 1 Cor. 8:4-13; 10:25-28) Paul addressed the implications for Christians of the widespread practice in the Gentile world of offering flesh foods to idols. The issue among the early Christians was whether the eating of food offered to idols was an act of worship. Those strong in their faith did not believe it was, and thus they would eat all edible things offered to idols. Paul urged that no one should despise those who eat vegetables, or judge those who "eat all things" suitable for food (Rom. 14:2).

Paul warned against future heresies that would forbid believers to partake of the two things God gave humanity at Creation—marriage and food. The foods involved are all foods God had created for human consumption. Paul's words here should not be taken to mean that unclean foods were "created to be received with thanksgiving by those who believe and know the truth" (1 Tim. 4:3).

28. Pepper, spices, mustard, pickles, and similar substances hurt the stomach. At first they irritate the lining of the stomach. Then they break down its mucous barrier, destroying its resistance to injury. Irritation of the stomach affects the brain, which in turn influences the temperament, often producing irritability. Cf. M.A. Schneider et al., "The Effect of Spice Ingestion on the Stomach," *American Journal of Gastroenterology* 26 (1956): 722, as quoted in "Physiological Effects of Spices and Condiments," (Loma Linda, CA: Department of Nutrition, School of Health, Loma Linda University [mimeographed]). White, *Counsels on Diet and Foods*, pp. 339-345.

29. Condiments and spices can also produce inflammation of the esophagus and destroy the mucous barrier of the small intestine and colon. They irritate the kidneys and may contribute to hypertension. Some contain carcinogens. See Kenneth I. Burke and Ann Burke, "How Nice Is Spice?" *Adventist Review*, Jan. 89, 1987, pp. 14-15; Department of Nutrition, "Spices and Condiments"; Marjorie V. Baldwin and Bernell E. Baldwin, "Spices—Recipe for Trouble," *Wildwood Echoes*, Winter 1978-79, pp. 8-11.

30. William G. Johnsson, "On Behalf of Simplicity," *Adventist Review*, March 20, 1986, p. 4.

31. *The SDA Bible Commentary*, vol. 1, p. 417.

32. See *Year-End Meeting Actions of the North American Division of Seventh-day Adventists* (1986), pp. 23-25.

33. The use of cosmetics is not totally harmless. Some of the chemicals used in their preparation can enter the blood circulation through absorption by the skin and, depending on the chemical and the sensitivity of the person, may injure the health. See N. Shafer, R.W. Shafer, "Potential Carcinogenic Effect of Hair Dyes," *New York State Journal of Medicine*, March 1976, pp. 394-396; Samuel J. Taub, "Cosmetic Allergies: What Goes on Under Your Makeup," Eye, Ears, Nose, and Throat, April 1976, pp. 131, 132; S.J. Taub, "Contaminated Cosmetics and Cause of Eye Infections," Eye, Ears, Nose, and Throat, Feb. 1975. pp. 81, 82; Cf. White, "Words to Christian Mothers," *Review and Herald*, Oct. 17, 1871.

34. White, *The Desire of Ages*, p. 668.

Ellen G. White Selected Quotations on Health and Ministry

The Purpose of the Health Message

1. Relieve suffering; purify the church

The work of health reform is the Lord's means for lessening suffering in our world and for purifying His church...I am instructed to say to health reform educators: Go forward. The world needs every jot of the influence you can exert to press back the tide of moral woe (*Testimonies*, vol. 9, pp. 112, 113).

2. Secure the highest development of body, mind and soul

In teaching health principles, keep before the mind the great object of reform—that its purpose is to secure the highest development of body and mind and soul. Show that the laws of nature, being the laws of God, are designed for our good: that obedience to them promotes happiness in this life, and aids in the preparation for the life to come (*The Ministry of Healing*, p. 146).

3. Elevate the moral standards

If we would elevate the moral standard in any country where we may be called to go, we must begin by correcting their physical habits (*Counsels on Health*, p. 505).

4. Serve as an entering wedge

I can see in the Lord's providence that the medical missionary work is to be a great entering wedge, whereby the diseased soul may be reached (*Counsels on Health*, p. 535).

5. To open doors

The right hand is used to open doors through which the body may find entrance. This is the part the medical missionary work is to act. It is to largely prepare the way for their reception of the truth for this time (*The Ministry of Healing*, p. 238).

6. To clarify thought processes

He (God) designs that the subject shall be agitated, and the public mind deeply stirred to investigate it; for it is impossible for men and women, while under the power of sinful, health destroying, brain enervating habits, to appropriate sacred truth (*Counsels on Health*, p. 21).

7. To sow the seed and reap a harvest

When connected with other lines of gospel effort, medical missionary work is a most effective instrument by which the ground is prepared for the sowing of the seeds of truth, and the instrument also by which the harvest is reaped (*Medical Ministry*, p. 240).

8. To restore the image of God

This is the work that will restore the moral image of God in man (*Medical Ministry*, p.160).

9. To prepare a people for Christ's return

As he thus instructs the people in the principles of true temperance, and as a guardian of souls gives advice to those who are mentally and physically diseased, the physician is acting his part in the great work of making ready a people prepared for the Lord. This is what medical missionary work is to accomplish in its relation to the third angel's message (*Counsels on Health*, p. 336).

In the preparation of a people for the Lord's second coming, a great work is to be accomplished through the promulgation of health principles (*Medical Ministry*, p. 206).

Origin of Health Evangelism

The medical missionary work is of divine origin, and has a most glorious mission to fulfill (*Medical Ministry*, p. 24).

Medical missionary work is a sacred thing of God's devising (*Medical Ministry*, p. 131).

Health Evangelism; Christ's Method

Christ's method alone will give true success in reaching the people. The Saviour mingled with men as one who desired their good. He showed His sympathy for them, ministered to their needs, and won their confidence. Then He bade them, "Follow Me!" (*The Ministry of Healing*, p. 143).

Christ came to this world as the great medical missionary. When His example is followed, medical missionary work will be carried forward on a much higher plane than it is at the present time. God calls for a reconversion among gospel teachers, and especially among physicians and other medical missionary workers, that Christ may not be misrepresented and put to shame. The cleansing must begin in the heart and mind, and flow forth in the actions. The characters of our medical missionary workers need to be refined and ennobled. This result can be brought about only as these workers are made partakers of the divine image, escaping the corruption that is in the world through lust (*Review & Herald*, Aug. 20, 1903).

Christ, the great Medical Missionary, is our example. He healed the sick and preached the gospel. In His service, healing and teaching were linked together. Today they are not to be separated (*Testimonies*, vol. 9, pp. 170, 171).

During His ministry, Jesus devoted more time to healing the sick than to preaching. His miracles testified to the truth of His words, that He came not to destroy, but to save.... Where he had passed, the objects of His compassion were rejoicing in health (*The Ministry of Healing*, p. 19).

In order to impress upon man his obligation to obey the law of God, Christ began His work of redemption by reforming the physical habits of man (*Testimonies*, vol. 3, p. 486).

His work did not stop with an exhibition of His power over disease. He made each work of healing an occasion of implanting in the heart the divine principles of His love and benevolence (*Counsels on Health*, p. 249).

Health Should be a Part of Church Ministry

Christ is no longer in this world in person, to go through our cities and towns and villages healing the sick. He has commissioned us to carry forward the medical missionary work that He began, and in this work, we are to do our best (*Counsels on Health*, p. 212).

Read the Scriptures carefully, and you will find that Christ spent the largest part of His ministry in restoring the suffering and afflicted to health....

We shall have success if we work on practical lines. Ministers, do not confine your work to giving Bible instruction. Do practical work. Seek to restore the sick to health. This is true ministry. Remember that the restoration of the body prepares the way for the restoration of the soul (*Medical Ministry*, p. 240).

There are precious blessings and a rich experience to be gained if ministers will combine the presentation of the health question with all their labors in the churches (*Gospel Workers*, p. 231).

You will never be ministers after the gospel order till you show a decided interest in medical missionary work, the gospel of healing and blessing and strengthening (*Counsels on Health*, p. 533).

Too little attention is generally given to the preservation of health. It is far better to prevent disease than to know how to treat it when contracted (*The Ministry of Healing*, p. 128).

Our ministers should become intelligent on health reform. They need to become acquainted with physiology and hygiene; they should understand the laws that govern physical life and their bearing upon the health of mind and soul.

In their own lives and homes they should obey the laws of life, practicing right principles and living healthfully. Then they will be able to speak correctly on this subject, leading the people higher and still higher in the work of reform. Living in the light themselves, they can bear a message of great value to those who are in need of just such a testimony (*Testimonies*, vol. 6, p. 376).

Those who go forth to engage in the work of the ministry must be intelligent upon the subject of health reform. Those men who after many years' experience have yet no appreciation of the medical missionary work, should not be appointed to preside over our churches (*Medical Ministry*, p. 238).

In new fields no work is so successful as medical missionary work. If our ministers would work earnestly to obtain an education in medical missionary lines, they would be far better fitted to do the work Christ did as a medical missionary....

Then will the work of the ministry be after the Lord's order; the sick will be healed, and poor, suffering humanity will be blessed.

Begin to do medical missionary work with the conveniences which you have at hand. You will find that thus the way will open for you to hold Bible readings. The heavenly Father will place you in connection with those who need to know how to treat their sick ones (*Medical Ministry*, p. 239).

The subject of health reform has been presented in the churches; but the light has not been heartily received. The selfish, health-destroying indulgences of men and women have counteracted the influence of the message that is to prepare a people for the great day of God. If the churches expect strength, they must live the truth which God has given them. If the members of our churches disregard the light on this subject, they will reap the sure result in both spiritual and physical degeneracy. And the influence of these older church members will leaven those newly come to the faith. The Lord does not now work to bring many souls into the truth, because of the church members who have never been converted, and those who were once converted but who have backslidden. What influence would these unconsecrated members have on new converts? Would they not make of no effect the God-given message which his people are to hear? (*Testimonies*, vol. 6, pp. 370, 371).

Ministers and people must make greater advancement in the work of reform. They should commence without delay to correct their wrong habits of eating, drinking, dressing, and working. I saw that quite a number of the ministers are not awake upon this important subject. They are not all where God would have them. The result is, some can show but little fruit of their labors (*Testimonies*, vol. 1, p. 466).

The Lord has presented before me that many, many will be rescued from physical, mental, and moral degeneracy through the practical influence of health reform. Health talks will be given, publications will be multiplied. The principles of health reform will be received with favor, and many will be enlightened. The influences that are associated with health reform will commend it to the judgment of all who want light, and they will advance step by step to receive the special truths for this time (*Testimonies*, vol. 6, pp. 378, 379).

Much of the prejudice that prevents the truth of the third angel's message from reaching the hearts of the people, might be removed if more attention were given to health reform. When people become interested in this subject, the way is often prepared for the entrance of other truths (*Counsels on Diet and Foods*, p. 76).

Those who labor in our conferences as ministers should become acquainted with the work of ministering to the sick. No minister should be proud that he is ignorant where he should be wise (*Medical Ministry*, p. 250).

The gospel ministry is needed to give permanence and stability to the medical missionary work; and the ministry needs the medical work to demonstrate the practical working of the gospel. Neither part of the work is complete without the other (*Counsels on Health*, p. 514).

Health Evangelism

We have come to a time when every member of the church should take hold of the medical missionary work (*Testimonies*, vol. 6, p. 289).

The medical missionary work should be a part of the work of every church in our land (*Counsels on Health*, p. 514).

Every city is to be entered by workers trained to do medical missionary work. As the right hand of the third angel's message, God's method of treating disease will open doors for the entrance of present truth (*Testimonies*, vol. 7, p. 59).

I wish to tell you that soon there will be no work done in ministerial lines but medical missionary work (*Counsels on Health*, p. 533).

Nothing will open doors for the truth like evangelistic medical missionary work (*Evangelism*, p. 513).

Medical missionary work gives opportunity for carrying forward successful evangelistic work. It is as these lines of effort are united, that we may expect to gather the most precious fruit for the Lord (*Evangelism*, p. 516).

The health reform is one branch of the great work which is to fit a people for the coming of the Lord (*Counsels on Health*, p. 20).

The Importance of Healthful Living for Church Workers

So far as health is concerned, physical exercise would be of the greatest value to all our ministers (*Testimonies*, vol. 4, p. 408).

The reason why many of our ministers complain of sickness is, they fail to take sufficient exercise, and indulge in overeating. They do not realize that such a course endangers the strongest constitution. Those who, like yourself, are sluggish in temperament, should eat very sparingly, and not shun physical taxation. Many of our ministers are digging their graves with their teeth. The system, in taking care of the burden placed upon the digestive organs, suffers, and a severe draught is made upon the brain. For every offense committed against the laws of health, the transgressor must pay the penalty in his own body (*Testimonies*, vol. 4, pp. 408, 409).

If they worked intelligently, giving both mind and body a due share of exercise, ministers would not so readily succumb to disease. If all our workers were so situated that they could spend a few hours each day in outdoor labor, and felt free to do this, it would be a blessing to them; they would be able to discharge more successfully the duties of their calling. If they have not time for complete relaxation, they could be planning and praying while at work with their hands, and could return to their labor refreshed in body and spirit.

Some of our ministers feel that they must every day perform some labor that they can report to the Conference. And as the result of trying to do this, their efforts are too often weak and inefficient. They should have periods of rest, of entire freedom from taxing labor. But these cannot take the place of daily physical exercise.

Brethren, when you take time to cultivate your garden, thus gaining the exercise needed to keep the system in good working order, you are just as much doing the work of God as in holding meetings. God is our Father, he loves us, and he does not require any of his servants to abuse their bodies (*Gospel Workers*, p. 92).

The Bible says of Jesus, "And the child grew, and waxed strong in spirit, filled with wisdom: and the grace of God was upon him." As He worked in childhood and youth, mind and body were developed. He did not use His physical powers recklessly, but gave them such exercise as would keep them in health, that He might do the best work in every line. He was not willing to be defective, even in the handling of tools. He was perfect as a workman, as He was perfect in character.

The time spent in physical exercise is not lost (*Fundamentals of Christian Education*, p. 418).

Continued inactivity is one of the greatest causes of debility of body and feebleness of mind (*Testimonies*, vol. 2, p. 524).

The chief if not the only reason why many become invalids is that the blood does not circulate freely, and the changes in the vital fluid, which are necessary to life and health, do not take place. They have not given their bodies exercise nor their lungs food, which is pure, fresh air; therefore it is impossible for the blood to be vitalized, and it pursues its course sluggishly through the system. The more we exercise, the better will be the circulation of the blood. More people die for want of exercise than through overfatigue; very many more rust out than wear out. Those who accustom themselves to proper exercise in the open air will generally have a good and vigorous circulation. We are more dependent upon the air we breathe than upon the food we eat. Men and women, young and old, who desire health, and who would enjoy active life, should remember that they cannot have these without a good circulation. Whatever their business and inclinations, they should make up their minds to exercise in the open air as much as they can. They should feel it a religious duty to overcome the conditions of health which have kept them conined indoors, deprived of exercise in the open air (*Testimonies*, vol. 2, pp. 525, 526).

Healthful Living: Prerequisite to Effectual Ministry and Child Rearing

Those who give proper attention to physical development will make greater advancement in literary lines than they would if their entire time were devoted to study.... Physical inaction lessens not only mental, but moral power. (*Education*, pp. 208, 209).

Healthful exercise in the open air will strengthen the muscles, encourage a proper circulation of blood, help to preserve the body from disease, and will be a great help in spirituality (*Medical Ministry*, p. 81).

Because of imprudence in eating, the senses of some seem to be paralyzed, and they are sluggish and sleepy. These pale-faced ministers who are suffering in consequence of selfish indulgence of the appetite, are no recommendation of health reform. When suffering from overwork, it would be much better to drop out a meal occasionally, and thus give nature a chance to rally. Our labor - ers could do more by their example to advance health reform than by preaching it. When elaborate preparations are made for them by well-meaning friends, they are strongly tempted to disregard principle; but by refusing the dainty dishes, the rich condiments, the tea and coffee, they may prove themselves to be true, practical health reformers. Some are now suffering in consequence of transgressing the laws of life, thus causing a stigma to rest on the cause of health reform. Excessive indulgence in eating, drinking, sleeping, or seeing, is sin (*Gospel Workers*, p. 92).

Overeating prevents the free flow of thought and words, and that intensity of feeling which is so necessary in order to impress the truth upon the heart of the hearer. The indulgence of appetite beclouds and fetters the mind, and blunts the holy emotions of the soul. The mental and moral powers of some of our preachers are enfeebled by improper eating and lack of physical exercise. Those who crave great quantities of food should not indulge their appetite, but should practice self-denial, and retain the blessings of active muscles and unoppressed brains. Overeating stupefies the entire being by diverting the energies from the other organs to do the work of the stomach (*Gospel Workers*, p. 92).

A gospel minister will be twice as successful in his work if he understands how to treat disease (*Medical Ministry*, p. 245).

A minister of the gospel who is also a medical missionary, who can cure physical ailments, is a much more efficient worker than one who cannot do this. His work as a minister of the gospel is much more complete (*Medical Ministry*, p. 245).

You should be teaching your children. You should be instructing them how to shun the vices and corruptions of this age. Instead of this, many are studying how to get something good to eat. You place upon your tables butter, eggs and meat and your children partake of them. They are fed with the very things that will excite their animal passions, and then you come to meeting and ask God to bless and save your children. How high do your prayers go? You have a work to do first. When you have done all for your children which God has left for you to do, then you can with confidence claim the special help that God has promised to give you (*Counsels on Diet and Foods*, p. 366).

Seventh-day Adventist Positions on Health Issues

Living in the midst of a sinful world, Christians often are confronted with moral issues for which they can find no easy answers, and no clear "Thus saith the Lord" to follow.

Responding to such dilemmas, the Seventh-day Adventist Church commissioned a number of task forces to wrestle with some of the most significant issues and to prepare guidelines and position statements that would be faithful to scriptural principles and would offer a clear voice in providing moral help for its members. Four of these documents were voted at the Annual Council of the General Conference Executive Committee (October 5-12, 1992): Abortion, Caring for the Dying, Temperance, and Caring for God's Creation. The AIDS document and the Statement regarding Smoking and Ethics were voted at the Annual Council (October 1-10, 1996) in Costa Rica.

As you read these items, remember that the documents on abortion and care for the dying are guidelines, not church policy. They are intended to be pastoral in nature, providing help to individual members as they personally struggle with the issues. The other four state the official church position on temperance principles, the environment, AIDS and tobacco.

Abortion

Many contemporary societies have faced conflict over the morality of abortion.* Such conflict also has affected large numbers within Christianity who want to accept responsibility for the protection of prenatal human life while also preserving the personal liberty of women. The need of guidelines has become evident, as the church attempts to follow Scripture, and to provide moral guidance while respecting individual conscience. Seventh-day Adventists want to relate to the question of abortion in ways that reveal faith in God as the Creator and Sustainer of all life and in ways that reflect Christian responsibility and freedom. Though honest differences on the question of abortion exist among Seventh-day Adventists, the following represents an attempt to provide guidelines on a number of principles and issues. The guidelines are based on broad Biblical principles that are presented for study elsewhere on these pages.

1. Prenatal human life is a magnificent gift of God. God's ideal for human beings affirms the sanctity of human life, in God's image, and requires respect for prenatal life. However, decisions about life must be made in the context of a fallen world. Abortion is never an action of little moral consequence. Thus prenatal life must not be thoughtlessly destroyed. Abortion should be performed only for the most serious reasons.

2. Abortion is one of the tragic dilemmas of human fallenness. The church should offer gracious support to those who personally face the decision concerning an abortion. Attitudes of condemnation are inappropriate in those who have accepted the gospel. Christians are commissioned to become a loving, caring community of faith that assists those in crisis as alternatives are considered.

3. In practical, tangible ways the church as a supportive community should express its commitment to the value of human life. These ways should include: (a) strengthening family relationships, (b) educating both genders concerning Christian principles of human sexuality, (c) emphasizing responsibility of both male and female for family planning, (d) calling both to be responsible for the consequences of behaviors that are inconsistent with Christian principles, (e) creating a safe climate for ongoing discussion of the moral questions associated with abortion, (f) offering support and assistance

Principles for a Christian View of Human Life

"*N*ow this is eternal life: that they may know you, the only true God, and Jesus Christ whom you have sent" (John 17:3, NIV). In Christ is the promise of eternal life; but since human life is mortal, humans are confronted with difficult issues regarding life and death. The following principles refer to the whole person (body, soul, and spirit), an indivisible whole (Gen. 2:7; 1 Thess. 5:23).

Life: Our Valuable Gift from God

1. God is the Source, Giver, and Sustainer of all life (Acts 17:25, 28; Job 33:4, Gen. 1:30; 2:7; Ps. 36:9; John 1:3, 4).
2. Human life has unique value because human beings, though fallen, are created in the image of God (Gen. 1:27; Rom. 3:23; 1 John 2:2; 1 John 3:2; John 1:29; 1 Peter 1:18, 19).
3. God values human life not on the basis of human accomplishments or contributions, but because we are God's creation and the object of His redeeming love (Rom. 5:6, 8; Eph. 2:2-9; 1 Tim. 1:15; Titus 3:4, 5; Matt. 5:43-48; John 1:3; 10:10).

Life: Our Response to God's gift

4. Valuable as it is, human life is not the only or ultimate concern. Self-sacrifice in devotion to God and His principles may take precedence over life itself (Rev. 12:11; 1 Cor. 13).
5. God calls for the protection of human life and holds humanity accountable for its destruction (Ex. 20:13; Rev. 21:8; Ex. 23:7; Deut. 24:16; Prov. 6:16, 17; Jer. 7:3-34; Micah 6:7; Gen. 9:5, 6).
6. God is especially concerned for the protection of the weak, the defenseless, and the oppressed (Ps. 82: 3, 4; James 1:27; Micah 6:8; Acts 20:35; Prov. 24:11, 12; Luke 1: 52-54).
7. Christian love (agape) is the costly dedication of our lives to enhancing the lives of others. Love also respects personal dignity and does not condone the oppression of one person to support the abusive behavior of another (Matt. 16: 21; Phil. 2:1-11; 1 John 3:16; 4:8-11; Matt. 22:39; John 18:22, 23; 13:34).
8. The believing community is called to demonstrate Christian love in tangible, practical, and substantive ways. God calls us to restore gently the broken (Gal. 6:1, 2; 1 John 3:17, 18; Matt. 1:23; Phil. 2:1-11; John 8:2-11; Rom. 8:1-14; Matt. 7:1, 2; 12:20; Isa. 40-42; 62:2-4).

Life: Our Right and Responsibility to Decide

9. God gives humanity the freedom of choice, even if it leads to abuse and tragic consequences. His unwillingness to coerce human obedience necessitated the sacrifice of His Son. He requires us to use His gifts in accordance with His will and ultimately will judge their misuse (Deut. 30:19, 20; Gen. 3; 1 Peter 2:24; Rom. 3:5, 6; 6:1, 2; Gal. 5:13).
10. God calls each of us individually to moral decision-making and to search the Scriptures for Biblical principles underlying such choices (John 5:39; Acts 17:11; 1 Peter 2:9; Rom. 7:13-25).
11. Decisions about human life from its beginning to its end are best made within the context of healthy family relationships with the support of the faith community (Ex. 20:12; Eph. 5; 6).
12. Human decisions should always be centered in seeking the will of God (Rom. 12:2; Eph. 6:6; Luke 22:42).

to women who choose to complete crisis pregnancies, and (g) encouraging and assisting fathers to participate responsibly in the parenting of their children. The church also should commit itself to assist in alleviating the unfortunate social, economic, and psychological factors that may lead to abortion, and to care redemptively for those suffering the consequences of individual decisions on the issue.

4. The church does not serve as conscience for individuals; however, it should provide moral guidance. Abortions for reasons of birth control, gender selection, or convenience are not condoned by the church. Women at times, however, may face exceptional circumstances that present serious moral or medical dilemmas, such as significant threats to the pregnant woman's life, serious jeopardy to her health, severe congenital defects carefully diagnosed in the fetus, and pregnancy resulting from rape or incest. The final decision whether to terminate the pregnancy or not should be made by the pregnant woman after appropriate consultation. She should be aided in her decision by accurate information, biblical principles, and the guidance of the Holy Spirit. Moreover, these decisions are best made within the context of healthy family relationships.

5. Christians acknowledge as first and foremost their accountability to God. They seek balance between the exercise of individual liberty and their accountability to the faith community and the larger society and its laws. They make their choices according to Scripture and the laws of God rather than the norms of society. Therefore, any attempts to coerce women either to remain pregnant or to terminate pregnancy should be rejected as infringements of personal freedom.

6. Church institutions should be provided with guidelines for developing their own institutional policies in harmony with this statement. Persons having a religious or ethical objections to abortion should not be required

to participate in the performance of abortions.

7. Church members should be encouraged to participate in the ongoing consideration of their moral responsibilities with regard to abortion in light of the teaching of Scripture.

* Abortion, as understood in these guidelines, is defined as any action aimed at the termination of a pregnancy already established. This distinguished from contraception, which is intended to prevent a pregnancy. The focus of the document is on abortion.

Care For the Dying

For people whose lives are guided by the Bible, the reality of death is acknowledged as part of the current human condition, affected by sin (Gen. 2:17; Rom. 5; Heb. 9:27). There is "a time to be born, and a time to die" (Eccl. 3:2). Although eternal life is a gift that is granted to all who accept salvation through Jesus Christ, faithful Christians await the second coming of Jesus for complete realization of their immortality (John 3:36; Rom. 6:23; 1 Cor. 15:51-54). While waiting for Jesus to come again, Christians may be called upon to care for the dying and to face personally their own death.

Pain and suffering afflict every human life. Physical, mental, and emotional traumas are universal. However, human suffering has no expiatory or meritorious value. The Bible teaches that no amount or intensity of human suffering can atone for sin. The suffering of Jesus Christ alone is sufficient. Scripture calls Christians not to despair in afflictions, urging them to learn obedience (Heb. 5:7, 8), patience (James 1:2-4), and endurance in tribulations (Rom. 5:3). The Bible also testifies to the overcoming power of Jesus Christ (John 16:33) and teaches that ministry to human suffering is an important Christian duty (Matt. 25:34-40). This was the example and teaching of Jesus (Matt. 9:35; Luke 10:34-36), and this is His will for us (Luke 10:37). Christians look in anticipation to a new day when God will end suffering forever (Rev. 21:4).

Developments in modern medicine have added to the complexity of decisions about care for the dying. In times past, little could be done to extend human life. But the power of today's medicine to forestall death has generated difficult moral and ethical questions. What constraints does Christian faith place upon the use of such power? When should the goal of postponing the moment of death give way to the goal of alleviating pain at the end of life? Who may appropriately make these decisions? What limits, if any, should Christian love place on actions designed to end human suffering?

It has become common to discuss such questions under the heading of euthanasia. Much confusion exists with regard to this expression. The original and literal meaning of this term was "good death." Now the term is used in two significantly different ways. Often euthanasia refers to "mercy killing," or intentionally taking the life of a patient in order to avoid painful dying or in order to alleviate burdens for a patient's family or society. (This is so-called active euthanasia.) However, euthanasia is also used, inappropriately in the Seventh-day Adventist view, to refer to the withholding or withdrawal of medical interventions that artificially extend human life, thus allowing a person to die naturally. (This is so-called passive euthanasia.) Seventh-day Adventists believe that allowing a patient to die by foregoing medical interventions that only prolong suffering and postpone the moment of death is morally different from actions that have as their primary intention the direct taking of life.

Seventh-day Adventists seek to address the ethical issues at the end of life in ways that demonstrate their faith in God as the Creator and Redeemer of life and that reveal how God's grace has empowered them for acts of neighbor love. Seventh-day Adventists affirm God's creation of human life, a wonderful gift worthy of being protected and sustained (Gen. 1; 2). They also affirm God's wonderful gift of redemption that provides eternal life for those who believe (John 3:15; 17:3). Thus, they support the use of modern medicine to extend human life in this world. However, this power should be used in compassionate ways that reveal God's grace by minimizing suffering.

Since we have God's promise of eternal life in the earth made new, Christians need not cling anxiously to the last vestiges of life on this earth. Nor is it necessary to accept or offer all possible medical treatments that merely prolong the process of dying.

Because of their commitment to care for the whole person, Seventh-day Adventists are concerned about the physical, emotional, and spiritual care of the dying. To this end, they offer the following Biblically-based principles:

1. A person who is approaching the end of life, and is capable of understanding, deserves to know the truth about his or her condition, the treatment choices, and the possible outcomes. The truth should not be withheld, but shared with Christian love and with sensitivity to the patient's personal and cultural circumstances (Eph. 4:15).

2. God has given human beings freedom of choice and asks them to use their freedom responsibly. Seventh-day Adventists believe that this freedom extends to decisions about medical care. After seeking divine guidance and considering the interests of those affected by the decision (Rom. 14:7), as well as medical advice, a person who is capable of deciding should determine whether to accept or reject life-extending medical interventions. Such persons should not be forced to submit to medical treatment that they find unacceptable.

3. God's plan is for people to be nourished within a family and a faith community. Decisions about human life are best made within the context of healthy family relationships after considering medical advice (Gen. 2:18; Mark 10:6-9; Ex. 20:12; Eph. 5, 6). When a dying person is unable to give consent or express preferences regarding medical intervention, such decisions should be made by someone chosen by the dying person. If no one has been chosen, someone close to the dying person should make the determination. Except in extraordinary circumstances, medical or legal professionals should defer decisions about medical interventions for a dying person to those closest to that individ-

ual. Wishes or decisions of the individual are best made in writing and should be in agreement with existing legal requirements.

4. Christian love is practical and responsible (Rom. 13:8-10; 1 Cor. 13; James 1:27; 2:14-17). Such love does not deny faith nor obligate us to offer or to accept medical intervention whose burdens outweigh the probable benefits. For example, when medical care merely preserves bodily functions, without hope of returning a patient to mental awareness, it is futile and may, in good conscience, be withheld or withdrawn. Similarly, life-extending medical treatments may be omitted or stopped if they only add to the patient's suffering or needlessly prolong the process of dying. Any action taken should be in harmony with legal mandates.

5. While Christian love may lead to the withholding or withdrawing of medical interventions that only increase suffering or prolong dying, Seventh-day Adventists do not practice "mercy killing" or assist in suicide (Gen. 9:5, 6; Ex. 20:13; 23:7). They are opposed to active euthanasia, the intentional taking of the life of a suffering or dying person.

6. Christian compassion calls for the alleviation of suffering (Matt. 25:34-40; Luke 10:29-37). In caring for the dying, it is a Christian responsibility to relieve pain and suffering to the fullest extent possible, not to include active euthanasia. When it is clear that medical intervention will not cure a patient, the primary goal of care should shift to suffering.

7. The Biblical principle of justice prescribes that added care be given the needs of those who are defenseless and dependant (Ps. 82:3, 4; Prov. 24:11; Isa. 1:1-18; Micah 6:8; Luke 1:52-54). Because of their vulnerable condition, special care should be taken to ensure that dying persons are treated with respect for their dignity and without unfair discrimination. Care for the dying should be based on their spiritual and medical needs and their social worthiness (James 2:1-9).

As Seventh-day Adventists seek to apply these principles, they take hope and courage from the fact that God answers the prayers of His children and is able to work miraculously for their well-being (Ps. 103:1-5; James 5:13-16). Following Jesus' example, they also pray to accept the will of God in all things (Matt. 26:39). They are confident that they can call on God's power to aid them in caring for the physical and spiritual needs of suffering and dying individuals. They know that the grace of God is sufficient to enable them to endure adversity (Ps. 50:14, 15). They believe that eternal life for all who have faith in Jesus is secure in the triumph of God's love.

Temperance

From the very inception of the Seventh-day Adventist Church, temperance has been a major focus, and the church has played a key role in struggling against the inroads of alcoholic beverages, tobacco, and other drugs. While some Christian denominations have lessened their emphasis on temperance, Seventh-day Adventists have continued to vigorously oppose the use of alcohol, tobacco, and improper drugs. The stand of the church advocating abstinence from harmful substances is well established in the church's fundamental beliefs.

There is evidence indicating that in some areas there has been a relaxation in the promotion within the church of the principles of true temperance. This development, coupled with the relentless advertising campaigns of the alcohol and tobacco industries, has revealed that some Seventh-day Adventists have not been impervious to such negative and insidious influences.

An issue that arises from time to time is the offer of funds to religious organizations by the alcohol or tobacco industries. It is the position of the Seventh-day Adventist Church that such offers of funds shall not be accepted by the church, nor by any of its institutions. Such money is tainted by human misery and, in the case of the alcohol industry, "has come through the loss of souls of men" (Ellen G. White, in *Review and Herald*, May 15, 1894). The gospel mandate of the Seventh-day Adventist Church is to rebuke evil and not praise or encourage those who manufacture "poisons that bring misery and ruin" and whose "business means robbery" (*The Ministry of Healing*, p. 337).

The Seventh-day Adventist Church reaffirms its historic stand for the principles of temperance, upholds its policies and programs supporting Article 21 of the Statement of Fundamental Beliefs, and calls upon each member to affirm and reveal a life commitment to abstinence from any form of alcohol and tobacco and irresponsible use of drugs. The 1992 Annual Council calls for a revival of temperance principles within the church and urges individuals and church organizations to refuse donations and favors from identifiable alcohol or tobacco industries.

Caring For God's Creation

The world in which we live is a gift of love from the Creator God, from "him who made the heavens, the earth, the sea, and the springs of water" (Rev. 14:7, NIV; cf. Rev. 11:17, 18). Within this creation He placed humans, set intentionally in relationship with Himself, other persons, and the surrounding world. Therefore, as Seventh-day Adventists, we hold its preservation and nurture to be intimately related to our service to Him.

God set aside the seventh-day Sabbath as a memorial and perpetual reminder of His creative act and establishment of the world. In resting on that day, Seventh-day Adventists reinforce the special sense of relationship with the Creator and His creation. Sabbath observance underscores the importance of our integration with the total environment. The human decision to disobey God broke the original order of creation, resulting in a disharmony alien to His purposes. Thus our air and waters are polluted, forests and wildlife plundered, and natural resources exploited. Because we recognize humans as part of God's creation, our concern for the environment extends to personal health and lifestyle. We advocate a wholesome manner of living and reject the use of substances such as tobacco, alcohol, and other drugs that harm the body and consume earth's resources; and we promote a simple vegetarian diet.

Seventh-day Adventists are committed to respectful, cooperative relationships among all persons, recognizing our common origin and realizing our human dignity as a gift from the Creator. Since human poverty and environmental degradation are interrelated, we pledge ourselves to improve the quality of life for all people. Our goal is a sustainable development of resources while meeting human needs.

Genuine progress toward caring for our natural environment rests upon both personal and cooperative effort. We accept the challenge to work toward restoring God's overall design. Moved by faith in God, we commit ourselves to promote the healing that rises at both personal and environmental levels from integrated lives dedicated to serve God and humanity.

In this commitment we confirm our stewardship of God's creation and believe that total restoration will be complete only when God makes all things new.

The Seventh-Day Adventist Church and the AIDS Epidemic: Guidelines
Rationale

The global epidemic of Acquired Immune Deficiency Syndrome (AIDS) profoundly impacts the worldwide gospel mission of the Seventh-day Adventist Church. Church leaders are called to respond through initiatives in education, prevention, and community service, and through personal acts of kindness to persons and families involved in the crisis. AIDS is no respecter of national boundaries, church membership, gender, marital status, education, income, or position in life. In many countries of the world, it is decimating the population, taking the lives of many individuals, including Seventh-day Adventist Church members. All persons, especially young people growing up in an era of moral laxity, need to be taught biblical principles regarding sexuality and God's design that sexual intimacy be experienced within the protection of the marriage covenant. Leadership should provide credible information to members presented in their own language and sensitive to their own culture. The Church is called to be both a prophetic and a compassionate voice the mouthpiece and hands of God as it extends the ministry of Christ into the community.

The global mission of the Church, in reaching out to all races and peoples, draws into church fellowship many who are infected by the AIDS virus prior to joining the church or who are affected by having family members with AIDS. The epidemic is of such magnitude that no family will ultimately remain untouched. Many are infected through no action of their own. A judgmental attitude is always inappropriate, especially since the source of the infection cannot be determined with certainty. Many have experienced shame, fear, and agony as family members suffered and died with AIDS, often feeling compelled to secrecy regarding their painful situation. Just as Christ came to offer healing to a suffering world, so Seventh-day Adventists are commissioned to compassionately care for those who suffer and are affected with the virus of AIDS. Members can safely serve as care givers, at home or in health care facilities, if they are educated in appropriate ways of doing so.

Recommendations

The Seventh-day Adventist Church recognizes its Christian responsibility to respond to the global AIDS crisis and the devastating effect on humanity and wishes to respond in multiple ways which include:

1. Extending the teaching and healing ministry of Christ, who without prejudice cared for all in need, by engaging in efforts to reduce the risk of individuals acquiring AIDS, and compassionately and nonjudgmentally caring for all those affected when an individual suffers from AIDS.
2. Designating a person in each division, along with such personnel and financial resources as may be secured, to respond to AIDS challenges through appropriate initiatives and cooperative efforts with other entities in the community or country at large.
3. Developing and managing AIDS education programs using the resource HIV/AIDS Guide when applicable. Programs should be

contextualized for relevant cultural and linguistic needs and directed to:
  a. **Pastors:** Through continuing education and ministerial meetings designed to equip pastors to deal with members touched by the AIDS crisis. Pastors need information on prevention, compassionate ministry, and applied ecclesiastical functions such as conducting a funeral service for a person infected with AIDS.
  b. **Teachers:** As continuing education and in-service training with emphasis on conveying spiritual values and developing skills among youth for coping with sexual pressures.
  c. **Church members:** Through sermons, Sabbath School lessons, premarital counseling and marriage strengthening activities, seminars regarding AIDS, and educational curricula are avenues for providing information regarding sexuality in general and AIDS in particular.
  d. **Communities:** By recognizing the opportunity for Christian witness and ministry in the community at large, providing appropriate community outreach, and participating in cooperative endeavors.
4. Protecting and strengthening marriage by:
  a. Upholding the ideal of abstinence from premarital sex.
  b. Advocating premarital HIV testing for both potential partners as part of the church-based preparation for marriage.
  c. Elevating God's ideal for fidelity in marriage.
  d. Recommending protective measures against sexually transmitted diseases, including HIV.
5. Intentionally transmitting Christian values to the next generation, recognizing that individual sexual values are established in youth. Priority should be given to providing accurate information, a forum for open discussion, and emphasis on the moral dimension of decision making regarding sexuality.

A Statement Regarding Smoking and Ethics

Smoking is the single greatest preventable cause of death in the world. It is a universal ethical concept that prevention is better than cure. When it come to smoking, most countries are faced by an ethical paradox: while many decades of research have provided incontrovertible evidence of the health hazards of cigarette smoking, the tobacco industry still flourishes, often with either tacit or overt government support. The ethics of smoking are made even more serious by alarming revelations about the deaths and health risks caused by second-hand smoke.

A serious question of international ethics is the exportation of cigarettes to developing countries, especially cigarettes higher in lethal ingredients than admissible elsewhere.

For over a century, the Seventh-day Adventist Church has warned its youth and the general public regarding the addictive and health destroying nature of tobacco smoking. Cigarettes are a world-wide health hazard because of the combination of addiction coupled with the economic greed of the tobacco industry and segment of the marketing community. Seventh-day Adventists believe that the ethics of prevention require public policies that will reduce smoking, such as:

1. A uniform ban on all tobacco advertising,
2. Regulations protecting children and youth who are being targeted by the tobacco industry,
3. Stricter laws prohibiting smoking in public places,
4. More aggressive and systematic use of the media to educate young people about the risks of smoking.
5. Substantially higher taxes on cigarettes, and
6. Regulations requiring the tobacco industry to pay for the health cost associated with the use of its products.

Policies such as these would save millions of lives every year.

Statement on Meeting the Challenges of Sexually Transmitted Diseases (9/27/98)

The contemporary world is confronted by grave ethical, medical, and social problems resulting from increasing sexual permissiveness and associated promiscuity. Because Christians are a part of the larger social community, these attitudes and behaviors have infiltrated the Seventh-day Adventist Church as well, demanding that we address them.

So serious are the challenges presented by sexually transmitted diseases (STDs) that the United Nations, in conjunction with most of the world's governments, the health-care community, religious, political, and economic leaders have instituted a series of major research and health-education programs that focus on prevention and treatment. The goal is to prevent, cure, and minimize the effectsCor at least slow the spreadCof these diseases.

At particular risk are youth entering puberty at increasingly younger ages, when they are especially vulnerable to peer pressure and a barrage of media and peer messages that treat casual sex outside marriage as acceptable and normal. Many youth are sexually active early in their teen years and soon become well established in patterns of sexual activity. Correlated with increased sexual activity is a dramatic increase in STDs associated with serious physical and emotional problems.

Advances have been made along several lines:

- research has provided more accurate data;
- benefits of using condoms to reduce unwanted pregnancy and the spread of STDs have been documented;
- dangers of promiscuity have been recognized;
- more effective treatment has reduced the spread and progression of many STDs;
- risk of long-term emotional damage resulting from casual sex has been recognized; and
- support has grown for the position that abstinence from extramarital sex promotes sexual and emotional health.

These advances, despite their limitations, have proved beneficial and should be encouraged for their positive effects. Seventh-day Adventist care givers should be encouraged to participate in promoting such efforts and deserve the support of church members as they do so. A pragmatic approach to dealing with these serious problems and the use of appropriate interventions should by no means be interpreted as endorsement or encouragement of sexual activity outside marriage or of unfaithfulness within marriage. Instead, these efforts must be seen as compassionate attempts to prevent or reduce the negative consequences of detrimental sexual behaviors.

At times, family members, and pastors, teachers, counselors, physicians, and others in helping professions may find themselves working with individuals who, despite strong counsel, refuse to turn from sexual decadence and live by God's high standard of morality. In such cases, those entrusted with ministry may, as a last resort, counsel specific individuals to use contraceptive and prophylactic methods such as condoms in an attempt to prevent pregnancy and reduce the risk of spreading life-decimating STDs. Utmost care should be taken when making such an intervention to make it clear to the individual(s) and members of the community involved that this extreme measure should in no way be misconstrued as a scriptural sanction for sexual intimacy outside marriage. Such action on the part of professionals should be considered interim and utilized only in individual cases. Though such interventions may provide a little time for grace to do its work in human hearts, they do not provide a viable long-term solution. The Church must remain committed to making the most of every opportunity to reinforce the wisdom of God's design for human sexuality and to calling men and women to the highest standard of moral conduct.

Biblical Principles

Although the efforts described above are in many ways beneficial, they are only a response to existing situations created by the impact of sin.

In the Scriptures, God has set out a superior plan to guide our use of His gift of sexuality. Built upon a series of guiding principles, it presents in practical terms God's ideal for His people who must live in a sin-stricken world.

1. **Sexual intimacy is reserved for marriage.** Sexuality is a loving gift of the Creator to humanity (Gen 1:26, 27). The gospel calls believers to an appreciation for and stewardship of their sexuality in harmony with the divine purposes (1 Cor 3:16, 17; 6:13-20; Eph 5:1-8; Phil 1:27; 1 Thess 4:3-7). In God's plan, sexual intimacy is reserved for a man and a woman within the bounds of the marriage covenant (Gen 2:24, 26; Exod 20:14; Proverbs 5; Song of Sol 4:12; 8:8-10; 2:6, 7; 3:5; 8:3, 4; Hos 3:3; Heb 13:4). Sexual fidelity within marriage is crucial to convey a full understanding of God's metaphor comparing marriage to His relationship with His people (Isa 54:5; Hos 2:14-23; 2 Cor 11:2; Rev 19:6-9; 21:9).

2. **Sexual intimacy outside of marriage is immoral and harmful.** Such intimacy has detrimental effects on individuals (Lev 18:6-3; Rom 1:24-27; 1 Cor 6:18), as well as on the marriage relationship (Prov 5:1-23). It is identified by Scripture as part of the sinful life (Gal 5:19; Col 3:5).

3. **God recognizes human frailty.** His divine will for human beings and His intent for creation are unchangeable (Mal 3:6; Matt 5:17-20; Acts 20:27). His absolute love for human beings and His redemptive intent are equally unchangeable (John 3:16; Rom 5:8; 8:35-39; Eph 1:1-14; 3:14-19; 1 John 4:7-10). The gospel message, centered in Jesus Christ, binds these truths together (Ps 85:10; 1 John 2:1, 2).

   God's grace is the only hope for fallen humanity (Rom 3:23, 24; 5:1, 2, 20; Eph 2:1-5). He is patient and long-suffering with human frailty (Num 14:18, 19; Ps 86:15; 103:13, 14; Hos 11:8, 9; Jonah 3:1; 4:10, 11; Matt 23:37; 1 Tim 1:15, 16). Though God's grace does not give license to sin (Rom 6:1, 2), it is through such grace that God accomplishes His redemptive intent in the circumstances resulting from sin (Rom 5:12-21). God's practical dealings in cases of divorce (Deut 24:1-5; Ezra 10:10, 11; Matt 19:7, 8), polygamy (Exod 21:10; Deut 17:17; 21:15-17; Matt 19:4, 5), the introduction of flesh foods (Gen 1:11, 12, 29, 30; 9:3; Lev 3:17; 11:47), and provision for an earthly monarch (1 Sam 8:7; 10:19; Hos 13:11) offer examples of interventions short of God's ideal. Through such cases, we see His grace and mercy at work in a world deformed by sin.

4. The Church conducts its mission in a fallen world. Existing conditions contrast sharply with God;s ideal. Both believers and unbelievers are vulnerable to sexual immorality as one of the tragic results of sin (John 17:15; 1 John 2:15). The Church is called to minister to believers and unbelievers alike, reaching and reclaiming sinners (Matt 28:19; Mark 2:17; 2 Cor 5:20, 21), nurturing the growth of believers (Eph 2:19-22; 4:11-13, 15; 1 Thess 5:11; 2 Peter 3:18), uplifting the infinite worth of each individual (Isa 43:3, 4, 7; Matt 12:12; Luke 12:7; 15:1-32; 1 Peter 1:18, 19), protecting the weak and vulnerable (Rom 15:1; 1 Thess 5:14; Heb 13:3), promoting and preserving life and health (John 10:10; 1 Cor 6:19; 3 John 2), and calling men and women to take up their lofty position as God's chosen and holy people (Eph 4:1; 5:8; 1 Peter 1:15, 16; 2:5, 9). The ministry of the Church is both to meet individuals where they are (1 Cor 3:1, 2; 7:1-28), and to call them to a higher standard (Luke 19:5-10; John 8:3-11; Acts 17:18-34).

5. A spiritual development process is anticipated in the Christian life. Change for the Christian involves both conversion (John 3:3, 7; Acts 3:19; Rom 12:2; 2 Cor 5:17) and growth (Prov 4:18; Luke 2:52; Eph 3:17-19; 4:11-15; 2 Peter 3:18). At conversion, believers accept Christ's perfect life as their own by faith and experience a Spirit-led transformation of values (John 3:5; Gal 2:20). Both external and internal forces may provoke relapses in thought or conduct (Gal 5:16-18; 1 John 3:20), but commitment to grace-induced progress in the Christian life (1 Cor

15:10; Phil 3:12-14; Col 1:28, 29) and reliance upon God-provided resources (Rom 8:5-7; Gal 5:24, 25) will produce growth toward Christlikeness (Gal 5:22-25; Eph 5:1).

The Scriptures call for human beings to progress morally and spiritually throughout their lives (Luke 2:52; 1 Cor 13:11; 14:20). Planning for and facilitating such growth is integral to fulfilling the gospel commission (Matt 28:20; Eph 3:14-24). It is the task of religious education to attend to individual development and to present truth in ways that hearers can understand (Matt 11:15), causing them to stretch but not to stumble (Rom 14:1-21; 1 Cor 8:9-13). Though some allowance may be made for the unlearned or immature (Matt 13:34; John 16:12; Acts 17:30; 1 Cor 3:1, 2), over time individuals should progress toward a more complete understanding of God's will (John 16:13) and a fuller expression of love for God and one another (Matt 22:37-39; John 13:35; 8:9; 13:11; 1 John 3:14; 4:11, 12). Under God's blessing, the clear presentation of the gospel and careful attention to the disciple-making process will bear spiritual fruit, even among those who have been involved in sexual sin (1 Cor 6:9-11).

Implications

1. The Church affirms the biblical view of sexuality as a wholesome attribute of human nature created by God to be enjoyed and used responsibly in marriage as part of Christian discipleship.

2. The Church is committed to sharing a biblical view of human sexuality in an intentional and culturally sensitive manner. Emphasis is placed on appreciating and understanding the human body and its functions, upholding sexual chastity outside and fidelity within marital relationships, and developing skills for decision-making and communication about sexual behavior. The Church is committed to conveying the truth that the misuse of one's own sexuality and the abuse of power in relationships are contrary to God's ideal.

3. The Church calls people to dedicate themselves before God to sexual abstinence outside the marriage covenant and sexual faithfulness to one's spouse. Apart from the wholesome expression of sexual intimacy in marriage, abstinence is the only safe and moral path for the Christian. In any other context, sexual activity is both harmful and immoral. This high standard represents God's intention for the use of His gift, and believers are called upon to uphold this ideal, regardless of the prevailing standards in the culture around them.

4. The Church recognizes the sinfulness of humanity. Human beings make mistakes, use poor judgment, and may deliberately choose to engage in sexual practices that are contrary to God's ideal. Others may not know where to turn for help to live sexually pure lives. Nothing, however, can spare such individuals from the consequences of departing from the divine plan. Emotional and spiritual wounds left by sexual activity that violates God's plan inevitably leave scars. But the Church extends Christ's ministry of mercy and grace by offering God's forgiveness, healing, and restorative power. It must seek to provide the personal, spiritual, and emotional support that will enable the wounded to lay hold of the gospel's resources. The Church must also help persons and families identify and access the full network of professional resources available.

5. The Church recognizes as morally acceptable the use of contraceptive measures, including condoms, by married couples who seek to control conception.[1] Condoms in particular may be indicated in some marital circumstances—for example, when one partner has been exposed to or has contracted a sexually transmitted disease, thus putting the spouse at high risk for infection.

On the other hand, the premarital or extramarital use of condoms—either in an attempt to lower the risk of unwanted pregnancy or to prevent the transmission of a sexually transmitted disease raises moral concerns. These concerns must be considered in the context of the divine plan for human sexuality, the relationship between God's creative intent and His regard for human frailty, the process of spiritual growth and moral development within individuals, and the nature of the Church's mission.

Though condoms have proved to be somewhat effective in preventing pregnancy and the spread of disease,[2] this does not make sex outside of marriage morally acceptable. Neither does this fact prevent the emotional damage that results from such behavior. The Church's appeal to youth and adults alike, believers and nonbelievers, is to live lives worthy of the grace extended to us in Christ, drawing as fully as possible upon divine and human resources to live according to God's ideal for sexuality.

6. The Church acknowledges that in cases where a married person may be at risk for transmitting or contracting a sexually transmitted disease such as Human Immunodeficiency Virus (HIV) from his or her marriage partner, the use of a condom is not only morally acceptable but also strongly recommended if the husband and wife decide to continue having sexual intercourse. Users of condoms must be alerted to the limits of their effectiveness in preventing the transmission of HIV infection and to the importance of using them properly.

Appeal

We are facing a crisis that threatens the lives and well-being of many people, including church members. Both youth and adults are in peril. The Church must develop, without delay, a comprehensive strategy of education and prevention. The resources of health, social services, educational, ministerial, and other professionals, both within and without the Church, must be mobilized. This crisis demands priority attention—using every legitimate resource and method at the Church's disposal to target the home, school, church, and community. The destiny of an entire generation of human beings is at stake, and we are in a race against time.

[1] See Birth Control: A Seventh-day Adventist Statement of Consensus (160-98G).

[2] Research indicates that condoms, when correctly used, have about a 97 percent success rate in prevention of pregnancy and about an 85 to 90 percent success rate in prevention of virus transmission, as used by the general population. In those groups who use them consistently and correclty, the effectiveness is about 97 percent.

Statement on Ethical Considerations Regarding Human Cloning (9/27/98)

For a number of decades, the prospect that new members of the human family might be produced by cloning was considered farfetched. Recent advances in genetic and reproductive biology, however, indicate that techniques for cloning humans may soon be developed. With this prospect comes the Christian responsibility to address profound ethical issues associated with human cloning. As Christians, with firm belief in God's creative and redemptive power, Seventh-day Adventists accept the responsibility to enunciate ethical principles that emerge from their faith commitments.

Cloning includes all those processes by which living plants or animals are replicated by asexual means—methods that do not involve the fusion of egg and sperm. Many natural processes are forms of cloning. For example, microorganisms, like common yeast, reproduce by splitting into two daughter cells that are clones of the parent cell and each other. Cutting a twig from a rose bush or grapevine and propagating it into a complete plant also creates a clone of the original plant. Similarly, many simple animals, such as starfish, can regenerate complete organisms from small parts of a predecessor. Thus the biological principle of cloning is not new.

The new technique is known as *somatic cell nuclear transfer*. The essence of this method is to take a cell from an existing individual and manipulate it so that it behaves like an embryonic cell. Given the proper conditions, an embryonic cell can proliferate and generate a complete individual. At present, this cellular reprogramming is accomplished by putting a complete adult cell inside a larger egg cell whose nucleus has been removed. The egg that is used in this process serves the role of an incubator, providing an essential environment to reactivate genes of the adult cell. The egg contributes to the offspring only the small amount of genetic material associated with its cytoplasm, not its nuclear genetic material, as occurs in sexual reproduction. The altered egg must then be implanted in an adult female for gestation.

Biologists have developed this technique as a tool for animal husbandry. By this means, they hope to create a herd of valued animals that are genetically identical to a selected individual. The potential benefits from this technology, including the expectation of products for treating human diseases, are of great interest to researchers and to the biotechnology industry. However, the same technological capacity could be used for human reproduction and thus raises serious ethical concerns.

First among these concerns is medical safety. If the current technique of somatic cell nuclear transfer were to be used in humans, ova would need to be obtained from donors. Most of these would perish because of cellular manipulations during early embryonic growth in the laboratory. Others would be lost after implantation, spontaneously aborted at various stages of fetal development. In this respect, sensitivity to the value of embryonic and fetal life would be similar to the development of other methods of assisted reproduction, such as *in vitro* fertilization. There would likely be an increased risk of birth defects in children brought to term. At present, concern about physical harm to developing human lives is sufficient to rule out the use of this technology.

However, even if the success rates of cloning were to improve and the medical risks were diminished, a number of major concerns would remain. For example, is there anything intrinsically problematic with creating an individual who is not produced through fertilization of an egg by a sperm? Further study is needed to resolve questions regarding the essential nature of procreation in God's design.

Another of the most often expressed concerns is that the dignity and uniqueness of a cloned person may be jeopardized. This risk includes the psychological harm that might be experienced by an individual who would be what some have called the "delayed identical twin" of the individual who provided the initial cell. Do existing persons have the right to exercise such a level of control over the genetic destiny of a new individual?

Concern also exists that human cloning might undermine family relationships. Commitments to both the unitive and the procreative functions of human sexual relationships might be diminished. For example, the questionable practice of using a gestational surrogate may, at times, be considered. The use of a donor cell from an individual other than the married couple may introduce problems of relationships and responsibilities.

An additional major risk is that cloning could lead to expedient uses of those who are cloned, with their value assigned primarily on the basis of their utility. For example, there could be a temptation to clone individuals to serve as sources of transplantable organs. Others have worried about the deliberate creation of subservient individuals whose autonomy would be violated. Egotistical or narcissistic individuals might be inclined to use the technology in order to "duplicate" themselves.

Finally, the financial costs of cloning would likely be considerable even after significant technological improvements. If human cloning were commercialized, conflicting interests might add to the risk of abuse.

While this is only a partial list of potential risks and misuses of human cloning, it should be sufficient to give pause to Christians who wish to apply the moral principles of their faith to the matter of human cloning. Still, it is important that concerns about the abuses of a technology not blind us to the possibilities of using it to meet genuine human needs.[1] The possibility of human cloning, even if remote, motivates this statement of relevant Christian principles.

The following ethical principles are intended to apply to somatic cell nuclear transfer if that technology is ever applied to human beings. The rapid pace of progress in this field will require

periodic review of these principles in light of new developments.

1. Protection of vulnerable human life. Scripture is clear in its call to protect human life, especially those lives that are most vulnerable (Deut 10:17-19; Isa 1:16-17; Matt 25:31-46). The biological technology of cloning is ethically unacceptable whenever it poses disproportionate risk of harm to human life.

2. Protection of human dignity. Human beings were created in the image of God (Gen 1:26, 27) and were thus endowed with personal dignity that calls for respect and protection (Gen 9:6). Cloning may threaten human dignity in a number of ways and must thus be approached with resolute moral vigilance. Any use of this technology that undermines or diminishes the personal dignity or autonomy of human beings must be rejected. This moral prohibition applies to all human cloning that would value human life primarily for its utilitarian function or commercial value.

3. Alleviating human suffering. It is a Christian responsibility to prevent suffering and to preserve the quality of human life (Acts 10:38; Luke 9:2). If it is possible to prevent genetic disease through the use of somatic cell nuclear transfer, the use of this technology may be in keeping with the goal of preventing avoidable suffering.

4. Family support. God's ideal plan is for children to develop in the context of a loving family with the presence, participation, and support of both mother and father (Prov 22:6; Ps 128:1-3; Eph 6:4; 1 Tim 5:8). Any use of somatic cell nuclear transfer as a means of assisting human reproduction should thus be within the context of the fidelity of marriage and support of stable family life. As with other forms of assisted reproduction, the involvement of third parties, such as surrogates, introduces moral problems that are best avoided.

5. Stewardship. The principles of Christian stewardship (Luke 14:28; Prov 3:9) are

important for all types of assisted human reproduction including the possibility of somatic cell nuclear transfer, which is likely to be very costly. Married couples seeking such assistance should consider the expenses involved in terms of their exercise of faithful stewardship.

6. Truthfulness. Honest communication is one of Scripture's mandates (Prov 12:22; Eph 4:15, 25). Any proposed use of cloning should be informed by the most accurate information available, including the nature of the procedure, its potential risks, and its costs.

7. Understanding God=s creation. God intends for human beings to grow in their appreciation and understanding of His creation, which includes knowledge regarding the human body (Matt 6:26-29; Ps 8:3-9; 139:1-6; 13-16). For this reason, efforts to understand the biological structures of life through ethical research should be encouraged.

Given our present state of knowledge and the current refinement of somatic cell nuclear transfer, the use of this technique for human cloning is deemed unacceptable by the Seventh-day Adventist Church. Given our responsibility to alleviate disease and to enhance the quality of human life, continued appropriate research with animals is deemed acceptable.

Glossary

Allele. One of the alternative forms of a particular gene. Each gene of an organism can exist in slightly different forms. These small differences are responsible for some of the variations that we observe in different individuals within natural populations. Different alleles for genes that produce the blood protein hemoglobin, for example, will affect how well the blood cells will carry oxygen.

Clones. Two or more individuals with identical genetic material. Human clones occur naturally in the form of "identical twins." Though twins begin life with the same genetic material they, nevertheless, develop distinct physical differences (fingerprints, for example). Furthermore, they become fully unique individuals with distinct personalities as a result of their different experiences and independent choices. An individual conceived by somatic cell nuclear transfer would be at least as different from his or her progenitor as natural twins.

Cytoplasm. All the contents of a cell, other than the nucleus. The cytoplasm is the site where many important processes occur, including the assembly of proteins and enzymes, and the manufacture of cell products. The cytoplasm also contains the mitochondria, small bodies that are responsible for the breakdown of food to produce the energy needed for the activities of the cell.

Embryo. The early stages of development of a fertilized egg. In somatic cell nuclear transfer, it refers to the early developmental stages of an enucleated egg after it has been fused with a somatic cell.

Enucleated egg. An egg cell from which the nucleus has been removed. This is usually accomplished by penetrating the cell with a fine glass needle and withdrawing the nucleus while observing the process under a microscope.

Germ cell. Reproductive cell. In mammals and humans, the germ cells are the sperm and eggs (ova).

Gestation. The period of time it takes an embryo to develop in the uterus from a fertilized egg to a newborn offspring. Gestation begins with implantation of the embryo in the uterus and ends with birth.

Nucleus. The structure within a cell that contains the genetic material or genes. The nucleus is surrounded by a membrane that separates it from the remainder of the cell.

Ovum (plural: ova). An egg cell. A female reproductive cell.

Somatic cell. Any cell from the body of a mammal or human, other than the germ cells.

Somatic cell nuclear transfer. The technical name for the method used to produce the first animal clone, a sheep called "Dolly." Though the name suggests that a nucleus from a somatic cell was used, in fact, the complete somatic cell was fused with an enucleated egg.

Sperm. A male reproductive cell.

[1] There may be future situations in which human cloning could be considered beneficial and morally acceptable. It is possible, for example, to imagine circumstances in which cloning may be comtemplated within the context of marriage as the only available means of reproduction for a couple who cannot participate in normal procreation. In other cases, potential parents may be carriers of defective genetic alleles, and they may wish to avoid the risk of giving birth to a child with a genetic disease. The use of somatic cell nuclear transfer might assist such parents in having a child who would be free of genetic disorder. Of course, many of the concerns about personal identity and dignity would still remain even in the context of family fidelity. As with other forms of assisted human reproduction, potential blessings of somatic cell nuclear transfer must be weighed against the risks.

Birth Control: A Seventh-day Adventist Statement of Consensus (9/29/99)

Scientific technologies today permit greater control of human fertility and reproduction than was formerly possible. These technologies make possible sexual intercourse with the expectation of pregnancy and childbirth greatly reduced. Christian married couples have a potential for fertility control that has created many questions with wide-ranging religious, medical, social, and political implications. Opportunities and benefits exist as a result of the new capabilities, as do challenges and drawbacks. A number of moral issues must be considered. Christians who ultimately must make their own personal choices on these issues must be informed in order to make sound decisions based on biblical principles.

Among the issues to be considered is the question of the appropriateness of human intervention in the natural biological processes of human reproduction. If any intervention is appropriate, then additional questions regarding what, when, and how must be addressed. Other related concerns include:

- Likelihood of increased sexual immorality which the availability and use of birth control methods may promote;
- Gender dominance issues related to the sexual privileges and prerogatives of both women and men;
- Social issues, including the right of a society to encroach upon personal freedom in the interest of the society at large and the burden of economic and educational support for the disadvantaged; and
- Stewardship issues related to population growth and the use of natural resources.

A statement of moral considerations regarding birth control must be set in the broader context of biblical teachings about sexuality, marriage, parenthood, and the value of children—and an understanding of the interconnectedness between these issues. With an awareness of the diversity of opinion within the Church, the following biblically based principles are set forth to educate and to guide in decision making.

1. Responsible stewardship. God created human beings in His own image, male and female, with capacities to think and to make decisions (Isa 1:18; Josh 24:15; Deut 30:15-20). God gave human beings dominion over the earth (Gen 1:26, 28). This dominion requires overseeing and caring for nature. Christian stewardship also requires taking responsibility for human procreation. Sexuality, as one of the aspects of human nature over which the individual has stewardship, is to be expressed in harmony with God's will (Exod 20:14; Gen 39:9; Lev 20:10-21; 1 Cor 6:12-20).

2. Procreative purpose. The perpetuation of the human family is one of God's purposes for human sexuality (Gen 1:28). Though it may be inferred that marriages are generally intended to yield offspring, Scripture never presents procreation as an obligation of every couple in order to please God. However, divine revelation places a high value on children and expresses the joy to be found in parenting (Matt 19:14; Ps 127:3). Bearing and rearing children help parents to understand God and to develop compassion, caring, humility, and unselfishness (Ps 103:13; Luke 11:13).

3. Unifying purpose. Sexuality serves a unifying purpose in marriage that is God-ordained and distinguishable from the procreative purpose (Gen 2:24). Sexuality in marriage is intended to include joy, pleasure,

and delight (Eccl 9:9; Prov 5:18, 19; Song of Sol 4:16B5:1). God intends that couples may have ongoing sexual communion apart from procreation (1 Cor 7:3-5), a communion that forges strong bonds and protects a marriage partner from an inappropriate relationship with someone other than his or her spouse (Prov 5:15-20; Song of Sol 8:6, 7). In God's design, sexual intimacy is not only for the purpose of conception. Scripture does not prohibit married couples from enjoying the delights of conjugal relations while taking measures to prevent pregnancy.

4. Freedom to choose. In creation—and again through the redemption of Christ—God has given human beings freedom of choice, and He asks them to use their freedom responsibly (Gal 5:1, 13). In the divine plan, husband and wife constitute a distinct family unit, having both the freedom and the responsibility to share in making determinations about their family (Gen 2:24). Married partners should be considerate of each other in making decisions about birth control, being willing to consider the needs of the other as well as one's own (Phil 2:4). For those who choose to bear children, the procreative choice is not without limits. Several factors must inform their choice, including the ability to provide for the needs of children (1 Tim 5:8); the physical, emotional, and spiritual health of the mother and other care givers (3 John 2; 1 Cor 6:19; Phil 2:4; Eph 5:25); the social and political circumstances into which children will be born (Matt 24:19); and the quality of life and the global resources available. We are stewards of God's creation and therefore must look beyond our own happiness and desires to consider the needs of others (Phil 2:4).

5. Appropriate methods of birth control. Moral decision making about the choice and use of the various birth control agents must stem from an understanding of their probable effects on physical and emotional health, the manner in which the various agents operate, and the financial expenditure involved. A variety of methods of birth control—includ-ing barrier methods, spermicides, and steril-ization—prevent conception and are morally acceptable. Some other birth-control meth-ods[1] may prevent the release of the egg (ovu-lation), may prevent the union of egg and sperm (fertilization), or may prevent attach-ment of the already fertilized egg (implanta-tion). Because of uncertainty about how they will function in any given instance, they may be morally suspect for people who believe that protectable human life begins at fertilization. However, since the majority of fertilized ova naturally fail to implant or are lost after implantation, even when birth con-trol methods are not being used, hormonal methods of birth control and IUDs, which represent a similar process, may be viewed as morally acceptable. Abortion, the inten-tional termination of an established pregnan-cy, is not morally acceptable for purposes of birth control.

6. Misuse of birth control. Though the increased ability to manage fertility and pro-tect against sexually transmitted disease may be useful to many married couples, birth control can be misused. For example, those who would engage in premarital and extramarital sexual relations may more read-ily indulge in such behaviors because of the availability of birth control methods. The use of such methods to protect sex outside of marriage may reduce the risks of sexually transmitted diseases and/or pregnancy. Sex outside of marriage, however, is both harm-ful and immoral, whether or not these risks have been diminished.

7. A redemptive approach. The availability of birth-control methods makes education about sexuality and morality even more imperative. Less effort should be put forth in condemnation and more in education and redemptive approaches that seek to allow each individual to be persuaded by the deep movings of the Holy Spirit.

---

[1] Some current examples of these methods include intrauterine devices (IUD's), hormone pills (including the "morning-after pill"), injections or implants. Questions about these methods should be referred to a medical professional.

A Seventh-day Adventist Statement on Gambling

Gambling-defined as a paid game of chance-increasingly impacts more and more people all over the world. The concept of winning at the expense of others has become a modern curse. Society pays the escalating costs of associated crime, victim support, and family breakdown which erodes the quality of life. Seventh-day Adventists have consistently opposed gambling as it is incomparable with Christian principles. It is not an appropriate form of entertainment or a legitimate means of raising funds.

Gambling violates Christian principles of stewardship. God identifies work as the appropriate method for gaining material benefit; not the playing of a game of chance while dreaming to gain at the expense of others. Gambling has a massive impact on society. Financial costs result from crime committed to pay for the gambling habit, increased policing, and legal expenses, as well as associated crimes involving drugs and prostitution. Gambling does not generate income; rather it takes from those who often can ill afford to lose and gives to a few winners, the greatest winner of course being the gambling operator. The idea that gambling operations can have a positive economic benefit is an illusion. In addition, gambling violates the Christian sense of responsibility for family, neighbors, the needy, and the Church.[1]

Gambling creates false hopes. The gambling dream of "winning big" replaces true hope with a false dream of a statistically—improbable chance of winning. Christians are not to put their hope in wealth. The Christian hope in a glorious future promised by God is "sure and certain"—unlike and opposite to the gambling dream. The great gain that the Bible points to is "godliness with contentment."[2]

Gambling is addictive. The addictive quality of gambling is clearly incomparable with a Christian lifestyle. The church seeks to help, not blame, those suffering from gambling or other addictions. Christians recognize that they are responsible before God for their resources and lifestyle.[3]

The Seventh-day Adventist Church organization does not condone raffles or lotteries to raise funds and urges members not to participate in any such activities, however well- intentioned. Neither does the Church condone state-sponsored gambling. The Seventh-day Adventist Church calls on all authorities to prevent the ever -increasing availability of gambling with its damaging effects on individuals and society.

The Seventh-day Adventist Church rejects gambling as defined above and will not solicit nor accept funding that is clearly derived from gambling.

---

1   I Thess. 4:11; Gen. 3:19; Matt. 19:21; Acts 9:36; 2 Cor.9:8,9

2   I Tim. 6:17; Heb. 11:1; I Tim.6:6

3   I Cor. 6:19,20

This statement was voted by the General Conference of Seventh-day Adventist Administrative Committee (ADCOM), for release at the time of the General Conference Session in Toronto, Canada, June 29-July 9, 2000.

Adventist Health Speakers

It is impossible to provide a "current" list of speakers. God is calling individuals to this work on a daily basis. Your conference health ministries director or the health ministries director in the conference where a speaker lives will usually be able to provide feedback and resource information on possible speakers. For those speakers who were accidently overlooked in the following list, please send information to the NAD Ministries Department. Some names and items in this list are out of date. Others on the previous list were dropped because of an inability to check their present status or contact information.

The following individuals are recommended as weekend seminar or camp meeting speakers.

Micky Ask, M.D., Behavioral Medicine, School of Medicine, Loma Linda University, Loma Linda, CA 92350, (909) 558-2353. Topics: Addictions and substance abuse.

Leonard Bailey, M.D., World-known pediatric heart surgeon and chairman of the department of surgery at Loma Linda University, School of Medicine, Loma Linda, CA 92350; (909) 558-4922. An inspirational speaker on health, and the experiences he has had preforming heart transplants on infants.

Bernell Baldwin, Ph.D. and **Marjorie Baldwin, M.D.,** Editors of the *Journal of Health and Healing*. They have taught for the schools of medicine and health at Loma Linda University and are teaching/practicing at Wildwood Lifestyle Center and Hospital. P.O. Box 129, Wildwood, GA 30757; (706) 820-1493 or (800) 634-WELL [9355]. Topics: general health, lifestyle, and neurophysiology.

Carol Bearce, Education Dept. Eden Valley, 6263 North County Rd. 29, Loveland, CO 80538-9598; (970) 667-1770 or (800) 637-WELL [9355]; Fax (970) 663-7072. A graduate of Wildwood Sanitarium, Carol is available to speak on nutri-

tion, cooking classes, the laws of the mind and Christian counseling, health reform and the Three Angels Message, sleep and the spiritual consequences of fatigue. Available for women's retreats and camp meetings.

Melvin Belz, M.D., and **Muriel,** Black Hills Health Center, P.O. Box 19, Hermosa, SD 57744; (800) 658-5433 or (605) 255-4101; home (605) 255-4789. Excellent speakers on general health. Muriel has written a number of cookbooks and presents cooking schools.

The Benton Sisters: Audrey, Trishonna & Emberly, P.O. Box 552, Lakeport, CA 95453; (707) 263-5871; Answering machine (707) 262-0901. These three young adults conduct community cooking schools and sing together. They provide a very inspiring and educational program.

Duane Bietz, M.D., Cardiac-thoracic surgeon who is an excellent communicator. He has produced various health news spots for television, and has a private practice. 9155 SW Barnes Road, Suite 240, Portland, OR 97225; (503) 297-1419. Topics: Medical issues such as lung cancer, pulmonary and heart disease and their prevention; general health, lifestyle and managed care.

Maxine Blome, M.S.N.E., C.N.A.A., Parish Nurse Coordinator for Adventist Health in Rocklin, California. Contact Adventist Health, 2100 Douglas Boulevard, Roseville, CA 95661-9002 or call (916) 781-2000 or (916) 781-4691. Topics: Medical missionary work, local health "evangelism" and the Parish Nursing program.

Gordon Botting. Dr.H.Sc., M.P.H., Pacific Union Conference,101 Lifton Court, Roseville, CA 95747; (916) 782-7163. Conducts various seminars including: Life in the Middle of a Stress Sandwich, Are You Rusting, Holding, or Burning Out, The Winning Weigh, Smoking Cessation Training, and more.

Brian Bull, M.D., Vice President for Clinical Faculty and Dean of the School of Medicine.

Contact: School of Medicine, Loma Linda University, Loma Linda, CA 92350, (909) 558-4481. Topics: Excellent speaker on general health and medical concerns.

DeWayne Butcher, M.D., Volunteered to do medical work in Russia. Contact: Rt. 5, Box 159-B, Hendersonville, NC 28792 Topics: General medicine and health. Paul and Carol Cannon, Co-founders and directors The Bridge. 1745 Logsdon Rd., Bowling Green, KY 42101; (502) 777-1094.

Ben Carson, M.D., Pediatric Neurosurgery. Contact: Johns Hopkins, 600 Wolfe St/Meyer 5-109, Baltimore, MD 21205; (410) 955-7888; Fax (410) 955-0626. Topics: A motivational and inspirational speaker on health and personal experiences of trusting in God. His family is musical and makes an excellent camp meeting or weekend presentation.

Zeno Charles-Marcel, M.D., Director, Faculty of Health Sciences, Montemorelos University, Apartado 16, Montemorelos, Nuevo Leon 67500 Mexico; and also Associate Clinical Professor of Medicine, Department of Internal Medicine, Loma Linda University School of Medicine. Topics: General health and lifestyle changes.

Wendall Cheatham, M.D., Endocrinologist Contact: 7610 Carroll Avenue, Takoma Park, MD; (301) 891-6020; home (301) 596-2857. Topics: Diabetes, general health.

Charles Cleveland, M.P.H., Director of Health Education. Contact: Wildwood Lifestyle Center and Hospital, P.O. Box 129, Wildwood, GA 30757-0129; (706) 820-1493 or (800) 634-9355. Topics: General health/lifestyle.

Joan C. Coggin, M.D., M.P.H., Cardiac surgeon and director of the international heart team. Contact: Loma Linda University, Loma Linda, CA 92350; (909) 558-4420. Topics: Joan is a dynamic, entertaining speaker who will energize any audience.

Winston Craig, Ph.D., Chairman, Department of Nutrition and Family Studies. Contact: Andrews University, Berrien Springs, MI 49104; (616) 471-3351. Topics: General nutrition.

Milton Crane, M.D., NEWSTART Director of Medical Research and Endocrinology. Contact:

Weimar Institute, 20601 W. Paoli Lane, P.O. Box 486, Weimar, California 95736 (916) 637-4111; (800) 525-9192; Fax (916) 637-4408. Topics: Scientific oriented authority on diabetes and neuropathy. His presentations will particularly appeal to the scientifically oriented and health professionals.

James Crawford, D.D.S., M.P.H., Former dean of the School of Public Health and currently associate dean of the School of Dentistry. Contact: Loma Linda University, Loma Linda, CA 92350, (909) 558-4607. Topics: Excellent speaker on general health and lifestyle.

Paul O. Davis, Ph.D., Exercise Physiologist Contact: Applied Research Associates, Inc., 15312 Spencerville Court, Burtonsville, MD 20866 ; (301) 384-0800. Topics: Physical fitness and lifestyle.

Samuel DeShay, M.D., former Director of the General Conference Health and Temperance Department. Author of *Plus Fifteen* and producer of line of health products. Now in private practice. (301)774-9007(h) or (301)439-7376(store). Topics: General health, nutrition; "Bacon or the Bananas".

David DeRose, M.D., M.P.H., and **Sonja DeRose, M.D.,** staff physicians and involved in research. David and Sonja would be an excellent speaking team. Contact: Lifestyle Center of America, Rt. 1, Box 4001, Sulphur OK 73086; (405) 993-2327; (800) 596-5480; Fax (405) 993-3902. Topics: general health, maternal and child health, and nutrition.

Hans Diehl, Dr.H.Sc., M.P.H., Founder and Director of The Lifestyle Medicine Institute. Author and producer of videos. He and his wife, Lily (who is a concert pianist and vocalist) make an outstanding duo for camp meetings and weekend seminars. Contact: Better Health Productions, P.O. Box 1761, Loma Linda CA 92354; (909) 825-1888, or The Lifestyle Medicine Institute, 11538 Anderson, Loma Linda, CA (909) 796-7676. Adventist CHIP Association, (866) 732-2447 toll free for a CHIP information kit and Director application. (Web site: www.sdaCHIP.org; e-mail: info@sdaCHIP.org). Topics: C.H.I.P. (coronary health improvement project) lecture series and general lifestyle medicine.

P. William (Bill) Dysinger, M.D., M.P.H., and **Yvonne Dysinger, R.N.,** Bill was the former senior health advisor for the Adventist Development and Relief Agency (ADRA.) He spent many years in academic administration at Loma Linda University School of Public Health. They have lived and worked in both Africa and Asia and are now retired. Contact: 684 Dry Prong Road, Williamsport, TN 38487; (615) 583-2792. Topics: General health, international health, medical topics, and prevention.

Harvey Elder, M.D., is chief of the infectious disease section, and spends much of his time doing AIDS education for pastors and lay people. Contact: Jerry L. Pettis Memorial Veteran's Center, Loma Linda California 92354; (909) 558-7084, Ext 2942; Fax (909) 777-3225. Topics: Expert in the clinical aspect of AIDS.

Martin W. Feldbush, D.Min., B.C.C., Associate Director, Adventist Chaplaincy Ministries. Contact: General Conference of Seventh-day Adventists. 12501 Old Columbia Pike, Silver Spring, MD 10904; (301) 680-6784. Topics: Health issues and spiritual health. Winston Ferris Contact: Andrews University, Berrien Springs, MI 49104; office (616) 471-3433; home (616) 471-3970. Topics: Drugs.

Gary E. Fraser, M.B., C.H.B., Ph.D., M.P.H., F.R.A.C.P., is a practicing cardiologist at Loma Linda University Medical Center and professor of epidemiology and cardiology at Loma Linda University. He was appointed director of the Adventist Health Study in 1987. Contact: Center for Health Research, Loma Linda University, Loma Linda, CA 92350; (909) 558-4988. Topics: Adventist Health Study; general health.

Helmuth F. Fritz, MD. Board certified in Internal Medicine. Contact: Weimar Institute, 20601 W. Paoli Lane, P.O. Box 486, Weimar, CA 95736; (530) 637-4111; (800) 525-9192; Fax (530) 637-4408. Topics: General health and lifestyle.

Gwen Foster, M.P.H., Health Czar for the City of Philadelphia. A dynamic speaker who was formerly Health Ministries Director for the Allegheny East Conference, talk radio host and the author of the lifestyle seminar, Fitness for Life. Contact: (215) 868-2000; web site:

www.phila.gov. Topics: General health and lifestyle: city ministry.

Phil Garver, Ed.D., Dean, School of Physical Education, Health and Wellness, Southern Adventist University. Contact: Southern Adventist University in Collegedale, TN 37315; (423) 238-2850 or 2852. Topics: Lifestyle change and wellness issues.

Hal Gates, Pastor, Director of SDAxA Regeneration. Contact: 1172 Prospect Ave., Raymond, WA 98577 or call (360) 875-4189; e-mail: sdaxahal@hotmail.com. Topic: Addiction recovery.

Carla Gober, R.N., M.P.H., Spiritual Care Nursing Specialist and Marriage and Family Therapy. Contact: Loma Linda University, Loma Linda, CA 92350; (909) 558-5163. Topics: Spiritual health and nurture; mental health and woman's issues. Carla is a popular speaker for women's retreats.

Norman Gulley, Ph.D., Retired Professor of Systematic Theology with a special interest in health education, and his wife **Leona, Ed.D., R.N.C.S., N.C.C.** Professor of Psychology in the graduate school Southern Adventist University. Contact: Southern Adventist University, P.O. Box 370, Collegedale, TN 37315-0370 for Leona (423) 238-2960; e-mail: lgulley@southern.edu. Norman can be reached at (423) 472-5652. Topics: General health and mental health issues.

John Goley, Dr. P.H., M.P.H., Director of Education. Contact: Lifestyle Center of America, Rt. 1, Box 4001, Sulphur OK 73086; (405) 993-2327; (800) 596-5480; Fax (405) 993-3902. Topics: Chronic disease and general health.

Vicki Griffin, Ph.D., Nutrition Counseling, co-founder with her husband Dane of Sure Word Productions, host on a video series Let's Eat! For Strength, and co-editor of the *FastFacts* health newsletter. Contact: Vicki Griffin at P.O. Box 19009, Lansing, MI 48901; (517) 485-2226; E-mail: vgriffin@misda.org. Topics: Excellent presentations on nutrition and creative cooking schools.

Lloyd Griffith, D.D.S., Dentist. Volunteered to do medical work/education in Russia. Contact: 407 Viewcrest, Port Angeles, WA 98362; (206) 457-4991. Topics: General health/dental education.

Scott Grivas, M.D., Staff physician at Wildwood Lifestyle Center and Hospital Contact: Wildwood Institute, P.O. Box 129, Wildwood, GA 30757-0129; (706) 820-1493 or (800) 634-9355. Topics: General health/medicine/lifestyle.

Don Hall, Dr. P.H., Founder and president of Wellsource, Inc. Contact: P.O. Box 569 Clackamas, OR 97015; (503) 656-7446. Topics: Health Screening and lifestyle. Note: Wellsource has speakers in all areas of health.

Ted Hamilton, M.D., Senior Vice President, Florida Hospital, columnist for *Vibrant Life* and dynamic speaker. Contact: Florida Hospital, 601 E. Rollins Street, Orlando, FL 32803; (407) 896-6611. Topics: General health, lifestyle, and medicine and spiritual factors.

Fred Hardinge, Dr.P.H. Founder and director of Total Life Creations. Contact: P.O. Box 41, Selah, WA 98942; (800) 283-6040; (509) 698-3990; Fax (509) 698-3656; e-mail fghard@totallife.com Topics: Eight easy ways to enhance your performance; Natural ways to beat chronic tiredness; Fatigue, family, and your witness; Making your health outreach programs soul-winning.

Mervin Hardinge, M.D. Ph.D., M.P.H., Founding dean of the School of Public Health, Loma Linda University, and producer of the Hardinge slide/video health education products. Now retired. Contact: 412 Valley Road, Rt. 1, Box 37B, Brewster, WA 98812; (509) 689-9103. Topics: General health and lifestyle.

Richard Hart, M.D., Dr.P.H., Vice President, LLU, formerly Dean, School of Public Health. Contact: Loma Linda University, Loma Linda, CA 92350, (909) 558-4578. Topics: Excellent speaker: General health/lifestyle and international health.

Patti Herring, Ph.D., RN. Director of the Office of Public Health. Practice in School of Public Health & Director of Black Recruitment in Adventist Health Study-2, (909) 558-7282 or (909) 558-8729. Topic: Speaks on Adventist Health Study & Minority health in general.

Carl Hinds, M.A., Pastor and Health lecturer Contact: 227 Herman St. Haskensack, NJ 07601; (201) 996-0807. Topics: Prevention from a Biblical perspective; E.G. White as a health authority; and the eight natural remedies.

Marshall Hollingsead, M.D., Medical Director of Pacific Health Education Center, and **Gladys Hollingsead, R.N., P.H.N., B.S.N.,** C.E.O. and Board Chairman. Contact: Pacific Health Education Center, 5300 California Ave., Suite 200, Bakersfield, CA 93309; (616) 633-5300. Topics: Dr. Hollingsead's topics include: General health, nutrition and medicine; Gladys speaks on communication, breast cancer, and diet. Excellent camp meeting duo.

Jerry Hoover, M.D., Director of Abundant Health Lifestyle Center and his wife, LaVonne, a cooking school instructor. Dr. Hoover has written, *Natural Medicine.* LaVonne has written the cookbook, "A Taste of Nature Cookbook and Nutritional Guide" and presents cooking schools. Contact: Rt. 2, Box 451A, Webster, FL 33597-3512; (904) 568-1119. Topics: They are an excellent team, speaking on general health, lifestyle and nutrition.

Gary L. Hopkins, M.D., Dr.P.H., C.H.E.S., is director of the Institute for the Prevention of Addictions. Contact: Andrews University, Berrien Springs, MI 49104; (616) 471-3558. Topics: Teen pregnancy prevention; AIDS research and program development; substance abuse prevention in the community and with incarcerated individuals.

Joyce Hopp, Ph.D. R.N., Dean of the School of Allied Health Professions. Contact: Loma Linda University, Loma Linda, CA 92350; (909) 558-4545; Fax (909) 824-4809; e-mail: jhopp@ccmail.llu.edu. Topics: Excellent communicator on health education and lifestyle.

Bruce R. Hyde, M.D., Med director working with Leamons, Contact: 101 N. 20th St. Battle Creek, MI 49015; (616) 963-0368; home (616) 964-6092; Fax (616) 964-4686; e-mail: yleamon@aol.com. Fine speaker on preventive medicine.

Luke Inankur, MD. Pediatrician, allergist. Health ministry leader, Collegedale Seventh-day Adventist Church. Contact: 5534 Barrington Country Circle, Ooltewah, TN 37363. (423) 396-3936. E-mail: vba@prodigy.net. Stop smoking and preventive medicine.

Clarence S. F. Ing, MD, MPH. Weimar College. Contact: Weimar Institute, 20601 W. Paoli Lane, P.O. Box 486, Weimar, CA 95736; (530) 637-4111; (800) 525-9192; Fax (530) 637-4408; e-mail: csfing@juno.com. Topics: General health and lifestyle.

Bethany Jackson, Ph.D., R.D. Former Department Chairman of Nutrition at Andrews University; recently retired from working with NIH funded programs at the University of North Carolina, Chapel Hill. Contact: 18 Preakness Dr., Durham, NC, 27713; home (919) 493-0848; e-mail: bethany.jackson@verizon.net. Topic: Nutrition.

Audray Johnson, R.N., Health Ministries and Family Life Director of the Southeastern California Conference. Contact: P.O. Box 8050, Riverside, CA 92515; (909) 359-5800. Topics: General health, addictions, family violence, and child abuse.

Cameron Johnston. Contact: WellChoices Seminars, P. O. Box 2398, Stn. R, Kelowna BC V1X 6A5. CANADA; (888) 973-3388; web site: http://www.wellchoices, com. Topics: Conducts a health ministry emphasis weekend and community seminars on wellness and stress reduction.

Patricia Johnston, Dr.P.H., M.S., R.D., Dean, Professor, Chairman of Department of Nutrition. Contact: School of Public Health, Loma Linda University, Loma Linda, CA 92350, (909) 558-4578. Topics: nutrition.

Don G. King, Dr.P.H.,President of Northeastern Conference. Formerly a pastor, and the secretary of the Alberta Conference in Canada. Contact: Northeastern Conference, 115-50 Merrick Boulevard, St. Albans, NY 11434; (718) 291-8006. Topics: General health and lifestyle issues.

Charles Knapp, M.D., Founder and Director of Fitness for Witness. Charles is a consultant in executive health: human resource/health risk prevention, healthcare programs, and cost containment, with special emphasis on cardiovascular disease, diabetes and cancer. He operates Project Assist: The State of Carolina Tobbaco Use Prevention Program for the National Institute of Health and the American Cancer Society. Contact: Fitness for Witness, 500 Rooster Ridge Rd.,

Lansing , NC 28643; office (336) 384-1111, home (336) 384-2747. E-mail: cknapp@skybest.com; Website: http://www.lost-province.com/hcassist. Topics: An outstanding speaker on health and lifestyle issues.

Kay Kuzma, Ed.D., Family specialist, speaker and founder of Family Matters. She has authored more than a dozen books on family life and compiled with her husband and DeWitt Williams the 1998 adult devotional on health, Energized! Contact: Family Matters, 1105 Big Creek Rd., LaFollette, TN 37766; e-mail: kaykuzma@aol.com. Topics: family health, "What I Wish I Would Have Done to Raise "Healthy" Children, Ten Traits of a Strong Healthy Family, Turning the Terrible into the Terrific, One Strike Doesn't Mean You're Out, and Keep it Between the Lines.

Dale and Yolanda Leamon, Pastor and midwife. Contact: 101 N. 20th St. Battle Creek, MI 49015; (616) 963-0368; home (616) 964-6092; Fax (616) 964-4686. Topics: Medical evangelism, CHIP for Churches.

Jim LeVos, M.D., and Sandee LeVos Contact: Rt. 1, Box 131 A; Pennsboro, WV 26415; (304) 659-3915. Topics: General health and lifestyle

Kathleen H. Liwidjaja-Kuntaraf, M.D., M.P.H., Associate Director for Prevention; General Conference Health Department. Contact: 12501 Old Columbia Pike, Silver Spring, MD. 20904; (301) 680-6716. Topics: Healthy lifestyle, smoking cessation, drug-free living.

Aileen Ludington, M.D., a graduate of Loma Linda University with over 25 years of practice which has focused on preventive medicine. Not only has she been a staff physician and consultant at Weimar, but she has authored a number of books and co-authored several with Hans Diehl. She and her husband are both physicians and have recently returned from coordinating a health education center in Thailand. Contact: 6775 Matell Rd., Paradise, CA 95969; Topics: General health and lifestyle. Topics: General health and lifestyle.

Richard Lukens, M.D., M.P.H., NEWSTART staff physician. Popular lifestyle physician, warm communicator, easily understood by lay people.

Pioneered and directed a mission hospital in Africa for several years. Contact: Weimar Institute, 20601 W Paoli Lane, P.O. Box 486, Weimar, California 95736 (530) 637-4111; (800) 525-9192; Fax (530) 637-4408. Topics: Medicine and lifestyle.

Perus A. Malkiah, Ph.D., and his wife **Sheila, R.N.,** Contact: 5602 Downey Ave., Lakewood, CA 90712; (562) 529-5778. Topics: This East Indian couple make an excellent team, presenting worldwide medical missionary outreach, health and spiritual matters.

Dan Matthews, Speaker Emeritus of Faith for Today and host of Lifestyle Magazine television. Contact: Faith For Today at PO Box 320, Newbury Park, CA 91319; (805) 955-7700; Fax (805) 955-7701. Topics: Mental/social and spiritual health.

Henry Martin, Vice President for Public Affairs. Contact: Weimar Institute, 20601 W. Paoli Lane, P.O. Box 486, Weimar, CA 95736; (530) 637-4111; (800) 525-9192; Fax (530) 637-4408. Hmartin@psyber.com/Topics: Henry is an enthusiastic health promoter. One of his favorite topics is "Ancient Diet Promotes Health." Henry and his wife, Robin, give the following seminars "Guest Relations: on how to make people feel truly welcome at the front door of your church", and "Reentry: Dining out the NEWSTART Way Choices in the Real World".

Alfred Mazat, M.D., and **Alberta Mazat, R.N.,** Former professors at Loma Linda University, the Mazats are now retired. Contact: 25659 Lawton Ave. Loma Linda, CA 92354; (909) 796-2402. Topics: Alfred in general medicine/health and Alberta in marriage and family issues, with a specialty in sexuality.

Wilfred McCleary, M.D., (pediatrician) and **Geneva, Dr.P.H.,** (exercise physiologist). An entertaining, witty, yet scientific team. Contact: 24141 Asbury Drive, Denton MD 21629; (410) 479-4837. Topics: Prevention, eight natural remedies, exercise, etc.

J. Wayne McFarland, M.D., Former associate director of General Conference Health Department and co-developer the popular Five-Day Plan for smoking cessation. Also has served

as a volunteer in Russia. Contact: 12114 Country Club Lane, Grand Terrace, CA 92324; (909) 824-3555. Topics: General health/smoking cessation.

Gerard McLane, Dr. P.H., Director of Patient Programming, and his wife, Kathryn, R.N., who gives cooking schools. They are an excellent team for health presentations. Contact: Lifestyle Center of America, Rt. 1, Box 4001, Sulphur, OK 73086; (405) 993-2327; (800) 596-5480; Fax (405) 993-3902. Topics: Topics: Health education.

Len McMillian, Ph.D., M.Div., Family Life Director, Pacific Health Education Center. Contact: 5300 California Ave., Suite 200, Bakersfield, CA 93309; (616) 633-5300. Topics: Mid-life crisis, marriage, child rearing, male/female differences, and male issues. Excellent speaker for men's retreats.

David Miller, M.D., Director of Lifestyle Center. Uchee Pines Institute, 30 Uchee Pines Road, Seale, AL 36875-5703; (334) 855-4781 or (334) 855-3912. Topics: general health/lifestyle, natural remedies, and nutrition.

Tom Mullen, M.D., Former director of NEW-START at Weimar, private practice. Contact: P.O. Box 909, Dalton, GA. (706) 278-6359. Topics: General medical/health with a spiritual component.

Lamont Murdoch, M.D., Professor and Head of Endocrinology. Contact: School of Medicine, Loma Linda University, Loma Linda, CA 92350; (909) 824-4911. Topics: General health and medical issues.

Pat Mutch, Ph.D., is the Academic Dean of the College of Arts and Sciences at Andrews University. For many years she was the director of the Institute for the Prevention of Addictions at Andrews University and an assistant director for the General Conference Department of Health and Temperance. Contact: Andrews University, Berrien Springs, MI 49104; (616) 471-3411. Topics: Addictions.

Edwin Nebblett, M.D., A family practice physician who is featured on Lifestyle Magazine and Janice's Attic television productions. A highly effective advocate of healthful living. His family (wife Maria and children) all sing and play stringed instruments. The Nebblett's make a wonderful family team for camp meetings or special presentations. Contact: 57001 Butcher Rd., Lawrence, MI 49064; (616) 674-4999; Fax (616) 674-4990. Topics: General health/lifestyle.

Neil Nedley, M.D., and **Ericka Nedley, P.T.** Volunteered to do medical work and education in Russia. Contact: 1010 Fourteenth St., NW Ardmore, OK 73401; (405) 223-5980. Topics: General medicine, physical fitness and health.

Christine Neish, R.N., M.P.H., Ph.D., Associate Professor, Chairman of Health Promotion and Education. Contact: School of Public Health, Loma Linda University, Loma Linda, CA 92350; (909) 558-4575. Topics: Health education/lifestyle.

Dorothy Nelson, Ph.D., M.P.H., Weimar Institite. Currently carrying on her husband's work in China and other countries. Contact: P.O. Box 486, Weimar, CA 95736; (800) 525-9192 ext. 7013. Topics: Eight natural principles of health.

Richard (Dick) Neil, M.D., M.P.H., formerly from the School of Public Health at Loma Linda University and currently founder and director of Rilenco Associates. Dr. Neil also provides consultation services for healthcare organizations concerned about optimal efficiency and target marketing. Contact: Rilenco Associates at 1743 Orange Tree Lane, Redlands, CA 92374; (909) 798-8359; Fax (909) 824-5801. Topics: He is an incredibly dynamic speaker on general health topics, health care trends, stress, nutrition, and the spiritual components of wellness.

Tom Neslund, Former Associate Director, General Conference Department of Health Ministries, Director of ICPA. Contact: 21562 Andorra, Mission Viejo, CA 92690; (949) 581-5513. Topics: Alcohol, tobacco and other drugs; Youth 2 Youth

Edna Nkechi Oyoyo, R.N., D.T.R, M.A. Contact: 5524 Wellesley Avenue, Pittsburgh, PA 15206; (412) 361-1667. Topics: Natural foods and how to utilize ethnic/cultural cuisine.

Patricia Pagan, M.D., Staff physician. Contact: Black Hills Health Center, P.O. Box 19, Hermosa, SD 57744; (800) 658-5433 or (605) 255-4101. Topics: Lifestyle medicine, food additives, nutrition.

Warren R. Peters, M.D., Director of the Center for Health Promotion and assistant professor. Contact: School of Public Health, Loma Linda University, Loma Linda, CA 92350; (909) 558-4496. Topics: Excellent speaker on lifestyle medicine and general health.

Ralph Peterson, M.D., and **Joycelyn M. Peterson, M.P.H., R.D., L.D.,** Nutrition consultant. Contact: Vegetarian Institute of Nutrition & Culinary Arts, Inc., P O Box 1032, Columbia, MD 21-44; (301) 854-0853 or (909) 862-2155, Fax: (909) 86404898. Topics: Excellent team on lifestyle and nutrition.

Stoy Proctor, M.P.H., and his wife, **Leilani.** Stoy is the Associate Director of Health and Temperance for the General Conference and author of the Breathe Free™ stop smoking manual. Leilani produces **The Health Connection Catalog** and is an authority on health education resources. Contact: Health and Temperance Department, General Conference of Seventh-day Adventists, 12501 Old Columbia Pike, Silver Spring, MD 20904; (301) 680-6702. Topics: General health/lifestyle/resources.

Vivian Raitz. Enthusiastic promoter of health lifestyles. Lay assistant to the Health Director of the Georgia-Cumberland Conference, Chairperson of the Health Evangelism Council. Contact: 806 Judd Terrace, Dalton, TN 30720; (706) 278-6685; e-mail: raitz@vol.com. Topics: Eight natural ways to live longer and healthier, how to shed pounds, how every member can be a health evangelist.

E. John Reinhold, D.D., D.N., Founder and Director of Christian Care Ministry, a not-for-profit organization where Christians help Christians pay medical expenses. Contact: Christian Care Ministry, P.O. Box 120099, West Melbourne, FL 32902-0099; (407) 726-6811 or (800) 374-2562. E-mail: ejr@tccm.org. Topics: John has an incredible testimony of how the health message changed—and probably saved his life, and led him to additional Bible truth in the Adventist Church. In addition to his inspirational testimony his field of expertise is nutrition.

Ron Rockey, Ph.D., and **Nancy Rockey, Ph.D.,** Former Family Life Directors of the

Dakota Conference and now seminar speakers for Faith For Today. Contact: Faith for Today (805) 955-7700, or Ron and Nancy's address is 10007 West Lancaster Dr., Sun City, AZ 85351; (602) 815-6867; e-mail: 74532,644 @compuserve.com. Topics: Hungry for Healing, Returning the Prodigal, spiritual understanding for past hurts, and mental health topics.

Joan Sabate, M.D., Dr.P.H., Associate professor, nutrition and epidemiology; working with the Adventist Health Study. Contact: School of Public Health, Loma Linda University, Loma Linda, CA 92350; (909) 558-7238. Topics: Nutrition and the Adventist Health Study.

Monte Sahlin, M.A., Former Assistant to the North American Division President for Ministries and the North American Division ADRA Director. He has been a pastor and is involved in research and development in the North American Division. Contact: Columbia Union Conference, 5427 Twin Knolls Road, Columbia, MD 21045; (301) 596-0800 or (410) 997-3414. Topics: Health evangelism, especially in the cities.

Elmar Sakala, M.D., M.P.H., Director of Medical Student Education in the OB/GYN Department at Loma Linda University's School of Medicine. As an obstetrician, his primary emphesis is preventive medicine. He hosts the daily syndicated radio spot, *Got A Minute for Your Health & Lifelines?* Contact: Loma Linda University, Loma Linda, CA 92350; (909) 558-4762, or home (909) 798-0061. Topics: He is an excellent speaker on general health, maternal health, and mental health.

Albert Sanchez, Dr.P.H., Former Director of Spanish Health and Coordinator of Community Health Education. Contact: Pacific Health Education Center, 5300 California Ave., Suite 200, Bakersfield, CA 93309; (616) 633-5300. Topics: Nutrition and the role that plant proteins play in preventing heart disease.

Dawna Sawatzky, M.P.H., R.N., Popular speaker who has done health education in Russia as well as at home. Contact: 3500 Tree Top Lane, Willets, CA 95490; (707) 459-4547. Topics: General health and fitness.

Richard Schaefer, Author of the history of Loma Linda called *Legacy.* Contact: Heritage Room, Del Webb Library, Loma Linda University, Loma Linda, CA 92350; (909) 558-7175. Topics: History of Adventist healthcare and current stories of. God's medical evangelistic work at Loma Linda Medical Center.

John Scharffenberg, M.D., M.P.H., Assistant Director of Health and Temperance for the General Conference. Formerly from Loma Linda University and Pacific Health Education Center. Author/developer of HeartBeat. Contact: P.O. Box 787, 60005 Cascadel Road, Northfork, CA 93643; (209) 877-2518. Topics: He is a dynamic speaker on nutrition, hypertension, heart disease, and lifestyle issues.

Blondel Senior, Ph.D., Co-founder and director of Advent Home, a residential home for troubled boys, 12-16. Contact: 900 Country Road 950, Calhoun TN 37309; (423) 336-5052. Topics: Dynamic and motivational speaker on mental health issues.

Roby Ann Sherman, M.D., Staff physician at Wildwood, who has given health education programs in Russia. Contact: Wildwood Lifestyle Center and Hosptial, P.O. Box 129, Wildwood, GA 30757-0129; (706) 820-1493 or (800) 634-9355. Topics: Medical issues, general health/lifestyle.

Nichole Sidenham, Nichole, a mother and pastor's wife, is a dynamic speaker (English and French). Contact: 198 Tu-Pelo Ave. Winnipeg, MB, Canada R2K 3W6; (204) 669-4469. Topics: Spiritual focus on health and survival of crisis.

John Sines, D.D.S., and **Jane Sines, R.N.,** John is a practicing dentist who is assisted by Jane. They are very active in ASI and health evangelism in their community, having recently raised up a church in Benton and build a model health education center there. Contact: P.O. Box 3105, Collegedale, TN 37315, (423) 396-3154 (office); (423) 472-8842 (home): . Topics: General health/lifestyle, nutrition, dental health and spiritual health.

Mireille St. Pierre, Women's Ministries Director for Northeastern Conference. Contact: 760 Broadway, Brooklyn NY 11206; (718) 630-3024. Topics: Teens, ministering to the AIDS patient, women's issues, and health.

Ernest Steed, Former Director of General Conference Department of Temperance and author of several books. Contact: 13 Pine Glen Drive, DeBary, FL 32713; (407) 668-9618. Topics: Temperance

Gary D. Strunk, M.A., M.Div., M.P.H., Pastor of the Templeton Hills Church in Central California. Prior Director of Religious Studies for the Pacific Health Education Center in Bakersfield California. Contact: 470 Lysandra Court, Templeton, CA 93465; (805) 434-0804 (home). Topics: General health and the spiritual connection; lifestyle changes.

Arlene Taylor, Ph.D., Founder and Director of Realizations Inc. and Director of Risk Management and Infection Control at St. Helena Hospital. She has a nursing background with a Masters in epidemiology and health education. Her doctorate degrees are in health and human services, and clinical pastoral counseling. Contact: Realizations, P.O. Box 2554, Napa, CA 94558-0255; (707) 554-4981, or St. Helena Hospital, 650 Sanitarium Road, Deer Park, CA 94576; (707) 963-6260. Topics: Presents the weekend seminar "Brainworks Unlimited," in addition to topics such as codependency, male/female personality differences, health and personal growth.

Milton Teske, MD. Health Department Director at Weimar College. Contact: Weimar Institute, P.O. Box 486, Weimar, CA 95736; (530) 637-4111 or (800) 525-9192; Fax (916) 637-4408; e-mail: teske@spiralcomm.net . Topics: He is an excellent lecturer on diabetes, stress and NEW-START topics.

Charles Thomas, Ph.D., P.T., Founder and Director of Desert Hot Springs Therapy Center. Contact: Desert Hot Springs Therapy Center, 66705 E. 6th St., Desert Hot Springs, CA 92240; (619) 329-5066 or 251-6205; Fax (619) 251-6206. Topics: Seminars on water treatments, hydrotherapy and natural remedies. A popular camp meeting speaker.

Walter C. Thompson, M.D., Surgeon, author of numerous books on health and active promoter of the 3-ABN television ministry. Contact: His Image Medical Mission Society, 718 North York Road, Hinsdale, IL 60521 (708) 887-1807or (630)

887-1735(h). Topics: General health and lifestyle; including *Freedom from Alcohol, Freedom from Smoking and Tobacco, Sexual Fulfillment,* and *Weight Management,* which are the titles of his books.

Agatha Thrash, M.D., co-founder of Uchee Pines Institute, popular speaker, TV host, and author of dozens of books on the health, natural remedies and the complete vegetarian diet. Agatha is a dynamic, popular camp meeting and seminar speaker. Contact: Uchee Pines Institute, 30 Uchee Pines Road, Seale, AL 36875-5703; (334) 855-4781 or (334) 855-3912. Website: www.ucheepines.org.Topics: general health/lifestyle, natural remedies, and nutrition.

Leo Van Dolson, Ph.D.,MPH. Former editor of *Life and Health,* the *Adventist Review* and *Adult Sabbath School Lessons* and Associate Director of Church Ministries at the General Conference. Also a former professor at the School of Public Health, Loma Linda University. He is the author of a number of books on health and is active in local health evangelism. Contact: 792 Brock Road, SW, McDonald, TN 37353; (423) 559-2733. Topics: health evangelism, lifestyle, spiritual health, and the Take 10 Laws of Life and Health.

Tracey Wallace, M.D. is in family practice in Atlanta and his wife, **Debbie, Dr.PH.** Specializes in preventive health care. Together they run the Preventive Health Care practice in Atlanta, GA. Contact: PO Box 930129, Norcross, GA 30010-0129; (770) 7797-2950. He speaks about the Biblical principles of alternative medicine, with a medical emphasis on Jesus' kind of ministry. She speaks on the laws of health, weight management, and the prevention of lifestyle diseases.

Robert Watts, B.Th, M.A., (Religion), NEW-START chaplain. One of NEWSTART's favorite speakers. Contact: Weimar Institute, 20601 W Paoli Lane, P.O. Box 486, Weimar, California 95736; (530) 637-4111; (800) 525-9192; Fax (530) 637-4408. Topics: Strategies for happy, healthful and victorious living; the role of truth in strengthening the immune system; the effects of the mind on the brain, body and behavior; renewing thought life; forgiving the unforgivable; inner healing; and causes, prevention and overcoming of depression.

Arthur Weaver, M.D., Cancer surgeon. Contact: Office 4201 St. Antoine, Detroit, MI 48201; (313) 745-8775; Home: 49285 Ridge Court, Northville, MI 48167; (313) 349-5683. Topics: Smoking cessation.

Donald Weaver, M.D., Surgeon (son of Arthur) Contact: Office 4201 St. Antoine, Detroit, MI 48201; (313) 745-8775; Home: 27258 Cecile, Dearborne Heights, MI 48127; (313) 274-7968. Topics: General medicine.

Raymond West, M.D., Formerly at the School of Public Health, Loma Linda University and in private practice. Now retired. Writer of HealthWise columns. Contact: P.O. Box 2237, Bel Fair, WA 98528; (206) 275-3777. Topics: General medicine and health.

Albert Whiting, M.D., former Director of the General Conference of Health Ministries. Contact: 1911 E. 16th Street, Ada, OK 74820-7110; (580) 436-4654. Email: bertw@adacomp.net. General health/lifestyle.

Marcel Wiggers, MD. Contact: Weimar Institute, 20601 W. Paoli Lane, P.O. Box 486, Weimar, CA 95736; (530) 637-4111; (800) 525-9192; Fax (530) 637-4408; e-mail: marcelwiggers@hotmail.com. Topics: General health and lifestyle.

DeWitt S. Williams, Ed.D., M.P.H., C.H.E.S., Director of NAD Health Ministries Department. Contact: 12501 Old Columbia Pike, Silver Spring, MD 20904; (301) 680-6733. Topics: General health/lifestyle. Certification programs.

Donna Willis, M.D., graduated from Loma Linda University; Formerly health education for The Today Show; Currently directing the Heart, Body and Soul African-American Program for Baltimore, sponsored by Johns Hopkins University. Contact: email: willdomd@aol.com. Topics: General health and lifestyle.

Walter L. Wright, Secretary, Lake Union Conference of SDA, P. O. Box C, Berrien Springs, MI 49103-9094; (616) 473-8200; Fax: (616) 473-8309; e-mail: 105515,530@compuserve.com. Topics: Family rituals and strengths.

Adventist Resource People and Speakers on HIV/AIDS

Mack Bonner, M.D., M.P.H., One Commerce Center 10320 Little Patuxent Parkway #901, Columbia, MD 21044; (410) 740-8160; Fax (410) 740-8197

Eunice Diaz, Ph.D., M.P.H., 2064 Las Tunas Rd. Santa Barbara, CA 93103; (805) 899-4660; Fax (805) 681-7332

Grace Emori, R.N., Epidemiology Centers for Disease Control, Atlanta, GA 30333 (404) 639-6438; Fax (404) 639-6458.

Wayne Greaves, M.D., Howard University Hospital, 2041 Georgia Ave. Washington, DC 20060; (202) 865-6736/5; Fax (202) 865-6800.

Betty Macomber, 2725 Summerbreeze Place, Redding, CA 96001 (916) 244-3503 phone & fax.

Duane McBride, Ph.D., Behavioral Science Department, Andrews University Berrien Springs, MI 49104; (616) 971-6532.

Bruce Moyer, S.T.D., Sutherland House, Andrews University, Berrien Springs, MI 49104; (616) 471-6532; Fax (616) 471-6252; CompuServe 74617,2465; Internet: bcmoyer@andrews.edu. .

Lester Wright, M.D., 15 Claremont Ave, New York, NY 10027; (212) 961-0978; Fax (518) 457-2115.

Appendix E

Books Advocating the Adventist Lifestyle

Books on Health Authored by Adventists

Books listed here are Adventist-authored, but may not reflect the NAD philosophy of health in every respect. An attempt was made to list as many current books in print as possible (and a few older ones), but there obviously will be omissions.

Adventist authored books usually can be found at your local Adventist Book Center, or from TEACH Services, Inc., (800) 367-1844).

Andress, William, with Ghode, Winnie, *Grandma Whitney: Queen of the Mountain.* Brushton, NY:TEACH Services, Inc., 1996. (800) 367-1844

The incredible story of Hulda Crooks, and how following good health habits allowed her to climb major mountain peaks into her eighties. The book was published to celebrate her 100th birthday.

Bacchiocchi, Samuele, *Wine in the Bible.* Brushton, NY: TEACH Services, Inc. (Fall, 2001 Catalog.)

Dr. Bacchiocchi shows that the Bible consistently teaches total abstinence as a divine imperative.

Cannon, Carol, *Never Good Enough.* Boise, ID: Pacific Press Publishing Association, 1993. Growing up imperfect in a "perfect" family. How to break the cycle of codependence and addiction for the next generation.

Craig, Winston J.,Ph.D., *Nutrition for the Nineties.* Eau Claire, MI 49111: Golden Harvest Books, 1992.

Chairman of the Nutrition Department at Andrews University. Discusses issues like the calcium craze, vitamin B 12 status of vegetarians, what our children are eating and safe water.

Craig, Winston J.,Ph.D., *Eating for Good Health.* Brushton, NY: TEACH Services, Inc., First produced in 1993. (Available through The Health Connection.)

Discusses many current dietary issues.

Crane, Milton G., M.D., *Preparation for Translation.* Brushton, NY: TEACH Services, Inc., 1988, 1992.

This book deals with many intricate subjects besides our health message, such as: vital lessons from the 1888 experience, God's true remedies, the secret of success, development of the "omega" of deception, the ministry of the spirit, perfection versus maturation and the nature of humanity (227 pages).

Dail, Clarence, M.D., and Thomas, Charles, Ph.D., *Hydrotherapy: Simple Treatments for Common Ailments.* Brushton, NY:TEACH Services, Inc., 1989.

This book describes how to use hydrotherapy in calming nerves and relaxing muscles, as well as relieving headaches, ulcers, insomnia, hemorrhoids, arthritis, hypertension, common cold, chest congestion and more. Dr. Charles Thomas was a former professor at Loma Linda University and is the founder and director of Desert Hot Springs Therapy Center.

Dawson, Ron, *Nature Bound.* Boise, ID: Pacific Press Publishing Association, 1985.

Pocket field guide—a handbook of wilderness appreciation and survival.

Diehl, Hans, *Reversing High Blood Pressure,* and *Reversing Obesity Naturally* (small booklets). Available from Better Health (909) 825-1888 or TEACH Services, Inc. (Fall, 2001 Catalog.)

Dr. Diehl founded the Lifestyle Medicine Institute in Loma Linda, CA. Diehl, Hans,

Dr.H.Sc., M.P.H., *To Your Health.* Loma Linda, CA: Lifestyle Medical Institute, 1987.

DeShay, Samuel, MD., and DeShay, Bernice A., RN., *Plus Fifteen.* Here's Life Publishers, Inc. (Now a part of Thomas Nelson: Nashville, TN) 1990.

This book offers a 15 day plan to lower blood pressure and cholesterol. Includes menus and recipes.

Grahm, Rhonda, *Nowhere to Turn.* Boise, ID: Pacific Press Publishing Association, 1993.

A deeply moving story of self-discovery that offers hope to Christians enduring crises of faith and family.

Griffin, Vicki, Ph.D., *Calamity in a Cup,* Sure Word Productions, P.O. Box 38, Hot Springs, NC. 28743; (800) 453-8732. Also: Dieting: *Victory from the Jaws of Defeat,* and *Mooove Over Milk.*

Hoover, Jerry, M.D., *Natural Medicine,* 1993. (Available from Jerry Hoover, Rt. 2, Box 451A Webster, FL 33597; (904) 568-1119.)

Natural remedies and the importance of a healthy lifestyle.

Hullquist, Gary, *Garlic—Nature's Perfect Prescription.* Brushton, NY: TEACH Services, Inc., 1995.

This bulb is a potential antibiotic, anticancer, antioxidant, anti-aging, and anti-inflammatory agent. It's worth considering.

Kuzma, Jan W., Ph.D., and Kuzma, Kay, Ed.D., and Williams, DeWitt S., Ed.D.,*Energized!: One-a-day devotionals for body, mind and soul.* Hagerstown, MD: Review and Herald Publishing Association, 1997.

365 devotionals on all aspects of the Adventist lifestyle written by over 165 health professionals and inspirational writers. (The 1998 adult devotional for the Seventh-day Adventist Church.)

Lee, Celeste, *Understanding the Body Organs,* Brushton, NY: TEACH Services, Inc., 1992.

Illustrated book on how the body organs function and relate to each other, and the benefits derived from following God's eight natural remedies.

Ludington, Aileen, M.D., and Hans Diehl, Dr.H.Sc., M.P.H., *Dynamic Living: How to Take Charge of Your Health.* Hagerstown, MD: Review and Herald Publishing Association, 1995.

Formerly entitled *Lifestyle Capsules.* 52 short nuggets that will help improve your health, one for each week. Better health in easy doses (204 pages). There is also a *Dynamic Living Workbook* (112 pages), (Available at ABC (800) 765-6955.)

Marshall, David, *Is God Still In the Healing Business?,* Autumn House Limited at Alma Park, Grantham, Lincs., NG31 9SL England, 1994.

Dr. David Marshall has pastoral, teaching, and journalism experience. From 1979 to 1993 he edited *Family Life Magazine.* From his rich background he tackles difficult questions using the Bible and recent well documented case histories of healings and non-healings (128 pages).

McLaughlin, Kate, *My Son, Beloved Stranger.* Boise, ID: Pacific Press Publishing Association, 1995.

Written from a mother's perspective and how she dealt with her son being homosexual. A real life drama that faces our church today.

Moore, Marvin, *Conquering the Dragon Within.* Boise, ID: Pacific Press Publishing Association, 1995.

Excellent advice drawing on the 12-Step program in overcoming sin and enslaving addictions that taunt us with our failures.

Moore, Raymond, Ph.D., and Dorothy, M.A., *Home Made Health.* Waco, TX: Word Books Publisher: 1986.

Raymond and Dorothy, known as the primary promoters for the rebirth of the home-school movement, build a strong case for Adventist health. This book is now available through The Moore Foundation, P.O. Box 1, Camas, WA 98607, (206) 835-2736.

Neil, Richard, M.D., Stress: *Taming the Tyrant.* Brushton, NY: TEACH Services Inc., 1994.
What stress is, how it affects the body, and how to manage it. Dr. Neil has his own health consulting organization called Rilenco Associates in the Loma Linda area and was a former professor of health promotions at Loma Linda University.

Nieman, David C. Dr.P.H., *The Adventist HealthStyle: Why it Works.* Hagerstown, MD: Review and Herald Publishing Association, 1992.
David Nieman, former professor at Loma Linda University, School of Public Health, gives an excellent overview of the Adventist lifestyle with research references.

Nedley, Neil, MD, *Proof Positive.* Published by Neil Nedley, 1010 14th St., NW, Ardmore, OK 73401, 1999. Available through Adventist Book Centers.
How to reliably combat disease and achieve optimal health through nutrition and lifestyle.

Nelson, Ethel, *Burkitt-Cancer-Fiber.* Brushton, NY: TEACH Services, Inc.
The story of Dr. Dennis Burkitt who discovered a grotesque cancer in children (Burkitt's Lymphoma) and skillfully lectured on prevention through nutrition.

Nolfi, Kristine, M.D., *Raw Food: Treatment of Cancer.* Brushton, NY: TEACH Services Inc., 1995.
A Denmark physician tells of her own cure from breast cancer and how she used raw foods to help herself and others (42 pages).

Peters, Warren, M.D., *Mystical Medicine.* Brushton, NY: TEACH Services, Inc. 1995.
A look at the connection between the physical, mental and spiritual aspects of our nature and more natural methods of treatments.

Potter, Russ L., *How to Live to A Healthy 100.* Siloam Springs, AR: Concerned Communications, 1996.
The fascinating interview of 100 people who have lived to be 100 or are nearly there.

Paulien, Gunther, *Divine Philosophy and Science.* Brushton, NY: TEACH Services, Inc., 1995.
All the principles of the Bible and the Spirit of Prophecy are designed to allow us to function in perfect harmony with God Himself. This book discusses the methods and means of healthful living.

Sabate, John, MD, DrPH, Ed., *Vegetarian Nutrition.* CRC Press, as part of the "Modern Nutrition" series, 2001.
Dr. Sabate along with a number of Loma Linda University faculty authored this book that is being used as a textbook in a number of classes taught at the university. This scientifically accurate book should be a special help to all in the field of nutrition.

Schaefer, Richard A, *Legacy.* Loma Linda, CA, Legacy Publishing Assoc., 1995.
The heritage of Seventh-day Adventist medicine. An updated version.

Scharffenberg, John A., M.D., *Diet and Heart Disease.* Bakersfield, CA: Pacific Health Education Center, 1987.
This little 25-page booklet shows how you can reduce your risk of heart attack by 90 percent.

Scharffenberg, John A., M.D., *Dietary Fats and Cholesterol.* Bakersfield, CA: Pacific Health Education Center, 1990.
This book represents the position of the North American Division of Seventh-day Adventists Nutrition Council on dietary fats and cholesterol. It reviews the current scientific information and gives recommendations for the health improvement of Seventh-day Adventists.

Stanley, Tyler, *Diet by Design.* Brushton, NY: TEACH Services, Inc. (Fall, 2001 Catalog.)
The keys to permanent weight loss and high energy levels.

Taylor, Arlene, Ph.D., and Lawrence, Lorna, Ph.D., *Thresholds to Thriving: A Power Pack of Practical Prescriptions.* Napa, CA: Success Resources International, 1995.

Available from Realizations, Inc., P.O. Box 2554, Napa, CA 94558-0255; (707) 554-4981. Factors contributing to problem behavior exhibited in adulthood.

Taylor, Arlene, Ph.D., *Brainworks: Success Smarts Unlimited,* Napa, CA: Success Resources International, 1997. Available from Realizations, Inc., P.O. Box 2554, Napa, CA 94558-0255; (707) 554-4981.

Designed to present cutting-edge brain function education to help people manage their lives and their relationships more effectively. This manual is also used as the syllabus for the Brainworks Unlimited™ seminar and the Whole Brain Success Strategies Seminar.

Thompson, Walter C., M.D., *Managing Stress by the Power of God's Love.* Siloam Springs, AR: Creation Enterprises International, 1991; (800) 522-4234.

A self-study stress control program based on getting to know and believe in God. This is a part of the Power of God's Love series, all of which are a medical and biblical approach to the problem.

Other books by Walter Thompson in this series are:

Freedom from Alcohol: Years of experience as a surgeon have given the author the convincing knowledge that this great evil of alcohol can and will only be defeated by the power of God's love.

Freedom from Smoking and Tobacco: Years of experience have supplied the background for this self-help manual written for people addicted to tobacco products, and other addicting substances.

Sexual Fulfillment: Discover the purest intent of God's gift of life to his earthly children as they experience sexual fulfillment by the power of God's love.

Weight Management: This manual seeks to integrate the experience of weight management with the experience of full restoration to the image of God.

Thrash, Agatha Moody, M.D., and Thrash, Calvin L., Jr., M.D., *The Animal Connection.* Seale, AL: New Lifestyle Books, 1983, (124 pages).

The Animal Connection is the culmination of a study extending over the past 20 years. It's 248 references to the ever growing scientific literature on the subject of the effects of animals and their diseases and animal products on the lives of humans presents a tiny but representative sampling of available material.

Other books by Agatha and Calvin Thrash:

Prescription Charcoal, Seale, AL: New Lifestyle Books, 1988, (108 pages).

This is the only book written on charcoal's medicinal properties by medical doctors.

Diabetes and the Hypoglycemic Syndrome, Seale, AL: New Lifestyle Books, 1993 (214 pages).

A complete discussion of all known ways to treat these diseases and avoid their complications. A must for anyone who has diabetes in the family history.

Home Remedies: Hydrotherapy, Massage, Charcoal, and other Simple Treatments. Seale, AL: New Lifestyle Books, 1981.

A detailed book that provides practical information to equip you to use natural remedies to promote health. It tells you not only how to use the remedies, but also why they work.

Nutrition for Vegetarians. Seale, AL: New Lifestyle Books, 1982.

A complete nutritional guide written for the average reader desiring to be informed on the subject.

(With Austin, Phyllis):

Fatigue: Causes, Preventions. Family Health Publications, 1989, (61 pages).

This book gives you all the information you need to treat fatigue.

Food Allergies Made Simple. Family Health Publications, 1985, (79 pages).

What you can do to relieve and eliminate allergies.

Natural Remedies: A Manual: Vol. 1. Family Health Publications, 1983, (171 pages).

A brief description of each disease and long lists of home remedies known to be effective in treating illnesses.

More Natural Remedies: Vol. 2. Family Health Publications, 1985, (125 pages).

Natural Healthcare for a Child, Family Health Publications, 1990. (255 pages).

How to intelligently care for your child's health and the treatment of diseases.

Booklets by Drs. Agatha and Calvin Thrash
- *Fertility, Contraception, Abortion* 1990, (23 pages).
- *Health Topics,* 1996, (58 pages).
- *Poison With a Capital C (Caffeine),* 1991, (22 pages).
- *Prostate: A Monograph,* 1991, (16 pages).
- *Simple Home Remedies Instructor Booklet,* 1996, 31 pages).

(Note: All the books by Agatha and Calvin Thrash are available from New Lifestyle Books; 30 Uchee Pines Road, Ste. 15. Seale, AL 36875-5702; (334) 855-4708; Fax (334) 855-3952: Orders only (800) 542-5695 or at your local ABC.)

Van Dolson, Leo. PhD, MPH, *Take 10.* Published by the Southern Adventist University Press, 2000. (Available from The Health Connections, Catalogue # 47010, plus an instructor's manual.)

Ten laws of life and health outlined by Ellen White, but written for a non-Adventist audience. Contains a Bible Study Guide at the end of each chapter.

Weimar Institute, *Reversing Diabetes Seminar Syllabus,* Weimar, CA: Weimar Institute, 1996.

Loose-leaf workbook includes 159 pages of course outline and physician's lecture material for the two-day NEWSTART® seminar presented by Weimar physicians and associates.

Wilson, Miriam J. Williams, R.N., *Help for Children: From Infancy to Adulthood.* Rocky River Publishers at P.O. Box 1679 Shepherdstown, WV 25443 (304) 876-2711, Updated periodically.

A national directory of hotlines, helplines, agencies, and other resources. A valuable resource for families and every person who works with children.

Wolfsen, Al, *Healing By God's Natural Methods.* Brushton, NY: TEACH Services, Inc., 1993.

In 1948 Al Wolfsen was at the point of death; the doctors gave him up. He found remedies in the Bible and nature. He has taught hundreds of sick people how to use simple nonpoisonous remedies.

A Few Selected Adventist Authored Cookbooks (Mostly Vegan)

The following cookbooks were selected as possible books to use with cooking schools. They generally feature natural foods, no animal products, no refined sugar and low fat.

Alderson, Leona, *Healthy Food Choices.* Brushton, NY:TEACH Services, Inc., 1994.

A compilation of some of the best recipes that have been used in vegetarian cooking classes over many, many years of time by an expert cook and nutrition teacher.

Beltz, Muriel, *Cooking with Natural Foods.* Brushton, NY: TEACH Services, Inc., 1978, and *Cooking with Natural Foods II,* Brushton, NY: TEACH Services, 1992. (Available from Black Hills Health and Education Center, HCR 89, Box 167, Hermosa, SD 57744; (605) 255-4789, 4101, or 9717.)

Ideal eating program for a preventive lifestyle, weight control and stress control.

Burnett, Reggi, *Adam's Table.* Brushton, NY: TEACH Services, Inc., 1994.

Originated from Adam's Table Restaurant in Albuquerque, NM. A true vegetarian cookbook.

Country Life Something Better Cookbook, Brushton, NY: TEACH Services, Inc. (Fall, 2001 Catalog.)

This cookbook was originally designed to be used as a reference book in local community vegetarian cooking schools. General health principles and wholesome vegetarian recipes.

Eakins, Paula A., MS, *Vegetarian Cooking Made E-Z.* Chicago, Illinois: National Center for Nutrition and Dietetics, 1994.

Fuller, Lucy, *Whole Foods for Whole People.* Brushton, NY: TEACH Services, Inc., 1994. Learn an exciting new way to cook with whole foods.

Hoover, LaVonne, *A Taste of Nature Cookbook and Nutritional Guide,* 1992. (Available from LaVonne Hoover, Rt. 2, Box 451A Webster, FL 33597; (904) 568-1119.)
These recipes are free from meat, dairy, refined fat and sugar.

Hullquist, Eriann, *Incredible Edibles Cookbook.* Brushton, NY: TEACH Services, Inc., 1992.
A four week planner with great tasting vegetarian recipes.

Hullquist, Eriann, *Nutrition Workshop Guide,* 2nd edition. Brushton, NY: TEACH Services, Inc., 1996.
Nutritional recipes as well as helpful nutritional tips for special situations, such as road trips. Designed to give out at cooking schools.

Hullquist, Eriann, *Oak Glen Apple Sampler Cookbook.* Brushton, NY: TEACH Services, Inc., 1991.
An apple a day is what you'll have with these delicious recipes. Included is all the health benefits from apples.

Hurd, Frank, D.C., M.D., and Rosalie, B.S., *Ten Talents Cookbook: Vegetarian Natural Food Cookbook and Health Manual,* is available in English and Spanish. Order from Dr. Frank and Rosalie Hurd, Rt. 1, Box 86-A Country Side Lane, Chisholm, MN 55719; (500) 442-4425.
Excellent recipes, but some of the nutritional information presented, such as the combination of certain foods, is not accepted by most nutritionists.

King, Penny, *Taste and See.* Family Health Publications, 1992. (Available from TEACH Services (800) 367-1844.)
Totally vegetarian and allergy free recipes. This book won a 1989 award from Vegetarian Times Magazine.

Knutsen, Lorrie, *Quick-n-Easy Natural Recipes.* Brushton, NY: TEACH Services, Inc., 1993.
Every recipe has five or fewer ingredients and most take only minutes to prepare! Simple, natural ideas.

Lawson, Gloria, *Caring Kitchens Recipes.* Brushton, NY: TEACH Services, Inc., 1989. Best selection of recipes featuring whole grains, vegetarian, dairy free cookery.

Living Springs, *Nature's Banquet.* Brushton, NY: TEACH Services, Inc., 1996.
Vegetarian cooking as an art and a science.

Lynch, Marcella, *Cooking by the Book.* Available only from author. Contact: (800) 655-9071. Or (650) 969-9838.
Accompanies the Cooking by the Book video series (from 3ABN) and features wholesome, nutritious food with simple recipes based on the nutrition principles of Scripture.

Nelson, Ethel, 375 *Meatless Recipes,* Brushton, NY: TEACH Services, Inc. 1974.
Continues to be a popular guide for nutritious cooking.

Nowack, Joanne Chitwood., *An Adventure in Cooking.* Brushton, NY: TEACH Services, Inc., 1995.
Step-by-step art of vegetarian cookery. Especially compiled to teach young people.

Peters, Betty-Ann, *Returning Back to Eden.* Brushton, NY: TEACH Services, Inc., 1994.
Makes vegetarian cooking easy and fun. These recipes have been taste tested by the world-wide travelers that have come to Back to Eden Restaurant and Bakery in Minocqua, Wisconsin.

Pickle, Julianne, *100% Vegetarian*. Brushton, NY: TEACH Services, Inc.

Rachor, JoAnn, *Of These Ye May Freely Eat: A Vegetarian Cookbook*. Sunfield, MI: Family Health Publications, 1990.

This cholesterol free vegetarian cookbook packs in over 250 recipes. JoAnn Rachor uses basic natural foods which yield maximum nutrition without a sacrifice.

Stepaniak, Joanne. *The Uncheese Cookbook*. Brushton, NY: TEACH Services, Inc. (Fall, 2001 Catalog.)

The recipes in this book are just like the ones you grew up with, but have no dairy products.

Tadej, Lorine, *Absolutely Vegetarian*. Brushton, NY: TEACH Services, Inc., 1984.

A cookbook based on the NEWSTART concepts and statements from the Spirit of Prophecy (160 pages).

Thomas-Peters, Cheryl, D.T.R., *Choices,* Hagerstown, MD: Review and Herald Publishing Association, 1994.

This book was a best seller in 1996.

Thomas-Peters, Cheryl, D.T.R., *Fabulous Food for Family and Friends*. Hagerstown, MD: Review and Herald Publishing Association, 1990.

Thomas-Peters, Cheryl, D.T.R., *Quick and Easy Cooking*. Hagerstown, MD: Review and Herald Publishing Association, 1988.

Thrash, Agatha, M.D., *Eat For Strength; A Vegetarian Cookbook*. NewLifestyle Books, 30 Uchee Pines Road, Ste 15, Seale, AL 36875-5702; (334) 855-4708, Fax (334) 855-3952. Orders only (800) 542-5695. 1978.

Oil-free, sugar-free, dairy-free.

Vierra, *Vegetarian Cooking School Cookbook*. Brushton, NY: TEACH Services, Inc., 1994.

This unique cookbook contains more than 170 of the tastiest vegetarian recipes as well as

many facts and charts supporting why it is wise to avoid eating animal foods.

Weimar Institute, *NEWSTART® Lifestyle Cookbook,* 1997. (Available from Weimar Institute (800) 525-9192.)

260 vegan recipes, plus helpful information on menu planning, food preservation, feeding infants, and more.

Weimar Institute, *Recipes from the Weimar Kitchen*. Boise, ID: Graphic House, Inc. 1992.

(Available from Weimar Institute (800) 525-9192.) Recipes using natural foods that contain no cholesterol, fat or sugar.

Note: The Adventist Heritage Library at Andrews University has a complete list of books on health authored by Adventists. This can be accessed by Internet in two ways:

- Telnet library.libr.andrews.edu (then go to Jewel)

  Select L for limited.

  Select W for where.

  Select A for Adventist Heritage Center
- Internet: http://www.andrews.edu/library

Ellen G. White Books on Health

A Call to Medical Evangelism, Brushton, NY: TEACH Services, Inc, 1954.

Adventures in Adventist Living. (Compiled by Leo R. Van Dolson with a study guide after each lesson.) Brushton, NY: TEACH Services, Inc., 1998 (Distributed by Boston Van Ministry, GMF, Box 1600, Boston, MA 02205. (781) 438-3838; Fax: (781) 438-8908. E-mail: bostonvan@juno.com.

Better Living for Your Home: The Book of Health and Happiness. Harvestime Books, 1988.

Counsels on Diet and Foods. Hagerstown, MD: Review and Herald Publishing Association, 1938.

Counsels on Health, Boise: ID: Pacific Press Publishing Association, 1951.

Healthful Living, (the first health compilation) Brushton, NY: TEACH Services, Inc., 1994.

Medical Ministry. Boise, ID: Pacific Press Publishing Association, 1963.

The Ministry of Healing. Boise, ID: Pacific Press Publishing Association, 1909. (The health classic).

Mind, Character, and Personality, (Vol. 1 & 2), Hagerstown, MD: Review and Herald Publishing Association, 1977.

Place of Herbs in Rational Therapy, (Compiled by D. E. Robinson, secretary to Ellen White.) Brushton, NY: TEACH Services, Inc. (800) 367-1844.

Temperance. Boise, ID: Pacific Press Publishing Association, 1949.

Welfare Ministry. Hagerstown, MD: Review and Herald Publishing Association, (1952)

(With James White) *Christian Temperance and Bible Hygiene*, 1890. (Available from: Brushton, NY: TEACH Services, Inc. (800) 367-1844. (Fall, 2001 Catalog.)

Recommended Non-Adventist Books on Health

Charles R. Attwood, MD, *Dr. Attwood's Low-Fat Prescription for Kids: A pediatrician' program of preventive nutrition*. New York, NY: Viking Penquin, 1995.

You would think Dr. Attwood was following Ellen White's counsel on nutrition as he makes a strong case for a plant-based diet for children. He shows how food choices in childhood result in adult disease.

Bradley, Doc, *Let the Mocking Bird Sing Herbal Praise from the Old Barn*, Brushton, NY: TEACH Services, Inc., 1996.

Scientific documentation showing that prayer, herbs and diet work to combat disease and medical conditions in both man and animals.

Cooper, Kenneth H., MD, *Antioxidant Revolution*. Nashville, TN: Thomas Nelson, Inc., 1994.

Delay the signs of aging and reduce the risk of cancer and heart disease with this powerful new prevention program.

Cooper, Kenneth H., MD, *It's Better to Believe*. Nashville, TN: Thomas Nelson, Inc., 1995.

The famous father of aerobics shows the relationship between faith and fitness and pinpoints the relationship between spiritual faith and physical health and shows why belief can lead to better health and fitness (248 pages).

Draper, Harry L., *Haunted Memories, Healing the Pain of Childhood Abuse*. Grand Rapids, MI: Flemming H. Revell:, 1996.

Harry L. Draper is a licensed marriage and family therapist and is the survivor of child abuse. He offers suggestions on how parents can protect their children from child abuse. Incest and sexual abuse are not popular subjects and most people don't want to talk about them, but Draper talks about them frankly and puts them in a Christian context (280 pages).

Fuhrman, Joel, MD, *Fasting and Eating for Health*. St. Martin's Press: New York, NY, 1995.

Dr. Fuhrman discusses how therapeutic fasting accelerates the healing process and allows the body to recover from serious disease in a dramatically short period of time. He has used fasting successfully to relieve lupus and arthritis, remove chronic skin conditions, heal the digestive tracts, and quickly improve cardiovascular diseases such as high blood-pressure and angina.

Malkmus, George H., Dye, Michael, *God's Way to Ultimate Health*. Destiny Image Publishers, Inc. at PO Box 310, Shippensburg, PA 17257-0310; (800) 722-6774. 1995.

Urges Christians to return to God's original plan for nourishing the human body. Tries to show what the Bible says about diet and how it is supported by scientific knowledge and real life testimonials, many from his Hallelujah Acres Farm in Tennessee (270 pages).

McDougall, John A., MD, and McDougall, Mary A. *The McDougall Plan*. New Century Publishers, Inc. at 220 Old New Brunswick Road, Piscataway, NJ 08854, 1983.

Although John is not an Adventist, he practices at St. Helena Hospital and appeared on Lifestyle Magazine on a regular basis. His nutrition plan is close to that of Adventists, with a few minor exceptions.

McMillan, S.I., MD, *None of These Diseases.* Old Tappan, NJ: Flemming H. Revell, Company, 1963, 1984.

This classic, which has sold well over a million copies, goes back to the Bible to show the extraordinary medical benefits that are hidden in God's word. The latest edition has been updated by David E. Stern, MD, the grandson of Dr. McMillan (224 pages). A classic!

Messina, Mark, PhD, and Messina, Virginia, RD, *The Simple Soybean and Your Health.* Garden City Park, NY: Avery Publishing Group, 1994.

How soyfoods can lower your cholesterol and reduce your risk of heart disease and cancer. Mark speaks at many Adventist conventions about his research on soy.

Ornish, Dr. Dean, *Reversing Heart Disease.* New York, NY: Random House, 1990.

The only system scientifically proven to reverse heart disease without drugs or surgery. Dr. Ornish's program promotes a lifestyle very similar to the Adventist lifestyle.

Oski, Frank A., M.D., *Don't Drink Your Milk!* Brushton, NY: TEACH Services, 1983.

New frightening medical facts about the world's most overrated nutrient. Dr. Oski was the Director, Department of Pediatrics, Johns Hopkins University School of Medicine and physician-in-chief, the Johns Hopkins Children's Center.

Robbins, John, *Diet for a New America.* Stillpoint Publishing at Box 640, Walepole, NH 03608, (800) 847-4014, 1987.

A must for your library. One of the best books giving scientific reasons to be a vegetarian. Written by the son of the Baskin and Robbins Ice Cream fame. Very well researched but easy to read with lots of graphs and charts and information (423 pages). Excellent!

Adventist Retirement Facilities and Nursing Homes

The following list of Adventist owned or operated facilities was updated in 2001. Readers must recognize that there is a large turnover in these facilities. Although an effort was made to obtain a complete list, there probably are a number of omissions, as well as additions. No effort was made to determine quality and costs. For an up-to-date list go to Orglinks on the Adventist PlusLine website. Type "retirement" in "specialty" field.

CANADA
Alberta
Sherwood Park
Sherwood Park Nursing Home Limited
2020 Brentwood Blvd.
Sherwood Park, Alberta, Canada T8A 0X1
(403) 467-2281

British Columbia
Sidney
Rest Haven Lodge
2281 Mills Rd.
Sidney, BC, Canada V8L 2C3
(604) 656-0717

Manitoba
Winnipeg
East Park Lodge, Inc.
301 Redonda St.
Winnipeg, Manitoba, Canada R2C 1L7
(204) 222-3251

Park Manor Personal Care Home
301 Redonda St.
Winnipeg, Manitoba, Canada R2C 1L7
204) 222-3251

West Park Manor Personal Care Home, Inc.
3199 Grant Ave.
Winnipeg, Manitoba, Canada R3R 1X2
(204) 889-3330

New Brunswick
Saint John
Kennebec Seniors Housing
475 Woodward Ave.
St. John, New Brunswick, Canada E2K 4N1
(506) 632-9628

Ontario
Oshawa
Kingsway Pioneer Home, Inc.,
1250 King Street, East
Oshawa, Ontario, Canada L1H 7Y8
(905) 571-1584

Stoney Creek
Heritage Green Senior Centre and Nursing Home
353 Isac Brock Dr.
Stoney Creek, Ontario, Canada L8J 1Y1
(905) 573-7177

Toronto
Carter Manor Limited*
103 Tyndall Ave.
Toronto, Ontario, Canada M6K 2G1
(416) 531-1621

Saskatchewan
Saskatoon
Sunnyside Nursing Home
2200 St. Henry Ave.
Saskatoon, Sask., Canada S7M 0P5
(306) 653-1267

*Adventist operated but not church affiliated.

UNITED STATES
California
Deer Park
Crystal Springs Manor
P.O. Box C.
Deer Park, CA 94576

Linda Valley Convalescent Home
25383 Cole St.
Loma Linda, CA 92354
(909) 796-0235; Fax: (909) 796-4401

Linda Valley Villa
11075 Benton
Loma Linda, CA 92354
(909) 796-7501; Fax: (909) 796-4401

Newbury Park
Ventura Estates
915 Estates Drive
Newbury Park, CA 91320-1198
(805) 498-3691; Fax 498-9838

St. Helena
Silverado Orchards
601 Pope St.
St. Helena, CA 94574
(707) 963-3688; (800) 339-1229

Rose Haven Residential Care Facility
520 Sanitarium Road
St. Helena, CA 94574
(707) 963-3748: Fax: (707) 963-9301

Yountville
Napa Valley Adventist Retirement Estates
306 Vista Drive
Yountville, CA 94599
(707) 944-2994

Colorado
Denver
Porter Place Retirement Residence
(An affiliate of PorterCare Hosptial)
1001 East Yale
Denver, CO 80210
(303) 778-1520

Florida
Altamonte Springs
Stanford Center: Quality Retirement Living
433 Orange Drive
Altamonte Springs, FL 32701
(407) 260-2433

Apopka
Florida Living Retirement Community
3425 E. Semonran Blvd.
Apopka, FL 32703
(800) 729-8017: Fax: (407) 862-6769
E-mail: shschlipp@aol.com

Georgia
Symrna
Smyrna Towers, Inc.,
4000 S. Cobb Dr.
Smyrna, GA 30080
(707) 435-4010

Maryland
Baltimore
Elesy Manor
4012 Buckingham Road
Baltimore, MD 21207
(410) 484-0814

Dayton
The Elternhaus: Assisted Living in a Family
    Setting, Residential Ambulatory Care, Primary
    Nursing Care
4201 Linthicum Rd.
Dayton, MD 21036
(301) 854-2776 or (301) 704-0638

Olney
Brooke Grove Convalescent Home
18201 Marden Lane
Olney, MD 20832
(562) 924-5176

Massachusetts
Clinton
Ferguson Rest Home
88 Walnut Street
Clinton, MA 01310

Stoneham
Sunshine Nursing Home
12 Benton Street
Stoneham, MA 02180

Michigan
Bloomingdale
Bethany Nursing Home
42235 C. R. 390
Bloomington, MI 49026

Eaton Rapids
Island View Adult Care Home
746 Michigan Rd.
Eaton Rapids, MI 48827

Lawton
White Oaks Residence Assisted Living
300 White Oak Rd.
Lawton, MI 49065
(616) 624-4811:Fax: (616) 624-7368
E-mail: goldenoak@aol.com

Nebraska
Lincoln
Orchard Park: A Residential Care and
    Retirement Community
3110 South 48th St.
Lincoln NE 68506
(402) 488-8191; Fax: 9402) 463-2931
E-mail: virgilearner@juno.com

New York
East Syracuse
Sunnyside Nursing Home
7000 Collamer Rd.
East Syracuse, NY 13057
(315) 656-7218

North Carolina
Hendersonville
Fletcher Park Inn: Gracious Southern
    Retirement Living (Designed for Independent
    Living with Parkridge Hospital across street)
150 Tulip Trail
Hendersonville, NC 28792
(704) 684-2882

Oklahoma
Harrah
Summit Ridge Retirement Center
18501 N.E. 63rd Street
Harrah, OK 73045
(405) 454-2431

Oregon
Canyonville
Forest Glen Senior Residence
P.O. Box 726
Canyonville, OR 97417
(503) 839-4266

Gresham
Regency at Gresham
405 N.E. Fifth
Gresham OR 97030
(503) 666-5600; Fax 667-9633

Woodburn
Colonial Gardens (Assisted Living)
1890 Newberg Highway
Woodburn, OR 97071
(503) 982-4000: Fax: (503) 982-0139

Tennessee
Madison
Cumberland View Towers*
    Retirement Living
1202 Cheyenne Blvd.
Madison, TN 37115
(615) 868-8653; Fax (615) 868-9942

Portland
Highland Manor
215 Highland Circle Drive
Portland, TN 37148-0510
(615) 325-9263; Fax; (615) 325-5776

Highland Rim Terrace Retirement Center*
100 Woodland Dr.
Portland, TN 37148
(615) 325-3245

Texas

Burleson
Huguley Nursing Center
301 Huguley Boulevard
Burleson, TX 76028-7517
(817) 551-5900; Fax: (512) 293-2388

San Marcos
Hays Nursing Center
1900 Medical Parkway
San Marcos, TX 78666-7520
(512) 396-1888; Fax: (512) 396-1920

Wisconsin
Villa Pines Living Center
201 S. Park Street
Friendship, WI 53934
(608) 339-3361; Fax: (608) 339-9468

*Adventist operated but not church affiliated.

Helplines and Hotlines for Health

There is a great deal of advice and referral information available from toll-free phone numbers. The Health Connection distributes two frequently updated books that provide comprehensive listings of carefully selected help lines:

- *The Directory of National Help* Lines is updated annually and includes fax numbers and Internet sites as well as toll-free numbers.
- *Help for Children,* lists over 450 agencies that can help with almost every problem related to children.

The following numbers may be helpful as a quick reference for health information. (Some numbers may not be available from Canada.)

Adoption
International Child Care (USA)
 (800) 722-4453
National Adoption Center
 (800) TO-ADOPT

Aging
Medicare Telephone Hotline
 (800) 638-6833
National Institute on Aging Information Center
 (800) 222-2225

AIDS
CDC National AIDS Hotline
 (800) 342-2437; (800) 344-7432
National AIDS Clearinghouse-Center For Disease Control (800) 458-5231

Air
Indoor Air Quality Information Clearinghouse
 (800) 438-4318

Albinism
National Organization for Albinism and Hypopigmentation (NOAH) (800) 473-2310

Alcohol/Drug Abuse/Addictions
Al-Anon Family Group Headquarters, Inc.
 (800) 356-9996
Alcohol and Drug Abuse Hotline
 (800) ALCOHOL or (800) 821-4357
Alcoholics for Christ
 (800) 441-7877
American Council on Alcoholism, Inc.
 (800) 527-5344
Cocaine Anonymous
 (800) 347-8998
CONTACT 609 ALA-CALL (alcohol hotline)
 (800) 322-5525
Families Anonymous
 (800) 736-9805
Hazelden Foundation (chemical dependency, recovery and education) (800) 257-7800
KIDSRIGHTS (publications)
 (800) 892-5437
Mothers Against Drunk Driving
 (800) 438-6233
National Association of Alcoholism and Drug Abuse Counselors (800) 548-0497
National Clearinghouse for Alcohol and Drug Information (800) 662-HELP
National Cocaine Hotline (nationwide substance abuse treatment referrals (800) 262-2463
National Council on Alcoholism and Other Drug Dependence, Inc. (800) 622-2255
Occupational Program Consultants Association (employee substance abuse program) (800) 436-7747
Rapha Treatment Centers (Christian psychiatric and substance abuse treatment) Recovery Options Network (referrals for chemical dependency) (800) 662-2873; (800) 383-4673
Substance Abuse and Mental Health Services Administration (800) 729-6686
Sunburst Communications, Inc. (substance abuse publications) (800) 431-1934

TARGET, National Federation of State High School Association (800) 366-6667
The Kids on the Block, Inc. (800) 368-5437

Alzheimer's
Alzheimer's Association (800) 272-3900
Alzheimer's Disease Education and Referral Center (800) 438-4380
National Headquarters Alzheimer's Disease (800) 621-0379
National Institute on Aging—Alzheimer's Disease Education (800) 438-4380

Arthritis
Arthritis Consulting Services (800) 327-3027

Asthma and Allergy
Allergy and Asthma Network/Mothers of Asthmatics, Inc (800) 878-4403
Asthma and Allergy Foundation of America (800) 7-ASTHMA [727-8462]
Asthma Information Line (800) 822-2762

Autism Society of America
Autism Society of America (800) 3AUTISM

Burn
American Burn Association (800) 548-2876

Cancer
American Brain Tumor Association (800) 886-2282
Cancer Information Service (800) 4-CANCER
Leukemia Society of America (800) 955-4LSA
National Marrow Donor Program (800) MARROW-2
United Leukodystrophy Foundation (800) 728-5483

Y-ME National Organization for Breast Cancer Information Support Program (800) 221-2141
US Too International, Inc. (Prostate Cancer) www.ustoo.com.

Cerebral Palsy
United Cerebral Palsy Associations (UCPA) (800) 872-5827

Child Abuse
National Child Abuse Hotline (800) 422-4453
National Clearinghouse on Child Abuse and Neglect (800) 394-3366
National Resource Center on Child Abuse and Neglect (800) 227-5242

Child Birth
American Academy of Husband-Coached Childbirth (800) 4A-BIRTH
International Childbirth Education Association (800) 624-4934

Children
American Academy of Pediatrics (800) 433-9016

Children: Missing/Runaway
National Hotline for Missing Children (800) 843-5678
National Runaway Switchboard (800) 621-4000; (800) 621-0394 (TDD)

Crohn's and Colitis
Crohn's and Colitis Foundation of America, Inc. (CCFA) (800) 932-2423

Chronic Fatigue Syndrome
Chronic Fatigue Immune Dysfunction Syndrome (CFIDS) Association of America, Inc. (800) 442-3437

Cleft Palate
Cleft Palate Foundation (800) 242-5338
Cleft Palate Parent's Council (800) 676-5727

Continence
Simon Foundation for Continence
   (800) 237-4666

Cystic Fibrosis
Cystic Fibrosis Foundation (CF)
   (800) 344-4823

Deaf
Deafness Research Foundation
   (800) 535-3323
National Hearing Aid Foundation
   (800) 521-5247

Diabetes
American Diabetes Association
   (800) 232-3472

Dietetic
American Dietetic Association
   (800) 877-1600
American Dietetic Association's Consumer
   Nutrition Hotline (800) 366-1655

Down Syndrome
National Down Syndrome Congress
   (800) 232-6372
National Down Syndrome Society
   (800) 221-4602

Dyslexia
Orton Dyslexia Society
   (800) 800-ABC-D123

Eating Disorders
Bulimia Anorexia Self-Help
   (800) 227-4785

Endometriosis
Endometriosis Association
   (800) 992-3636

Epilepsy
Epilepsy Foundation of America
   (800) 332-1000

Estrogen
DES Action USA (information on synthetic
   estrogen drug, DES) (800) DES-9288

Headache
National Headache Foundation
   (800) 843-2256

Head Injury
American Trauma Society
   (800) 556-7890
National Head Injury Foundation, Family
   Helpline (800) 444-6443

Heart
American Heart Association
   (800) 242-8721

Hemophilia
National Hemophilia Foundation
   (800) 42-HANDI

Human Growth
Human Growth Foundation
   (800) 451-6434

Huntington's Disease
Huntington's Disease Society of America, Inc.
   (800) 296-4433

Immune Deficiency
Immune Deficiency Foundation
   (800) 296-4433

Impotence
Impotence Information Center
   (800) 843-4315; (800) 543-9632

Kidney
American Kidney Fund (Nephrology)
   (800) 638-8299
National Kidney Foundation
   (800) 622-9010

Liver
American Liver Foundation
   (800) 223-0179

Lung Disease

Lung Line National Jewish Center for
  Immunology and Respiratory Medicine (800)
  222-5864; (800) 552-LUNG (lung facts)

Lupus

Lupus Foundation of American
  (800) 558-0121

Lyme Disease

Lyme Disease Foundation
  (800) 886-5963

Lymphedema

National Lymphedema Network
  (800) 541-3259

Marfan

National Marfan Foundation
  (800) 8-MARFAN

Medic Alert

MedicAlert Foundation
  (800) 432-5378; (800) 344-3226

Mental Health

Depression Awareness, Recognition, and
  Treatment (800) 421-4211
National Alliance for the Mentally Ill
  (800) 950-NAMI
National Clearinghouse on Family Support and
  Children's Mental Health (800) 628-1696
National Depressive and Manic Depressive
  Association (800) 82-NDMDA
National Foundation for Depressive Illness
  (800) 248-4344
National Mental Health Association
  (800) 969-6642
Panic Disorder Information
  (800) 64-PANIC

Multiple Sclerosis

National Multiple Sclerosis Society
  (800) FIGHT-MS

Neurofibromatosis

National Neurofibromatosis Foundation, Inc.
  (800) 323-7938
Neurofibromatosis, Inc.
  (800) 942-6825

Ostomy

United Ostomy Association
  (800) 826-0826

Osteoporosis

National Osteoporosis Foundation
  (800) 223-9994

Paralysis

Christopher Reese Foundation
  (800) 225-0292
National Spinal Cord Injury Association
  (800) 962-9629

Parkinson Disease

American Parkinson Disease Association, Inc.
  (800) 223-2732
National Parkinson Foundation
  (800) 327-4545

Plastic Surgery

American Society of Plastic Reconstructive
  Surgeons, Inc., (800) 635-0635
Facial Plastic Surgery Information
  (800) 332-3223

Psoriasis

National Psoriasis Foundation
  (800) 723-9166

Retardation

American Association on Mental Retardation
  (800) 424-3688
National Clearinghouse on Family Support and
  Children's Mental Health (800) 628-1696
Siblings for Significant Change
  (800) 841-8251

Reye's Syndrome

National Reye's Syndrome Foundation
  (800) 233-7393

Safety

National Fire Protection Association
(800) 344-3555
National Highway Traffic Safety Administration
Auto Safety Hotline (800) 424-9393
U.S. Coast Guard Boating Safety Hotline
(800) 368-5647
U.S. Consumer Product Safety Commission
(800) 638-2772

Sclerosis

National Tuberous Sclerosis Association
(800) 225-6872

Scoliosis

The Scoliosis Association, Inc.
(800) 800-0669

Sickle Cell Disease

Sickle Cell Disease Association of America, Inc.
(SCDAA) (800) 421-8453

Skin Disease

United Scleroderma Foundation, Inc.
(800) 722-4673

Speech

National Stuttering Association
(800) 364-1677

Spina Bifida

Spina Bifida Association of America
(800) 621-3141

Spinal Muscular Atrophy

Families of S.M.A.—Spinal Muscular Atrophy
(800) 886-1762

Spondylitis

Spondylitis Association of America
(800) 777-8189

STD

CDC National STD Hotline
(800) 227-8922

Stroke

American Heart Association Stroke Connection
(800) 553-6321
National Stroke Association
(800) STROKES
National Institute of Neurological Disorders and
Stroke (800) 352-9424

Sudden Infant Death

American Sudden Infant Death Syndrome
Institute (800) 232-7437
SIDS Alliance
(800) 221-7437

Terminally Ill

Hospice Education Institute
(800) 331-1620
Make-A-Wish Foundation
(800) 722-9474

Tourette Syndrome

Tourette Syndrome Association, Inc.
(800) 823-2055

Urology Problems

American Foundation for Urologic Disease
(800) 242-2383

Visually Impaired/Blindness/Eye

American Council of the Blind
(800) 424-8666
American Foundation For The Blind, Inc.
(800) 232-5463
American Printing House for the Blind
(800) 223-1839
Blinded Veterans Association
(800) 669-7079
Braille Institute of America
(800) BRAILLE
Christian Record Services (Free publications/
audio cassettes for blind) (402) 488-0981)
Council of Citizens with Low Vision International
(800) 733-2258
Division of Services for the Blind
(800) 960-9270
Guiding Eyes for the Blind
(800) 942-0149

National Association for Parents of the Visually
Impaired (800) 562-6265
National Braille Press
(800) 548-7323
National Eye Care Project
(800) 222-3937
National Eye Research Foundation
(800) 621-2258
National Federation of the Blind
(800) 638-7518
National Library Service for the Blind and
Physically Handicapped (800) 424-8567
National Society to Prevent Blindness
(800) 331-2020
Research to Prevent Blindness
(800) 621-0026
Retinitis Pigmentosa International
(800) 344-4877
RP Foundation Fighting Blindness (retinitis pig-
mentosa)
(800) 683-5555
Science Products (product for blind)
(800) 888-7400
The Lighthouse, Inc. (information about visual
impairment and resources in your area
(800) 334-5497
Xavier Society for the Blind
(800) 637-9193
Xerox Imaging Systems (portable reading
machine) (800) 248-6550

Water
Safe Drinking Water Hotline
(800) 426-4791

Miscellaneous Information Associations:
Consumer Health Information Research Institute
(800) 821-6671
ETR Associates/Network Publications (family life
and health publications) (800) 321-4497
Food Labelling Hotline
(800) 535-4555
National Black Women's Health Project
(800) ASK BWHP
National Health Information Center
(800) 336-4797
National Library of Medicine
(800) 272-4787
National Reference Center for Bioethics Literature
(specialized collection of books, journals and
articles concerned with biomedical issues)
(800) MED-ETHX
National Vaccine Information Center
(800) 909-SHOT
National Youth Crisis Hotline
(800) 448-4663
Office of Minority Health Resource Center
(800) 444-6472
Social Health Association
(800) 227-8922
Women's Sport Foundation
(800) 227-3988
YMCA of the USA
(800) 872-9622

Published References

This handbook was compiled from many sources. The following is a list of published references that were used in the compilation of this book.

Chapter 1: The Adventist Philosophy of Health Ministry

Roger Coon, "What is the Adventist 'Health Message'?" *Adventist Review*, Dec. 9, 1993, p. 17.

P. William Dysinger, J. Robert Spangler, and Mark Finley, "Chapter 14: A Blended Ministry," *Aims Study Guide*. Siloam Springs, AK: Creation Enterprises, International, 1991.

Jan W. Kuzma, Kay Kuzma, and DeWitt S. Williams, Devotional selections from *Energized!* One-a-day devotionals for body, mind and soul, Hagerstown, MD: Review and Herald Publishing Association, 1997.

J. R. Spangler, "An Imaginary Interview Between J. R. Spangler and Ellen White" *Ministry* Vol. 43, No. 9, September, 1970.

DeWitt S. Williams, "Change or Not to Change." *HT Update*, Vol 4, #2, 1996, p. 7.

Gary D. Strunk, Unpublished manuscript.

Chapter 2: Community Health Promotion

David C. Nieman, *The Adventist Healthstyle: Why it Works*. Hagerstown, MD: Review and Herald Publishing Association, 1992.

Monte Sahlin, et. al, "Chapter 10: Health Screening and Education," *Ministries of Compassion*, Lincoln NE: AdventSource,1994, pp. 143-156.

DeWitt S. Williams, "Prevention: The New Philosophy of Health Education," *HT Update*, Vol 2 #2, pp. 6-7, 1994.

DeWitt S. Williams, "Closing the Health Gaps," *HT Update*, Vol. 3 #1, p. 7, 1995.

Chapter 3: The Mission and Organization of NAD Health Ministries

SDA Encyclopedia

Chapter 4: Getting Started: Help for the New Health Ministries Leader

DeWitt S. Williams, "Help for the New Health and Temperance Leader." *HT Update*, Vol 2, #1, p. 1-2, 1994.

Jayney Scandiff, "Marketing the Adventist Health Message," *HT Update*, Vol. 2, #2, 1994.

Chapter 5: Step-by-step in Health Evangelism

Elvin Adams, "Health Evangelism Needs a Home," *Worker*.

Chapter 6: Health Behavior Change

Elvin Adams, "God's Formula for Behavior Change," slide script.

Don G. King, "The Relationship of Religious Commitment to Health Behaviors: Implications for the Church." General Conference: Health 2000 and Beyond Study Paper.

Chapter 7: Natural Remedies

Bernell E. Baldwin, *Natural Remedies,* Unpublished manuscript.

Warren Peters, "The Use of Natural Therapeutics In A Contemporary Medical Setting," Prepared for the General Conference of Seventh-day Adventists. June 14, 1993.

Agatha and Calvin Thrash, *Home Remedies*, Seale, AL: Thrash Publications, 1981.

Chapter 8: Divine Healing and Prayer for the Sick

Leo Van Dolson and J. R. Spangler, "Prayer for the Sick" *Health, Happy, Holy,* Hagerstown, MD: Review and Herald Publishing Association, 1975, pp. 112-123.

Chapter 9: Nutrition Education

Stoy Proctor, John A. Scharffenberg, and Joycelyn M. Peterson: Unpublished manuscripts.

Chapter 10: Health Promotion with Youth

"Substance Use Among Seventh-day Adventist Youth," A NAD Leadership Briefing Paper pre-pared by the Institute of the Prevention of Addictions, Andrews University.)

Gary L. Hopkins, et. Al, "AIDS and Adventist Youth," *Ministry*, July, 1996, pp. 22-27.

Vikki Fields: Unpublished manuscript

Chapter 12: AIDS Ministries
Monte Sahlin, et. al, "Chapter 9: AIDS Ministries," *Ministries of Compassion*, Lincoln NE: Advent*Source*, 1994. pp. 133-142.
Harvey Elder: Unpublished manuscript

Chapter 13: Mental Health Ministries
Resources for Family Ministry, Southeastern California Conference, 1990. Compiled by Audray Johnson.
Wilma Hepker, "How to Choose a Counselor," *Adventist Review*, Sept. 2, 1993, p. 18-20.
Donna Davis Cameron: Unpublished manuscript

Chapter 14: Parish Nursing
Maxine Blome: Unpublished manuscript

Chapter 15: Health Education Centers
DeWitt Williams, "Following the Blueprint," *Adventist Review*, Oct, 1995, pp. 22-23.

Chapter 16: The Adventist Health Network
DeWitt Williams, "Networking Realities," HT Update.

Chapter 17: Adventist Healthcare
Kimberly Carr: Unpublished manuscript

Chapter 18: Loma Linda University, School of Public Health
Richard A Schaefer, *Legacy*, Loma Linda, CA: Legacy Publishing Association, 1990

Chapter 19: Self-supporting Health Ministries
Bernell Baldwin: Unpublished manuscript.

Chapter 20: Health Media Ministries
Lee Anna Jackson: Unpublished manuscript

Chapter 21: Resources for Health and Temperance
Leilani Proctor and David DeRose: Unpublished manuscripts

Chapter 23: Research on Seventh-day Adventists and Health
Gary E. Frazier, "Epidemiologic Studies of Adventists," *Scope*, July-Sept., 1991, pp. 50-55.

Chapter 24: Health Fairs and Exhibits
Allan Handysides, Leilani Proctor, Stoy Proctor and Kathleen Kuntaraf, *"Fill Your Life With Celebrations!*®

Chapter 25: How to Start a Van Ministry
Steve Veres: Unpublished manuscript.

Chapter 26: "Alternative Methods" and Quackery
S. Barrett and W. T. Jarvis, editor. *The Health Robbers. A Close Look at Quackery in America.* Amherst, NY: Prometheus Books, 1993.

Chapter 27: Nutrition Fads, Fallacies, and Quackery
S. Barrett and W. T. Jarvis, editor. *The Health Robbers. A Close Look at Quackery in America.* Amherst, NY: Prometheus Books, 1993.

Chapter 28: Fitness and Wellness Camps.
Celeste Ryan, Unpublished manuscript.

Appendix A: What Seventh-day Adventists Believe about Healthful Living
Seventh-day Adventists Believe: A Biblical Exposition of 27 Fundamental Doctrines, Chapter 21: Christian Behavior, General Conference of Seventh-day Adventists, 1988, pp. 279-289.

Appendix C: Seventh-day Adventist Positions on Health Issues
"Taking a Stand," *Adventist Review*, Dec. 31, 1992, pp. 11-14.

Index